STORAGE
of Cereal Grains and Their Products

AMERICAN ASSOCIATION OF
CEREAL CHEMISTS, INC.

Monograph Series **Volume V – Revised**

CONTRIBUTORS

J. E. Bailey, Cargill, Inc., Minneapolis, Minnesota

G. R. Bauwin, Grain Division, Agricultural Marketing Service, U.S. Department of Agriculture, Chicago, Illinois

N. J. Burrell, Pest Infestation Control Laboratory, Ministry of Agriculture, Fisheries and Foods, Slough, Buckinghamshire, England

Clyde M. Christensen, Department of Plant Pathology, University of Minnesota, St. Paul, Minnesota

Richard T. Cotton, Stored-Product Insects Division, U.S. Department of Agriculture, Washington, D.C.

Ernesto De Las Casas, University of Minnesota, St. Paul, Minnesota

Philip K. Harein, University of Minnesota, St. Paul, Minnesota

Kenton L. Harris, O'D. Kurtz, Inc., Baltimore, Maryland

W. V. Hukill, U.S. Department of Agriculture, Iowa State University, Ames, Iowa

W. Haward Hunt, Grain Division, Agricultural Marketing Service, U.S. Department of Agriculture, Beltsville, Maryland

Mary B. Hyde, Ministry of Agriculture, Fisheries and Food, Pest Infestation Control Laboratory, Slough, Buckinghamshire, England

Henry H. Kaufmann, Cargill, Inc., Minneapolis, Minnesota

S. W. Pixton, Ministry of Agriculture, Fisheries and Food, Pest Infestation Control Laboratory, London Road, Slough, Buckinghamshire, England

Yeshajahu Pomeranz, U.S. Department of Agriculture, ARS, U.S. Grain Marketing Research Center, Manhattan, Kansas

H. L. Ryan, Grain Division, Agricultural Marketing Service, U.S. Department of Agriculture, Chicago, Illinois

Donald E. Schaetzel, General Mills, Inc., Minneapolis, Minnesota

C. A. Southwick, Jr., Modern Packaging Magazine, New York, New York

Donald A. Wilbur, Department of Entomology, Kansas State University, Manhattan, Kansas

STORAGE
of Cereal Grains and Their Products

Edited by Clyde M. Christensen, *University of Minnesota*
St. Paul, Minnesota

Published by the

AMERICAN ASSOCIATION OF CEREAL CHEMISTS, Incorporated
St. Paul, Minnesota

LIBRARY OF CONGRESS CATALOG CARD NUMBER: 73-82902

ISBN 0-913250-05-8

Printed in the UNITED STATES OF AMERICA

Preface to the First Edition

STORAGE OF CEREAL GRAINS AND THEIR PRODUCTS is the second in a series of monographs sponsored by the American Association of Cereal Chemists. The subject seems especially timely; for in spite of recent advances in technology, millions of tons of cereals are wasted each year through spoilage of various sorts. Yet hunger is widespread, and populations increase ever more rapidly. Protection of food supplies through sound storage practices is thus a matter of the most vital importance.

Each of the eleven chapters of the book has been written by one or more experts. The chief aim was to produce a useful treatise by combining comprehensive reviews of the scientific literature with knowledge drawn from other sources. In pursuit of that aim some unevenness among chapters could not be avoided; for some aspects of the subject are brightly illuminated by the light of scientific knowledge; on others that light is dim, and we must depend largely on practical experience; and elsewhere, even practical experience is limited, and we grope in semi-darkness.

The first six chapters deal with moisture, chemical and physical changes with time, microflora, respiration and heating, insects, and rodents. Their main purpose is to provide the scientific background for a consideration of storage problems, though all, and especially those on insects and rodents, do full justice to practical matters also. The last five chapters, by contrast, deal largely with areas in which practical experience is the chief source of knowledge. Two describe grain storage facilities in the country and at terminal points, and discuss their operation; one deals with grain drying; and the last two with cereal products themselves, namely, with bulk storage of flour and with packaging of various types.

Three further comments may appropriately be made on the book as a whole. Firstly, since authors were urged to deal fully with their subjects it was inevitable that some topics should be discussed in more than one chapter. We did not attempt to remove all such repetition since we believed that the reader would prefer to have each chapter essentially complete in itself. Secondly, while the treatment is often both comprehensive and detailed, not all cereals and their products are fully covered. The aim was primarily to elucidate and illustrate the main principles governing storage rather than to discuss specific problems presented by individual grains or products. And lastly, as might be expected, since all authors—and the editors—are citizens of the United States or Canada, the book gives most emphasis to North American investigations and practices.

We are deeply indebted to our authors for the time and labor they gave to the preparation of their chapters, and for their patience, forbearance, and cooperation, in dealing with the many matters, some important and some trivial, that authors and editors are bound to discuss. Circumstances beyond our control made it necessary to find a number of new authors when about half the book had been written, and as a result, the completion of the work was considerably delayed. We are therefore especially grateful to those authors who turned manuscripts in early and were later kind enough to bring them up to date; and to those who, coming to their tasks late in the day, made special efforts to meet our postponed deadlines.

In carrying out our part in the preparation of this book we received much help and valuable advice from the chairman of the Monograph Committee, W. F. Geddes. The other members of this committee were C. N. Frey, George Garnatz, Majel M. MacMasters, Betty Sullivan, J. A. Shellenberger, and ourselves. The committee chose the subject for the book, prepared an outline of its contents, selected authors for the various chapters, and asked them to contribute.

We were particularly fortunate in persuading Kathleen Webb, who helped with Volume I of this series, to undertake the technical editing of Volume II also; her painstaking work has added immeasurably to the quality of this book. Eunice R. Brown, Margaret Hilligan, V. G. Martens, and R. J. Cheale also gave us valuable assistance. Lastly, we pay a well-earned tribute to R. J. Tarleton, Managing Editor of *Cereal Chemistry,* who undertook the final work of publishing the book for the American Association of Cereal Chemists.

J.A.A.
A.W.A.

October, 1953.

Preface to the Second Edition

The 1954 edition of *Storage of Cereal Grains and Their Products* had a justifiably good reception among those concerned with problems in this diverse field; it was reissued in paperback form in 1969, and has continued to be almost the only summary source of information on many facets of storage and handling of cereal grains and their products. However, during the past 20 years that have elapsed since the first edition appeared in 1954, there have been many new developments and significant advances in both basic knowledge and in practical technology in this field, or these fields, and a largely new book seemed justified to present these advances and to embody some of the new concepts that have accompanied them. It is hoped that the present book, contributed to by world-recognized authorities in their separate fields, will effectively summarize these advances and concepts, and that it will be of even greater value than the 1954 edition. Although the contents deal primarily with cereal grains and their products, many of the principles, practices, and concepts apply equally well to the storage and handling of many other raw and processed materials that in one way or another constitute an important part of our food- and feedstuffs. The understanding of the principles and the application of the practices outlined in the book should enable those concerned with the storage and handling of these many and various products to approach their problems with informed and intelligent understanding in place of intuition. For whatever success the book may attain, thanks must be given to the authors of the individual chapters, who gave so freely of their time and talents to the end that the idea of a new edition might be realized. Acknowledgment is made of the invaluable assistance of Carl Eide who prepared the Subject Index.

C. M. Christensen

CONTENTS

CHAPTER 1

MOISTURE—ITS SIGNIFICANCE, BEHAVIOR, AND MEASUREMENT

W. HAWARD HUNT

Grain Division, Agricultural Marketing Service
U.S. Department of Agriculture, Beltsville, Maryland

S. W. PIXTON

Ministry of Agriculture, Fisheries, and Food
Pest Infestation Control Laboratory, London Road, Slough, Bucks, England

I. INTRODUCTION

No serious discussion of the storage behavior of cereal grain and their products can take place without reference to their moisture content and temperature. Moisture content, i.e., the quantity of water held by the grain or product, is usually expressed as mass of water per unit mass of wet grain (wet-weight basis), or as mass of water per unit mass of dry grain (dry-weight basis). In trade and industry the wet-weight basis is used most often. In pure science, the dry-weight basis is used.

Water is weight, and must be paid for when grain is bought or sold. For example: A big-John freight carload of wheat will hold approximately 200,000 lb. of wheat. With 14% moisture, 200,000 lb. of wheat contain 28,000 lb. of water. With 8% moisture, the same carload contains only 16,000 lb. of water—a difference of 12,000 lb. of water. Since a gallon of water weighs 8.345 lb., the 14%-moisture wheat contains 3,355.3 gal. of water, and the 8%-moisture wheat contains only 1,917.3 gal. of water. Assuming 60 lb. of wheat per bu., the quantity of water present would be equivalent to 466.7 and 266.7 bu. of wheat, respectively.

If wheat is selling at $1.50 per bu., then the water would be valued at $700.05 and $400.05, respectively. Thus, the grain buyer is paying 20.9 cents per gal. for water, or $50 for each 1% moisture. Such differences in intrinsic values may or may not be reflected in market prices.

Further, an increase in moisture content reduces bulk density so that wet grain occupies more shipping or storage space than drier grain. Damp grain flows less readily than drier grain, a factor to be considered when grain is to be conveyed from one point to another. But most important of all, at low moisture content, grain and other agricultural products will store for longer periods without deteriorating. The rates of growth and development of microorganisms, insects, and mites as well as the rate at which chemical and physical changes take place, increase very greatly with increase in moisture content of the grain, and also of temperature,

1

up to certain well defined optima. The moisture content of a product, and such changes of moisture content as we wish to promote, must be taken into account when a product is handled. The design of food packets and the design of ventilation of warehouses and ships' holds as a rule must prevent the excessive uptake of water, but sometimes these may be required to encourage the loss of water, or even to prevent any water exchange.

In this context—of storing commodities free from deterioration—moisture content and temperature are interrelated. A product can safely contain more moisture if the temperature of the product is low and uniform throughout. If, however, there are differences in temperature in parts of a bulk of grain, moisture will move from a warm area to a cooler area, increasing the moisture content of the product in the cooler area and hence considerably increasing the risk of deterioration. Therefore, temperature gradients must be avoided, particularly if the moisture content is near the critical limit. The quantity of water a cereal grain contains, its influence on the behavior of the grain in store or transit, and the effect of temperature are, therefore, of paramount importance in grain technology.

To understand the role of water in cereal grains as related to the problems of storage, it is necessary to consider first the underlying principles involved when water is adsorbed by the various chemical constituents, e.g., carbohydrate and protein, in the grain. Only when such principles are clearly understood is it possible to appreciate the full scope of the more practical aspects of the relationship between water in grain to storage. A discussion of these basic considerations is therefore presented in the first section of this chapter. The second section describes some of the practical aspects involved, and the third section compares and discusses methods used for determining the moisture content of cereals.

II. BASIC CONSIDERATIONS

As a starting point we may inquire into what is known about the forces that hold water in biocolloidal systems such as grain: whether these forces are chemical or physical, how strong they are, and so on. This leads to a discussion of adsorption in relation to chemical structure and hence to a consideration of what may be learned from water-sorption isotherms. Information on isotherms for cereals is then presented, followed by a discussion of the concept of "bound water". The section ends with a brief consideration of the practical implications of the isotherm, of moisture migration caused by temperature gradients, and of moisture diffusion into and out of grain.

A. Forces Involved in Adsorption

For purposes of the present discussion it is convenient to consider water absorption as several distinct phenomena. A certain quantity of water may be held in the intergranular spaces and within the pores of the material, i.e., held loosely in the system by capillary forces. Such water may be termed *absorbed* water. It possesses the usual properties of free water and the molecules of the absorbing substance are not concerned except as a supporting structure.

Another portion of the water is more closely associated with the absorbing substance. There is an interaction between the water molecules and those of the substance; the properties of one substance influence the properties of the other.

Water is then said to be *adsorbed*, i.e., held in the system by molecular attraction, being more closely linked with the adsorbing substance and therefore being held more firmly. The general term *sorption* is used to denote such interaction. The terms adsorption and desorption are used specially to denote the process of taking up or giving off water of sorption.

Finally, some water may combine in a chemical union with the adsorbing substance. Conversely, water which is an integral part of a given substance may be removed under the rigorous conditions at times employed for moisture determination. This bound water, or water of constitution, is held in the system by very strong chemical forces and is in a chemical union with the adsorbing substance.

The foregoing classification must be regarded merely as a setting up of useful categories. It must be kept in mind that in a biocolloidal system such as grain, which is made up of various substances and which also possesses an organized structure, there will be many types of water binding, ranging from free water to the chemically bound water that forms an integral part of some organic molecule. For the purpose of the present exposition, the most pertinent inquiry is in that somewhat indefinite area between free water that remains uninfluenced by the grain, on the one hand, and water which is chemically bound, on the other: an area in which intermolecular forces play a dominant role. It is therefore necessary to examine what these intermolecular forces are.

When atoms unite to form molecules, all chemical bonds are satisfied, but the molecules can still exert an influence on other molecules by means of forces variously described as intermolecular forces, van der Waals (forces considered to be responsible for physical adsorption), and secondary valency forces. The forces of attraction emanating from a solid may be of two kinds, physical and chemical, giving rise to physical adsorption and chemisorption, respectively (Brunauer, 1943; Mark and Tobolsky, 1950; Gregg and Sing, 1967). These forces manifest themselves in the formation of liquids and crystals, of complexes and aggregates, and in other types of interactions between molecules of the same or different kind.

The origin of intermolecular forces has been attributed to several effects (Brunauer, 1943; Mark and Tobolsky, 1950). The first of these is the orientation effect of permanent dipoles, sometimes called the Keesom effect, which may be described as follows: If, by reason of the structure of a molecule, the center of gravity of positive charges does not coincide with the center of gravitiy of negative charges, that molecule is said to possess a permanent dipole moment. Water, alcohol, and ammonia are good examples of substances with dipole moments. When two such molecules approach each other there will be an electrostatic attraction between the positive end of one molecule and the negative end of the other.

A second effect is called the induction effect of Debye. When molecules which contain easily mobile charges are brought near a strong dipole or ion, or are placed in an electric field, a distortion of the negative-charge clouds surrounding the atoms takes place. As a result, the centers of gravity of negative and positive charges in the molecule will no longer coincide and the molecule is said to acquire an induced dipole moment. This process is broadly analogous to the induction of magnetic polarity in a piece of soft iron in the presence of a permanent magnet. Interaction between the inducing dipole and induced dipole gives rise to a force of attraction.

A third type of interaction between molecules is the London dispersion effect, which is also an attractive force. The term dispersion is derived from certain optical properties. As an example, consider an atom of hydrogen, which is generally thought to be nonpolar. Its dipole moment, however, is zero only statistically over a finite interval of time. But at any instant, the single electron of the hydrogen atom is always on one side, so that the atom possesses a dipole moment constantly fluctuating in direction. This will create a fluctuating field around the atom and will result in a displacement of charge in a nearby atom in phase with the fluctuation. This type of interaction then gives rise to a force of attraction.

Usually, the attraction between molecules will not be a simple effect but rather the combined effect of several kinds of interaction, such as dipole-dipole, dipole induced dipole, and ion-dipole. For example, the binding of water to the copper ion in the pentahydrate of copper sulfate is an ion-dipole interaction. The hydrogen bond deserves special mention. It may be visualized as consisting of a hydrogen atom forming a bridge between two electro-negative groups. The dipole forces and quantum-mechanical resonance cooperate to form a stable link.

Intermolecular forces are relatively weak. The heat of adsorption of one substance onto the surface of another may range from 4 to 15 kcal. per mole. When the energy involved is from 15 to 35, or even up to 50 kcal. per mole, the process is sometimes termed chemisorption to indicate that it is intermediate between sorption and chemical binding by means of covalent or ionic bonds. This latter type of bond may involve 50 to 150 kcal. or more.

Water occupies a prominent position in adsorption phenomena. It has already been pointed out that water has a permanent dipole. In addition, it is a small molecule and therefore has a large dipole moment per unit surface. Water would thus be expected to be strongly absorbed on polar substances, and especially so on substances containing ions.

B. Adsorption and Chemical Structure

It is logical to inquire next to what extent intermolecular forces may be expected to be involved in the process of sorption of water by cereal grains. To do this, it is necessary to note briefly the significant structural characteristics of the predominant constituent substances occurring in grain, and to identify the polar foci or functional groups which govern the behavior of these substances towards water. Starch and protein are the main constituents of wheat, together with moisture. They also provide most of the polar sites with which water can react, and have therefore been selected for a brief discussion.

Starch is a natural high polymer built up from the basic glucose unit by repetition into a long or branched chain. It may be represented by the formula:

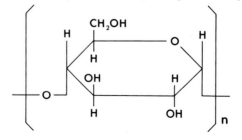

It is characterized by hydroxyl groups on the ring, ring oxygen, and bridge oxygen, all of which are points of polarity in the molecule and therefore suitable foci for interaction with water molecules through hydrogen bonding. Hunter (1950) suggests the following modes of linkage of the polysaccharide hydroxyl with water, through the hydrogen bond:

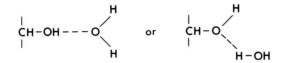

For the interaction of water with the bridge oxygen the same author suggests:

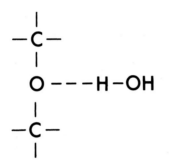

The exact nature of the hydrogen bond is still undecided (Finar, 1957). It is discussed in detail by Glasstone (1960).

The structure of protein is also that of a high polymer, but the repeating unit is not identical and may be any of the naturally occurring amino acids. One of the most significant structural characteristics of protein is the polypeptide backbone:

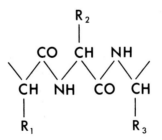

R_1, R_2, etc., are the amino acid side-chain residues. They carry a wide variety of polar and ionic groups:

-OH, in serine, threonine, hydroxyproline, and tyrosine;
-NH-, in tryptophan, histidine, and proline;
-NH_2, in lysine and in one of the terminal amino acids in the polypeptide chain;

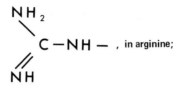

-COOH, in aspartic and glutamic acids and in one of the terminal amino acids in the polypeptide chain; and

-CONH$_2$, in glutamine and asparagine.

Accordingly, there is ample opportunity for water to interact with a variety of polar groups.

This approach to the problem of binding of water has been adopted by several investigators. Lloyd (1938) recognized the multipolar character of proteins and pointed out the various groups coordinating with water. Pauling (1945) also concluded that water adsorbed in the first layer by proteins was bound primarily by the polar side chains. He attached less importance to the effect of the peptide link. Hunter (1950), however, suggested that water is bound by the peptide link according to the scheme:

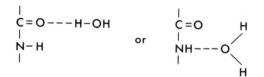

Sponsler et al. (1940) give an interesting estimate of the amount of water which may be held by various groups in proteins. The carboxyl group can coordinate or bind four to five molecules of water; the amino group, three molecules; hydroxyl group, three molecules; imino and carbonyl groups, two molecules each. Mellon et al. (1947, 1948b) determined the extent to which the amino and peptide groups in proteins participate in water binding. For casein, they concluded that 24 to 33% of the total water adsorbed was held by the amino groups and an additional 45% by the peptide linkages. In zein, the peptide linkage adsorbed 70% of the total water taken up at a relative humidity of 80%.

C. The Water-Sorption Isotherm

A useful approach to the study of the adsorption of water by solid substances, such as those occurring in cereal grains, is given by means of the isotherm. An isotherm is a curve describing the amount of water adsorbed by a substance at a particular constant temperature as a function of the equilibrium vapor pressure, water activity, or relative humidity. The water activity, or equilibrium relative humidity, is defined as

$$\text{Water Activity} = A_w = p/p_0 = \frac{\text{\% Relative Humidity}}{100}$$

where p = the vapor pressure exerted by the water held by the food, at a given temperature, and p_0 = saturation vapor pressure of water at the same temperature.

The moisture content of a food in equilibrium with a given relative humidity may have two values, one when the food is adsorbing moisture, and another when it is desorbing or drying out. An isotherm may, therefore, be an adsorption or a desorption isotherm, and it is important when quoting sorption data to state to which the data refer. Procedures for obtaining water-vapor isotherms for foods have been described by many workers, including Ayerst (1965a) and Labuza (1968).

In general the isotherm may be described as a sigmoid curve, as shown in Figure 1. In the low-humidity range the curve is concave to the humidity axis; in the mid-range it has a region of inflection which is approximately linear; and in the high-humidity range the curve is concave to the moisture-content axis. The sigmoid isotherm is characteristic of cellulose (Sheppard and Newsome, 1934) and of proteins, e.g., casein (Mellon et al., 1948a) and edistin (Greenberg, 1938). It is also common to numerous other materials including cereal grains and their products. The shape, described as the Type II isotherm according to the classification of Brunauer et al. (1938), is significant and its implications merit discussion in greater detail.

Various isotherm models have been discussed in detail by Labuza (1968), Chung and Pfost (1967a), Gregg and Sing (1967), and Strohman and Yoerger (1967). Most theories, however, can predict adsorption of water only in one of the three main regions of the isotherm. Labuza (1968) suggests that the Brunauer-Emmett-Teller (B.E.T.) equation (Brunauer et al., 1938), which is discussed in detail by Gregg and Sing (1967) is probably the most useful in the study of isotherms of concern to the processing and storage of food materials, particularly for predicting the monolayer value of coverage and the heat of adsorption.

According to the B.E.T. theory of multilayer adsorption, the first portion of the isotherm—where the curve is concave to the humidity axis—represents the adsorption of the first layer of water vapor onto the surface of the absorbing material; the region of inflection represents the deposition of a second layer of water molecules; and the final curved portion represents the continued adsorption of additional layers. McLaren and Rowen (1952) have shown that for many

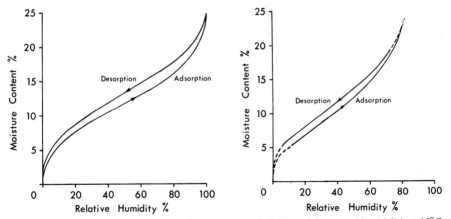

Figure 1. Moisture-sorption isotherms for maize starch (left) and for egg white (right) at 10°C. (FAO, 1970.)

proteins the number of water molecules adsorbed is very close to the number of polar sites on the polymer chain. Labuza (1968) points out that while the nitrogen surface area is closely related to the particle-size distribution of a food material, the water surface area is not. Various modifications to the B.E.T. equation have been suggested, the main one proposing that the radius of the capillary determines the upper limit of layers of water that can be accommodated within the capillary. A full and detailed discussion of the proposed modifications is given by Gregg and Sing (1967) and by Labuza (1968), who is of the opinion that, in the modified form, the B.E.T. equation reasonably represents the part of the isotherm that is concave to the humidity axis and the region of inflection, but cannot account for the capillary region, i.e., the final curved section of the isotherm. The initial portion of the isotherm may thus include only the deposition of water on polar sites, whereas the region of inflection includes the deposition of a first layer on nonpolar sites as well as an entire second layer. An alternative hypothesis—that water is adsorbed at polar sites as clusters of molecules rather than in layers—has also been suggested (Theimer, 1951). For a discussion on various theories of sorption of water by proteins and polymers, the reader is referred to a review by McLaren and Rowen (1952).

In each of the three segments of the isotherm there is a different relationship between vapor pressure and moisture content. In the initial portion of the isotherm, the vapor pressure/moisture content relationship is governed by the energy of binding between the water molecules and the adsorbing surface. The binding energy depends on the surface and its chemical constitution, and on the physical and chemical properties of the water. The magnitude of the binding energy will thus be the resultant of various effects. The extent to which the isotherm is displaced towards the moisture-content axis is an indication of binding energy between the water and the adsorbing surface.

In the intermediate, almost linear, portion of the isotherm, water molecules are being deposited on the water molecules already present in the first layer, and to a smaller extent on the nonpolar sites which have little influence on the properties of water. The energy involved in this process is predominantly that of condensation of water. In this range the amount of adsorption is strongly dependent on the water-vapor pressure. Park (1971), in a study of the adsorption kinetics of water vapor by yellow corn, found that the factors influencing the adsorption rate, in order of importance, were vapor pressure, initial moisture content, and temperature. Becker (1960) states that the absorption of liquid water by a wheat kernel proceeds by a heterogeneous mechanism, there being a very rapid initial absorption in which the pericarp is saturated by capillary imbibition, giving an activation energy of 12.3 kcal. per mole. He also found that the average moisture gain due to this absorption was 0.045 g. per g., dry basis, at 22°C. and observed that it decreased with increasing temperature.

In the high-humidity range the vapor pressure is determined primarily by the second layer, which covers the entire surface. Addition of third and fourth successive layers appears to be a kind of capillary condensation. The water deposited in each layer possesses nearly the same properties as water in the preceding layer. Thus the amount of water sorbed increases very rapidly in this range, but the vapor pressure of the system is influenced only moderately. The equation of Smith (1947) describes this portion of the isotherm for biological materials (Becker and Sallans, 1956).

The most interesting part of the isotherm is the initial portion, which is generally considered to describe the forces of interaction between the grain constituents and water. The strong displacement of this part of the isotherm towards the moisture-content axis is interpreted as indicating that strong intermolecular forces, and perhaps chemisorption, are involved in the adsorption of the water by the grain at low vapor pressures. Something of the magnitude of the forces involved is indicated by the observation of Babbitt (1949) that 3% moisture was retained by wheat at 25°C. and 0.8% at 34°C. in systems evacuated by a mercury-diffusion pump. Heats of hydration for flour, gluten, and starch, which are also indicative of the binding energy, have been measured by Winkler and Geddes (1931) and by Schrenk et al. (1949). Values of 27 calories for flour and 20 calories for gluten were obtained when 1 g. of these moisture-free substances was added to a large quantity of water. These values are average heats of hydration. A value of 260 calories has been reported by Greenberg (1938) when 1 g. of water was taken up by a large amount of moisture-free casein.

When a quantity of water vapor is adsorbed on a surface, a quantity of heat, the heat of adsorption, is given out. When water vapor is desorbed a quantity of heat is taken up, the heat of desorption. A measure of the heat of adsorption or desorption is an indication of the binding energy of the intermolecular force between the water vapor and the surface of the absorbent. Chung and Pfost (1967a) obtained the free energy changes and heats of adsorption and desorption from isotherms for corn and corn products at from 4 to 20% moisture content at 31°C. and reported them to range from 16 to 10.5 kcal. per mole, observing that these values are comparable to the values determined by Rodriguez-Arias et al. (1963) for corn; Becker and Sallans (1956), for wheat; and Bushuk and Winkler (1957), for flour, starch, and gluten.

D. Hysteresis

The moisture-sorption isotherms for carbohydrate polymers, such as starch and cellulose, are smooth sigmoid curves showing no discontinuities. The adsorption and desorption isotherms for such substances, however, are not necessarily the same. With many substances, including cereals and their products, the desorption isotherm is markedly displaced to the left of the adsorption isotherm (Figure 1), i.e., the moisture content corresponding to a given relative humidity may have two values, depending on whether the material is adsorbing or desorbing moisture. For material such as cereal grains and their products the moisture content in equilibrium with a given relative humidity is higher when the product is desorbing than when it is adsorbing moisture. One characteristic feature of such isotherms is that they demonstrate this phenomenon, which is known as hysteresis. It is a reflection of the direction from which the equilibrium state is approached, and may make a difference of as much as 1.5 to 2.0% in the moisture content represented by a particular value of equilibrium relative humidity (ERH). It is important, therefore, to know the previous history or treatment of a sample, and when quoting sorption data to state clearly whether they refer to an adsorption or to a desorption isotherm.

Babbitt (1949) was one of the first workers to demonstrate the effect of hysteresis in sorption and desorption of water from wheat and flour. Hubbard et al. (1957) investigated this phenomenon for wheat and corn. Other workers have reported the phenomenon of hysteresis in different commodities such as rough rice (Juliano, 1964) and brown rice (Houston, 1952).

The reasons for the hysteresis effect noted in this class of foods are not fully understood at the present time, and are the subject of continuing investigations. Many theories have been proposed to explain the phenomenon of hysteresis in the sorption behavior of porous solids, including foodstuffs (Gregg and Sing, 1967; Labuza, 1968). Young and Nelson (1967) studied the hysteresis effect in wheat and developed a theory relating equilibrium moisture content to temperature, relative humidity, and to the previous moisture condition of the material. They hypothesized three mechanisms by which water was held by the material: a) a unimolecular layer of water molecules bound to the surface of the cells, b) multimolecular layers stacked on top of the first layer, and c) moisture within the cells. Mathematical equations were developed, theoretically, to relate each of the three types of moisture to the condition of the environment and to the previous condition of the material. Chung and Pfost (1967b) postulated that the heat of desorption is greater than that of adsorption, or that sorptive sites are more available on the absorbent to water vapor in desorption than in adsorption. They investigated the effect of successive desorption and adsorption cycles on wheat at 50°C. and found that in the third cycle of desorption and adsorption the hysteresis effect disappeared.

Both chemical and physical factors have been advanced in various hypotheses to account for the phenomenon of hysteresis, based mainly on the effect of water condensing in the capillary structure of the material. Babbitt (1949) observed that hysteresis is not as pronounced with flour as with whole wheat, inferring that the structure of the cereal grains had an influence. Swelling that results from the absorption of water by a gel system may also be associated with structure (Smith, 1947). Pierce and Smith (1950) point out that plane surfaces with no capillary structure may also show hysteresis. They suggest that hysteresis results from energy changes which take place in the system when water, deposited first as clumps at active centers, merges to form a layer covering the adsorbing surface. Benson et al. (1950) showed that adsorption of water on proteins may be blocked by other substances, such as oxygen of the air. They found that in the absence of oxygen, adsorption and desorption equilibria could be reached in 1 to 3 hr. In comparison, previous work showed that, in the presence of oxygen, 6 to 8 days were required for adsorption and over 18 days for desorption equilibrium to be attained. Hart (1964), using intimate mixtures of marked grains of different moisture contents, found that only a few days were required for equilibrium to be achieved, though equality of moisture contents was not obtained due to the effect of hysteresis. Ayerst (1965b) observed that when products are exposed to an atmosphere of controlled relative humidity until a state of constant weight is attained, the observed hysteresis is large (1.5 to 2.0% moisture content) and pointed out that, in practice, relative humidity is never constant. If products are prepared to different moisture contents, either by adding moisture to them or removing moisture by drying, and the ERH relationship is determined, a smaller hysteresis effect is observed. Both Ayerst (1965b) and Pixton and Warburton (1971), using the same technique, found that with prepared samples the hysteresis effect was in the order of 0.5 to 1.0% moisture content. Becker and Sallans (1956) explain that, especially when products are artificially dried, the outer layers of particles change in moisture content more rapidly than do the inner layers, and in subsequent equilibration the moisture from the inside diffuses to the outer layers, i.e., the direction of water exchange in the outer layers is reversed. Tuite and Foster (1963) state that corn dried artificially at temperatures up to 60°C. should be stored at 0.5 to 1.0% lower moisture content than naturally dried grain in order to prevent mold development, because of its higher interseed humidity. Drying may, in some products, produce a reversed hysteresis effect (Ayerst, 1965b).

Thus, several factors may be involved in the hysteresis effect. In materials such as cereal grains, which possess an organized structure and which are made up of widely different substances, a multiple effect can indeed be expected.

E. Sorption Isotherms for Cereals and their Products

Cereals and their products, being colloids, are hygroscopic, i.e., they will sorb moisture from, or give it up to, the surrounding atmosphere until they are in equilibrium with it. The relative humidity of an atmosphere in equilibrium with a product increases with the moisture content of the product until saturation of the atmosphere is reached.

The relationship between the moisture content of different cereal grains, and cereal products, and their ERH has been studied by many workers. A useful summary of results obtained by different workers is given by Davey and Elcoate (1965). Oxley (1948a) observed that while published results differ among themselves, there is general agreement that the relationship between moisture content and relative humidity is best represented by a sigmoid curve rising steeply above 80% relative humidity.

A classic study of the water-sorption isotherm of cereals is that of Coleman and Fellows (1925). They equilibrated various grains with atmospheres of known relative humidities. In addition to wheat of various types, corn, oats, barley, rye, rice, buckwheat, and flaxseed were also studied. In general, the moisture contents of all cereals in equilibrium with the same relative humidity were much the same. Flaxseed, however, had a much lower moisture content. Figure 2 shows that while the moisture content/ERH relationship of starchy cereal grains differ only slightly, they differ widely from oilseeds. The evidence suggests that the oil content of a product simply acts as a weighting factor and reasonably comparable results for oilseeds may be expected if the moisture content is expressed on a fat-free basis.

Adsorption isotherms from flour have been obtained by Bailey (1920), Fairbrother (1929), Anker et al. (1942), and by Babbitt (1949). Knight and Larmour (1950) obtained isotherms for flour, bran, shorts, screenings, and middlings. Ayerst (1965b) obtained adsorption and desorption data, at two temperatures, for groundnuts, wheat, sorghum, coffee beans, coffee cherry, hazel nuts, black seed pepper, and pimento.

F. Effect of Temperature on ERH

When the temperature of a product is changed, the vapor pressure exerted by the moisture in the product (i.e., its moisture content) changes so that the humidity of the product atmosphere remains an almost constant fraction of that of a saturated atmosphere at the same temperature. Ayerst (1965b) and Pixton and Warburton (1971) found that, for wheat, if the moisture content remained constant, in the range 10 to 20%, the ERH increased or decreased approximately 3% for every 10°C. rise or fall in temperature. Above and below this range the effect of temperature decreased. Conversely, if the relative humidity remains constant, the moisture content of wheat decreases approximately 0.6 to 0.7% per 10°C. rise in temperature (Oxley, 1948a).

Morey et al. (1947) studied the equilibria between moisture content and vapor pressure for flour over a temperature range of 50° to 90°C. and found that vapor pressure increased markedly with temperature. The relationship between temperature and the logarithm of vapor pressure at a specified moisture content is essentially linear and can be expressed mathematically as

$$t = a \log p + b$$

where t is the temperature, °C.; p is vapor pressure; and a and b are constants. Pixton and Warburton (1971) studied the effect of temperature on the ERH relationship of different cereal grains, and tick beans, at temperatures from 0° to 40°C., and showed that over this temperature range there was a linear relationship between percent relative humidity and temperature, expressed mathematically for a given moisture content as:

$$\frac{1}{T} = b \log rh + k$$

where T is the absolute temperature, °C.; and b and k are constants. An example, for soft wheat, of this plot of log ERH for grain at a given moisture content against temperature, expressed as the reciprocal of the absolute temperature but labeled in degrees centigrade, is given in Figure 3. The lines of equal vapor pressure, also given in Figure 3, enable the fall in atmospheric temperature required to cause condensation to be found. Data on the effect of temperature on the ERH relationship have been obtained for sunflower seeds and oats (Colvin et al., 1947), rice (Karon and Adams, 1949), and starch (Hellman and Melvin, 1948, 1950; and Sair and Fetzer, 1944). Other related data may be found in the literature. For moderate ranges of temperature, relative humidity is often assumed to be independent of temperature; but the temperature effect must be included if accuracy is required or if a wide range of temperatures is to be considered.

G. Bound Water

Now that the forces involved in adsorption and the significance of isotherms have been discussed, the concept of bound water may be briefly considered. The isotherm has been considered in three sections: the initial curved portion, the intermediate linear portion, and the final curved portion. It has been pointed out that the energy of binding involved in the last two sections of the isotherm is principally that of condensation of water. Accordingly, it is the initial portion of the isotherm that must be emphasized, since it is in this region that interaction between water and the adsorbing substance is involved. It has also been pointed out

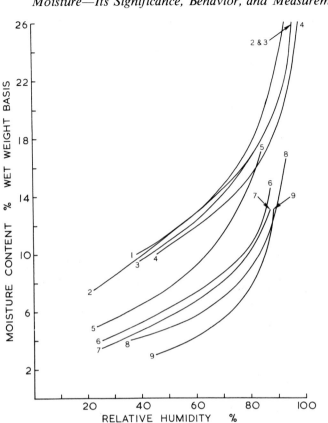

Figure 2. Absorption. The ERH relationship of various products, showing the difference between nonoily and oily grains. 1. English maize. 2. Cappelle wheat. 3. Barley. 4. American maize. 5. Soya beans. 6. Linseed. 7. Sunflower. 8. Groundnuts. 9. Smoked copra. (Pixton and Warburton. Unpublished.)

that adsorption of water on substances of which grain is composed takes place on specific active groups such as the carboxyl group, amino group, peptide linkage, and hydroxyl group. Thus, there is no single type of binding, but rather many types, each with a characteristic energy of reaction between water and the group on which adsorption takes place. The result of all these types of binding, ranging from inactive sorption to chemisorption, is represented by the isotherm, i.e., the isotherm represents "the normalization integral of the distribution function of site energies" (Katchman and McLaren, 1951).

The concept of bound water implies that some water adsorbed by the grain, for example, is held by forces stronger than those of simple cohesion between water molecules themselves. From what has been said so far, such a view certainly seems justified. This concession, however, does not endorse the bound water in its historical sense. Traditionally, bound water also implies a quantitative stoichiometric relationship between water and the adsorbing substance. Numerous

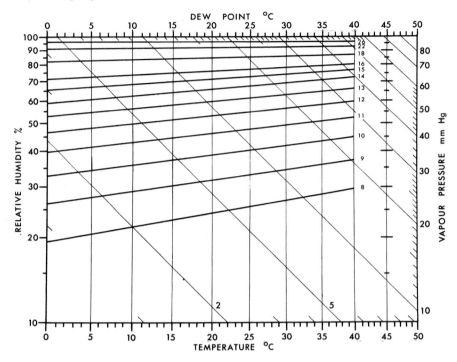

Figure 3. Adsorption. The ERH relationship, for a given moisture content, of Cappelle wheat at different temperatures. (Pixton and Warburton, 1971.)

attempts have been made to determine the amount of bound water and a variety of procedures have been developed.

It should be kept in mind, however, that the adsorption isotherm is a complete description of the water-binding relationship in the system, and that any method which is used to determine "bound water" is one which more or less arbitrarily selects some point on the curve. Water present and possessing a vapor pressure above this point is called "free water", whereas water adsorbed with a greater energy than that corresponding to this point is called "bound". The term "bound water" is thus relative, and methods for the estimation of bound water are arbitrary. In estimating "free water", it is assumed that the free water can be removed by the normal heat of vaporization, whereas bound water requires heat in excess of this (Becker and Sallans, 1956).

The above condition is not analogous to hydrate systems containing water of crystallization in which the presence of a hydrate can be sharply distinguished by the vapor pressure of the system. Isotherm studies on the more complex biocolloidal systems show clearly that no such point of demarcation between bound and free water can be selected. A discontinuity or break in the isotherm would be required, and such a break can hardly be expected in isotherms of systems in which a multiplicity of types of water-binding are involved.

Although at the present time bound water should probably be regarded as an indefinite concept, future qualitative studies will increasingly be focused on adsorption energies at specific sorptive sites and on the energy contribution of various chemical groups.

III. PRACTICAL CONSIDERATIONS

A. The Practical Significance of Isotherms for Stored Products

In discussion of the isotherm so far, emphasis has been placed on the description of water-binding in a biocolloidal system given by an isotherm. It is pointed out that a sorption isotherm is a graph of the moisture content of the product as a function of the ERH at a single temperature. This relationship can relate to a product adsorbing or desorbing moisture, and it varies for different products mainly because of differences in chemical composition. Storage of products becomes hazardous in conditions represented by the final curved portion of the isotherm, which begins between 75 and 80% relative humidities. In this region sufficient water is present to disperse the colloidal constituents and eventually fill the capillary spaces between particles when very high levels of ERH are reached. At this point a relatively large amount of water becomes available and may be utilized by the grain or microorganisms.

Industry and commerce require a reasonable estimate of the moisture content of a product, if only as a guide to the amount of dry matter being bought or sold. In considering storage potential, however, the ERH of the product is more important than the moisture content, since it is a measure of the availability of water to microorganisms associated with the product, i.e., the ERH at a given temperature gives an indication of the biological activity, or potential activity, of the product at that temperature (Ayerst, 1965a; Jones, 1969). Above 75% relative humidity molds will develop rapidly during storage, and heating of the product will occur with subsequent deterioration and loss. For products such as grain, the "safe" storage-moisture content is usually accepted as that in equilibrium with 70% relative humidity or less, and the chances of deterioration through development of microorganisms and subsequent heating are considerably reduced. The moisture content in equilibrium with 70% relative humidity varies with different products. Cereal grains are similar in this respect, but they differ widely from oily seeds (Figure 2).

The ERH relationship is particularly important for wrapped goods where the permeability of the wrapping material must be taken into consideration. The ERH of the product influences the interchange of moisture between the product and the atmosphere or free air space inside the wrapper. If the wrapping material is permeable to moisture the product may lose water and so lose weight; or, if it gains weight, increasing the ERH inside the wrapper, the product may deteriorate. If the wrapper is impermeable it will prevent loss of moisture from the product, but there might be a dangerously high increase in the ERH inside the package if there were a sudden fall in temperature. Condensation may result on the surface of the product, where the excess moisture would only be absorbed slowly. This problem is not serious if the product has a low moisture content, i.e., a low ERH, because of the small amount of water available to influence the hygroscopic state of the package; but for products with an initially high ERH, a wrapper should be somewhat permeable to moisture so that any excess moisture can escape (Jones, 1969).

B. Moisture Translocation

Deterioration may occur in stored grain even if the grain is at a safe and uniform moisture content if there are marked differences in temperature in different parts of the bulk. The intergranular air is not static, but is in constant motion through convection currents. When air moves from a warm to a cooler region it gives up moisture to maintain its relative humidity. This interchange usually takes place in the vapor phase (Anderson et al., 1943; Oxley, 1948b). Moisture moves along the vapor-pressure gradient caused by a temperature gradient in material of fairly uniform moisture content. Movement of moisture from a warm to a cooler region may cause the ERH to exceed the safe level. In extreme cases the air, on striking a cold surface, may be cooled below the dew-point (Figure 3), and water will condense onto the walls of the storage structure or onto the surfaces of the grain bulk, considerably increasing the ERH in that region and consequently increasing the risk of deterioration of the grain. Usually, however, the buffering effect of grain at a normal storage moisture content reduces the formation of dew, or condensation, on surfaces in which the grain is in contact, and, even if dew is deposited, the grain would probably be able to reabsorb the moisture. Anderson et al. (1943) found that a temperature difference of 35°C. across 6 ft. of grain with an initial moisture content of 14.6% caused the moisture content of the grain in the cold region (0°C.) to increase to 20% in 316 days. Moisture movement along a vapor-pressure gradient caused by a temperature gradient is a slow process, and equilibrium conditions are never established for any practical length of time or mass

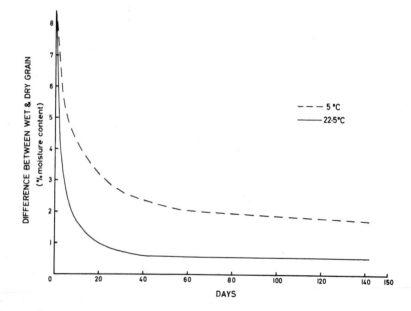

Figure 4. Rate of equalization of moisture content when 120 g. of wet wheat (22.1% moisture content, wet-weight basis) was embedded in 550 g. of dry wheat (13.7% moisture content, wet-weight basis). (Pixton and Griffiths, 1971.)

of grain. Diffusion is said to be the dominant mechanism of moisture transfer, assisted by convection currents. Disney (1969) suggests that damage to grain near the walls of bins arises from the continuous migration of moisture from a warm to a cooler area, combined with convected air currents rising from the center of a bulk of grain and falling down the cooler walls of the bin. Translocation of moisture resulting from temperature gradients is responsible for the mold development, caking, sprouting, and rotting which occur at the surface of a warm bulk of grain. By itself heating may not damage the grain, but the secondary effects caused by the translocation of moisture are the main cause of serious damage.

C. Diffusion of Moisture Through Grain

Liquid water is seldom intentionally allowed to come into contact with grain in storage. It is more important to consider the movement of water through grain in the vapor rather than in the liquid phase. The rate at which grain will adsorb or lose moisture depends on the amount by which its equilibrium humidity differs from that of the surrounding atmosphere, and on the extent to which the individual grains are exposed. The rate of moisture diffusion into and out of grains, i.e., the rate of moisture exchange with the atmosphere, is slower than usually expected, particularly when a large quantity of grain is stored in bulk.

Diffusion is the process by which matter is transported from one part of a system to another as a result of random molecular motions, similar to the transfer of heat by conduction. Fick (1855) first enunciated the mathematical theory of diffusion. This theory has been considered in detail by Crank (1956) and others.

The theory of diffusion in an isotropic medium is based on the hypothesis that the rate of transfer of the diffusing substance through a unit area of section is proportional to the concentration gradient normal to the section, i.e.,

$$F = \frac{-D\,\delta C}{\delta x}$$

where F is the rate of transfer per unit area of section, C is the concentration (mass per unit volume), and x is the space coordinate measured normal to the section. D, a constant of proportionality, is defined as the coefficient of diffusion and has dimensions $(length)^2$, $(time)^{-1}$. The negative sign in the equation arises because diffusion occurs in the direction of decreasing concentration.

Many workers have studied the movement of heat and water in stored grain (Anderson et al., 1943; Oxley, 1948a; Joffe, 1958) and the thermal properties of grain in bulk (Babbitt, 1945; Oxley, 1948b), but most of the work on the rate of moisture diffusion through grain has been concerned with drying problems. In their study of this phenomenon, Becker and Sallans (1955, 1957) used single grains of wheat and found that a standard solution of the diffusion equation for diffusion out of spheres was applicable to the drying of wheat. In the commercially important drying range of 10 to 23% moisture content (wet-weight basis), it was observed that the diffusion coefficient was independent of moisture content and was calculated to be between 0.069×10^{-6} and 2.77×10^{-6} cm.^{2} sec.$^{-1}$ in the temperature range 20° to 80°C. Fan et al. (1961) found that diffusion coefficients at temperatures below 65°C. are practically independent of variety. The rate of moisture transfer may be expected to be slow, and hence the diffusion coefficient will be small if the change in ERH with moisture content is small (Pixton and Griffiths, 1971). If the hygroscopic relationship has the well-known sigmoid form, then it is not unreasonable to suppose that the diffusion coefficient will be greatest at intermediate moisture contents and will decrease at high and low moisture contents. The movement of moisture in corn meal by diffusion alone was observed by Whitney and Porterfield (1968), though their main concern was the effect of internal heat generation.

Moisture transfer in bulk grain in the absence of temperature gradients has received little attention. Pixton and Griffiths (1971), using wheat, studied this phenomenon at two temperatures, 5° and 22.5°C., approaching the problem in two different ways. First they demonstrated that a wet patch of grain embedded in a dry bulk did not completely attain equilibrium with the dry bulk (Figure 4); and that, at 22.5°C., 65 days were required for the system to reach equilibrium. A difference in moisture content of 0.5% between the wet patch and the dry bulk remained after 140 days at 22.5°C. Equilibrium conditions had not been established after 140 days at 5°C. These authors further exposed columns of dry wheat to a high relative humidity at the surface, and other columns of high-moisture wheat to a low humidity, and observed the rate at which the moisture passed into and out of the columns of grain at the two controlled temperatures. The approach to the equilibrium state was more rapid at the higher temperature. The diffusion coefficients were calculated to be 2.4×10^{-6} to 2.6×10^{-6} cm.^{2} sec.$^{-1}$ at 5°C., and 7.1×10^{-6} to 8.9×10^{-6} cm.^{2} sec.$^{-1}$ at 22.5°C., for adsorption and desorption, respectively, over the range 8 to 18% moisture content (dry-weight basis).

If grain is exposed in a layer only a few kernels deep, the time to reach equilibrium with the relative humidity of an atmosphere may be a week or more. Further small increases in the thickness of the layer will greatly extend the time required for equilibration. Theoretically, after 12 months at a constant temperature

Back of Oven

11.86	11.87	11.87	11.91	11.87	11.96	11.98	
11.94	11.94	11.95	11.92	11.96	11.99	11.98	Direction
12.09	12.09	12.09	12.01	12.00	12.04	12.06	◄———
12.16	12.15	12.10	12.12	12.08	12.12	12.14	of
12.13	12.12	12.16	12.12	12.16	12.19	12.24	◄———
12.14	12.12	12.12	12.11	12.16	12.09	12.22	air flow
12.15	11.99	12.16	12.12	12.15	12.14	12.08	

Moisture values, top shelf of oven

Back of Oven

12.15	12.16	12.17	12.12	12.14	12.12	12.14	
12.23	12.22	12.19	12.20	12.23	12.26	12.22	Direction
12.25	12.24	12.24	12.24	12.27	12.30	12.31	◄———
12.16	12.20	12.18	12.19	12.18	12.24	12.31	of
12.20	12.20	12.21	12.21	12.22	12.23	12.26	◄———
12.18	12.21	12.24	12.22	12.23	12.21	12.27	air flow
12.20	12.21	12.21	12.21	12.23	12.22	12.26	

Moisture values, lower shelf of oven

Figure 5. Test for uniformity of heating in an oven.

of 22.5°C. and constant relative humidity, no change in moisture content would have taken place in grain 50 cm. below the surface of a large bulk (Pixton and Griffiths, 1971). Further, the rate of dispersion of moisture by diffusion alone, from a damp patch contained in an infinitely large bulk of dry grain at constant temperature, is extremely slow. This is well known from the behavior of grain of uneven moisture content in storage, but the calculations of Pixton and Griffiths (1971) are useful in indicating the effect of the size of the damp patch, and the temperature, on the rate of moisture transfer. The time is greatly increased as the patch becomes larger, as well as being influenced, to a lesser extent, by the change in diffusion coefficient with temperature.

It is essential that future studies should continue to include the elucidation of the concept of bound water, with special reference, perhaps, to the monolayer condition. It is equally essential that the whole range of moisture relations and behavior in products should be included, to determine conditions required to enable cereal grains and their products to be stored, or transported, without loss of quality.

IV. DETERMINATION OF WATER CONTENT

A. Basic Methods

Methods for determining grain moisture content which are generally classified as basic or primary methods are relatively accurate, but in general are too time consuming for most practical purposes.

OVEN METHODS

The most widely recognized methods for determining moisture content in grain are based on drying known weights of grain in various types of ovens and calculating moisture content from the weight lost in the drying operation. These methods appear to be rather simple and direct and usually constitute the "basic" methods against which rapid, practical moisture-testing equipment is calibrated. Actually, however, all oven methods for determining moisture content in grain are more or less empirical in nature, the results depending on the degree of subdivision of the material being tested, the time of drying, and the temperature and atmospheric pressure under which the drying is accomplished. In most biological materials, including grain, it is difficult if not impossible to remove all moisture by the application of heat without at the same time driving off small amounts of other volatile substances or causing decomposition of some of the constituents with the formation and release of moisture not initially present as such. Comprehensive surveys of the various oven-drying methods have been made by Bausch and Woller (1951), Bennett and Hudson (1954 a and b), Bruckner et al. (1950), Common (1951), Dubois (1952), Fetzer (1954), Hart et al. (1959), Hecht (1964), Senborn and Senborn (1953), Tsutsumi and Nagahara (1963), and Zeleny (1961).

The difficulty encountered in removing all moisture from biological material, even when it is finely ground, seems to be due principally to the fact that the water is present in different forms. When an inorganic material such as wet sand is heated at 100°C. or higher at atmospheric pressure, the water is lost at a rapid and essentially uniform rate until the material is completely dry. In drying finely ground grain, however, a much longer time is required to remove the moisture, the rate of moisture loss decreases rapidly as the drying progresses, and the ultimate loss in weight differs with the temperature employed for drying.

In biological materials such as grain, part of the moisture present appears to be tightly held or "bound" by powerful physical forces to proteins, high-molecular-weight carbohydrates, and perhaps other colloidal substances. This moisture, sometimes spoken of as "bound" water, is much more difficult to remove than "free" water. The tenacity with which water may be held to colloidal substances probably varies with the nature of the colloidal material and with the amount of water so held. Thus in the case of wet grain there are all gradations between "free" water that is removed by heat as readily as the water from wet sand, and water that is so tightly held that it can be removed only under conditions of temperature and pressure that may permit volatilization or decomposition of other constituents. For these reasons oven methods, as well as most other "basic" methods for determining moisture content in grain, are actually empirical; and to obtain comparable results, standard procedures that have usually been rather arbitrarily established must be followed precisely.

AIR-OVEN METHODS

The methods for determining moisture content as specified in the Official Grain Standards of the U.S. and in the U.S. Standards for Beans, Peas, Lentils, and Rice are all air-oven methods. These methods have been accepted by the AACC (Method 44-15). (See Appendix A, page 46.)

The proper method of grinding grain samples for moisture determination has been the subject of much controversy. There is no loss or gain of moisture when samples having 16% or less moisture (10% for soybeans and 13% for rough rice) are ground in the Wiley Intermediate Mill with an 18- or 20-mesh sieve. To determine whether the mill heats when used for a long time, a quart of hard red winter wheat was put through the mill as rapidly as possible and a portion was taken for moisture determination from each filling of the 4-oz. sample holder. Uniform results were obtained on all portions.

Special attention has to be given to grinding rough and brown rice and oats. For rice, the grinding chamber must be allowed to empty completely in order to obtain a representative sample. For oats, the grinding cannot be forced because the material will pack in the mill and give erroneous results.

Another commonly used air-oven method provides for heating a weighed portion of the finely ground grain for 2 hr. at 135°C. This method gives slightly higher results than the previously described method and is an official method of analysis for grain of the Association of Official Analytical Chemists (1970).

In addition to the conventional types of air oven, special types of air ovens are available which have built-in balances for weighing dried samples while they are still hot and without removing them from the oven. In some instances the balances may be used also for the initial weighings and are calibrated directly in terms of moisture percentage (see Figure 5). This type of oven is ideal for research on time and temperature studies on drying grain. It is also practical for the small laboratory, since it eliminates need for separate analytical balance, desiccator, and moisture dishes.

Safflower and sunflower seed cannot be satisfactorily dried for moisture determination in the ground state, as oxidation of the oil is so rapid that the samples will actually gain weight after partial drying.

Methods involving heating 10 g. of whole safflower seed for 1 hr. and whole sunflower seed for 3 hr. at 130°C. in an air oven yield results that agree with the Karl Fischer-method values (Johnson et al., 1956).

VACUUM-OVEN METHOD

One of the most widely accepted methods for determining the moisture content of grain is based on drying the finely ground grain at a temperature of 98° to 100°C. in an oven chamber maintained at a pressure of 25 mm. Hg or less. Heating is continued until no appreciable further loss of weight occurs (usually about 5 hr.). This method is one of the official methods of the Association of Official Analytical Chemists for grain and gives results in reasonably good agreement with the 1 hr., 130°C. air-oven method. Table I gives oven methods used by various technical societies and by Canada, England, France, and the U.S. Department of Agriculture as official methods.

DRYING WITH DESICCANTS

The moisture content of grain and other materials may be determined by placing a weighed portion of the finely ground material in a closed container with a relatively large quantity of an efficient desiccant. The desiccant chosen must have a lower vapor tension than the material being dried. The moisture in the material is gradually vaporized, and is then absorbed by the desiccant. Moisture content is determined by the loss in weight of the original material after it finally attains constant weight. Reducing and maintaining the atmospheric pressure in the container to a low level will greatly reduce the time required to complete the operation, but even when this is done the time required is too great for most practical purposes. However, one of the official methods of the Association of Official Analytical Chemists for determining moisture content in grain provides for holding the finely ground material under vacuum in the presence of anhydrous sulfuric acid until constant weight is attained. One advantage of the method is that it avoids the hazard of possible decomposition of organic material by heat. However, grain of high moisture content may decompose as a result of the action of molds and bacteria before the moisture content is reduced sufficiently to inhibit the growth of these organisms. Ethylene oxide or propylene oxide could probably be used to prevent such growth without affecting the results. Ethylene oxide (ETO) is used (12% ETO in 88% Freon 12) to preserve very wet samples, and has been found to have no effect on moisture determinations by the oven method or by electric moisture meters. Under positive pressure ETO will destroy molds, bacteria, and viruses but will not prevent souring or browning resulting from enzyme activity.

TOLUENE DISTILLATION METHOD

One of the official methods of the Association of Official Analytical Chemists and of the Corn Industries Research Foundation provides for boiling the finely ground grain in toluene in an apparatus that condenses the volatilized materials, collects the condensed water in a graduated tube, and returns the condensed

TABLE I

Official methods of various countries and technical societies for moisture determination of cereal grains and their products

Crop	AACC[a]	AOAC[b]	AOCS[c]	ASBC[d]	USDA[e]	U.S.S.R.	Canada	England	France	ICC[f]	ISO[g]	CEE[h]
Barley	9,18,27	9,18		14,17	9,27	6,8,19	9,27	2,9,10	5,10,22	10,22	10,22	10
Beans, dry, edible	3,27				3,27		3,27	2,9,24,25				
Brewers grains				1[i]				2,9				
Buckwheat		9,18		1		6,8,19	9,27	2,9,10				
Cereal adjuncts	18	1		1			1,18					
Corn, whole	3,27				3,27	6,8,19	3,27		13			
Corn, ground	9,18	9,18				6,8,19		2,9,10	5,12,22	12,22	12,22	12
Corn gluten feed		14,17,21,25							4,15			4,15
Corn-oil meal		14,17,21,25						2,4,17,24,25	4,15			4,15
Feed and feeding stuffs	18	14,17,21,25						2,4,9,17,24,25	4,15			4,15
Flaxseed, whole	2,27		11		3,27		11,27	4,17,24,25	4		4	
Flour	9,12,18				9	6,8,19		9,10	5,10,22	10,22	10,22	10
Grain	9,18	9,18			9,27		9,27	5,23	5,10,22			
Malt	1			1								
Oats, ground	9,27	9,18			9,27	6,8,19	9,27	9,10	5,10,22			
Peas and lentils	9,27				9,27	8,19		2,9,24,25	4		4	
Rice	9,27	9,18			9,27	6,8,19		9,10	5,10,22	10,22	10,22	10
Rye	9,27	9,18			9	6,8,19		9,10	5,10,22	10,22	10,22	10
Semolina	9,18	9,18			9,27	6,8,19		9,10	5,10,22	10,22	10,22	10
Soybeans	9,27		11		9,27		9,27	2,9,10,24,25	4		4	4
Safflower seed, whole					9			2,4,17,24,25	4			
Sunflower seed, whole					11	5		2,4,17,24,25	4		4	
Wheat, ground	9,18,27	9,18			9,27	6,8,19	9,27	9,10	5,10,22	10,22	10,22	10

[a] American Association of Cereal Chemists. [b] Association of Official Analytical Chemists. [c] American Oil Chemists' Society. [d] American Society of Brewing Chemists. [e] United States Department of Agriculture. [f] International Association for Cereal Chemistry. [g] International Standardization Organization. [h] European Economic Community. [i] Predried at 50° to 60° C.

Legend: Official Methods

1. Air-oven, 103° to 106°C. for 3 hr.
2. Air-oven, 103°C. for 4 hr.
3. Air-oven, 103°C. for 72 hr.
4. Air-oven, 100° to 105°C. for 3 hr., plus 1-hr. intervals to constant weight.
5. Air-oven, 102° for 17 hr., constant weight-corrective for relative humidity (CNERNA[a]).
6. Air-oven, 105°C. for 30 min., plus 130°C. for 40 min.
7. Air-oven, 130°C. for 30 min.
8. Air-oven, 130°C. for 40 min.
9. Air-oven, 130°C. for 1 hr.
10. Air-oven, 130°C. for 2 hr.
11. Air-oven, 130°C. for 3 hr.
12. Air-oven, 130°C. for 4 hr.
13. Air-oven, 130°C. for 38 hr.
14. Air-oven, 135°C. for 2 hr.
15. Vacuum-oven, 70°C. at 10 mm. Hg pressure-constant weight (CEE).
16. Vacuum-oven, 100°C. for 3 hr.
17. Vacuum-oven, 95° to 100°C. for 5 hr., or constant weight.
18. Vacuum-oven, 98° to 100°C. for 5 hr., or constant weight.
19. Vacuum-oven, 105°C. for 30 min., plus 130°C. for 1 hr.
20. Vacuum-oven, 80°C. for 20 hr.
21. Vacuum-desiccator, no heat, to constant weight.
22. Glass drying tube, at 10 to 20 mm. Hg pressure, temperature of 45° to 50°C., with P_2O_5 as desiccant (CNERNA, ISO, and ICC Basic Method).
23. Aluminum plate, 140°C. for 15 min.
24. Bidwell-Sterling, benzene.
25. Bidwell-Sterling, toluene.
26. Karl Fischer titration method.
27. Model 919 moisture meter (Motomco, CAE, Halross).

---

[a]CNERNA = Centre National d'Etudes et Recherches en Nutrition et Alimentation.

toluene to the boiling flask (Dean and Stark, 1920; Bidwell and Sterling, 1925). The boiling is continued as long as water accumulates in the graduated tube, and the moisture content of the grain is calculated from the volume of water condensed. Since the boiling of toluene is 111°C., all substances that boil at or below this temperature, including all water that will be released at this temperature, are distilled. Also, since the water is measured volumetrically, no water-insoluble volatile material can be measured as moisture. A modification of this method has been adopted for corn by the wet-corn-milling industry. Rauscher and Korn (1961) developed an improved apparatus which they claim increases the speed and accuracy of the method.

KARL FISCHER METHOD

In recent years considerable attention has been given to the method of Karl Fischer for determining the moisture content of a wide variety of materials. The method depends upon the reaction of iodine with water in the presence of sulfur dioxide and pyridine to form hydriodic acid and sulfuric acid. Since the method is strictly stoichiometric it is, theoretically at least, one of the most accurate methods for determining moisture content. In applying the method to grain, the grain must be finely ground and the moisture extracted with anhydrous methyl alcohol. Because of certain practical difficulties in its application, the Karl Fischer method has been used only infrequently in determining moisture content in grain, although Fosnot and Haman (1945) applied the method to wheat and barley. Hart and Neustadt (1957) have adapted the method to all cereal grains and have used it to test the accuracy of official oven methods. The technical skill required and the time-consuming nature of this analytical method make its usefulness likely to remain limited.

B. Practical Methods

Practical methods designed for the rapid routine determination of grain moisture content are for the most part secondary or indirect methods which must be standardized against one of the basic or primary methods.

BROWN-DUVEL DISTILLATION METHOD

For many years moisture content was determined in the routine inspection of grain by heating a weighed portion of unground grain in oil. The moisture volatilized by this heating is condensed, and then collected and measured in a graduated cylinder. The apparatus used for this purpose must be standardized to provide a definite amount of heat in a definite period of time. The method is highly arbitrary and the exact procedure to be followed must be established for each kind of grain in order to obtain results equivalent to those obtained by the applicable official oven method. The method was first proposed by Brown and Duvel (1907).

The Brown-Duvel method has been replaced by an electric moisture meter in the routine inspection of grain in the U.S. and Canada. The method was official for some of the grains in Canada until recently. Canada now uses the air-oven and vacuum-oven methods for calibrating the Model 919 moisture meter which is used in Canadian grain inspection.

DIRECT HEATING METHODS

Various modified air-oven methods with special heating equipment have been devised to shorten the time required as compared with standard oven methods. In general these methods provide for heating the material to temperatures considerably higher than those employed in the usual oven methods. Heating may be accomplished by ordinary electric heating coils; by radiation from infrared radiators; or by a high-frequency, high-voltage field. When employing these methods and devices, it is customary to determine in advance the time of heating and the temperature or other adjustment of the equipment required for each type of material to be tested in order to obtain results in reasonably good agreement with those obtained by one of the more basic methods.

CALCIUM CARBIDE METHODS

Calcium carbide (CaC_2) reacts readily and completely with water to form calcium hydroxide and acetylene. Parks (1941) was the first to utilize this reaction as a basis for determining the moisture content of plant materials. An excess of CaC_2 is mixed with a weight of plant material. The moisture in the material tested reacts with the CaC_2 and the acetylene escapes. The moisture content of the material is calculated from the weight lost by escape of the gas. A special balance for the weighings was devised so that the final reading is made directly in terms of percent moisture. Although the method is theoretically sound, practical difficulties appear to have prevented any extensive use of it in the testing of grain.

A moisture-testing device is available in which the material to be tested is mixed with CaC_2 in a tightly sealed, heavy metal container equipped with a pressure gage. For any given type of plant material, the pressure developed by the evolution of acetylene should be proportional to the moisture content of the material. This method and equipment are limited in use for measuring the moisture content of grain.

Gnezdov (1958) utilizes a 5-g. sample heated at $200°$ to $210°C$. in a vessel containing CaC_2. After 15 min. the loss of weight is determined. Dahl (1965a, 1966) speeds up the reaction by heating the sample and CaC_2 in a closed system and collecting the acetylene over mercury in a measuring buret. The French "Chopin" tester uses CaC_2 at an operating temperature of $200°C$. for approximately 5 min.

DICHROMATE METHOD

A method for measuring the moisture content of fruits and vegetables based on oxidation of the organic material by potassium dichromate has been proposed by Launer and Tomimatsu (1952). An excess of dichromate is used in the reaction, and the part that remains after oxidation is complete is determined by titration. A "dichromate factor" based on results obtained by a standard oven method for determining moisture content is established for each type of product to be tested. Although the method is intended primarily for products of high moisture content, it is applicable to rice containing from 10 to 15% moisture. Presumably it could be used for other grains.

Siddappa and Das (1954) modified the above procedure to reduce the time required to make the test. A finely ground portion of material is diluted with a known quantity of water. To this solution, 25 cc. of 1.835N dichromate and 40 cc. of concentrated sulfuric acid are added, and the mixture is allowed to stand 3 to 5 min. A portion of the mixture is placed in a test tube and rapidly cooled to room temperature under tap water. The color is measured in a colorimeter. The accuracy and reproducibility are stated to be high.

METHODS BASED ON RELATIVE HUMIDITY MEASUREMENT

When grain is freely exposed to the air it will gradually lose or gain in moisture content until it reaches a level in equilibrium with the relative humidity of the air to which it is exposed. Likewise the interstitial air in unventilated stored grain will tend to become stabilized at a relative humidity in equilibrium with the moisture content of the grain. Thus, after equilibrium is established, a measurement of the relative humidity of the interstitial air may be used as a rough index of the moisture content of the grain. Actually such relative humidity measurements may be better indexes of the keeping quality of grain than direct moisture-content measurements, since the activity of molds and other microorganisms that develop on the surfaces of and within grain kernels, and that are largely responsible for grain spoilage, is probably more closely dependent upon the relative humidity of the surrounding air than upon the moisture content of the grain. Molds develop very slowly on grain when the relative humidity is below 75%, but rapid deterioration as a result of mold growth is likely to occur at ordinary temperatures if the relative humidity of the interstitial air is greater than 75% (Milner and Geddes, 1946). For long storage the moisture content should be low enough so that the relative humidity is considerably below 75, and probably below 65%.

Wet- and dry-bulb thermometers have been used by Gaus et al. (1941) to determine the moisture content of seed cotton prior to ginning by measuring the relative humidity of air drawn by suction from bulk lots of the product. Manufacturers of electric hygrometers are investigating the application of these devices to the measurement of moisture content in grain and other products.

Ives (1952) made ingenious use of dew-point depression as a measure of relative humidity in a closed jar of grain, and hence of the moisture content of the grain.

Certain inorganic salts, notably those of cobalt, undergo marked change in color at different relative-humidity levels as a result of degree of hydration. Practical use of this phenomenon has been made by Solomon (1945) in estimating the relative humidity of air in small spaces, and by Dexter (1948) in estimating the moisture content and keeping quality of grain and other farm products. Although the accuracy of any such method is not high, its simplicity may make it valuable for farm use.

To translate relative-humidity measurements into terms of grain moisture content, it is obviously necessary to know the relationship between the two. This relationship differs for different kinds of grain, and to some extent among different lots of the same kind of grain, probably because of the effect of hysteresis and of differences in the tenacity with which part of the water is held by colloidal constituents. Although various investigators have published data in respect to these relationships, there is a considerable amount of disagreement among the published reports. Perhaps the most thorough study of this subject is that of Hubbard et al. (1957).

The "previous history" of a sample of grain will affect its equilibrium moisture content at various relative humidities. In studies on corn by the Grain Division[1], it was desirable to bring all samples to 15% moisture. Samples were placed on wire screens in a walk-in environmental chamber controlled at a temperature and humidity designed to bring all samples to the desired moisture content. However, the moisture content of the samples at equilibrium ranged from 14.2 to 16.4%. This study and studies by other workers demonstrate that accurate moisture results cannot be obtained by relative humidity measurement.

PRACTICAL APPLICATION OF RELATIVE HUMIDITY TO MOISTURE DETERMINATION FOR GRAIN INSPECTION

Tests on grain with various hygrometers have shown that when the samples were transferred from the mailing container to a test cell, about 2 hr. were required for the relative humidities to come to equilibrium. To determine the minimum time for a sample to come to moisture-relative humidity equilibrium, a completely closed system was designed in which a diaphragm-type pump forced air over the sample as it was being agitated in a container. The air, filtered to eliminate dust, was passed over the sensing element of an electric hygrometer in another container and then back to the pump. By this method, uniform relative humidity measurements could be made at the end of 5 min.

C. Sources of Error in Moisture Measurement

Accuracy in moisture determination is dependent upon many factors. Some of these are:

a) *Representative sample.* Usually the sample selected for oven drying consists of a few grams which may represent as much as an entire carload. Proper sampling methods must be used, or the error from this source will be great. (See Chapter 3 for details.)

b) *Protection of the sample.* The condition of the sample must be maintained by use of moistureproof containers. There should also be: a minimum exposure to air during reduction to degree of fineness required for oven drying, and during weighing before drying; proper desiccation during cooling; and rapid weighing after cooling.

c) *Accurate weighing of sample.* The precision of weighing required to produce the degree of accuracy desired should be determined, and only equipment and techniques which will guarantee this accuracy should be used.

d) *Preparation of samples.* For samples that require grinding before drying, several factors are involved:

1) Mills that provide little or no exposure of the sample to air should be used.

2) The mill should be easy to clean between samples.

3) There should be little or no heating during reduction of the sample.

4) Fineness of grind is critical with grains. An 18-mesh screen (wire diameter is 0.018 in. and openings are 0.96 mm.) on the Wiley Intermediate laboratory

---

[1]Grain Division, Agricultural Marketing Service, U.S. Department of Agriculture, Beltsville, Md.

mill will give reliable results, but a 16-mesh screen will not. However, even with the 18-mesh screen, low moisture values will be obtained if the grain is forced rapidly through the mill or if the cutting blades of the mill are dull. Under these conditions, larger, grittier particles are produced, and will not dry completely during the prescribed time for oven drying.

5) High-moisture material may require a two-stage drying procedure. In such cases, a weighed portion of the sample is air-dried in a warm place (preferably on top of the heated oven) until it reaches a moisture level at which it can be ground without moisture loss (two-stage method). For example, with grains that are normally ground on the Wiley mill before oven drying, the direct and the two-stage drying methods produced no difference in results up to 16% moisture content, except with soybeans and rough rice. Between 16 and 18% moisture, the direct method averaged 0.09% lower than the two-stage method; above 18%, the differences were erratic.

e) *Sample size.* Sample size is critical in moisture determination. The U.S. Department of Agriculture and AACC oven methods for grain specify a 2- to 3-g. sample of the ground material for moisture determination. Since the density of grains such as oats and wheat differs greatly, it is often difficult for a technician to estimate sample size. Duplicate portions of a sample of ground wheat ranging from 3 to 10 g. were tested for moisture content. The values (average of closely agreeing duplicates) ranged from 12.30% for a 3-g. sample to 12.06% for a 10-g. sample. The results showed that a sample weighing 2 to 5 g. can be used with moisture dishes 55 mm. in diameter and 15 mm. high. However, even with the larger dishes (3-1/4 X 5/8 in.) which are used with the Brabender oven, samples of ground material weighing more than 5 g. gave very low moisture values.

It has been observed that surface caking takes place when larger-sized samples are used. This prevents complete removal of moisture, and may also explain why large, gritty particles do not dry readily.

f) *Ovens.* Either convection or forced-draft ovens can be used for moisture determination. Forced-draft ovens are preferred. Preferably, ovens should operate continuously when in use, to ensure uniform heating and greater stability of temperature.

Each oven should be checked for stability of temperature, uniformity of heating, ventilation, rate of airflow, rate of recovery after insertion of samples, and accuracy of the thermometer or other temperature-measuring device.

1) *Temperature Stability.* The oven should maintain a temperature at all times within $\pm 1°C$.

2) *Heating Uniformity.* To check this, prepare a large sample of the commodity to be tested. Place a weighed aliquot in each of a large number of moisture dishes. Distribute the dishes over the shelf or shelves, and record the position of each dish. Plot moisture content of each sample according to its position in the oven to determine if there are any hot or cold spots. (See Figure 5.)

3) *Ventilation.* Inadequate ventilation of an oven can result in low moisture values of as much as 1% or more. A dried sample of wheat was placed in an oven containing a tray of water and the forced-air draft was cut off. Under these conditions, the sample picked up 1.4% of water at $130°C$.

4) *Airflow.* The airflow in the oven should be adjusted to the maximum rate possible without blowing the material from the dish. If the airflow is not adjustable, it may be necessary to install baffles.

5) *Recovery Rate.* The oven should regain temperature within 15 to 20 min. after insertion of the samples. Timing of the drying period should begin when the oven is within one degree of the desired temperature.

6) *Thermometer Accuracy.* Mercury thermometers held constantly at high temperature may become inaccurate after several months. Usually the thermometer will not be off more than 2°C., but one was found to be off 7°C. Occasionally new thermometers are inaccurately calibrated. Each thermometer should be checked against a standard precision thermometer when it is new and again after each 6 months of use.

g) *Desiccant.* Dried grain is about as hygroscopic as phosphorus pentoxide. Presumably other dried biological material would behave similarly. As mentioned earlier, dried wheat picked up moisture even at 130°C. Dried wheat will also restore the deep blue color to exhausted indicating-type silica gel. Therefore, activated alumina beads, of 1/16-in. pellets of "Molecular Sieves", type 4A or 4AXW, are preferred desiccants. The molecular sieves will reduce the moisture vapor in a desiccator to such a low level that an electric hygrometer with a sensing element calibrated for the 0 to 10% range of relative humidity does not show a reading.

h) *Room humidity.* The moisture content of grain samples dried at 103°C. is affected by room humidity. When the humidity of the air going into the oven was controlled at various levels, humidity levels of 90 to 100% gave sample-moisture values 0.2% lower than when the humidity was at the normal 40 to 60%. Room humidity has no effect on samples dried at 130°C.

i) *Nonaqueous losses.* The U.S. Department of Agriculture and AACC oven methods for grain have been subjected to critical examination by comparison with the Karl Fischer chemical-titration method and by analysis of the effluents driven off by heating. For all grains except corn, flaxseed, and soybeans, the nonaqueous loss was insignificant, and the average deviation between the Karl Fischer results and the oven results was less than 0.1%. A 2-year study on corn showed that there was an average nonaqueous loss of 0.34%. Since this loss occurred in the early heating stages, the present method of drying whole corn for 72 hr. at 103°C. was deliberately chosen to leave approximately 0.3% of the moisture in the sample to compensate for this loss.[2] Drying whole flaxseed at 130°C. results in an average nonaqueous loss of 0.6%. This can be eliminated by drying the whole seed for 4 hr. at 103°C. Soybeans showed a nonaqueous loss from 0.0 to over 1.0%, with an

---

[2]As this is submitted for publication, collaborative studies between the senior author and Dr. Andre Guilbot, Directeur de Recherches A l'I.N.R.A., Massey, France, showed that corn grown in France gave moisture values about 1% too low when dried by this procedure. Since French corn is very hard and is essentially identical to flint corn grown in the U.S., additional studies were made on 66 samples of corn containing from 6 to 100% flint corn. These samples also gave low moisture values (mean deviation from standard of −0.97%) when dried for 72 hr. at 103°C. Additional drying for 120 hr. showed little or no increase in loss of moisture. The Committee on Moisture Determination, International Organization for Standardization (ISO)—chaired by Dr. Guilbot—has proposed that ground corn be dried for 4 hr. at 130°C. as the reference standard. Although this procedure gives abnormally high results on dent corn, both Karl Fischer and gas-chromatographic analyses indicate that it is more accurate for hard corn such as flint corn or corn grown in France. However, before a recommendation is made to adopt the ISO proposed method for use with flint corn, further research will be conducted on the 1972 corn crop. Flint corn, dent corn, and various mixtures of these will be evaluated.

average of 0.5%. This loss occurs mostly at low temperatures in the early stages of drying, and a satisfactory oven method has not been developed to counteract this. Limited research on the vacuum-desiccator method proposed by the International Standardization Organization indicates that this may be a satisfactory method for soybeans.

Too often it is assumed that nonaqueous loss owing to decomposition occurs near the end of the heating period. Actually, much of this loss occurs as the sample is heating up to the temperature of the oven. When thermocouples were embedded in kernels of corn in an oven, there was the usual endothermic absorption of heat until the internal temperature reached approximately 70°C. The reaction then became strongly exothermic until the internal temperature was approximately 80°C., when it again became endothermic. The strong exothermic reaction around 70°C. was attributed to highly accelerated decomposition resulting from enzymatic activity. The nonaqueous volatiles in soybeans are driven off well under 100°C.

Leroy (1954) reports that vapor pressure of the sample should be taken into consideration during drying. The influence of drying temperature (105° and 130°C.) was tested in about 1,000 samples by Nehring (1952). At both temperatures no final equilibrium value was found.

According to Oxley and Pixton (1960), water as vapor or liquid added to a soft wheat was accurately determined by the oven method (heating 4 hr. at 113°C.), but a hard wheat was over-assessed 1% in proportion to the amount added, when the moisture content was raised from 9 to 25%, dry-weight basis. Since changes in weight are not directly proportional to change in water content on wet basis, dry basis of calculation was found more convenient for presentation and statistical treatment. The amount of water removed from both wheats by drying in a current of warm air was over-assessed. That from hard wheat was over-assessed in proportion to the amount removed, about 0.25% on drying from 25 to 0%, while over-assessment was inversely proportional in the case of soft wheat. Apparently, the ability of an oven-drying method to measure known amounts of water in wheat is related to the type of wheat.

According to Schild and Wegh (1962), the new E.B.C. mill did not break down barley other than by grinding, so that there was no chance of error from vapor loss by grinding.

Veijola (1949a and b) lists four types of errors: errors in methods, sampling errors, errors in procedure, and accidental errors. Of these, the third is by far the most important.

Samples must be stored or shipped in airtight and moistureproof containers. Plastic bags are suitable, provided they are at least 4 mm. (0.004 in.) thick. Moisture-loss tests were made with grain and water sealed in plastic bags of various thickness. These tests were: a) Storing under vacuum in a desiccator; b) storing at high humidity; and c) shipping back and forth to various points in the U.S. by both rail and air.

With 4-mm. (0.004-in.) or heavier bags, there was no loss or gain in weight over extended periods. A 6-mm. (0.006-in.) bag is preferred for its greater durability in mailing. Heavier bags are hard to seal adequately.

By calculation of maximum possible vapor loss, and by actual tests, it has been

TABLE II

Effect on electrical moisture-meter results of tempering grain

Grain	Test Condition[a]	Oven Moisture %	% Deviation from Oven			
			Meter A	Meter B[b]	Meter C[b]	Meter D
Dark	A	9.99	+0.14	+1.28	+0.08	−0.07
hard	B	15.55	+4.53	+3.60	+1.66	+1.06
red	C	15.64	+0.66	+0.00	−0.54	−0.44
winter	D	15.66	+0.06	−0.39	−1.02	−0.57
wheat	E	15.49	+0.21	−0.34	−0.82	−0.48
	F	15.62	+0.04	−0.39	−0.95	−0.64
Dark	A	10.89	−0.58	+1.55	−0.50	−0.44
hard	B	15.90	+2.03	+1.57	+0.37	+0.46
red	C	16.00	+0.15	−0.12	−0.79	−0.23
winter	D	15.86	−0.16	−0.46	−1.04	−0.40
wheat	E	15.73	−0.11	−0.31	−0.85	−0.24
	F	15.80	−0.17	−0.37	−0.97	−0.33
Dark	A	10.63	−0.08	−0.05	−0.18	−0.14
Northern	B	16.16	+4.03	+6.54	+1.28	+0.91
spring	C	16.19	+0.90	+1.61	−0.73	−0.32
wheat	D	16.21	+0.15	+0.16	−1.18	−0.63
	E	16.17	+0.14	+0.25	−1.19	−0.26
	F	16.08	+0.28	+2.81	−1.03	−0.50
Dark	A	10.89	−0.25	−0.22	−0.42	−0.06
Northern	B	16.44	+1.74	+2.49	−0.85	+0.06
spring	C	16.27	+0.24	+0.91	−1.05	−0.36
wheat	D	16.27	−0.14	+0.01	−1.26	−0.46
	E	16.27	−0.19	−0.11	−1.27	−0.52
	F	16.26	−0.17	+0.02	−1.21	−0.41
Soft	A	11.51	−0.80	−0.26	−0.11	+0.11
red	B	14.24	+1.35	−0.07	−0.44	−0.48
winter	C	14.13	+0.34	−0.64	−0.69	−0.52
wheat	D	14.13	−0.11	−0.42	−0.85	−0.58
	E	14.12	−0.14	−0.76	−0.93	−0.60
	F	13.99	−0.07	−0.90	−0.84	−0.47
Soft	A	11.48	−0.81	−0.63	−0.62	−0.11
red	B	14.40	+0.84	−0.35	−0.78	−0.49
winter	C	14.29	−0.07	−0.84	−0.90	−0.55
wheat	D	14.29	−0.36	−1.01	−0.96	−0.65
	E	14.28	−0.50	−1.02	−1.11	−0.66
	F	14.25	−0.47	−0.87	−1.15	−0.56
White	A	11.27	−0.17	+0.11	+0.29	−0.01
club	B	12.88	+1.34	−0.06	+0.29	+0.14
wheat	C	12.75	+0.18	−0.45	+0.29	+0.00
	D	12.75	+0.15	−0.50	+0.15	+0.04
	E	12.68	+0.13	−0.29	+0.14	+0.13
	F	12.86	−0.01	−0.57	+0.04	+0.08

(Continued on next page)

TABLE II, *Continued*
Effect on electrical moisture-meter results of tempering grain

Grain	Test Condition[a]	Oven Moisture %	% Deviation from Oven			
			Meter A	MeterB[b]	Meter C[b]	Meter D
White club wheat	A	0.69	−0.21	+0.40	+0.20	+0.13
	B	12.70	+1.70	+0.07	+0.30	+0.30
	C	12.85	+0.34	−0.45	−0.01	−0.03
	D	12.73	+0.03	−0.51	+0.05	+0.11
	E	12.78	−0.19	−0.51	−0.05	+0.06
	F	12.67	−0.12	−0.60	−0.01	−0.04

[a]Test Conditions: A, initial test before tempering; B, tested 1 hr after tempering; C, tested 4 hr. after tempering; D, tested 24 hr. after tempering; E, tested 48 hr. after tempering; and F, tested 72 hr. after tempering.
[b]Meters B and C are different models of the same machine.

shown that the container does not have to be completely full in order to avoid moisture loss in the sample.

AACC National Check Sample Service mails samples in plastic bags with no apparent adverse effects on moisture content.

Most instrument manufacturers and many investigators of moisture meters temper samples to various moisture levels to prepare moisture-conversion charts. Several investigations of this procedure have been made by the Grain Division. Table II is a summary of one such study which shows clearly that tempered samples cannot be used for evaluation of an instrument's performance or for preparation of conversion charts. However, the Motomco Moisture Meter can be used to determine the moisture content of grain as it is being dried if the internal temperature of the grain does not exceed 140°F. Samples taken from the first-stage dryer at 140°F., and then from the second- and third-stage cooling-drying operations, showed good agreement with oven-moisture tests on each portion. Grain dried at internal temperatures higher than 140°F. has shown considerable deviation between oven and meter values. These tests on grain during drying were not made on other makes of meters (except the McGill-Tag), so their accuracy in this situation has not been determined. The Tag gave very poor results on these samples.

D. Electric Moisture Meters

Certain electrical properties of grain depend largely on the moisture content, and these properties have been used as the basis for a number of devices for determining moisture content.

The possibility of determining the moisture content of grain by resistance measurements was first demonstrated by Briggs (1908). Using as electrodes 12-in. brass rods inserted into a jar of wheat, and, with a Wheatstone bridge, measuring the resistance of the wheat to the flow of current from an electromotive force of 17 volts, he found a linear relationship between the moisture content of the wheat and the logarithm of its resistance, over the moisture range of about 11 to 16%. He also showed the effect of temperature on the electrical resistance of wheat.

In 1909, Zeleny (Anthony) devised an electrical instrument for determining the moisture content of corn. Electrodes in the form of spaced metal points were pressed into the germs of individual kernels of corn. The two electrodes were of dissimilar metals, so that they formed a simple voltaic battery. The current produced depended upon the moisture content of the corn and was registered on a sensitive galvanometer. Thus, no battery or other external source of current was required. In a later modification of the instrument a battery was added to the circuit and the electrodes were made of the same metal, so that the galvanometer deflection became essentially a measure of conductivity of the corn kernel.

Although neither the Briggs nor the Zeleny devices were used extensively for practical purposes, they stimulated interest in electric grain-moisture testing and were the forerunners of a number of electric moisture meters now widely used in the grain trade. Most modern meters are based on conductance or capacitance measurements. Various measurement techniques, devices utilizing these techniques, their relative accuracy—both among the various devices and the devices as compared to basic methods—are cited by Nuret and Dubois (1949); Hlnyka et al. (1949); Duma (1958); Groves and King (1946); Guilbot (1949a and b,1952); Ivaska (1949); Kubo (1955); Kuhne (1956); Leroy (1965); Martens and Hlynka (1965); Platonov (1967); Shiba and Ichinose (1965); Urion (1956); and USDA Bulletin AMS-511, Grain Division (1963).

For testing the accuracy of moisture-measuring devices, at least two identical models of each device should be used. For example, two identical models of a new moisture meter were tested side by side with corn. One meter showed a mean deviation of standard (MDS) from the oven of +2.61%, with a range from +0.84 to +3.95%; and the other, a MDS of +1.28% with a range from −0.43 to +2.25%.

CONDUCTANCE-TYPE MOISTURE METERS

In conductance-type moisture meters the grain is pressed between two electrodes connected in series with a suitable source of current and a galvanometer. A series of fixed resistors may be introduced individually into the circuit so that the full range of the galvanometer may be utilized for separate relatively narrow ranges in moisture content.

In one type of conductivity meter a weighed or measured portion of grain is pressed to a standard thickness between two electrodes in a small cylinder. In another type of meter, formerly used in the inspection of grain under the Official Grain Standards of the U.S., the electrodes are in the form of corrugated steel rolls, one of which is motor-driven. The grain, which need not be weighed or measured, is poured between the two rolls, which are accurately spaced with respect to each other and rotate in opposite directions, subjecting the grain passing between them to high pressure.

Conductance-type moisture meters are relatively easy to keep in adjustment and to maintain in satisfactory alignment with one another. They are very rapid in operation, particularly the meter using motor-driven electrodes. One of the principal disadvantages of conductance meters is that their accuracy is dependent in large measure upon a normal distribution of moisture within the kernels of grain. Grain that has recently been dried gives low readings since the surfaces of the kernels are abnormally dry in relation to the moisture content of the grain as a whole. Likewise freshly tempered (moistened) grain gives high readings because of the high surface-moisture content. (See Meter A in Table II.) Mixtures of wet and dry grain and grain that is musty or sour also often fail to produce correct readings with conductance-type meters. Furthermore, conductance meters are quite limited in the range of moisture content they can measure. At moisture levels below about 7%, moisture in grain appears to be so tightly "bound" that it contributes very little to the conductivity, hence satisfactory readings may not be obtained at such levels. At moisture levels above about 23%, grain conductivity is so great that increases are not measurable with further increase in moisture content. At these moisture levels, therefore, conductance meters are subject to error.

CAPACITANCE-TYPE MOISTURE METERS

Since the dielectric properties of grain depend largely on its moisture content, the capacity of a condenser in which grain is the dielectric will vary in accordance with the moisture content of the grain. This principle has been utilized in the development of a number of grain moisture meters. In some the circuits are designed so as to utilize the change in impedance resulting from the change in capacitance as a means of measuring the moisture content. Impedance decreases with increases in grain moisture content.

Moisture meters of this type have certain inherent advantages over conductance-type meters. They are less subject than conductance meters to errors resulting from uneven moisture distribution within or among the kernels of the grain being tested, and to errors associated with mustiness or moldiness of grain. They are also capable of testing grain over a wider range of moisture content than are conductance meters. Capacitance meters are particularly useful in testing freshly dried or tempered grain, mixtures of wet and dry grain, out-of-condition grain, and grain of very high or low moisture content.

Good replicability of results is somewhat more difficult to obtain with capacitance meters than with conductance meters, particularly in the higher moisture ranges. This appears due to a degree of nonuniformity in the packing and orientation of the grain kernels when they are dropped into position between the plates of the condenser. Another disadvantage encountered with many capacitance moisture meters is the difficulty in keeping them in proper adjustment, particularly in maintaining accurate alignment among instruments. Marked improvements, however, have been made in capacitance meters both in respect to precision in manufacture and to means for maintaining proper adjustment and alignment.

NUCLEAR MAGNETIC RESONANCE METHOD

Shaw et al. (1953) observed that the magnetic resonance absorption due to hydrogen nuclei can be used to measure the moisture content of various materials. Equipment and methods for determining moisture content by means of this principle are described by Rubin (1958), Skripo and Neiganz (1964), and Miller and Kaslow (1963). Although this method is rapid and may be the most accurate of the various secondary methods for determining grain moisture content, it still has to be calibrated against some basic method, and the present cost of the essential equipment would prohibit its adoption for routine use.

E. Inaccuracies in Moisture Testing

The basic methods of determining moisture under the grain standards of the U.S. are oven methods. These methods are empirical and may be subject to errors owing to decomposition and loss of nonaqueous volatile matter. The Karl Fischer method, as modified by Hart and Neustadt (1957), apparently gives the true moisture content of grain. Therefore, all U.S. Department of Agriculture oven methods have been designed to give results which agree with those obtained by the Karl Fischer method.

Fortunately the 130°C., 1-hr. oven method on ground material, which has been the standard for most grains for many years, gave results which agreed within 0.1% of those of the Karl Fischer method, and did not need revision. The water-oven method formerly used for corn and beans was shown to underestimate moisture content by approximately 1%, while air-drying the ground sample at 130°C. for 1 hr., or the whole grain at 103°C. to constant weight, gave results approximately 0.3% too high. Trapping of the vapors from the oven operated at 130° and at 103°C. showed that the value of 0.3% was due to a nonaqueous loss. Therefore a drying time (72 hr.) which yielded values equivalent to those of the Karl Fischer method was incorporated as the basic method for corn and beans.

The Grain Division has from time to time tested many of the moisture-measuring devices available in this country and from other countries. Much attention has been devoted to electrical moisture meters because they are rapid. But it has been obvious for many years that there are problems in measuring moisture electrically. Grains originating in different parts of the country, for example, frequently do not show the same electrical properties, and thus register different results. Consequently, moisture-meter conversion charts are based on the average of all the meter readings and, for any particular area, the results as compared with the oven may be higher or lower. On subsequent crop years the area difference may be reversed. Furthermore, it has been observed that the electrical properties may change from day to day on some samples even though the moisture values as determined by the oven method have not changed. Usually the changes are progressively greater in one direction, but at times the changes are in one direction and then reversed on successive tests. Several moisture meters were used in tests on the constancy of electrical properties of grain. They did not respond identically to the electrical changes which occurred. The Motomco was decidedly less influenced by electrical variations than the others. It has also been less subject to the area-to-area or season-to-season variations. The Motomco moisture meter was adopted for rice inspection in 1960, and for corn and soybean inspection on September 1, 1962. On May 1, 1963, it became official for all grain inspection under the U.S. grain standards. It is also an approved method of the AACC (Method 44-11).

The use of the Motomco in the inspection of grain has been substantiated by the Canadian Grain Commission. This meter (now called simply Model 919 in Canada) was one of ten meters tested by Hlynka et al. in 1949 when it was called the Halross moisture meter. It has been used in the official inspection of Canadian grain since then. In 1965 Martens and Hlynka reported that the "Model 919 moisture meter consistently gave better moisture results on grain than all other meters tested in the Grain Research Laboratory".

However, the Motomco is not the final answer to the need for a practical, accurate, yet rapid method of moisture determination. In individual instances it may still yield results that deviate more than is desirable from the oven-method values. Possible reasons for this behavior follow.

The main cause of electrical-property variation is probably the nature of water distribution within the grain. The first part of this chapter covers hydrogen bonding and other forces which influence the position and nature of water in organic structure. At this point we will discuss "free" and "bound" water as they relate to moisture measurement with electric meters. "Bound" water is water which is tightly linked within the molecular structure of starch, protein, and other components of grain to such an extent that it is essentially a part of the physical structure, although not the chemical structure, of the molecules. The dielectric constant of "bound" water is essentially the same as that of the molecule with which it is associated (Oehme, 1958); and, since it is not capable of dissolving mineral salts while so bound, it is a nonconductor of electricity (Hunt, 1965). "Bound" water, therefore, cannot be measured by conductance-type meters.

"Free" water is defined as water which is capable of acting as a solvent and is found in the interstitial spaces between the larger molecules. Since this water contains dissolved salts, it can conduct electricity, and its dielectric constant is close to the value of 80 for pure water when it does not contain much dissolved matter.

Theoretically, because of hydrogen bonding, there is no distinct line of demarcation between water that will conduct electricity and that which will not.

Since "bound" water is not measurable by conductance-type meters such as the McGill, Marconi, and Universal moisture meters, these meters measure "free" water only and add a constant value for the bound water. Charts for conductance-type meters are based upon the assumption that there is a fixed amount of bound water at all times. However, there is evidence that the ratio of free and bound water may not remain constant and, as changes occur, errors are introduced in the moisture measurement.

Although dielectric moisture meters such as the Motomco and Steinlite measure both "free" and "bound" water, the great difference in dielectric value of these two types of water may introduce errors in measurement when the ratio of the two shifts. However, the Motomco has consistently shown less deviation from the oven method value than any other electric meter tested.

F. Basic Reference or "True Moisture" Methods

In the early pages of this chapter various theories on the composition of water in grain are given. In spite of all these studies, there is still considerable doubt as to what exactly is meant by "true" moisture content of grain. Oven methods are shown to be empirical, and different oven methods will yield different results. In recent years studies on gas chromatography, Karl Fischer titration, nuclear magnetic resonance, microwave, and vacuum-desiccator methods have led to claims by researchers that they can determine the true moisture content of samples. We will examine these:

GAS CHROMATOGRAPHY

Apparently, Weise et al. (1965) of the National Bureau of Standards are the only ones to have reported on this procedure. Using samples supplied by the Grain Division, they prepared methanol extracts of the ground grain and tested the extracts by both gas chromatography (GC) and Karl Fischer. Extracts were made at room temperature. This required from 1 to 5 days. Five percent Polyethylene 400 on Polytetrafluoroethylene (30 to 60 mesh) was found to effectively elute water with minimal tailing. The procedure requires approximately one-half hour per sample. It also requires sophisticated equipment and a trained analyst. However, it may, on further study, prove to be an accurate measure of "true" moisture content. Agreement between the GC and Karl Fischer methods was excellent.

VACUUM DESICCATOR

Buré and Guilbot (1962) concluded that grain dried in a vacuum desiccator over phosphorus pentoxide at a temperature of 45° to 50°C. and under 10 to 20 mm. Hg pressure gave true moisture content without any nonaqueous loss due to decomposition. This method has been proposed as a basic international reference method by the International Organization for Standardization and the International Association for Cereal Chemistry. Limited studies by the Grain Division indicate the method has merit and warrants further investigation.

NUCLEAR MAGNETIC RESONANCE

Moisture determination by nuclear magnetic resonance (NMR) was listed earlier in the chapter as a practical method, since instrument readings had to be calibrated against some basic method such as the air-oven. However, recent developments in equipment and techniques have led to claims that free water, semi-bound water, and bound water can be measured accurately and independently. Substantiation of these claims should make the NMR a basic method for measurement of true moisture control. Toledo et al. (1968) report on "Quantitative Determination of Bound Water by NMR." Shanbhag et al. (1970) report on "Bound Water Defined and Determined at Constant Temperature by Wide-Line NMR."

KARL FISCHER TITRATION

The accuracy of the Karl Fischer titration method for detecting minute quantities of water is well known. Therefore, if water can be completely extracted from grain with a solvent such as methanol, then, theoretically, a very accurate measurement of true moisture is possible with the K. F. method. Hart and Neustadt (1957), Kostyrko and Plebansko (1965), and Kostyrko and Wyzykowska (1966) report on using a modified Stein Laboratory Mill to extract water from grain using methanol as a solvent. This extraction procedure requires only a few minutes per sample. Weise et al. (1965), in testing both the K. F. and the GC, extracted the samples from 1 to 5 days by soaking at ambient temperature. Blank determinations by both procedures indicated that no interfering substances were extracted along with the water. Although the K. F. method should be basic, repeatability between different operators is unsatisfactory.

NEAR-INFRARED ABSORPTION TECHNIQUES

Water exhibits absorption bands at 0.75, 0.97, 1.18, 1.45, and 1.94 μm. as well as at longer wavelengths. The bands at 0.97 and 1.94 μm. are the most useful for moisture analysis because most free from interfering absorption from the components. Three possible methods for moisture analysis by infrared absorption are by reflectance from the sample surface, transmittance through a thin layer of sample, and by transmittance of an extract from the sample. Each of these techniques has been applied, and the choice depends on the nature of the sample and the accuracy desired. Extraction with a solvent, as has been done by several investigators—Gold (1964); Goulden and Manning (1970a and b); Hart et al. (1962) and Rader (1966)—requires time and chemical manipulations, but this technique offers an accurate method of moisture determination which can be used as a standard. The most commonly used solvents are methanol, dimethyl sulfoxide, and dimethylformamide. Coefficients of variability of less than 1% have been obtained within a laboratory.

Direct spectrophotometric analysis by reflectance or transmittance measurements on suitably prepared samples offers essentially instant moisture analysis. Sample inhomogeneity represents the greatest source of error, and for best accuracy the sample must be ground uniformly. Coefficients of variability of less than 1% can be attained. An instrument is now available from Anacom Corporation and at least two other firms have instruments under development.

G. Interesting Experiments

NEUTRON MODERATION
Ballard and Ely (1961) and Marcesse et al. (1967) have experimented with this method on corn. The accuracy was not great and required very large samples.

SPECTROSCOPIC DETERMINATION OF TOTAL WATER CONTENT
Broida and Morowitz (1955) mixed the sample with heavy water. The initial $H_2O:D_2O$ ratio is about 0.99. The final mole ratio is measured and the weight fraction of water is calculated.

MICROWAVE ABSORPTION
Watson (1965) describes a nondestructive method in which the moisture content of nonmetallic porous solids and liquids containing water is determined by the absorption of a beam of electromagnetic microwaves sent through them.

TRITIUM (RADIOACTIVE ISOTOPE OF HYDROGEN)
See Walton and Wolfe, 1961. Calculations have shown that present methods of determination of tritium do not have the accuracy required.

EXTRACTING WITH SALT WATER AND TITRATING FOR CHLORIDE
See Walton and Wolfe, 1961. Wheat extracts water from salt solution, and concentrates, rather than dilutes it.

BOMBARDMENT WITH FAST NEUTRONS
See Walton and Wolfe, 1961. This method detects all hydrogen nuclei regardless of whether they are in liquid or solid matter. No practical solution to isolating water nuclei has been found.

THERMAL EFFECT OF MIXING CONCENTRATED SULFURIC ACID WITH WATER
See Visyagin and Lisina, 1950. A 3-g. sample of the grain, contained in an insulated test tube fitted with a thermometer, is treated with 2 cc. of concentrated sulfuric acid (d. 1.84) and the rise in temperature in 5 min. is determined. For the same kind of grain this temperature rise is a linear function of the moisture content.

RELATION BETWEEN MOISTURE CONTENT OF RICE GRAINS AND ITS RIGIDITY

See Morishima and Nakagawa, 1953. In samples of Norin No. 22 (small grain), the rigidities of rice containing 7, 10, 13, 14, 16, and 18% moisture were, respectively, 15.8, 14.5, 12.5, 11.5, 9.8, and 9.4 kg.

COLORIMETRIC METHOD

See Whitehead and Sherrill. The sample is placed in dry methanol containing dry CaC_2. The water in sample reacts with CaC_2 to release acetylene, which is swept out of the methanol into a cuprous salt solution. A red product forms which shows maximum absorbance at 595 nm. Accuracy, when compared to the Karl Fischer method, is ±0.01%.

SURFACE FRICTION

See Finn-Kelcey and Clayton, 1957. A meter operates on the principle that surface friction of grain varies with moisture content and, through measurement of the depth of penetration of a weighted blade into a mass of grain, moisture content can be obtained.

LITERATURE CITED

AMERICAN ASSOCIATION OF CEREAL CHEMISTS. 1969. *AACC Approved methods* (8th ed.). Publ. by the Association, 3340 Pilot Knob Road, St. Paul, Minnesota 55121.

ANDERSON, J. A., J. D. BABBITT, and W. O. S. MEREDITH. 1943. The effect of temperature differential on the moisture content of stored wheat. Can. J. Res. C21: 297-306.

ANKER, C. A., W. F. GEDDES, and C. H. BAILEY. 1942. A study of the net weight changes and moisture content of wheat flour at various relative humidities. Cereal Chem. 19: 128-150.

ASSOCIATION OF OFFICIAL ANALYTICAL CHEMISTS. 1970. *Official methods of analysis* (11th ed.). Publ. by the Association, P.O. Box 540, Benjamin Franklin Station, Washington, D.C. 20044.

AYERST, G. 1965a. Water activity – its measurement and significance in biology. Int. Biodeterior Bull. 1: 13-26.

AYERST, G. 1965b. Determination of water activity of some hygroscopic food materials by a dew-point method. J. Sci. Food Agr. 6: 71-78.

BABBITT, J. D. 1945. Thermal properties of wheat in bulk. Can. J. Res. 23F: 388-401.

BABBITT, J. D. 1949. Observations on the adsorption of water vapor by wheat. Can. J. Res. 27F: 55-72.

BAILEY, C. H. 1920. The hygroscopic moisture of flour exposed to atmospheres of different relative humidity. Ind. Eng. Chem. 12: 1102-1104.

BALLARD, L. F., and R. L. ELY, Jr. 1961. Moisture determination in corn by neutron moderation. U.S. At. Energy Comm. ORO485.

BAUSCH, H., and S. WOLLER. 1951. Determination of moisture content (in cereal grains). Brauerei Wissh. Beil. 4(1): 1-4.

BECKER, H. A. 1960. On the absorption of liquid water by the wheat kernel. Cereal Chem. 37: 309-323.

BECKER, H. A., and H. R. SALLANS. 1955. A study of internal moisture movement in the drying of the wheat kernel. Cereal Chem. 32: 212-226.

BECKER, H. A., and H. R. SALLANS. 1956. A study of the desorption isotherms of wheat at 25°C. and 50°C. Cereal Chem. 33: 79-91.

BECKER, H. A., and H. R. SALLANS. 1957. A theoretical study of the mechanism of moisture diffusion in wheat. Cereal Chem. 34: 395-409.

BEN-GERA, I., and K. H. NORRIS. 1968. Isr. J. Agr. Res. 18(3): 125-132.

BENNETT, A., and J. R. HUDSON. 1954a. Determination of moisture in cereals: Review of methods in common use. J. Inst. Brew. (London) 60(1): 29-34.

BENNETT, A., and J. R. HUDSON. 1954b. Study of methods for determination of moisture in malt. J. Inst. Brew. (London) 60(1): 35-42.

BENSON, S. W., D. A. ELLIS, and R. W. ZWANZIG. 1950. Surface area of proteins. III. Adsorption of water. J. Amer. Chem. Soc. 72: 2102-2105.

BIDWELL, G. L., and W. F. STERLING. 1925. Preliminary notes on the direct determination of moisture. Ind. Eng. Chem. 17: 147-149.

BOLLING, H. 1960. Weight losses incurred in moisture determination in grains. Getreide Mehl 9: 102-108.

BRIGGS, L. J. 1908. An electrical resistance method for the rapid determination of the moisture content of grain. U.S. Dep. Agr. Bureau of Plant Industry Circ. No. 20.

BROIDA, H. P., and H. J. MOROWITZ. May 17, 1955. Spectroscopic determination of total water content. U.S. Patent 2,708,387.

BROWN, E., and J. W. T. DUVEL. 1907. A quick method for the determination of moisture in grain. U.S. Dep. Agr. Bureau of Plant Industry Bull. 99.

BRUCKNER, G., M. HENGST, and M. ROHRLICH. 1950. A standard method for the determination of water in grain and grain products. Muhlen-Ztg. 4: 233-235; Chem. Zentralbl. II, 1296.

BRUNAUER, S. 1943. *The adsorption of gases and vapors.* I. Physical adsorption. Princeton University Press, Princeton, N.J. 08540.

BRUNAUER, S., P. H. EMMETT, and E. TELLER. 1938. Adsorption of gases in multimolecular layers. J. Amer. Chem. Soc. 60: 309-319.

BURÉ, J., and A. GUILBOT. 1962. Basic reference method for determination of water in cereals and their products. Fermentatio 6: 276-282.

BUSHUK, W., and C. A. WINKLER. 1957. Sorption of water vapor on wheat flour, starch, and gluten. Cereal Chem. 34: 73-86.

CHUNG, D. S., and H. B. PFOST. 1967a. Adsorption and desorption of water vapor by cereal grains and their products. II. Development of the general isotherm equation. Trans. Amer. Soc. Agr. Eng. (St. Joseph, Mich.) 10: 551-554.

CHUNG, D. S., and H. B. PFOST. 1967b. Adsorption and desorption of water vapor by cereal grains and their products. III. A hypothesis for explaining the hysteresis effect. Trans. Amer. Soc. Agr. Eng. (St. Joseph, Mich.) 10: 555-558.

COLEMAN, D. A., and H. C. FELLOWS. 1925. Hygroscopic moisture of cereal grains and flaxseed exposed to atmospheres of different relative humidity. Cereal Chem. 2: 275-287.

COLVIN, R., B. M. CRAIG, and H. R. SALLANS. 1947. Hygroscopic equilibria for hulls and kernels of sunflower seeds and oats. Can. J. Res. 25F: 111-118.

COMMON, R. H. 1951. Moisture determination. I. Some basic difficulties in testing for moisture. Can. Food Ind. 22(12): 6-9.

CRANK, J. 1956. *The mathematics of diffusion.* Clarendon Press, Oxford, England.

DAHL, S. 1965a. Determining moisture in solid materials by reaction with calcium carbide. Mater. Res. Stand. 5(9): 446-453.

DAHL, S. 1966. Determining moisture in solid materials by reactions with calcium carbide. J. Amer. Leather Chem. Ass. 61(2): 75-89.

DAVEY, P. M., and S. ELCOATE. 1965. Moisture content/relative humidity of tropical stored produce. Part I. Cereals. Trop. Stored Prod. Inf. 11: 439-467.

DEAN, E. W., and D. D. STARK. 1920. A convenient method for the determination of water in petroleum and other organic emulsions. Ind. Eng. Chem. 12: 486-490.

DEXTER, S. T. 1948. A colorimetric test for estimating the percentage moisture or the storage quality of farm products or other dry materials. Mich. Agr. Exp. Sta. Quart. Bull. 30: 422-426.

DEXTER, S. T. 1949. A modified wet and dry-bulb thermometer technique for determining the moisture content of storage qualities of so-called dry materials. Mich. Agr. Exp. Sta. Quart. Bull. 31: 275-286.

DISNEY, R. W. 1969. the formation of dew on a cooled surface in contact with dry wheat. J. Stored Prod. Res. 5: 281-288.

DOLEZALOVA, A., and H. VRTELOVA.

1966. Moisture determination in barley. Kvasny Prum. 12(6): 125-131.

DUBOIS, M. 1952. Rapid determination of water in cereals. Bull. Anciens Eleves École Fr. Meun. 129: 107-111.

DUMA, Z. 1958. Accuracy of grain moisture determination. Przegl. Zbozowo-Miynarski 2: 84-87.

DUVAL, C. 1954. Rapid automatic determination of water and of ash in cereals. Chim. Anal. (Paris) 36: 61-62.

FAIRBROTHER, T. H. 1929. The influence of environment on the moisture content of flour and wheat. Cereal Chem. 6: 379-395.

FAN, L.-T., D. S. CHUNG, and J. A. SHELLENBERGER. 1961. Diffusion coefficients of water in wheat kernels. Cereal Chem. 38: 540-548.

FETZER, W. R. March, 1954. Some anomalies in the determination of moisture. Agr. Eng. 35(3): 173-178.

FICK, A. 1855. Ann. Phys. (Leipzig) 170: 59.

FINAR, A. L. 1957. The fundamental principles. p. 19 in *Organic chemistry*, vol. 1. Longmans, Green and Co. Ltd., London and New York.

FINN-KELCEY, P., and P. E. CLAYTON. 1957. Measurement of surface friction of grain to determine its moisture content. p. 490 in *The Engineering Index*.

FISCHER, K. 1935. A new method for the analytical determination of the water content of liquids and solids. Angew. Chem. 48: 394-396.

FOOD AND AGRICULTURE ORGANIZATION OF THE UNITED NATIONS, World Food Program. 1970. *Food storage manual.* Tropical Stored Products Center, Ministry of Overseas Development, Rome, Italy.

FOSNOT, R. H., and R. W. HAMAN. 1945. A preliminary investigation of the application of the Karl Fischer reagent to the determination of moisture in cereals and cereal products. Cereal Chem. 22: 41-49.

GAUS, G. E., C. S. SHAW, and W. H. KLIEVER. 1941. A practical seed-cotton moisture tester for use at gins. U.S. Dep. Agr. Circ. 621.

GLASSTONE, S. 1960. p. 113 in *Textbook of physical chemistry*, 2nd ed. Macmillan and Co., Ltd., London.

GNEZDOV, S. V. 1958. A thermic moisture meter. Inst. Sel'sk Khoz. N 1-2, 76-77.

GOLD, J. J. 1964. Food Technol. (Champaign) 18:586.

GOULDEN, J. D. S., and D. J. MANNING. 1970a. Determination of water in methanol by near infrared absorption. Analyst (London) 95(1128): 308-311.

GOULDEN, J. D. S., and D. J. MANNING. 1970b. Determination of moisture in dairy products by near infrared absorption of methanol extracts. J. Dairy Res. 37: 107-112.

GREENBERG, D. M. 1938. Certain chemical and physical characteristics of the proteins. In: *Chemistry of the amino-acids and proteins* (C. L. A. Schmidt, ed.). Charles C. Thomas, Springfield-Baltimore.

GREGG, S. J., and K. S. W. SING. 1967. *Adsorption, surface area and porosity.* Academic Press, London and New York.

GROVES, L. G., and J. KING. 1946. Determination of the moisture content of cereals by measurement of specific inductive capacity. J. Soc. Chem. Ind. (London) 65: 320-324.

GUILBOT, A. 1949a. Water in wheat. Ind. Agr. Aliment. (Paris) 66: 423-427.

GUILBOT, A. 1949b. Critical comparison of short-time registering devices for the moisture of grain. Bull. École Meun. Belge 11: 98-113.

GUILBOT, A. 1952. Determination of water in cereals. Reference method standardization and selection of apparatus for rapid determinations. Bull. Anciens Éleves École Fr. Meun. 129: 103-106.

HART, J. R. 1964. Hysteresis effects in mixtures of wheats taken from the same sample but having different moisture contents. Cereal Chem. 41: 340-350.

HART, J. R., L. FEINSTEIN, and C. GOLUMBIC. 1959. Oven methods for precise measurement of moisture content of seeds. MQRD Report No. 304.

HART, J. R., and M. H. NEUSTADT. 1957. Application of the Karl Fischer method to grain moisture determination. Cereal Chem. 34: 26-37.

HART, J. R., K. H. NORRIS, and C. GOLUMBIC. 1962. Determination of the moisture content of seeds by near-infrared spectrophotometry of their methanol extracts. Cereal Chem. 39: 94-99.

HARTH, O., W. KREIENBERG, and D.

MERTZ. 1953. Simple procedure for the determination of water in biological material. Klin. Wochenschr. 31: 905-907.

HECHT, H. 1964. Analytical specification of barley. Bayer. Landwirt. Jahrb. 41(7): 853-861.

HELLMAN, N. N., and E. H. MELVIN. 1948. Water sorption by corn starch as influenced by preparatory procedures and storage time. Cereal Chem. 25: 146-150.

HELLMAN, N. N., and E. H. MELVIN. 1950. Surface area of starch and its role in water sorption. J. Amer. Chem. Soc. 72: 5186-5188.

HLYNKA, I., V. MARTENS, and J. A. ANDERSON. 1949. A comparative study of ten electrical meters for determining moisture content of wheat. Can. J. Res. 27F: 382-397.

HOUSTON, D. F. 1952. Hygroscopic equilibrium of brown rice. Cereal Chem. 29: 71-76.

HUBBARD, J. E., F. R. EARLE, and F. R. SENTI. 1957. Moisture relations in wheat and corn. Cereal Chem. 34: 422-433.

HUKILL, W. V. 1965. Moisture in grain. p. 116-122 in *Humidity and moisture measurement and control in science and industry* (A. Wexler, ed.), vol. 2. Van Nostrand, New York, N.Y. 10001.

HUNT, W. H. 1965. Problems associated with moisture determination in grain and related crops. p. 123-125 in *Humidity and moisture measurement and control in science and industry* (A. Wexler, ed.), vol. 2. Van Nostrand, New York, N.Y. 10001.

HUNT, W. H., and M. H. NEUSTADT. 1966. Factors affecting the precision of moisture measurement in grain and related crops. J. Ass. Offic. Anal. Chem. 49(4): 757-763.

HUNTER, L. 1950. The hydrogen bond in organic chemistry. In: Rep. Symposium on the hydrogen bond, March 25, 1949. Roy. Inst. Chem. Lect. Monogr. Rep. (London).

IVASKA, S. 1949. Moisture analysis methods, especially the use of certain automatic moisture meters in determining the moisture in grain. Suom. Kemistilehti 22A: 103-115.

IVES, N. C. 1952. A dew-point moisture indicator. Agr. Eng. 33: 85-87.

JOFFE, A. 1958. Moisture migration in horizontally-stored bulk maize: The influence of grain-infesting insects under S. African conditions. S. Afr. J. Agr. Sci. 1: 175-193.

JOHNSON, R. M., W. H. HUNT, M. H. NEUSTADT, and L. ZELENY. 1956. A rapid dielectric method for determining the oil content of safflower and sunflower seed. J. Ass. Offic. Anal. Chem. 33(7): 314-316.

JONES, N. R. 1969. The meaning and importance of relative humidity. B.F.M.I.R.A. Symp. Proc. No. 4: 2-7.

JULIANO, B. O. 1964. Hygroscopic equilibria of rough rice. Cereal Chem. 41: 191-197.

KARON, M. L, and MAYBELLE E. ADAMS. 1949. Hygroscopic equilibrium of rice and rice fractions. Cereal Chem. 26: 1-12.

KATCHMAN, B., and A. D. McLAREN. 1951. Sorption of water vapors by proteins and polymers. IV. J. Amer. Chem. Soc. 73: 2124-2127.

KNIGHT, E. P., and R. K. LARMOUR. 1950. Moisture equilibrium of cereal products. Presented at Annual Conference, Chem. Ind. of Canada. Toronto.

KOSTYRKO, K., and T. PLEBANSKO. 1965. Improved apparatus for moisture extraction from friable materials. p. 27 in *Humidity and moisture measurement and control in science and industry* (A. Wexler, ed.), vol. 4. Van Nostrand, New York, N.Y. 10001.

KOSTYRKO, K., and A. WYZYKOWSKA. 1966. Moisture determination in cereal grains. Przegl. Zbozowo-Miynarski 10(1): 10-13.

KUBO, R. May 26, 1955. Water-content measurement by use of a wave guide. Japan 3600.

KUHNE, P. F. April 19, 1956. Determination of moisture in vegetable products. Ger. 941, 876, (Cl. 42L, 951).

LABUZA, T. P. 1968. Sorption phenomena in foods. Food Technol. 22: 263-272.

LAUNER, H. F., and Y. TOMIMATSU. 1952. Rapid method for moisture in fruits and vegetables by oxidation with dichromate. I. Potatoes and peas. Food Technol. 6(2): 59-64.

LECOMTE, J. 1954. Detection and determination of water by infrared spectrography. Chim. Anal. (Paris) 36: 118-122.

LEIKIN, Z. I. April, 1965. Determination of

humidity of grain. Sov. Invent. Illus., p. 27.

LEROY, R. 1954. A correct procedure for determining water. Chim. Anal. (Paris) 36: 294-301.

LEROY, R. 1965. Moisture measurement by high frequency currents. Humidity Moisture Papers Intern. Symp., Washington, D.C. 4: 135-140.

LLOYD, DOROTHY J. 1938. Imbibition of water by proteins. Cereal Chem. 15: 25-34.

MARCESSE, J., P. COUCHAT, and M. JOSSOUD. 1967. Grain moisture measurement with neutrons. Chem. Abstr. 66: 952-953.

MARK, H. F., and A. V. TOBOLSKY. 1950. *Physical chemistry of high polymeric systems,* 2nd ed. Interscience, New York.

MARTENS, V., and I. HLYNKA. 1965. Determination of moisture in Canadian grain by electric moisture meter. p. 125 in *Humidity and moisture measurement and control in science and industry* (A. Wexler, ed.), vol. 4. Van Nostrand, New York, N.Y. 10001.

MARTIN, J. H., and A. KNEVEL. 1965. Gas chromatographic method of moisture determination. J. Pharm. Sci. 54(10): 1464-1467.

McLAREN, A. D., and J. W. ROWEN. 1952. Sorption of water vapor by proteins and polymers. A. review. J. Polym. Sci. 7: 289-324.

MELLON, E. F., A. H. KORN, and S. R. HOOVER. 1947. Water absorption of proteins. I. The effect of free amino groups in casein. J. Amer. Chem. Soc. 69: 827-831.

MELLON, E. F., A. H. KORN, and S. R. HOOVER. 1948a. Water absorption of proteins. II. Lack of dependence of hysteresis in casein on free amino groups. J. Amer. Chem. Soc. 70: 1144-1146.

MELLON, E. F., A. H. KORN, and S. R. HOOVER. 1948b. Water absorption of proteins. III. Contribution of the peptide group. J. Amer. Chem. Soc. 70: 3040-3044.

MILLER, B. S., and H. D. KASLOW. 1963. Determination of moisture by NMR and oven methods in wheat, flour, doughs, and dried fruits. Food Technol. 17(5): 142-145.

MILNER, M., and W. F. GEDDES. 1946. Grain storage studies. III. The relation between moisture content, mold growth, and respiration of soybeans. Cereal Chem. 23: 225-247.

MOREY, L., HELEN KILMER, and R. W. SELMAN. 1947. Relationship between moisture content of flour and humidity of air. Cereal Chem. 24: 364-371.

MORISHIMA, S., and K. NAKAGAWA. 1953. The simple methods for determination of the moisture content of grains. Bull. Fac. Agr., Mie Univ. 6: 62-75.

NEHRING, K. 1952. The determination of water in feeding. Landwirt. Forsch. 3: 217-224.

NORRIS, K. H., and J. R. HART. 1965. Principles and methods of measuring moisture in liquids and solids. p. 19-25 in *Humidity and moisture measurement and control in science and industry* (A. Wexler, ed.), vol. 4. Van Nostrand, New York, N.Y. 10001.

NURET, H., and M. DUBOIS. 1949. Rapid determination of water in grain. Bull. Anciens Éleves École Fr. Meun., pp.: 80-88.

OEHME, F. 1958. Methods of dielectric measurement. Monographie No. 70 for Angewanotg Chemie and Chemie-Ingenieur-Technik Vertag Chemie, GMBH, Weinheim/Bergstr.

OKAMURA, T. Drying characteristics of soybean in relation to minute structure. Abihro Chikuson Daigahas Gakujutsu Kenkyu Hokoku, Dai-1-5(5): 767-779.

OXLEY, T. A. 1948a. *The scientific principles of grain storage.* Northern Pub. Co., Liverpool.

OXLEY, T. A. 1948b. Movement of heat and water in stored grain. Trans. Amer. Ass. Cereal Chem. 6: 84-99.

PARK, S.-W., D. S. CHUNG, and C. A. WATSON. 1971. Adsorption kinetics of water vapor by yellow corn. I. Analysis of kinetic data for sound corn. Cereal Chem. 48: 14-22.

PARKS, R. Q. 1941. A rapid and simple method for determining moisture in forages and grains. J. Amer. Soc. Agron. 33: 325-335.

PAULING, L. 1945. The adsorption of water by proteins. J. Amer. Chem. Soc. 67: 555-557.

PIERCE, C., and R. N. SMITH. 1950. Adsorption desorption hysteresis in relation to capillarity of absorbents. J. Phys. Colloid Chem. 54: 784-794.

PIXTON, S. W., and H. J. GRIFFITHS. 1971. Diffusion of moisture through grain. J. Stored Prod. Res.

PIXTON, S. W., and S. WARBURTON. 1971. Moisture content/relative humidity equilibrium relationship of some cereal grains at different temperatures. J. Stored Prod. Res. 6: 283-292.

PLATONOV, P. N. March 1967. Measurement of moisture in loose materials, for instance grain. Soviet Invent. Illus. p. 21.

RADER, B. R. 1966. J. Ass. Offic. Anal. Chem. 49: 726.

RAUSCHER, K., and O. KORN. 1961. Water determination in food products by distillation procedures. Nahrung 5: 656-662.

RODRIGUEZ-ARIAS, J. H., C. W. HALL, and F. W. BAKKER-ARKEMA. 1963. Heat of vaporization for shelled corn. Cereal Chem. 40: 676-683.

RUBIN, H. 1958. Nuclear magnetic resonance. Cereal Sci. Today 3(9): 240-243.

SAIR, L., and W. R. FETZER. 1944. Water sorption by starches. Ind. Eng. Chem. 36: 205-208.

SCHILD, E., and H. WEGH. 1962. The determination of the moisture content of brewing barley—Grinding in the new E.B.C. mill results in a certain simplification of the analysis. Brauwelt 102: 1800-1801.

SCHNATZ, G., and L. RICHTER. 1967. Automatic moisture analyzer for grain. Chem. Abstr. 66(17): 114763.

SCHRENK, W. G., A. C. ANDREWS, and H. H. KING. 1949. Heat of hydration of certain wheat flours and gluten. Cereal Chem. 26: 51-59.

SENBORN, A., and B. SENBORN. 1953. Moisture determination in wheat and flour. Zemljiste Biljka 2: 109-127.

SHANBHAG, SUDHAKAR, M. P. STEINBERG, and A. I. NELSON. 1970. Bound water defined and determined at constant temperature by wide-line NMR. J. Food Sci. 35: 612-615.

SHAW, T. M., and R. H. ELSKEN. 1950. Nuclear magnetic resonance absorption in hydroscopic materials. J. Chem. Phys. 18: 1113-1114.

SHAW, T. M., R. H. ELSKEN, and C. H. KUNSMAN. 1953. Moisture determination of foods by

hydrogen-nuclei magnetic resonance. J. Ass. Offic. Agr. Chem. 36: 1070-1076.

SHEPPARD, S. E., and P. T. NEWSOME. 1934. The sorption of water by cellulose. Ind. Eng. Chem. 26: 285-290.

SHIBA, K., and T. ICHINOSE. 1965. Moisture balance. p. 49 in *Humidity and moisture measurement and control in science and industry* (A. Wexler, ed.), vol. 4. Van Nostrand, New York, N.Y. 10001.

SHKURUPIY, E. N., and T. VSESOYAZ. 1958. The work of the Ukrainian research institute of the oil and fat industry in the field of new control instrument design. Protsessov V. Maslozhir Pron., Leningrad 60-63.

SIDDAPPA, G. S., and D. P. DAS. 1954. A photoelectric method for the rapid determination of moisture in biological materials. Curr. Sci. (India) 23: 157-158.

SKRIPO, A. L., and A. B. NEIGANZ. 1964. Proton-resonance moisture meter PRV-63. Kraneniya i Pererabotki Zerna 10: 22-23.

SMITH, S. E. 1947. The sorption of water vapor by high polymers. J. Amer. Chem. Soc. 69: 646-651.

SOLOMON, M. E. 1945. The use of cobalt salts as indicators of humidity and moisture. Ann. Appl. Biol. 32: 75-78.

SOLOMON, M. E. 1957. Estimation of humidity with cobalt thiocyanate papers and permanent color standards. Bull. Entomol. Res. 48: 489-506.

SPONSLER, O. L., J. D. BATH, and J. W. ELLIS. 1940. Water bound to gelatin as shown by molecular structure study. J. Phys. Chem. 44: 996-1006.

STROHMAN, R. D., and R. R. YOERGER. 1967. A new equilibrium moisture content equation. Trans. Amer. Soc. Agr. Eng. (St. Joseph, Mich.) 10: 675-677.

THEIMER, O. 1951. Hutigs adsorption isotherm. Nature (London) 168: 873.

TOKMAKOVA, M. M. 1957. Determination of moisture in grain at higher moisture contents. Spirt. Prom. 23(5): 37.

TOLEDO, R., M. P. STEINBERG, and A. I. NELSON. 1968. Quantitative determination of bound water by NMR. J. Food Sci. 33: 315-317.

TOMIMATSU, Y., and H. F. LAUNER. 1952. Rapid method for moisture in fruits and vegetables by oxidation with dichromate. II. Pineapple-rice-pudding, rice, prunes, and corn. Food Technol. 6(8): 281-285.

TRIOEN, M. 1948. Electrical determination of moisture in grain. Rev. Int. Brass. Malt. 85-93.

TSUTSUMI, C., and T. NAGAHARA. 1963. Determination of moisture in legumes by oven-drying methods. II. Determination of moisture in whole soybeans and peanuts, soybean flour, and defatted soybeans. Kaname Muroi, and Kunihiko, Ogawa, Shokuryo Kenkyusho, Kenkyu Hokoku 16: 18-23; Cf. Ibid. 16: 1-4, 5-8.

TUITE, J., and G. H. FOSTER. 1963. Effect of artificial drying on the hygroscopic properties of corn. Cereal Chem. 40: 630-637.

URION, E. 1956. Moisture content of grain. Brasserie 11(123): 313-316.

U.S. DEPARTMENT OF AGRICULTURE, Grain Division. 1963. Comparison of various moisture meters with the oven method in determining moisture content of grain. U.S. Dep. Agr. Bull. AMS-511.

VEIJOLA, T. 1949a. Sources of error in commercial moisture analyses on grain. Suom. Kemistilehti 22A: 95-103.

VEIJOLA, T. 1949b. Sources of error in moisture analyses in the grain market. Valtion Tek. Tutkimuslaitos Tiedotus No. 79, 11 pp.

VISYAGIN, N. I., and A. I. LISINA. 1950. A rapid method for the determination of moisture in grain. Selek. Semenovod. 17(10): 53-55.

WARTON, W. W. June 14, 1961. Progress in the measurement of moisture in grain. Presented before the 46th National Conference on Weights and Measures, Washington, D.C.

WATSON, A. 1965. Measurement and control of moisture content by microwave absorption. p. 87 in *Humidity and moisture measurement and control in science and industry* (A.

Wexler, ed.), vol. 4. Van Nostrand, New York, N.Y. 10001.

WEISE, E., R. W. BURKE, and J. K. TAYLOR. 1965. Gas chromatographic determination of the moisture content of grain. p. 3-6 in *Humidity and moisture measurement and control in science and industry* (A. Wexler, ed.), vol. 4. Van Nostrand, New York, N.Y. 10001.

WHITEHEAD, T. H., and R. W. SHERRILL. A new method for the quantitative determination of water.

WHITNEY, J. D., and J. G. PORTERFIELD. 1968. Moisture movement in a porous hygroscopic solid. Trans. Amer. Soc. Agr. Eng. (St. Joseph, Mich.) 11: 716-719, 723.

WINKLER, C. A., and W. F. GEDDES. 1931. Heat of hydration of wheat flour and certain starches including wheat, rice and potato. Cereal Chem. 8:455-475.

WOLFE, W. 1963. Differential dielectric apparatus for determination of water added to solvents. Anal. Chem. 35(12): 1884-1887.

YAMAMOTO, Y., Y. TOMITA, and M. SATO. 1957. Foods. II. Simplified rapid measurement of moisture by infrared moisture balance. Kagoshima Daigaku Nogakubu Gakujutsu Hokoku 6: 69-74.

YOUNG, J. H., and G. L. NELSON. 1967. Research of hysteresis between sorption and desorption isotherms. Trans. Amer. Soc. Agr. Eng. (St. Joseph, Mich.) 10: 260-263.

ZELENY, A. 1909. An electrical method for the measurement of the amount of moisture in grain and other materials. The Minnesota Engineer 17: 163-170.

ZELENY, L. 1961. Ways to test seeds for moisture. In: *Yearbook of Agriculture.* Yearbook Separate No. 3115. U.S. Dep. Agr.: Washington, D.C.

APPENDIX A

Moisture—Air Oven Methods[a]

Definition

These methods determine moisture content as loss in weight of a sample when heated under specified conditions.

Scope

Applicable to flour, farina, semolina, bread, grain, soybeans, rice, beans, peas, lentils, corn meal, corn grits, rolled oats, bulgur rolled wheat, breakfast cereals (except those which are sugar-coated). This method gives results closely approximating those obtained by Method 44-40 (vacuum-oven).

This method is not recommended for feeds and feedstuffs when fat determination is to be made on dried samples.

Apparatus

1. Wiley Laboratory Mill, intermediate model, equipped with 18- or 20-mesh screen and 4-oz. receiving bottle; or any other mill that will grind to same degree of fineness without undue exposure to atmosphere and without appreciable heating.

2. Oven (either gravity-convection or mechanical-convection), capable of being maintained at $130°C.$ $(\pm 1°)$ and provided with good ventilation. Thermometer shall be so situated in oven that tip of bulb is level with top of moisture dishes but not directly over any dish.

3. Oven for drying corn and beans, meeting requirements of oven in item 2 except that it is maintained at $103°C.$ $(\pm 1°)$.

4. Moisture dishes having diameter of ca. 55 mm. and height of ca. 15 mm. They should be of heavy-gage aluminum with slightly tapered sides and provided with tightly fitting slip-in covers which are designed to fit snugly under dishes when they are placed in oven. Both dish and cover should be identified by the same number. Before using, dry for 1 hr. at $130°C.$, cool in desiccator, and obtain tare weight. (See Note 1.)

5. Airtight desiccator, containing activated alumina, molecular sieves (type 4A or 4AXW), or other equally suitable desiccant. (See Note 2.)

6. Balance, accurate to at least 1 mg.

Procedure

One-stage:

For samples containing less than 16% moisture, except soybeans and rough rice for which moisture values of 10 and 13%, respectively, apply; also for flour, farina, and semolina except for grinding.

1. Grind a 30- to 40-g. sample in mill, leaving minimum possible amount in mill. Mix rapidly with spoon or spatula and transfer immediately a 2- to 3-g. portion to each of two or more tared moisture dishes. Cover and weigh dishes at once. Subtract tare weights and record weight of sample. Dismantle and clean mill between samples.

---

[a]AACC Method 44-15 (American Association of Cereal Chemists, 1969).

2. Uncover dishes and place them with covers beneath on shelf of oven. Insert shelf in oven at level of thermometer bulb. Heat for exactly 60 min. after oven recovers its temperature. (See Note 3.)

3. Remove shelf and dishes from oven, cover rapidly (using rubber finger insulators), and transfer to desiccator as quickly as possible. Weigh dishes after they reach room temperature (45 to 60 min. usually). Determine loss of weight as moisture (see equation 1). Replicate determinations must check within 0.2% moisture; otherwise, repeat determination.

Two-Stage:

For samples containing 16% or more moisture (10 and 13% for soybeans and rough rice), loss of moisture incident to grinding is likely to be excessive; hence, following two-stage procedure should be used.

1. Fill two or more tared moisture dishes nearly full with representative portions of unground sample. Cover and weigh dishes. Subtract tare weights and record weight of sample.

2. Uncover dishes and place them with covers beneath in warm, well-ventilated place (preferably on top of heated oven protected from dust) so that sample will dry reasonably fast and reach approximate air-dry condition. This will usually be accomplished in 14 to 16 hr. when top of heated oven is used, or approximately 60 hr. when room temperature is used for this preliminary drying. In all cases, except for soybeans and rough rice, moisture content must be reduced to 16% or less (10% for soybeans and 13% for rough rice).

3. Cover dishes containing air-dried samples and weigh them soon after they cool to room temperature. Determine loss in weight and record it as moisture loss due to air-drying.

4. Using air-dried sample, follow one-stage procedure described above, starting with grinding step. Calculate total moisture loss by using equation 2 under *Calculation.*

Air-oven, for corn and beans, at 103°C.:

Place approximately 15 g. of representative portion of unground sample in each of two or more tared moisture dishes. Weigh covered dishes and contents. Subtract weight of each dish from total weight and record result as weight of sample. Put covers under dishes and heat for 72 hr. in oven regulated at 103° ± 1°C. Dishes should be placed on single shelf with bulb of oven thermometer as close as possible to them. At end of heating period, remove shelf containing dishes, cover dishes immediately and place in desiccator. Weigh dishes when they reach room temperature. Determine loss in weight as moisture by using equation 1 under *Calculation.*

Replicate determinations should check within 0.2% moisture.

Air-oven, for flax, at 103°C.:

Proceed as above for corn and beans, except use 5- to 7-g. sample and 4-hr. oven time.

Bread, two-stage:

1. Air-dry and grind sample as directed in Method 62-05. Using 2- to 3-g.

portion of ground air-dried sample, follow one-stage procedure described above. Calculate total moisture loss by using equation 2 under *Calculation*. To obtain % of total solids in fresh loaf, subtract % total moisture from 100.

Calculation

Equation 1 (one-stage and 103° air oven):

$$\% \text{ moisture} = \frac{A}{B} \times 100$$

in which
A = moisture loss in g.;
B = original weight of sample.

Equation 2 (two-stage):

$$\% \text{ moisture} = \frac{\frac{E\ B}{D} + C}{A} \times 100$$

in which
A = weight of original sample used for air-drying;
B = weight of sample after air-drying;
C = moisture loss due to air-drying;
D = weight of subportion of air-dried sample used in 130°C. oven; and
E = moisture loss due to oven-drying.

Notes

1. Tare weight will usually remain constant within few tenths of mg. for approximately 1 year if dishes are dumped and then carefully wiped with soft cloth.

2. Silica gel and anhydrous calcium chloride are not suitable desiccants.

3. Oven should regain temperature within 15 to 20 min. after insertion of full load (24 moisture dishes). If oven requires longer time to recover, it should not be used.

Since this monograph is intended for use as an international reference standard, we are including (on the following pages) the basic and practical methods of moisture determination proposed jointly by the International Organization for Standardization (ISO) and the International Cereal Chemists (ICC). Many countries have already adopted these methods as official for international trade purposes. The basic method has been evaluated in considerable detail by the senior author and it appears to be worth considering. During the testing, the equipment was markedly improved to make the method more practical. It has been submitted to the ISO and ICC for consideration.

APPENDIX B

International Association for Cereal Chemistry (ICC)

ICC - STANDARD Nr. 109

§ 1. TITLE. Basic Reference Method for the Determination of Moisture Content of Cereals and Cereal Products.

§ 2. SCOPE. This method is applicable to ground grain, the particle size of which is equal to or smaller than 1.7 mm., and of which less than 10% by weight is larger than 1 mm. and more than 50% is smaller than 0.5 mm. This method is also applicable to flours and other cereal products which, if necessary, are ground to the above particle sizes.

This method is to serve as a standard for working out one or several practical reference methods or in establishing the working conditions for existing methods in order to achieve results which are as concordant as possible. It is not to be used for the settlement of commercial disputes.

§ 3. DEFINITION. In general, the moisture content of a product is defined as the loss in weight sustained by the material under certain circumstances.

The basic reference method for cereals aims at avoiding any chemical change of the substance (especially oxidation and loss of volatile organic substances) and at removing the whole of the moisture in the product (as shown by reversibility and water addition tests). In the present state of knowledge, it is considered that this method permits the determination of the true moisture content of cereals and cereal products.

§ 4. PRINCIPLE. The material, ground if necessary without change of moisture content, is equilibrated in an anhydrous atmosphere at a temperature between 45° and 50°C. and at a pressure of 20 mbar $\pm$ 7 mbar, i.e. of approximately 10 to 20 mm. of mercury.

Attainment of a state of equilibrium is indicated by constancy of weight; measurement of the loss of weight enables the moisture content of the product to be calculated.

§ 5. REAGENTS.

§ 5.1. Sulfuric acid (H_2SO_4), reagent grade: d 20° C. $\geqslant$ 1.83.

§ 5.2. Phosphoric anhydride (phosphorus pentoxide) (P_2O_5), reagent grade.

§ 6. APPARATUS.

§ 6.1. Precision balance (precision: 0.1 mg.).

§ 6.2. Apparatus which reduces the pressure to 20 mbar $\pm$ 7 mbar (e.g. water jet pump).

§ 6.3. Grinder made from a material which does not absorb any moisture, is easily cleaned, grinds rapidly and uniformly without heating, avoids contact of the sample with the surrounding air as far as possible, and fulfills the requirements given under point 2, "Scope" (e.g., dismountable conical mill).

§ 6.4. Corrosion-proof metal dish with cover. Its utilizable surface should allow a sample distribution of 0.3 g. per square centimeter[1].

§ 6.5. Glass or porcelain bowl.

---

[1]See following drawing of the sample dish, Figure 1. Its utilizable surface is 16 cm.[2] and its inside height is 14 mm. It may be used in conjunction with the desiccation tube in Figure 2.

§ 6.6. Desiccation tube made of glass[2], with one end closed and the other end provided with a ground stopper equipped with a semicapillary tube socket and a tap for producing a vacuum. The sample, after drying, is cooled in the desiccation tube, eliminating the use of a desiccator.

§ 6.7. Electric drying oven with temperature regulation or any other apparatus which raises the temperature of the chamber containing the sample dish to between 45° and 50°C.

§ 6.8. Air-drying system: washing apparatus containing sulfuric acid, e.g., Durand's wash bottle connected with a tube which contains phosphoric anhydride (phosphorus pentoxide) dispersed on fiber glass.

§ 7. SAMPLING. According to I.C.C. standard method No. 101.

§ 8. PROCEDURE.

§ 8.1. *Preparation of the sample.* Weigh to a precision of ±0.2 mg. Approximately 3 g. of the substance is placed in the metal dish, which previously has been dried, cooled down to laboratory temperature in the desiccator, and weighed. Carry out the operations quickly when dealing with products of a very low or a very high moisture content.

§ 8.2. *Determination.*

§ 8.2.1. Conditioning (predrying or humidification) and grinding of grain, if required. Grain having a moisture content above 7% and below 17% does not require conditioning. The moisture content of drier or wetter grain should be adjusted to bring it within this range. If the moisture content is lower than 7% the sample must be humidified by bringing it into an appropriate atmosphere in order to increase the moisture content to between 7 and 17% (preferably between 9 and 15%). Predrying is necessary most frequently in order to bring the moisture content of wetter samples down to between 9 and 15%. The uncovered dish containing the sample is placed on the bottom of the ground tube, and beside it is placed a bowl containing a 1-cm. thick layer of phosphoric anhydride (phosphorus pentoxide). The tube is stoppered. The pressure in the surrounding atmosphere is reduced to a value between 10 and 20 mm. of mercury (gradually, in order to avoid scattering the material, e.g. by intercalating a semicapillary tube). The connection with the device producing the vacuum is interrupted. That part of the tube which contains the dish is heated to 50°C. in the drying oven. After 1-1/2 to not more than 2 hr. the tube is removed from the drying oven and allowed to cool to laboratory temperature. In order to re-establish atmospheric pressure in the tube, air which has passed through the drying system is slowly introduced through a capillary tube.
The dish is quickly removed, covered, and weighed immediately. The sample is then ground immediately. The ground material is replaced in the dish and weighed again.
These two weighings should be carried out within a period of less than 2 min.

§ 8.2.2. *Dehydration.* Replace the dish containing the sample in the tube, and proceed as during predrying, the first weighing being performed after 100 hr. Dehydration is continued until constant weight is attained. (The difference between two weighings made before and after an interval of 48 hr. should not exceed 0.6 mg.)

§ 8.2.3. *Remarks on the determination.* The range of moisture contents indicated, to which the grain should be conditioned before grinding, corresponds approximately to a temperature of 20°±2°C. and to a relative humidity of 40 to 70% in the laboratory. It should be modified for other products and other atmospheric conditions. The indicated time of predrying should be regarded only as an approximate value. Check whether the desired "conditioning" is obtained with the apparatus and with the particular cereal varieties.
The drying time required is at least 150 hr.

---

[2]See following drawing of the desiccation tube, Figure 2. It has standard grinding 40/50 (40 mm. diameter, 50 mm. length of the ground part). It can be used in conjunction with the sample dish.

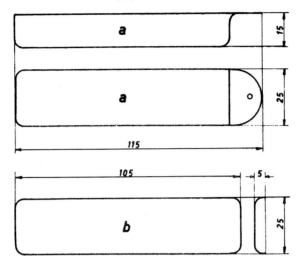

Figure 1. Sample dish, a) receptacle, b) lid.

Loss of traces of volatile organic substances is indicated by discoloration at the surface of the phosphoric anhydride (phosphorus pentoxide). This phenomenon serves as a "warning." If, in the case of certain adulterated products, there is a significant discoloration the heating temperature should be reduced. Prepare fresh phosphoric anhydride (phosphorus pentoxide) if it cakes at the surface.

Flours and flour products are to be handled in the same way as grain, but without conditioning and grinding.

§ 9. PRESENTATION OF RESULTS.

§ 9.1. *Method of calculation and formulae.*

E = initial weight of the sample, in g.
M = weight of the sample after conditioning, in g.
M' = weight of the sample after grinding, in g.
m = weight of the dry sample, in g.

The moisture content, in percent, of the product is given by one or other of the following expressions:

Without preliminary conditioning:

$$(E - m) \times \frac{100}{E}$$

With preliminary conditioning:

$$\left[\frac{(M' - m)\,M}{M'} + E - M \right] \times \frac{100}{E} = 100 \left(1 - \frac{Mm}{EM'} \right)$$

The determination shall be carried out in duplicate.

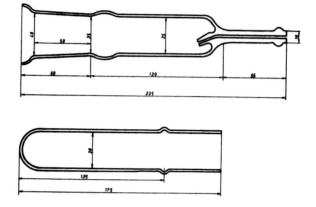

Figure 2. Desiccation tube (measurements in millimeters).

§ 9.2. *Precision of the determination.* The difference between the results of two moisture determinations on one and the same sample should not exceed 0.1% (absolute value). With a little practice, deviations of less than 0.05% (absolute value) are obtained within one laboratory.

Study Group:	Moisture Determination
Chairmen:	Prof. J. Buré, Prof. A. Guilbot
	Paris, France
Approved:	3 June, 1960, Vienna.

APPENDIX C

International Association for Cereal Chemistry (ICC)

ICC - STANDARD Nr. 110

§ 1. TITLE. Practical Method for the Determination of Moisture Content of Cereals and Cereal Products.

§ 2. SCOPE. This method of drying at 130° to 133°C. is applicable to ground grain. The particle size should be equal to or smaller than 1.7 mm.; less than 10% by weight should be larger than 1.0 mm., and more than 50% by weight should be smaller than 0.5 mm. This method is also applicable to flour, semolina, and other products of milling.

§ 3. DEFINITION. The moisture content of a material is defined as the loss in weight sustained by the material under certain circumstances.

§ 4. PRINCIPLE. The material is dried at 130° to 133°C. and at normal atmospheric pressure, the drying time being fixed empirically according to the particle size, so that the loss in weight sustained by 100 g. corresponds with the moisture percentage determined by the basic reference method.

§ 5. REAGENTS. Effective dehydrating agents, e.g., phosphoric anhydride (phosphorus pentoxide) (P_2O_5), reagent grade, anhydrous calcium sulfate ($CaSO_4$), granulated and impregnated with a cobalt chloride developer.

§ 6. APPARATUS.

§ 6.1. Precision balance (minimum precision: 1 mg.).

§ 6.2. Grinder made from a material which does not absorb any moisture, is easily cleaned, grinds rapidly and uniformly without heating, avoids contact of the sample with the surrounding air as far as possible, and fulfills the requirements given under point 2 (e.g., dismountable conical mill).

§ 6.3. Dish made from corrosion-proof metal or, failing that, from glass, with cover. Its utilizable surface should allow a sample distribution of 0.3 g. per square cm.

§ 6.4. Electric drying oven with temperature regulation to 130° to 133°C.[1] and adequate ventilation[2].

§ 6.5. Desiccator with thick perforated plate made of metal or, failing that, of porcelain. The desiccator contains phosphoric anhydride (phosphorus pentoxide), anhydrous calcium sulfate, or any other effective dehydrating agent.

§ 7. SAMPLING. According to I.C.C. standard method No. 101.

---

[1]Temperature of the air and of the plates supporting the shelves in the vicinity of the samples within the drying oven.

[2]The thermal capacity of the drying oven should be such that, after having regulated the temperature to 131°C. and having introduced the maximum number of samples to be dried, the same temperature is reestablished after less than 45 min. The adequacy of ventilation is tested by the use of durum semolina having a maximum particle size of 1 mm. The ventilation should be such that when simultaneously drying all the samples for 2 hr. and for 3 hr. at 130° to 133°C., the difference between the results does not exceed 0.15%.

§ 8. PROCEDURE.

§ 8.1. *Preparation of the sample.* Weigh to a precision of ± 1 mg. At least 5 g. of the substance is placed in the metal dish, which previously has been dried, cooled down to laboratory temperature in the desiccator, and weighed. Carry out the operations quickly when dealing with products of a very low or a very high moisture content.

§ 8.2. *Determination.*

§ 8.2.1. Conditioning (predrying or humidification) and grinding of grain, if required.
Grain having a moisture content above 7% and below 17% does not require conditioning. The moisture content of drier or wetter grain should be adjusted to bring it within this range. If the moisture content is lower than 7% the sample must be humidified by bringing it into an appropriate atmosphere in order to increase the moisture content to between 7 and 17% (preferably between 9 and 15%).
Predrying is required more frequently: place each uncovered dish with the samples in the drying oven for 7 to 10 min., then remove and allow to remain in the laboratory atmosphere for at least 2 hr. Weigh immediately after cooling down to laboratory temperature, and immediately thereafter grind the sample. Replace the ground material in the dish and weigh again. These two weighings should be carried out within a period of less than 2 min.

§ 8.2.2. *Dehydration.* Place the samples in the drying oven for 2 hr., reckoning the time from the moment when a temperature of 130° C. has been attained. Remove the samples by the procedure described above and weigh immediately after cooling in the desiccator.

§ 8.2.3. *Remarks on the determination.* The range of moisture contents indicated, to which the grain should be conditioned before grinding, corresponds approximately to a temperature of 20° ±2° C. and to a relative humidity of 40 to 70%, in the laboratory. It should be modified for other materials and other atmospheric conditions.
Avoid placing wet and nearly dry samples in close proximity to each other in the drying oven, as this would cause a partial rehydration of the nearly dry samples.
For flours a drying time of 1-1/2 hr. is sufficient.

§ 9. PRESENTATION OF RESULTS.

§ 9.1. *Method of calculation and formulae.*

E = initial weight of the sample, in g.
M = weight of the sample after conditioning, in g.
M' = weight of the sample after grinding, in g.
m = weight of the dry sample, in g.

The moisture content, in percent, of the material is given by one or other of the following expressions:
Without preliminary conditioning:

$$(E - m) \times \frac{100}{E}$$

With preliminary conditioning:

$$\left[\frac{(M' - m)\, M}{M'} + E - M \right] \times \frac{100}{E} = 100 \left(1 - \frac{Mm}{EM'}\right)$$

Carry out the determination in duplicate, at least.

§ 9.2. *Precision of the determination.* The difference between the results of two moisture determinations on one and the same sample should not exceed 0.1% (absolute value). In general, the differences between the results of this method and those of the basic reference method do not exceed 0.15% (absolute value).

Study Group:	Moisture Determination
Chairmen:	Prof. Buré, Prof. Guilbot
	Paris, France
Approved:	3 June, 1960, Vienna.

CHAPTER 2

BIOCHEMICAL, FUNCTIONAL, AND NUTRITIVE CHANGES DURING STORAGE

YESHAJAHU POMERANZ

U.S. Department of Agriculture, Agricultural Research Service,
U.S. Grain Marketing Research Center, Manhattan, Kansas

I. RESPIRATION

Early measurements of respiration of moist grains did not distinguish between respiration of the grain itself and respiration of the microflora on and within the grain (Bailey and Gurjar, 1918). Milner and Geddes (1945b) correctly attributed the respiration of moist soybeans primarily to fungi. In the only study using proven mold-free wheat, respiration at moisture contents of 16 to 31% and 35° C. was low and constant with time (Hummel et al., 1954). No one has measured respiration of grains infested with *Aspergillus glaucus* or *A. restrictus* at moisture contents in equilibrium with relative humidities of 70 to 75%, the moisture contents at which these ubiquitous species usually predominate.

A. Measurement of Respiration

Under aerobic conditions, the complete combustion of a typical carbohydrate and fat is represented by the following equations:

D-glucose:

$$C_6H_{12}O_6 \ + \ 6O_2 \longrightarrow 6CO_2 \ + \ 6H_2O \ + \ 677.2 \text{ Cal.}$$

180 g.	134.4 liters	134.4 liters	108 g.	
1.0 g.	0.747 liters	0.747 liters	0.60 g.	3.76 Cal.

1.0 liter of oxygen consumed = 5.04 Cal.
1.0 liter of carbon dioxide produced = 5.04 Cal.

Tripalmitin:

$$(C_{15}H_{31}COO)_3C_3H_5 \ + \ 72\tfrac{1}{2} O_2 \longrightarrow 51CO_2 \ + \ 49H_2O \ + \ 7616.7 \text{ Cal.}$$

806.8 g.	1,624 liters	1,142.4 liters	883 g.	
1.0 g.	2.88 liters	1.42 liters	1.09 g.	944 Cal.

1.0 liter of oxygen consumed = 4.69 Cal.
1.0 liter of carbon dioxide produced = 6.67 Cal.

The above equations reveal that heat equivalents of oxygen consumed and carbon dioxide produced vary with the type of substrate which is oxidized.

End products in anaerobic respiration are carbon dioxide and several simple organic compounds. The energy released per unit of substrate is much less than in the aerobic process.

The ratio of moles (or volumes) of carbon dioxide produced to the moles of oxygen consumed during respiration is called the respiratory quotient (R.Q.). This quotient is unity in aerobic respiration of glucose, but only 0.7 for tripalmitin (51/72.5). The caloric equivalents of oxygen corresponding to various respiratory quotients can be calculated from the average energy equivalents for the oxidation of carbohydrates (R.Q. = 1.0) and of fats (R.Q. = 0.7). These equations may be utilized in indirect calorimetry to compute the energy corresponding to a given oxygen consumption. In calculating R.Q., several corrections must be applied to experimental data for oxygen consumption and carbon dioxide production. Despite numerous factors which may influence R.Q.'s they are useful indexes of the relative extent of aerobic and anaerobic metabolism occurring in grain supplied with various oxygen levels at controlled temperatures.

Respiration of quiescent seeds can be measured either in closed or in aerated (intermittent or continuous) systems.

The closed system uses a static technique in which carbon dioxide produced after a fixed period is measured. The static method had great appeal because of its simplicity and also because it was assumed that it duplicates conditions which exist in bulk storage. It has been shown that accumulation of carbon dioxide in the interseed air depresses respiration, that air movements which occur in heating grain stored in bulk tend to prevent localization of inhibitory concentrations of carbon dioxide, and that the static method in which measurements are made after several days obscures valuable information which can be obtained by more frequent or continuous measurements.

To overcome the limitations of the static methods, Milner and Geddes (1945a) constructed a multiple respirometer in which grain held at constant temperature was aerated at desirable rates. Aeration was controlled by slow displacement of a calcium chloride solution (sp. gr. 1.40, in which carbon dioxide is only slightly soluble) in graduated respirometers; the control was accomplished by lowering leveling bulbs suspended from pulleys on a slowly rotating lineshaft. Carbon dioxide-free air, suitably humidified, was thus drawn into the respirometer through the grain container, which was maintained at constant temperature in a controlled water bath. The effluent air in the respirometer was measured at 24-hr. intervals, and a sample was analyzed for carbon dioxide and oxygen.

More recently, Pedersen et al. (1971) described the construction of experimental silos. The silos had a capacity of about 10 kg. grain; were equipped with systems to control humidity, temperature, quantity, and composition of air; and were designed to allow sampling during the experiment without disturbing the storage conditions.

To study respiration of one or several seeds, several microtechniques were developed. In addition to the Warburg-Barcroft manometric apparatus, several special micro apparatus were described. Stiles and Leach (1931) originated the Katharometer in which oxygen consumption was measured by following the change in electrical conductivity of heated wires in the atmosphere of the respiration vessel. Conductivity is affected by heat radiation from the wire which varies with the oxygen concentration of the atmosphere. A later modification of the apparatus (Leach, 1932) provided for determination of carbon dioxide by measuring the conductivity of standard alkali solutions used to absorb this gas.

The various forms of apparatus and technique described can yield valuable information on grain respiration under controlled laboratory conditions. The methods are not suitable for use in commercial grain practice as an aid in storage supervision. Accordingly, several investigators (Oxley, 1944, 1948; Milner and Geddes, 1945a) devised simple techniques for sampling and analysis of interseed carbon dioxide. In recent years, several types of analyzers for measuring carbon dioxide are available commercially.

B. Respiration of Dormant Grain

The principal factors which control grain respiration are moisture, temperature, aeration, and previous history ("condition").

Moisture. Of the various factors influencing the rate of deterioration, moisture is by far the most important. If the moisture content is maintained at a sufficiently low level, grain can be stored for many years with little deterioration even under otherwise unfavorable storage conditions. In actual practice, however, grain as it comes from the farm, and milled products of grain as they are normally produced, often have moisture contents near or above the critical levels for safe storage.

Deterioration in stored grain as a result of excessive moisture may occur, strangely enough, even though the grain when placed in storage is within what is normally considered a safe moisture limit and is uniform in its moisture content. This phenomenon may occur when marked temperature differences exist or develop in different parts of the storage space. Relative humidity of interstitial air in stored grain tends to remain in equilibrium with moisture in the grain. At any level of relative humidity, however, the actual amount of water vapor per cubic foot of air increases with rising temperature. The air in the storage space is in constant motion as a result of diffusion or convection. When air from a warm region in the grain reaches a cooler region, it must give up some of its moisture to the grain in order to maintain equilibrium. This interchange of moisture usually takes place entirely in the vapor phase but, in extreme instances, warm air reaching a cold region in the storage space may be cooled below the dew point, and water will be condensed on the cold surfaces of the grain or walls of the bin. Thus moisture is transported from warmer to cooler regions of stored grain, and spoilage as a result of excessive moisture may occur in parts of the storage space, even though none of the grain initially contained sufficient moisture to promote spoilage. Effects of atmospheric changes in temperature on the storage bin walls, and of heat produced by local pockets of insect infestation, are frequent causes of temperature gradients in stored grain that result first in the translocation of moisture, and then in deteriorative changes resulting from local accumulation of excessive moisture.

Moist_____ at which _____ marked rise in the respiratory rates occurred are near tho__ at which heating and spoilage start in storage. Different species exhibited somewhat different critical moisture values. Whereas critical values of cereal grains are around 14%, flaxseed is conspicuous with a low critical moisture value, somewhat under 11%, and a much higher respiratory rate than cereal grains. The difference between critical moisture contents for flaxseed and for cereal grains led Bailey (1940) to suggest that since the 40% (approximately) of oil in flaxseed is nonhygroscopic, only 60% of the dry matter retains water. A moisture content of 10% for the entire flaxseed implies a moisture of about 16.5% in the hydrophilic portion which agrees fairly well with the critical moisture in the hydrophilic portion of cereal grains. This explanation, however, fails to hold for soybeans which contain up to 20% oil and yet have a critical moisture value of about 14%.

Several investigators have shown that a relative humidity of 75% is about minimum for the germination of mold spores at ordinary temperatures. It is now quite generally agreed that the so-called critical moisture level for any individual species is the percentage moisture at which the seed is in equilibrium with an atmospheric relative humidity of about 75%.

The fact that the marked increases in respiration for different grains occur at a rather constant relative humidity of 75% in the interseed atmosphere, at which the equilibrium moisture content of different grains may vary markedly, clearly indicates that the total moisture content of the grain is not the controlling factor.

The absolute moisture content of grain is less important than the relative humidity with which food is in hygroscopic equilibrium (Rockland, 1969). Apparently, there is a critical limiting relative humidity at which molds can survive. This critical humidity varies with the microorganism and is about 75% for the more strongly osmophilic molds, though some Aspergilli and strongly osmophilic yeasts can develop at even lower humidities. In view of those findings, it is clear that the moisture content of a food is a less reliable criterion of shelf life than the relative humidity of the atmosphere with which one food is at equilibrium.

Bacterial growth is rarely encountered in stored grain, as the relative humidity requirement for these microorganisms exceeds 90%. Since mold growth is associated with heating and deterioration, the maximum moisture content for the safe, short-time commercial storage of a given grain at ordinary temperatures can be approximated from its moisture value when exposed to an atmosphere of 75% relative humidity. If grain is cracked or broken, or if storage is prolonged or at high temperatures, the maximum moisture limit should correspond to a lower relative humidity. For long-time storage (up to 2 or 3 years) a relative humidity as low as 65% must be accepted as a safe maximum. Typical hygroscopic moisture values for various grains maintained in an atmosphere of 75% relative humidity are summarized in Table I.

Milner, Linko, and their associates have shown that in addition to fungal respiration, the metabolism of the embryo itself is affected by wetting dry grain, the result being deleterious biochemical changes before fungal development reaches a damaging level (Linko, 1960). McDonald and Milner (1954) have shown that there is a consistent evolution of carbon dioxide in wetted embryos. The result was a high R.Q. This high carbon dioxide evolution subsided long before the germination of fungal spores affected the subsequent respiratory pattern. These results suggested that enzymatic patterns would be stimulated by increasing the moisture content of air-dry embryos.

A useful summary of the relationship between the moisture content of different cereal grains and their equilibrium relative humidity was published by Davey and Elcoate (1965).

An investigation on the relationship of tricarboxylic acid cycle intermediates with the carbon dioxide evolution indicated that pyruvate and alpha-ketoglutarate were readily decarboxylated by wheat germ (Linko and Milner, 1959a). At the same time, pyruvate slightly inhibited oxygen uptake. This resulted in high R.Q. values. The high values could not be explained by the activation of an alpha-keto acid decarboxylase, owing to the small quantities of pyruvic and alpha-keto-glutaric acids in the germ (Linko and Milner, 1959b). The observation that glutamic acid decarboxylase is readily activated by adding water to wheat embryos traced carbon dioxide evolution after wetting to enzymatic decarboxylation of glutamic acid (Linko and Milner, 1959c; Cheng et al., 1960).

The relative humidity of the interseed atmosphere in equilibrium with grain of a given moisture content is not greatly influenced by temperature. However, as adsorption is characterized by a negative temperature coefficient, there is a slight increase in relative humidity as the temperature is raised. In other words, at a given relative humidity the hygroscopic moisture increases slightly as the temperature is lowered. This effect amounts to about 0.6 to 0.7% moisture increase for each 10°C. drop in temperature (Milner and Geddes, 1954).

According to Ayerst (1965), the effect of changes of temperature on the equilibrium relative humidity is in the order of 3% per 10°C. rise or fall in temperature in the relative humidity range of 40 to 90%; at higher relative humidity values, the effect of temperature is decreased. Pixton (1968) found that the equilibrium relative humidity of Manitoba wheat was changed by heating at 70°C. but that very little further change occurred when the heating was prolonged for more than 1 hr. In wheat with 10% moisture, the equilibrium relative humidity increased by 6% but at 14% moisture the increase was only 2%. A heat-treated sample kept at 70% relative humidity was about 0.3% drier than an unheated sample; in a sample kept at 50% relative humidity the difference was about 0.9% moisture.

For many purposes the effect of temperature on equilibrium relative humidity is negligible for all practical purposes. It should be included if high accuracy is required or if a wide range of temperatures is to be considered. Pixton and Warburton (1971) presented graphs giving the equilibrium relative humidity at a given moisture for different temperatures of a soft wheat, barley, American yellow dent corn, English flint corn, and tick beans (*Vicia faba* L.).

There is a functional relation between relative humidity (or a_w - water activity; a_w = relative humidity/100) and moisture content. That relation is given by a sorption isotherm which has the shape of a sigmoid curve. The sigmoid shape of the isotherm has been attributed to the qualitative differences in the affinity of water for hygroscopic solids. Based on thermodynamic considerations (supported by X-ray, IR, and NMR spectroscopy, refractive index, water density, and molecular structure investigations) it was shown that water in foods is bound in three forms (Rockland, 1969). Type 1 water binding is regarded as water molecules bound to ionic groups (such as carboxyl or amino groups); type 3 is free water in interstitial pores, and type 2 has water hydrogen-bonded to

TABLE I

Hygroscopic moisture values for different grains at 75% relative humidity

Grain	Moisture Content[a] %	Temperature of Measurement	Reference
Barley	14.4	25°-28° C.	Coleman and Fellows (1925)
Buckwheat	15.0	25°-28° C.	Coleman and Fellows (1925)
Corn	14.3	25° C.	Bailey (1921)
Corn	14.4	25°-28° C.	Coleman and Fellows (1925)
Corn	14.7	80° F. (27° C.)	Brockington, Dorin, and Howerton (1949)
Cottonseed			
Whole seed	11.4	25° C.	Karon (1947)
Meats	10.0	25° C.	Karon (1947)
Hulls	13.7	25° C.	Karon (1947)
Flaxseed	10.0	25°-28° C.	Coleman and Fellows (1925)
Flaxseed	10.3	25° C.	Larmour, Sallans, and Craig (1944)
Flaxseed	10.5	28°-30° C.	Schricker (1948)
Oats			
Whole seed	13.9	25°-28° C.	Coleman and Fellows (1925)
Whole seed	13.4	25° C.	Colvin, Craig, and Sallans (1947)
Groats	14.1	25° C.	Colvin, Craig, and Sallans (1947)
Hulls	12.7	25° C.	Colvin, Craig, and Sallans (1947)
Peanuts			
Whole	10.5	25° C.	Karon and Hillery (1949)
Kernels	8.8	25° C.	Karon and Hillery (1949)
Rice			
Whole seed	14.4	25°-28° C.	Coleman and Fellows (1925)
Whole seed	14.0	25° C.	Karon and Adams (1949)
Artificially dried	13.2	25° C.	Karon and Adams (1949)
Polished	15.6	25° C.	Karon and Adams (1949)
Rye	14.9	25°-28° C.	Coleman and Fellows (1925)
Sorghum	15.3	25°-28° C.	Coleman, Rothgeb, and Fellows (1928)
Soybeans	14.4	25° C.	Ramstad and Geddes (1942)
Soybeans	14.0	25° C.	Larmour, Sallans, and Craig (1944)
Sunflower seed			
Whole seed	10.4	25° C.	Larmour, Sallans, and Craig (1944)
Whole seed	11.7	25° C.	Colvin, Craig, and Sallans (1947)
Meats	8.2	25° C.	Colvin, Craig, and Sallans (1947)
Hulls	14.6	25° C.	Colvin, Craig, and Sallans (1947)
Wheat			
Hard red winter	14.6	25°-28° C.	Coleman and Fellows (1925)
Hard red spring	14.8	25°-28° C.	Coleman and Fellows (1925)
White	15.0	25°-28° C.	Coleman and Fellows (1925)
Durum	14.1	25°-28° C.	Coleman and Fellows (1925)
Soft red winter	14.7	25°-28° C.	Coleman and Fellows (1925)

(Continued on next page)

TABLE I, *Continued*

Hygroscopic moisture values for different grains at 75% relative humidity

Grain	Moisture Content[a] %	Temperature of Measurement	Reference
Wheat			
Weak	16.1	10°C.	Gane (1941)
Medium	15.3	10°C.	Gane (1941)
Strong	15.4	10°C.	Gane (1941)
Wheat	14.5		Pap (1934)
Wheat	15.0	70°F. (21°C.)	Robertson, Lute, and Gardner (1939b)
Wheat	15.5	...	Hoffmann (1931)
Wheat	14.7	80°F. (27°C.)	Gay (1946)

[a]Calculated to damp-weight basis (from Milner and Geddes, 1954)

hydroxyl or amide groups. Numerous equations have been derived for the description of sorption isotherms which related moisture content to equilibrium relative humidity. Rockland (1969) described the applicability and limitations of those equations for the description of moisture sorption isotherms.

Temperature. Respiration is accelerated by an increase in temperature until it is limited by such factors as the thermal inactivation of the enzymes which are involved, exhaustion of substrate, limitation in oxygen supply, or accumulation of inhibitory concentrations of carbon dioxide. In addition, the effect of temperature on respiratory rate depends upon the moisture content of the seeds. It also depends on the relative contributions of seeds, molds, and insects to the total respiration, because of variable effects of temperature on those factors. The interrelation of the different variables is so complex that empirical determinations of optimum temperatures for grain respiration yield only approximate values and can be applied only to conditions under which the values were determined.

Aeration. Since aerobic respiration of grain and of the microorganisms associated with grain involves consumption of oxygen and liberation of carbon dioxide, the process tends to be limited by the oxygen supply.

Condition. The storage properties of grain are influenced by environmental conditions during growth and maturation, by the degree of maturity at harvest, by methods of harvesting, and by the handling the seed has received until it is placed in storage. Varietal differences in cereal grains may also influence their relative respiratory rates; softer types of wheat respire more rapidly than harder types at similar moisture levels and temperatures.

Respiratory activity and the tendency of grain and its products to deteriorate in storage are considerably influenced by the "condition" or "soundness" of the product. This is one of the major reasons why it is impossible to establish a maximum safe moisture limit for the storage of any grain or grain product. Bailey and Gurjar (1918) were the first to demonstrate experimentally that the rate of respiration under controlled conditions of temperature, oxygen supply, and moisture content was distinctly greater for unsound wheat than for sound wheat. It is commonly observed under practical storage conditions that grain containing a high percentage of damaged kernels, or showing other evidences of unsoundness, is much more likely to heat in storage than is sound grain of the same moisture content.

II. BIOCHEMICAL CHANGES

This section describes the major modifications which take place in the biochemical moieties of stored grain. Some biochemical changes are described in other sections of this chapter (mainly under Nutritive Changes). In addition, some of the changes are discussed under Indexes of Deterioration.

A. Carbohydrate Changes

Earlier studies on changes in carbohydrates were reviewed by Zeleny (1954).

Alpha- and beta-amylases attack the starches of grain and grain products during storage, converting them into dextrins and maltose. Amylase activity in wheat has been shown by Popov and Timofeev (1933) to increase during the early stages of storage. An increase in the dry weight of grain during storage has been observed under certain conditions and is explained by Gross (1919) by the fact that water is consumed in the starch hydrolysis reactions. Thus, the dry weight of the products of starch hydrolysis is greater than that of the original starch. Although this hydrolytic action might be expected to result in a significant increase in the reducing sugar content of grain, conditions that favor starch decomposition usually favor respiratory activity also, so that the sugars are consumed and converted into carbon dioxide and water. Under these conditions, which usually occur at moisture levels of 15% or more, the grain loses both starch and sugar and the dry weight decreases. Leavitt and LeClerc (1909), however, showed that the total sugar content of wheat tends to increase during storage. Ramstad and Geddes (1942) found a marked increase in reducing sugars in soybeans stored at more than 15% moisture. The increase was followed by an equally significant decrease in nonreducing sugars. Milner and Geddes (1946) demonstrated a disappearance of sugars in stored, heating soybeans during the initial biological phase of the heating process, but a later increase in reducing substances when the heating had reached a nonbiological phase in which the heat produced was the result of direct chemical oxidation. Bottomley et al. (1950, 1952) have demonstrated a marked disappearance of nonreducing sugars in corn stored under conditions favoring deterioration. Grain resembling spelt, taken from an ancient Egyptian tomb, and said to be more than 3,000 years old, was reported by Geddes (1935) to contain dextrins and considerable amounts of reducing sugars. This would appear to indicate that amylase activity continued after the condition of the grain became such that respiration could no longer take place. At higher moisture levels, however, active carbohydrate fermentation may occur with the production of alcohol or acetic acid and resulting characteristic "sour" odors (Davies, 1928).

Montgomery and Smith (1956) postulated that the quantity of soluble carbohydrates in wheat is likely to depend on the highest moisture level to which the grain has been exposed. Linko et al. (1960) studied soluble carbohydrates of wheat germ stored at moisture levels and temperatures pertinent to conditions which produce germ-damaged ("sick") wheat (for explanation see later in this

TABLE II

Effect of atmosphere and moisture level on mold count and on reducing and nonreducing sugar content of wheat after storage for 16 weeks at 30°C.[a]

| | Moisture Content of Wheat, and Atmosphere | | | | | | | |
| | 15% | | 16% | | 17% | | 18% | |
	Air	Nitro-gen	Air	Nitro-gen	Air	Nitro-gen	Air	Nitro-gen
Mold count[b]	0.7	0	1.4	0	10.6	0	40	0
Nonreducing sugars[c]	186	188	133	176	127	144	98	129
Reducing sugars[d]	32	38	44	52	44	83	48	108

[a]Data of Glass et al. (1959).

[b]Mold count per g. $\times 10^{-6}$.

[c]Expressed as mg. sucrose per 10 g. wheat (dry-matter basis). Initial value for wheat before storage trial was 232 mg. sucrose per 10 g.

[d]Expressed as mg. maltose per 10 g. wheat (dry-matter basis). Initial value for wheat before storage trial was 37 mg. maltose per 10 g.

chapter). Storage for 8 days at moisture levels from 9 to 25% and temperatures from 29° to 50°C. produced characteristic increases of reducing sugars at the expense of nonreducing sugars. Those changes preceded the appearance of browning. An increase in fluorescence occurred at moisture levels above 15% only after browning was visually detectable. Several unknown compounds believed to be intermediates in nonenzymatic browning were formed. Glucose and fructose did not increase as much as might have been expected from the breakdown of sucrose and raffinose. It was postulated that the difference resulted from reaction of reducing sugars with amino acids. Dubois et al. (1960) observed noticeable changes in the composition of sugars in embryos exposed for approximately 1 day to water vapors. During this time the moisture content increased from 9.2 to 13%.

Glass et al. (1959) carried out laboratory studies on aerobic and anaerobic storage of wheat. The values in Table II show that marked changes in nonreducing and reducing sugars occurred in an atmosphere of nitrogen, even though mold growth was prevented. The decrease in nonreducing sugars was almost exactly compensated for by the increase in reducing sugars. When damp wheat was stored in air, extensive mold growth occurred, and the increase in reducing sugars was only about one-fourth as great as the decrease in nonreducing sugars, owing to the utilization of the former by the molds.

Expressing the nonreducing and reducing sugars as sucrose and maltose, respectively, was arbitrary, but subsequent chromatographic studies have shown the changes in the individual components. Glass and Geddes (1960) isolated and characterized galactose, myo-inositol, and glycerol from the monosaccharide fraction obtained from a sample of wheat which had been stored under an atmosphere of nitrogen for 24 weeks at 18% moisture and 30°C. In addition, glucose and fructose were obtained in chromatographically pure form. The control wheat sample yielded glucose and fructose, together with trace amounts of what appeared to be galactose and myo-inositol.

Lynch et al. (1962) applied quantitative chromatographic techniques in an investigation of the changes in the mono- and disaccharides in moist wheat stored for 8 weeks in different atmospheres (Table III). In the air-stored sample, the reducing sugars remained unchanged or decreased slightly during storage, whereas sucrose decreased. The decrease in the latter, however, was not great, as was indicated by the ferricyanide estimation of nonreducing sugars, since raffinose and glucofructans are also measured by this procedure. In the wheat stored under anaerobic conditions, maltose remained unchanged, whereas fructose and glucose each increased threefold and galactose four- to fivefold. The increase in galactose reveals that sucrose and glucofructans are not the only nonreducing sugars hydrolyzed during storage. Galactose can arise from raffinose by the action of an alpha-galactosidase, simultaneously producing sucrose, or from cleavage of galactolipids. In the air-stored sample, extensive utilization of the reducing sugars occurred.

Taufel et al. (1959) investigated the changes in the di- and trisaccharide contents of wheat during storage under good and poor conditions (Table IV). Under good conditions, concentrations of various sugars remained essentially unchanged, except for a slight decrease in sucrose content. When the wheat was stored at high moisture contents and temperatures, sucrose, glucodifructose, and raffinose contents decreased; the maltose content increased materially only in the sample stored at 35.4% moisture. Pixton and Hill (1967) reported that storage of sound wheat for 6 years reduced the total sugar content, and especially the nonreducing sugars.

Taufel et al. (1960) reported, on the basis of qualitative and quantitative paper chromatographic analyses, that legumes (including soybeans) contain traces of glucose and fructose and significant quantities of raffinose, stachyose, and verbascose. During storage for 1 month there was practically no change in

TABLE III

Changes in the mono- and disaccharides of wheat stored under various atmospheres for 8 weeks at 30° C. and 20% moisture[a]
(Concentration of sugars, mg. per 10 g., dry-matter basis)

Sugar	Control	Stored in Air	Stored in Nitrogen	Stored in Carbon Dioxide
Fructose	6	5	18	16
Glucose	8	7	24	23
Galactose	2	3	9	9
Sucrose	54	21	39	36
Maltose	5	1	4	3
Total reducing sugars, as maltose	41	41	117	117
Total nonreducing sugars, as sucrose	190	43	100	115

[a]Data of Lynch et al. (1962).

content of lower carbohydrates. With abnormal storage (high temperature and humidity), the amounts of verbascose and stachyose decreased slightly; sucrose and raffinose increased, and free galactose became detectable.

Gracza (1965) stored flours with about 9% moisture for 51 weeks in closed containers at temperatures alternating between 24° and 32°C. in 6-hr. cycles. Maltose values were unchanged. However, if the flours were stored in cotton bags exposed to relative humidities of 58 and 90%, maltose values decreased considerably within 30 weeks.

Iwasaki and Tani (1967) reported that rice with 16% moisture stored for 1 year at −2° to 33°C. and at low oxygen concentrations showed decreases in acidity of water extract, formation of limited amounts of alcohol, and a great increase in reducing sugars although amylase activity was essentially unaffected by oxygen concentration.

B. Changes in Nitrogenous Compounds

Total protein. According to Pixton and Hill (1967), in wheat stored for 8 years under conditions which might be used for long-term commercial storage, crude protein remained unchanged. Daftary et al. (1970b) found that protein content determined by the Kjeldahl method was slightly, but consistently, higher in mold-damaged samples than in the corresponding sound flours. The relative increase on a percentage basis can be explained by respiratory losses of carbohydrates. In samples stored at 37°C., protein values determined by a dye binding method were lower than protein values determined by the Kjeldahl method. The results indicated damage to proteins, in addition to breakdown and changes in lipids.

Protein fractions. Jones and Gersdorff (1941) conducted extensive studies on changes during storage in proteins of wheat, whole wheat flour, and white flour. Their results for wheat are summarized in Table V.

More recently, Kozlova and Nekrasov (1956) studied changes in quality of 4 types of spring and 7 types of winter wheat during storage for up to 16 years in

TABLE IV
Changes in the di- and trisaccharide contents of wheat stored under good and poor conditions[a]
(Sugar concentration, dry-matter basis)

Storage Time days	Moisture Content %	Temperature °C.	Relative Humidity %	Sucrose %	Maltose %	Difructose %	Raffinose %
0		16-21	50-70	0.88	0.04	0.26	0.19
116				0.80	0.04	0.22	0.18
160				0.77	0.04	0.21	0.19
172				0.75	0.05	0.21	0.19
0	12.6	30-32	90-95	0.80	0.04	0.22	0.18
10	12.6			0.77	0.04	0.21	0.18
5	19.8			0.63	0.08	0.11	0.16
3	35.4			0.55	0.70	0.09	0.10

[a]Data of Taufel et al. (1959).

TABLE V
Effect of storage on the proteins of wheat kernels[a]
(Results expressed in milligrams per 100 g. wheat)

Determinations	Fresh Material	Stored in Jars			
		Months at 30° F. (−1° C.)		Months at 76° F. (24° C.)	
		9	24	9	24
Moisture	10,950	10,960	10,960	10,950	10,940
Total nitrogen	2,140	2,140	2,140	2,140	2,140
True protein nitrogen	1,682	1,653	1,574	1,632	1,519
Free ammonia nitrogen	37	37	37	38	38
Nitrogen soluble in 3% NaCl	756	620	606	557	516
Nitrogen soluble in 70% alcohol	910	770	748	722	713
Nitrogen soluble in 3% sodium salicylate	...	1,061	1,038	998	922
Nitrogen in NaCl precipitable by trichloracetic acid	616	518	509	134	163
Nitrogen in sodium salicylate precipitable by trichloracetic acid	...	943	919	874	788
Amino nitrogen in NaCl extracts	109	102	100	94	88
Nitrogen soluble in peptic-tryptic digests	2,050	2,033	1,987	2,026	1,878

[a] Data of Jones and Gersdorff (1941).

wooden and brick warehouses. Annual storage temperatures and humidities ranged from 1° to 20° C. and 42 to 80%, respectively. The fractional composition of high-quality grain was fairly stable for 3 to 4 years. Longer storage decreased hydrophilic characteristics and aggregation of the protein molecules. This resulted in a decrease in water-soluble substances. The quality of gluten deteriorated during storage; the rate of deterioration was greater for lower quality grain and for that which had been severely dried after harvest or fumigated in storage.

Enzymes and free amino acids. Proteolytic enzymes in grain and in organisms associated with grain hydrolyze the proteins into polypeptides and finally into amino acids. These reactions ordinarily proceed very slowly and are not readily measurable until the grain has reached an advanced stage of deterioration (Zeleny and Coleman, 1939). Zeleny and Coleman (1938) have shown that the free amino acid content of grain may be estimated by an adaptation of the method of Foreman (1920) in which acid phosphates and free carboxyl groups of amino acids in a 60% ethanol extract of fat-extracted meal were determined by titration in 85% ethanol solution. From the titration value thus obtained was subtracted the titration value of the acid phosphates alone, which was determined by titration of a similar extract in 5% ethanol solution. The resulting value may be considered an approximate measure of the free amino acid content of the grain, although it did not account quantitatively for any proline or dibasic amino acid that may be present. The amino acid content of corn (maize), measured in this manner and expressed as the number of milligrams of potassium hydroxide required to neutralize the free carboxyl groups in 100 g. of corn on a moisture-free basis, was found usually to be in the neighborhood of 110 mg. in sound, mature corn and as high as 320 mg. in severely damaged corn (Zeleny and Coleman, 1939).

Though the total quantity of free amino acids shows significant changes only at advanced stages of damage, several investigators have reported major qualitative transformations during incipient deterioration. DeVay (1952) observed changes in concentrations of gamma-aminobutyric acid in hard red spring wheat stored at 19.5% moisture. Linko and Milner (1959b) have shown a considerable change in the composition of free amino acids of wheat which has been wetted. Linko (1960) studied the effect of storage at 16.2% moisture at 37°C. on the free amino acids in the embryo and endosperm end of wheat. The most significant change during the first 2 days of storage was the almost total and irreversible decrease in free glutamic acid of the embryo accompanied by a striking increase in free gamma-aminobutyric acid, presumably from the activation of glutamic acid decarboxylase by the increased moisture content. Except for arginine, glutamic acid, and the amides, free amino acids in the endosperm end of the kernel generally increased as a result of proteolysis.

The activation of enzymes in cereal grains is characteristic of the early stages of germination. Linko and Milner (1959c) found that glutamic acid decarboxylase and glutamic acid-alanine transaminase are activated at early stages of water imbibition. Moisture levels as low as 15 to 18% activate both enzyme systems. The activity increases rapidly with increase in moisture content. Swanson (1935) observed that 27 to 30% moisture was adequate for starting amylolytic activity, but that 40% was required for more extensive degradation of starch. Similarly, moisture levels of about 40% are required for dehydrogenase activities.

C. "Sick" Wheat

One of the poorly defined types of damage in wheat associated with storage deterioration is the condition known to the grain trade as germ-damaged or "sick" wheat. It is manifested by kernels with a dull appearance, and the germs are dead and exhibit various degrees of darkening (Milner and Geddes, 1954). Mold growth is usually present in commercial samples of such grain, but germ damage also occurs when moist wheat is stored under anaerobic conditions. Cole and Milner (1953) found that increases in the absorbance of extracts of wheat and especially of wheat germ in the ultraviolet region (250 to 325 nm.) were associated with darkening of the germ. Increases in the fluorescence of the germ extracts also occurred and were negatively correlated with the viability of the grain. These spectrophotometric and fluorescence changes are characteristic of the browning reaction in other food products and lend support to the view that the discoloration associated with germ-damaged wheat is due primarily to a browning reaction of the Maillard type localized in the germ. This view was substantiated by McDonald and Milner (1954), who found that browning and the associated increases in absorbance and fluorescence were inhibited by sodium bisulfite. The onset of browning in fresh wheat germ, promoted by storage at elevated moistures and temperatures, invariably preceded mold growth.

Linko et al. (1960) reported that the fluorescence of germ extracts did not increase until after discoloration was visually apparent. Storage of wheat germ at moisture contents and temperatures which favored browning increased reducing sugars at the expense of the nonreducing ones. The development of fluorescence paralleled the appearance of several spots on chromatograms prepared from 70% ethanol extracts of the germ which did not coincide with any of the known simple carbohydrates. These compounds disappeared later as the fluorescence increased, indicating that they are not normal metabolites but rather compounds formed during storage after the embryo has lost its viability. These authors concluded that the enzymatic activity which occurs when wheat or wheat germ is stored at high moisture contents results in the production of reducing carbohydrates which form browning intermediates with available free amino acids.

Although germ damage can develop in the absence of fungi, "sick" embryos are generally infested by fungi. Discoloration of the germ depends on the pathogenicity of the fungi, wheat variety and history, and on storage conditions. Although the primary deteriorative processes resulting in germ damage appear to involve the metabolic processes in an embryo, the conditions that those processes create are conducive to fungal growth. While storage under conditions that exclude mold attack may result in germ discoloration, the changes are not typical of sick wheat encountered in commercial storage. It was concluded that under conditions of commercial grain storage, fungi are the primary cause of loss of germinability and germ damage (Christensen and Kaufmann, 1969).

D. Lipids

Deteriorative changes in grain fats or oils may be either oxidative, resulting in typical rancid flavors and odors, or hydrolytic, resulting in the production of free fatty acids. Grains contain fairly active antioxidants, and the fats in unbroken kernels of grain are rather effectively protected against effects of oxygen in the air. For these reasons the development of oxidative rancidity is rarely a problem in grain storage, although it is often a serious problem in the storage of grain oils and of milled products, particularly whole grain milled products. Whole wheat flour, for example, can be kept for only a relatively short time because it readily becomes rancid, regardless of its moisture content (Zeleny, 1954).

Fats in grain are readily broken down by lipases into free fatty acids and glycerol during storage, particularly when the temperature and moisture content are high and thus favorable to general deterioration. This type of change is greatly accelerated by mold growth because of high lipolytic activity of the molds. Fat hydrolysis takes place much more rapidly than protein or carbohydrate hydrolysis in stored grain. For this reason, the free fatty acid content of grain has been proposed as a sensitive index of incipient grain deterioration.

Deterioration of wheat during storage is generally accompanied by decreases in petroleum ether-extractable lipids. In studies reported by Pomeranz et al. (1956) a thousand-fold increase in mold count was accompanied by a reduction of about 20% in free lipids.

Daftary and Pomeranz (1965) studied changes in lipids of soft and hard wheat stored at elevated moisture levels and high temperatures. Increase in mold count from 1,000 to about 2,000,000 per gram was accompanied by a 40% decrease in total lipid content. Nonpolar lipids decreased about 25%; damaged wheat contained only one-third as much polar lipids as sound wheat. Grain deterioration was accompanied by rapid disappearance of glycolipids and phospholipids. The breakdown of polar lipids was more rapid and extensive than formation of free fatty acids or disappearance of triglycerides (Figures 1 and 2). Deterioration of grain was accompanied by formation of at least four compounds that showed fluorescence under ultraviolet light. When wheat flour containing 14.7% moisture was stored in polyethylene bags at room temperature for 6 months it developed lumps, an objectionable color, and a musty odor (Pomeranz et al., 1968). Those changes were accompanied by a substantial decrease of bound lipids and an almost complete breakdown of free flour lipids. Starch-gel electrophoresis patterns indicated that under the storage conditions used, proteins had undergone only minor changes.

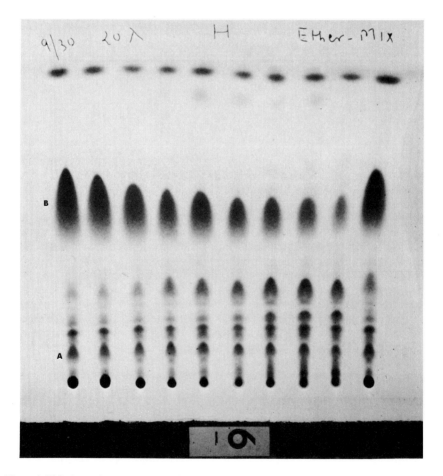

Figure 1. Thin-layer chromatography of benzene extracts of wheat stored for 0, 0, 14, 28, 42, 56, 70, 100, 132, and 0 days. First sample (extreme left) original wheat; others moistened to 22%. Tentatively identified: A — free fatty acids, B — triglycerides (from Daftary and Pomeranz, 1965).

As mentioned previously, moisture content and temperature are the main factors which determine respiration intensity and damage of stored grains and grain products. The kinds of molds that grow on cereals are influenced by the initial moisture, temperature, and oxygen concentration; by the direction and extent to which these and other factors (such as nutrient availability) change as molds grow; and by the inherent growth rates of the individual fungi. To investigate the effects of temperature on composition of damp flours, two hard red winter and two hard red spring wheat flours with moistures around 18% were stored for 16 weeks at 23°, 30°, and 37°C. (Daftary et al., 1970b).

The original mold count of the flours was 50 to 200 colonies per g. and at the end of storage increased up to 2,700,000 per g. The final count was much higher in flours stored at 23° and 30°C. than at 37°C. *Aspergillus niger* v. Tiegh, *A. candidus* [Lk.], and *A. versicolor* (Vuill.) Tiraboshi were the predominant

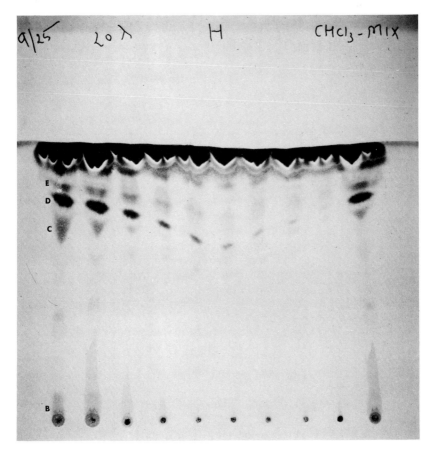

Figure 2. Thin-layer chromatography of polar lipids from benzene extract of 22% moisture wheat stored as in Figure 1. Tentatively identified: B — phosphatidyl serine, C — phosphatidyl choline, D — digalactosyl diglyceride, E — monogalactosyl diglyceride (from Daftary and Pomeranz, 1965).

TABLE VI
Lipids in flours stored at various temperatures[a]

Variety and Storage Temp. (°C.)	Free Lipids, %				Bound Lipids, %			
	Total	Nonpolar	Polar	Recovery	Total	Nonpolar	Polar	Recovery
Comanche								
4	0.75	61.7	34.4	96.1	0.74	15.7	79.0	94.7
23	0.17	93.5	8.1	101.6	0.70	25.4	70.3	95.7
30	0.21	96.7	4.5	101.2	0.67	36.1	60.5	96.6
37	0.22	96.2	5.2	101.2	0.48	65.1	34.5	99.6
C.I. 12995								
4	0.79	62.3	32.5	94.8	0.66	11.3	84.0	95.3
23	0.18	92.4	8.5	100.9	0.61	26.2	68.9	95.1
30	0.21	95.7	5.8	101.5	0.53	34.7	62.2	96.9
37	0.25	96.1	5.1	101.2	0.39	69.2	30.0	99.2
Thatcher								
4	0.89	69.1	26.2	95.3	0.86	8.2	86.3	94.5
23	0.19	96.5	6.0	102.5	0.85	31.8	63.1	94.9
30	0.25	96.5	4.8	101.3	0.76	39.2	56.1	95.3
37	0.30	97.4	4.1	101.5	0.50	71.3	26.6	97.9
Selkirk								
4	0.87	69.4	26.3	95.7	0.83	8.7	86.8	95.5
23	0.24	95.8	5.9	101.7	0.74	33.1	62.1	95.2
30	0.36	97.7	4.6	102.3	0.71	44.2	53.2	97.4
37	0.31	97.7	4.0	101.7	0.50	71.2	27.1	98.3

[a]Data of Daftary et al. (1970b).

species present. Free lipids decreased more in samples stored at 23° than at 30° or 37°C. Residual (bound) lipids in all storage-damaged flours contained markedly reduced amounts of polar components. The breakdown of bound lipids increased as temperature of flour storage was increased from 23° to 30° and 37°C. The breakdown of bound lipids was accompanied by transformation of polar to nonpolar-like components. The ratio of nonpolar to polar components in residual bound lipids increased as the storage temperature of the flours increased. The results are summarized in Table VI. The breakdown of free lipids was accompanied by disappearance of lipoprotein which was present in petroleum ether extracts of the sound flour.

Morrison (1963) followed changes in free fatty acids of wheat flours of 13 to 14% moisture in storage. Palmitic, oleic, linoleic, and linolenic acids were liberated at a steady rate, in proportions close to those of the total lipids. Yasumatsu and Moritaka (1964) studied fatty acid composition of lipids from polished rice. After 6 months' storage, fatty acids were released from neutral fat in the same proportion as they were combined in the neutral fat.

III. NUTRITIVE CHANGES

Implications of hygienic and nutritive deterioration have been studied only to a limited extent and are poorly defined, partly because the effects of feeding deteriorated stored products are sometimes difficult to demonstrate. Consumption of cereals infested by insects or mites may cause digestive or similar ailments. Certain insects may mechanically transfer bacteria from drains or other undesirable localities to foodstuffs. Workers handling infested commodities have been affected by skin rashes and various kinds of dermatitis from the presence of insects or mites or of their cast-off skins, hairs, or excreta.

Certain nutritional factors are destroyed in moldy cereals and feeds. A diet containing moldy oilseed meals may retard the growth of poults. Oxidation of unsaturated fatty acids in damaged grain is involved in the appearance of muscular dystrophy in pigs. In recent years there have been many reports on the formation of toxic compounds in mold-damaged food and feedstuff. They are discussed in detail in Chapter 4 of this book.

A. Mineral Changes

Although mineral matter is seldom gained or lost in storage, the availability of phosphorus, nutritionally important to animals and man, appears to increase in storage. Most phosphorus in grain is present in the form of phytin, a potassium-magnesium salt of inositol phosphoric acid. The phosphorus of this compound is not well utilized in the animal body, and about 60% of it is excreted in unchanged form by man (Harrison and Mellanby, 1939; Krieger et al., 1941). During the storage of flour (Greaves and Hirst, 1925) and more slowly in the storage of unmilled grain, phytin is acted upon by the enzyme phytase with the liberation of water-soluble, readily assimilable phosphorus compounds.

B. Changes in Carbohydrates

It has been reported by Sreenivasan (1939) that freshly harvested rice is not digested as readily as rice that has been stored for a time. Fresh rice is said to contain an active alpha-amylase that causes the rice to become sticky when cooked. This amylase presumably becomes partially inactivated during storage.

C. Protein Changes

Although the total protein content of grain as calculated from its nitrogen content is generally assumed to remain unchanged during storage, Shutt (1909, 1911) and Daftary et al. (1970b) demonstrated a progressive though small increase in the protein content of wheat during extended storage. As suggested previously, this protein increase on a percentage basis is doubtless the result of a loss in carbohydrate by respiration.

A sample of barley taken from an excavation in Asia Minor and claimed to be from 3,000 to 5,000 years old was found in Zeleny's (1954) laboratory to contain 3.2% of nitrogen, equivalent to 20% of protein on a moisture-free basis. This compares with an average protein content of modern barley of about 12%. The ancient barley was blackened with age, light in weight, and very fragile, although the characteristic shape of the kernels was well maintained. It is doubtful if this grain contained any true protein; the nitrogen was probably present in other forms. The high nitrogen content can probably be accounted for by the fact that the nitrogen-containing compounds were lost more slowly than other constituents of the grain.

Jones and Gersdorff (1938, 1939, 1941) and Jones, Divine, and Gersdorff (1942) studied changes occurring in the proteins of various seeds and their ground products during storage. The proteins of wheat, corn, and soybeans, and their ground products, were shown to decrease in solubility and in digestibility by pepsin and trypsin *in vitro*. Simultaneously there occurred an increase in amino nitrogen and a decrease in "true protein" nitrogen. Wheat containing approximately 11% of moisture showed a decrease in protein digestibility of 8% when stored in sealed jars at 76°F. (24°C.) for 2 years. Corn containing about 12% moisture similarly stored showed a decrease of 3.6% in protein digestibility in the same time. These changes, as well as changes in protein solubility, occur much more rapidly in the milled products of grain than in whole grain.

In a continuation of these studies, rats were fed ground corn stored at 76°F. for varying lengths of time. These experiments showed that the product decreased in palatability as well as in nutritive value as the length of the storage period increased.

This deterioration in nutritive value was assumed to be associated with the changes in protein solubility and digestibility mentioned previously. Similar feeding experiments using whole wheat flour, white flour, and wheat meal showed no significant decrease in nutritive value over a 24-month period. In all these feeding trials, grain and meal were sound and free from any evidence of insect infestation or mold growth throughout the period of the study.

Proteins from groats of barley, oats, corn, rice, wheat, buckwheat, peas, and millet were hydrolyzed by enzymes *in vitro* (Salun and Nadezhnova, 1971). Long storage decreased susceptibility to pepsin and trypsin.

Feeding experiments conducted at the University of Illinois (Fairbanks et al., 1940) showed that swine fed sound corn made more rapid gains and consumed less feed per day and less feed per 100 lb. of gain in weight than swine fed moldy corn. Whether the deterioration in nutritive value in this case was due to protein changes or to toxic substances resulting from mold growth was not clear.

Mitchell and Beadles (1949) were unable to detect any significant deterioration in the biological value or digestibility of corn and wheat proteins in grains stored for 2 to 3 years. The authors suggested that the earlier results of Jones and co-workers, based on *ad libitum* feeding trials, showed decreased growth because of diminished consumption of unpalatable feed. The investigations of Mitchell and Beadles (1949) involved N-balance studies.

Yannai and Zimmermann (1970) conducted studies on changes during controlled storage. The studies were to determine the influence of air and storage over a range of temperature and relative humidity levels on the protein nutritive value of staple foods. The nutritive value was determined in weanling rats fed lysine-limited diets. Protein nutritive value parameters used were protein efficiency ratio, net protein ratio, protein retention, and net protein utilization. Only minor changes took place during storage of wheat and rice.

Koch and Meyer (1957) concluded that feeding trials with large animals have generally shown that storage under adequate dry conditions does not change the value of cereal grains as a source of energy or as a source of proteins in a well-balanced diet. The authors fed barley grain for 4 crop years, both before and after storage, to growing rats. Data for feed consumption, weight gain, and N-balance were used as the criteria of measurement in the rat study. In another study, barley stored for 3 years was compared to fresh barley as the chief component of the ration of growing swine. Criteria of measurements were weight gain and food consumption. Koch and Meyer (1957) noted no significant differences in N-retention or weight gain of growing rats fed stored or fresh barley, either as the only or partial source of protein. In the case of swine, average comparable weight gains and feed efficiency values were obtained when fresh or stored barleys were supplemented with equal amounts of casein or equal amounts of a soybean-cottonseed meal mixture. Dobczynska (1966) studied changes in available lysine, the limiting amino acid, in wheat stored under various conditions. Changes were greatest during the first 6 weeks; only small changes were measured during subsequent 20 weeks. Decrease in available lysine ranged from 3.2% (in grain with 15% moisture, stored at 7° to 8°C.) to 19.9% (in grain with 20% moisture stored at 20° to 21°C.). Under practical conditions (moisture of 13.0 to 13.5% at 20° to 21°C., or 14.0 to 16.5% moisture at 7° to 8°C.) decreases were 6 to 8%. Losses in available lysine increased as initial moisture, rate, and temperature of drying damp grain increased. Drying under an atmosphere of nitrogen was not superior to drying in air. A linear relation was established between available lysine and reducing sugars.

Pawlak and Pion (1970) stored wheat samples for up to 4 years under standard conditions or for 2 years under controlled atmospheres. Storage for 1 year or longer slightly decreased growth rates and food consumption, without any change in lysine and threonine contents of blood and muscle, of growing rats. Wheat stored under N_2 or CO_2 atmospheres and a control stored at $-20°$C. gave similar results. Growth rates and food consumption were lowest with air-stored wheat samples.

Ferrel et al. (1970) infused lightly scarrified wheat kernels with up to 15% of lysine hydrochloride and then blended them with untreated wheat to provide lysine enrichment at any desirable nutritional level. The fortified grain and blends with 0.1% fortification were stored at 90° and 100°F. (32° and 38°C.) at moisture levels of 9, 11, and 13%; a control sample was stored at 0°F. ($-18°$C.) at a moisture level of 13%. The samples were evaluated chemically for added lysine, organoleptically for odor or color deterioration, and biologically for physiological availability of added lysine (PER assays). Stability during 1 year remained relatively high.

According to Trolle and Pedersen (1971), good feeding grain is characterized by high digestibility and biological value of the protein, by the absence of toxic substances (mycotoxins, fungicides, etc.), by the presence of lipids which have not been excessively hydrolyzed and/or oxidized, and by relatively minor changes in water-soluble and fat-soluble (especially tocopherol) vitamins. Damaged (in storage) barley was high in free fatty acids (fat acidity of 37.5), and its tocopherol content was only 30.5 γ/g., compared to 54.5 to 81.0 γ/g. of sound barley. The lysine content of the stored barley was decreased. This is of interest as Daftary et al. (1970b) have shown that whereas Kjeldahl-N changed relatively little during storage under adverse conditions, binding of the acidic dye, acid orange 12, decreased significantly. The dye is known to bind under acidic conditions to the epsilon-amino group of lysine, the imidazole group of histidine, or the guanidyl group of arginine.

Trolle and Pedersen (1971) also reported that in feeding experiments with rats digestibility of protein in storage-damaged barley was normal, but its biological value was low. The damaged barley had also a low net protein utilization. The damaged barley caused serious renal damage in pigs. The renal changes probably resulted from the action of the mycotoxin citrinin from *Penicillium viridicatum* Westling.

Lund et al. (1971) measured temperature, carbon dioxide production, germinative capacity, contents of reducing and nonreducing sugars, the predominant fungus flora, malting properties, and the feeding quality of barley stored for 30 weeks under controlled conditions at 20° C. and at moisture contents from about 12 to 26%. Barley at 12 and 14% moisture stored satisfactorily without mold development. At increasing moisture levels, a high correlation was found between increases in mold growth, carbon dioxide production, and reducing sugars; and decreases in germinative capacity and nonreducing sugars. Among the storage molds, *Aspergillus* spp. was the predominating genus in barley stored at up to 18% moisture and *Penicillium* spp. prevailed at higher moisture contents. At the highest moisture content, *Fusarium* spp. also developed rapidly. *Fusarium* and *Aspergillus* developed more rapidly in green (unkilned) malt than in barley, especially if the malt were produced from a high-moisture barley. To determine feeding quality for rats, digestibility, biological value, and net protein utilization (NPU) were determined on whole barleys stored at various moisture levels. There was a considerable drop in NPU at 18% moisture. NPU values at 18 and 20% moisture differed considerably from the corresponding values at 12 to 17% moisture. Digestibility at 18% moisture differed significantly from the corresponding values for all other samples, while a drop in biological value was significant only at 20% moisture. The less extensive damage implied for barley at higher moisture content may have resulted from the shorter storage period. Generally, as the barley moisture increased total lysine contents (determined in acid hydrolysates) decreased.

D. Vitamin Changes

Cereal grains and their products are important sources of certain vitamins in food and feed. Losses in vitamin content that may occur during storage are therefore of considerable practical importance. Cereal grains are generally good sources of thiamine, niacin, pyridoxine, inositol, biotin, and vitamin E. They also contain significant quantities of pantothenic acid. Vitamin A activity occurs in yellow corn but is practically absent in all other cereal grains (Fraps, 1931).

Bayfield and O'Donnell (1945) showed that wheat containing about 17% moisture lost approximately 30% of its thiamine in a 5-month storage period. This wheat deteriorated considerably during this period because of its high moisture content. They also showed that at normal moisture level of about 12%, the thiamine loss in a 5-month period was in the neighborhood of 12%. The same investigators made thiamine assays on a number of samples of apparently sound wheat of varying ages up to 51 years. No data on the original thiamine content of any of these samples were available for comparison, but the very low values obtained for some of the older samples indicated that considerable loss of thiamine must have occurred. However, some of these samples that were as much as 21 years old still had fairly high thiamine contents and thus appeared to have lost little thiamine during these long periods of storage. Fifield and Robertson (1945) reported the thiamine contents of 12 samples of wheat stored in a dry, unheated room at Fort Collins, Colorado, for 14 to 21 years. Here again, initial thiamine data were not available, but the relatively high thiamine contents of the stored wheats appear to indicate that the thiamine losses were, in most instances, probably rather small.

Experiments conducted at Iowa State College indicate that the thiamine content of yellow corn stored under ideal farm conditions does not appear to be affected during 4 years (Jones et al., 1943).

Studies on rice have also indicated that thiamine is quite stable during storage. Hulled rice stored in straw bags for 4 years retained most of its original thiamine content during the first 2 years, but a significant drop occurred during the second 2 years of storage (Kondo and Okamura, 1933a). After storage in airtight containers for 26 and 28 years, samples of hulled rice still had thiamine contents of more than half that found in fresh rice (Kondo and Okamura, 1933c). Hulled and unhulled rice stored in hermetically sealed concrete bins for 5 years showed no appreciable loss in thiamine (Kondo and Okamura, 1937). Kondo and Okamura (1933b), however, found that unhulled rice stored at a moisture content of more than 10% suffered appreciable losses in thiamine content and that these losses did not parallel the decrease in viability of the seed.

A few studies have been conducted by commercial flour mills on vitamin losses in enriched flour. Results indicate that significant losses of thiamine may occur during storage and that the extent of the losses, although quite variable, depends considerably on the time and temperature of storage and upon the moisture content of the flour. High temperatures and high moisture contents accelerate the rate of thiamine destruction.

When thiamine chloride hydrochloride is used as an enrichment ingredient, enriched flour may be expected to lose about 10% of its thiamine in 6 months of normal storage, although losses of 20% or more may occur under unfavorable storage conditions. Because of its greater stability, thiamine mononitrate has largely replaced thiamine chloride hydrochloride as a flour-enriching agent. When the mononitrate is thus used, thiamine losses in enriched flour are reduced by one-half or more (Hollenbeck and Obermeyer, 1952). No appreciable losses of riboflavin or niacin (nicotinic acid) have been found to occur in enriched flour during normal storage.

Very little definite information appears to be available concerning losses of the B vitamins, other than thiamine, found in grain (riboflavin, niacin, pyridoxine, pantothenic acid, para-amino benzoic acid, and inositol). But it is generally believed that these vitamins, with the possible exception of pantothenic acid, are rather stable and are not readily destroyed in unbroken grain under normal conditions of storage. Riboflavin and pyridoxine are rather sensitive to light and may therefore be unstable in milled products exposed to strong light.

Vitamin A activity of yellow corn, although equivalent to only about 3.5 to 5.0 international units per gram, is of considerable importance in animal feeding and may also be of significance in human nutrition in certain sections of the country where corn meal is an important item of the diet. No other grain has any appreciable vitamin A activity. The vitamin A activity of yellow corn is due primarily to its content of beta-carotene, cryptoxanthin, and neocryptoxanthin, and in lesser degree to alpha-carotene and K-carotene (Fraps and Kemmerer,

1941). These substances are spoken of as "provitamins" and are converted in varying degree into vitamin A in the animal body.

Considerable losses of vitamin A have been shown to occur in yellow corn during storage. Fraps and Kemmerer (1937) showed that yellow corn and corn meal may suffer losses in carotenoid pigment even in cold storage. With corn meal as much as 34% of the crude carotene was lost during the first week of storage at 35°C., although subsequent losses were much smaller. Studies conducted at the University of Illinois showed that corn stored in steel bins for 4 years contained less than half the crude carotene of fresh corn (Jones et al., 1943).

The Bureau of Animal Industry, United States Department of Agriculture, studied corn from the 1937 to 1941 crops that had been stored under government seal in Illinois and Iowa. Chemical and biological assays showed losses of both carotene and vitamin A as the result of storage. In corn more than 1 year old these losses ran as high as 70%. Loss of vitamin A appeared to occur more rapidly during the first year of storage than subsequently.

The cattle disease known as anasarca appears to be caused by vitamin A deficiency (Creech and Madsen, 1942; Madsen and Earle, 1947). The disease is manifested by loss of appetite, lameness, marked swelling of subcutaneous tissues, and defective vision, particularly night blindness. Serious economic losses may result from this disease. The apparent relationship between anasarca and vitamin A deficiency lends considerable practical importance to the loss of vitamin A activity in stored yellow corn. However, even diets containing new yellow corn need to be supplemented with roughages of relatively high vitamin A activity, such as alfalfa hay (Madsen and Earle, 1947).

Quackenbush (1963) stored shelled dent corn, from the seed of a single cross of a high carotene parentage, in the dark for 3 years at 3 and 11% moisture and at 7° and 25°C. Losses of total carotenoid pigments, not rapid during the early part of the storage period, were approximately a logarithmic function of time. Temperature exerted more effect than moisture content. The carotene fraction was the least stable pigment fraction. Half of the initial carotene was lost at 7°C., three-quarters at 25°C. Losses of zeinoxanthin and the carotendiols (lutein and zeaxanthin) were about equal, and all occurred at slower rates than losses of carotene. The author concluded that some of the recent corn hybrids, which are comparatively low in carotenoids initially, may contain negligible amounts of pigments after long storage.

Tocopherols are lost during storage of cereal grains. Losses are accelerated in grain stored under adverse conditions (Karp, 1959). Losses are correlated with decreases in unsaturated fatty acids of cereal lipids (linoleic and linolenic). Total tocopherols in freshly milled flour were 1,500 to 1,600 γ/100 g., but only 17 to 18% of this was alpha-tocopherol. Aerobic storage for 190 days reduced all tocopherols by 62 to 67%.

According to Stefanov and Gavrilenko (1970), intensive oxidation and hydrolysis took place when corn grain containing 14% moisture was stored. Vitamin, carbohydrate, and protein contents decreased; fat content of the bran increased; and grain processing was increasingly more difficult. During storage in a carbon dioxide atmosphere for 3 months, moisture and fat contents of the bran remained unchanged.

E. Drying Damp Grain

It is well established that drying damp grain at elevated temperatures may reduce its nutritive value, breadmaking potential, and germinative power and capacity. Stansfield and Cook (1932) have shown in their classic and comprehensive study that there is a relationship between grain moisture content and the "critical temperature" to which it may be dried without damage. Thus, Cashmore (1942) found that no damage to germination occurred in grain with a moisture content of 18% if the air temperature was below 67°C., and the critical air temperature of grain with 30% moisture was 43°C.

The use of heated air to dry high-moisture barley was compared with air-drying without heat, and field-drying (P. H. Hoskins, private communication). The study was conducted for several years by Anheuser-Busch, Inc., in cooperation with the University of Missouri. Evaluations were made on germination and malt quality. Drying 20% moisture barley with 43°C. heated air down to 12% moisture did not reduce germination percentage. Malting quality of the barley dried with heated air was similar to air- and field-dried barley. Finney and co-workers (1962) reported somewhat higher "critical" air temperatures for safe drying of immature wheat to be used in breadmaking. A comprehensive review on heat damage to functional properties during drying of cereals was published by Linko (1966). Emerick et al. (1961) dried corn in thin layers at 50° to 350°F. (10° to 177°C.). All dried grains incorporated into diets as sources of energy and supplementary protein supported growth of chicks and rats. However, drying at 450°F. (232°C.) for 2 1/2 hr. caused significant damage to the nutritive value of the corn (as measured by poorer weight gain, feed conversion, and feed consumption). Jensen et al. (1960) reported similar results for corn heated for rather long periods and fed to 2-week-old pigs or pigs fed from 45 to 190 lb. Vitamin assays indicated some destruction of pantothenic acid but no measurable damage to carotene, riboflavin, or nicotinic acid. Clanton et al. (1960) found no change in digestibility of corn dried at 190°F. (88°C.) and fed to cattle.

On the other hand, Cabell et al. (1958) found that very prolonged heating of wet corn above 135°F. (57°C.) decreased the nutritive value of corn proteins for rats; but even drying at 240°F. (116°C.) for 1.5 hr. had no significant deleterious effect. Milner and Woodforde (1965) suggested that the prolonged heating could lead to degradation of starch to reducing sugars and their interaction with the epsilon group of lysine, thus rendering the limiting amino acid unavailable.

Milner and Woodforde (1965) harvested wheat at 22% moisture and heated it in air at 180°F. (82°C.) for 37 min., 220°F. (104°C.) for 26 min., or 220°F. for 120 min. The wheat samples were incorporated into two series of diets for young growing chicks. No significant differences were found between the samples either when fed as the sole protein source or when fed as the major energy source in completely adequate rations. None of the samples was significantly different from a control sample of wheat dried at 80°F. (27°C.).

Chow and Draper (1969) studied the stability of saturated and unsaturated fatty acids and of tocopherols in corn dried artificially. Drying temperatures ranged from room temperature to 143°C. The moisture content decreased during drying from about 25 to 15%. Drying had no significant effect on fatty acids or on tocopherols.

According to Sato et al. (1971), brown rice dried by the sun (30°C.) or in storage at 90°C. gave milled and cooked rice with more soluble matter and higher starch-iodine blue value than rice dried at lower temperatures (10°C.) in storage.

Solubility of polysaccharides from the cooked rice increased as storage of the brown rice was prolonged, regardless of the drying method. Starch-iodine blue values tended to decrease. Brown rice dried at higher temperatures gave more broken kernels during milling than that dried at lower temperatures. Solubilization of steamed rice by amylase action at earlier stages of saccharification was greater in the rice dried at higher temperatures. Brown rice stored for longer periods gave cooked rice which was less susceptible to amylase action. Cooked rice prepared from brown rice dried during storage was more susceptible to amylase action than rice dried by the sun.

Grain with moisture levels of 20 to 35% can be stored after application of 0.75 to 1.50% propionic acid or 0.90 to 1.75% of a 40:60 mixture of propionic and acetic acids (Stevenson, 1972). The grain can be used for feed purposes only. The treatment kills the embryo.

IV. DORMANCY, VIABILITY, GERMINATION, AND MALTING

Germination of seeds is of interest for several reasons. It is the crucial step in the reproductive cycle, it is essential in several uses of grain (such as malting and brewing, several distilling industries, production of sprouts), serves often as an index of soundness of stored grain, and is fascinating from the standpoint of biochemistry and plant physiology.

A. Dormancy and Germination

Seeds of most species of cultivated plants germinate when they are morphologically mature and are placed under optimum conditions of moisture, temperature, and light. But even when provided with such conditions seeds of many species may fail to germinate. This stage is described as dormancy. Depending on species and variety, dormancy may range from several days to years. Eventually, the dormant seeds will germinate if they are stored under conditions that are conducive to physiological and chemical changes that eliminate dormancy. Such storage is referred to as after-ripening. The elimination of dormancy may result from environmental effects (e.g. a particular light or heat treatment) or from degradation of inhibitors as a result of slow metabolic changes (Amen, 1964; MacLeod, 1967; Black, 1970; Belderok, 1968a).

Amen (1964) distinguishes between dormancy and quiescence. Seed quiescence is an environmentally imposed temporary suspension of growth and reduced metabolic activity in viable seeds which occurs under conditions that are unfavorable to germination. Seed dormancy, on the other hand, is an endogenously controlled and/or environmentally imposed temporary suspension of growth which is independent of immediate environmental conditions. Consequently, dormant seeds do not germinate under conditions which may be favorable for normal growth.

According to Amen (1964), dormancy is a physiological adaptation which delays germination until favorable environmental conditions are likely to occur. The causes of seed dormancy generally fall into five classes: 1) rudimentary embryos, 2) physiologically immature embryos (inactive enzyme systems), 3) mechanically resistant seed coats, 4) impermeable seed coats, and 5) presence of germination inhibitors.

Dormancy contributes to the survival of wild plants. Seeds can survive low temperatures or dry weather that would kill seedlings. If rain occurs at harvest time, seeds that show no dormancy may sprout before they can be harvested. Sprouting in the ear decreases yield and, most important, impairs significantly functional properties and decreases value of the grain. Flour (or meal) from sprouted wheat or rye is rich in alpha-amylase and proteases and has a reduced breadmaking potential as a result of excessive starch and gluten degradation. Similarly, barley that sprouted in the field is of limited use in malting. However, breadmaking quality of wheat may actually be improved by a small amount of sprouted grain which raises the alpha-amylase level to an optimum.

On the other hand, prolonged dormancy is both troublesome and expensive if the grain is to be malted or sown shortly after harvest. In the case of malting barley, there is a conflict in the requirements of the growers and the maltsters. The growers, especially in countries with rain during harvest, prefer grain with some dormancy to resist field sprouting. On the other hand, maltsters prefer barley with a very limited dormancy. Use of such barley saves storage costs. In addition, brief dormancy is generally accompanied by rapid and uniform germination and optimum modification of barley during malting. Modification describes the sum total of desirable physical and biochemical changes that take place when grain is malted. With regard to sowing, short dormancy is important in areas in which two crops are grown in 1 year, in plant-breeding programs designed to increase rapidly available seed by inclusion of a greenhouse cycle, or in the case of winter cereals in regions where harvest is late and winter sets in early.

In addition to failure of viable dormant seeds to germinate, there are two other types of germination inhibition. One is called water-sensitivity and is exhibited by failure of seeds to germinate if the water uptake has been excessive. The second is steeping injury, as indicated by the harmful effect on germination of even short immersion in water. MacLeod (1967) considers all three types as different facets of dormancy. Water sensitivity and steeping injury are, according to her, dormancy types induced by exposure to excessive moisture.

B. Physiology of Germination

Inasmuch as dormancy is failure of germination to take place, it is appropriate to describe briefly the latter process. Black (1970) defines germination as the appearance of the first signs of growth, normally the visible protrusion of the radicle. Mayer and Poljakoff-Mayber (1963) describe germination as the consecutive steps which increase metabolic activity and initiate the formation of a seedling from a quiescent seed with low water content. The increase in metabolic activity takes place following water uptake by the dry seed. Thereafter there is a rapid rise in fresh weight of the embryonic axis. Generally, initiation of growth of the radicle is by cell enlargement followed by cell division. During the initial stage of water uptake, respiration rises slowly, reaches a plateau, and increases sharply with cell growth commencement. Amen (1964) outlined the following steps in the germination process: 1) imbibition and absorption of water, 2) hydration, 3) oxygen uptake, 4) increased enzymatic activity and metabolism, 5) initiation of cell division and elongation, 6) increased respiration and assimilation, 7) increased cell division and elongation, 8) cellular differentiation, 9) increased reducing sugar content, and 10) emergence of embryo. The exact sequence of those events has not been fully determined. In addition, there is a great deal of interspecies variation, especially between wild and cultivated species.

Investigations of Marcus (1969) have shown that as water is taken up, "activation" of the ribosomes renders the protein-synthesizing apparatus in wheat embryos functional. Ribosomes from imbibed seeds actively incorporate amino acids into protein. Ribosomes from dry seeds are sluggish in this respect, even though other RNA species (transfer RNA) are active. If, however, poly-uridylic acid (poly U) is added *in vitro* to the ribosomal preparation from dry seeds, the latter can reach the same activity as ribosomes from imbibed wheat. As poly U acts as an artificial messenger RNA, it was suggested that preparations from imbibed seeds contain an endogenous messenger RNA that is absent in dry seeds. It would seem, therefore, that polysome formation (i.e., union of ribosomes with messenger RNA) takes place during early stages of germination. Apparently, however, there is no need for *de novo* synthesis of messenger RNA, and only a combination of a preformed RNA with ribosomes to form polysomes is required. While it has become quite clear in recent years that the occurrence of those processes is essential to germination, it is not clear how those processes are prevented or blocked during dormancy.

Seed dormancy is not necessarily characterized by failure of the protein-synthesizing apparatus to function. Protein synthesis in some dormant seeds does not differ from that in nondormant seeds. In certain cases (e.g. *Avena fatua*) there is a significantly higher rate of RNA synthesis in dormant seeds. Black (1970) has emphasized that those results should not be interpreted to mean that regulation of nucleic acid or protein synthesis are not important features of dormant seeds. Apparently, some small changes take place in synthesis of selected key enzymes, and those small changes cannot be measured by available methods. It would seem that we cannot describe with certainty the dormant state in biochemical terms. We have, however, some information on the location of germination inhibitors in the grain.

C. Factors Inhibiting Germination

It is generally assumed that dormancy factors reside in the outer layers of the grain. Dormancy is generally broken when those layers are removed or damaged. This has led to establishing a procedure for measuring dormancy from the difference between germinative capacity and germinative vigor. To determine viability we can use tetrazolium dyes or measure growth of kernels which have been germinated after the outer covering layers have been removed. In the germination test, percentage of whole kernels which germinate under standard conditions is determined. Whole kernels which do not germinate are either dormant or dead. If tetrazolium staining or germination of mechanically abraded kernels gives a figure approaching 100% viability, it can be assumed that the ungerminated kernels are dormant (MacLeod, 1967).

Germinative vigor is often measured. Vigor is generally associated with rate of germination and seedling growth, and ability to germinate under adverse conditions.

In some cases where no germination was observed after the removal of the pericarp and testa, it has been shown that an additional germination factor was present in the embryo. Such embryo dormancy was found in freshly harvested *Hordeum spontaneum, Avena fatua,* and some wheats. No dormancy factors were detected or isolated in the endosperm. It has been suggested that dormancy in cereals results from the outer seed layers blocking oxygen transport to the embryo. This assumption is based on the fact that removal or damage of pericarp which breaks dormancy also facilitates oxygen transport. Similar effects are exerted by adding hydrogen peroxide to the water in the germination test. The evidence is indirect, as no measurements have been recorded of changes in oxygen permeability resulting from removal of seed coats. While oxygen uptake is higher in dormant than in nondormant barley, there is no such differentiation in lettuce seeds. Dormancy does not seem to depend on the rate of water uptake, which is the same in dormant and after-ripened grain. Similarly, respiration is not a factor inhibiting germination during dormancy as respiration of dormant and after-ripened grain is of almost equal intensity.

Several mechanisms have been proposed to explain the involvement of oxygen in dormancy. They are based on differences in available and required oxygen for germination and growth. According to some, breaking of dormancy does not alter oxygen permeability of seed coats but lowers oxygen tension required by the embryo for growth. According to others, during after-ripening increased oxygen permeability increases available oxygen. Recent findings point to another possible explanation. Respiration of nondormant seeds is characterized by a greater participation of the pentose phosphate pathway (as an alternative route to the glycolytic metabolism of carbohydrates) than in dormant seeds. Interestingly, some chemical reagents which break dormancy also increase the contribution of the pentose pathway to respiration.

Endosperm slices from freshly harvested barley produced after treatment with gibberellic acid (GA) little alpha-amylase, as compared with slices from barley stored up to 18 months at 4°, 25°, or 16° to 20°C. The response to GA was improved by heating for 3 days at 40°C. or by procedures which increased oxygen supply to the aleurone cells. No difference was detected in response to GA of dehusked kernels of the freshly harvested and stored (or treated) types of barley (Crabb, 1971). It was suggested that outer coverings of freshly harvested barley restricted permeability to oxygen to a greater extent than those of stored barley, probably because of increased microbial activity.

D. Germination Inhibitors

Numerous natural substances have been suggested as germination inhibitors. Evidence is based on findings that substances can be extracted from the seed and inhibit germination in nondormant seeds. In nature, dormancy is apparently broken in the soil by leaching out germination inhibitors from certain seeds after an adequate rainfall. Belderok (1968b) determined the sulfhydryl and disulfide contents in embryos of intact dormant and after-ripened grains. After moistening, embryos of dormant wheat and barley did not release glutathione and cysteine from soluble proteins or peptides. The release could be accomplished by embryos of post-ripened grain.

Most recent studies postulate involvement of plant growth regulators in breaking dormancy. Wild oats exhibit embryo dormancy. Excised embryos of freshly harvested wild oats cannot form or release (from a bound form) gibberellins (GA). That capacity is restored in after-ripened oats (Black, 1970). Treatment of dormant grains with GA increases production of glutathione and cysteine, which agrees with the finding that dormancy can be broken by either GA or thiol-containing compounds. Kinetin is as effective in overcoming dormancy as gibberellic acid. The effect of GA is on dormancy but not on water-sensitivity. The action is directly on the embryo.

Work of Paleg and MacLeod (see review by Belderok, 1968a) suggests an effect of gibberellins through activation of hydrolases that degrade high molecular weight moieties in the endosperm into amino acids and simple sugars which are essential for growth. A shortage of endogenous gibberellins would induce dormancy both by limiting liberation of SH-containing compounds which are essential for initiating germination and by reducing amounts of available sugars and amino acids.

Production of gibberellins in plant tissues takes place under aerobic conditions. Similarly, GA-induced stimulation of hydrolytic action requires the presence of oxygen. The interrelation of those factors has led Simpson (1965) to suggest that primary dormancy in mature seed of the wild oat (*Avena fatua* L.) is due to blocks in at least two metabolic pathways associated with the mobilization and use of endosperm reserves. The first block involves the production of sugar from endosperm starch and has been attributed to inability to produce or release maltase. The second block involves utilization of the sugar and has been related to the inability to synthesize the enzyme 3-nucleotidase. Both blocks can be overcome independently by exogenous gibberelic acid or endogenous gibberellin-like substances.

Chen and Varner (1969, 1970) compared carbohydrate metabolism, respiration, and protein synthesis in dormant and after-ripened seeds of *Avena fatua* L. In nondormant seeds ^{14}C-maltose administered to the endosperm was readily converted to sucrose in the scutellum and translocated to the embryo. In dormant seeds, little sucrose was synthesized from ^{14}C-maltose, and glucose and maltose accumulated in the endosperm. It was suggested that biosynthesis of sucrose is essential for effective transport of the endosperm reserve to the embryonic axis in germinating seeds. Respiration rate of imbibed dormant seeds was only about 20% less than that of imbibed nondormant seeds in the period before actual germination. Both were capable of synthesizing proteins at comparable rates. The results indicated that dormancy in wild oat is due to some specific metabolic block rather than to a state of general inactivity.

According to Roberts (1969), in some species there is good evidence for control of dormancy by germination inhibitors. In many cereals (especially the cultivated ones) even though several inhibitors have been isolated and characterized, their role in dormancy mechanisms in intact seeds remains uncertain.

Abscissic acid was isolated and characterized in 1965 and shown to be involved in bud dormancy and control of leaf abscission in cotton (Black, 1970). In the last 7 years it has been found in the covering layers, embryo, and endosperm of many seeds and shown to be involved in the mechanism of dormancy. In some seeds, inhibition of germination seems to be regulated by abscissic acid, and there is a positive correlation between abscissic acid content and dormancy. It is yet debatable whether abscissic acid controls dormancy in cereal grains. Reservations stem from its presence in the endosperm that has not been shown to be a site of dormancy factors. In addition, kinetin, but not GA, overcomes the effect of abscissic acid in lettuce seeds. GA is far less effective than kinetin in reversing abscissic acid inhibition of alpha-amylase and coleoptile growth in barley.

Khan et al. (1971) suggested that cytokinins (kinetin, zeatin, and benzyladenine) counteract the inhibition of germination caused by natural inhibitors (abscissic acid, coumarin, xanthatin). The authors proposed a hypothesis on the mechanism of dormancy and germination. According to this hypothesis, gibberellin is the primary stimulus for germination, and the roles of cytokinin and inhibitor are basically "permissive" or "preventive." Cytokinin is postulated to remove the block to germination and to permit the completion of gibberellin-mediated germinative processes. Accordingly, dormancy could result not only from the presence of an inhibitor but also from the lack of a gibberellin or a cytokinin.

E. Controlling Length of Dormancy

Duration of dormancy in most cereal grains is largely determined by genetic factors. Cultural practices (such as application of fertilizers) have little effect. On the other hand, environmental factors affect length of dormancy. Dry and sunny weather during grain development shortens postharvest dormancy. Belderok (1968a) studied effects of weather during the dough stage in grain development on dormancy. The dough stage is the intermediate phase of ripening which follows milk-ripeness and ends with harvest-ripeness. At that stage the grain matrix is soft and doughy. Hot weather during the dough stage shortens, and cool weather extends, dormancy. Dormancy depended on the temperature during, and duration of, dough stage. Dormancy of a given wheat variety depended on accumulated temperature during the dough stage, i.e. the sum of the daily mean temperatures above 12.5° C. reached during that stage. The length of dormancy was related to both variety and to accumulated temperature. According to Belderok (1968a), dormancy is in fact a varietal characteristic that can be modified by the environment. In The Netherlands, wheat varieties with a critical accumulated temperature of 50° or below are highly susceptible to sprouting after rain during harvest. Varieties with values over 80 are sprout-resistant. The critical values should be set somewhat lower in countries with cool summers, and higher if summers are hot. Those findings, combined with meteorological data, are used in The Netherlands and Germany to inform the farmer about danger of sprouting and the maltster about the projected dormancy period following harvest.

In seed testing, dormancy of freshly harvested grain can be broken artificially by predrying at 35° C., treatment with GA or hydrogen peroxide, or by removing (mechanically or chemically) the outermost layers of the seed coat (Heydecker, 1969).

The effect on germination of drying freshly harvested cereals was recorded as early as 1852 by Duchartre. The Swedes were among the first to recognize dormancy in cereals and its relation to storage and germination. Early work on methods of breaking dormancy by appropriate heat treatments, by removing semipermeable seed coats, by postharvest storage, and by genetic modification was reviewed by Brown et al. (1948). Those authors conducted extensive investigations (including 40,000 tests) on dormancy and the effects of storage on oats, barley, and sorghum. They concluded that most cereals completely after-ripen after storage for 1 to 6 months at 104° F. (40° C.). When freshly harvested seed of dormant barley and oats was kept at 36° F. (2° C.) at a relatively high humidity, dormancy was maintained for 3 years. Most freshly harvested dormant seeds germinated under favorable humidity conditions at 36° F. but not at 86° F. (30° C.). Removing the coat over the embryo enhanced germination at 36° F. Similarly, storage at 75° to 104° F. (24° to 40° C.) enhanced germination at 86° F. It was confirmed that dormancy is a varietal characteristic. There was an association between dormancy and winter growth habit. Dormancy was less common in sorghum than in barley or oats and disappeared after 2 months' storage at 104° F.

Increasing the partial pressure of oxygen surrounding rice seeds shortens length of dormancy (Roberts, 1969). Increasing the oxygen tension during germination or applying hydrogen peroxide also increases germination of partially dormant seeds. Over the range of 27° to 47° C. the relation $\log d = K_d - C_d t$ (where d = mean dormancy period, t = temperature, K_d and C_d constants) indicated that high storage temperatures increased the rate of breaking dormancy. The Q_{10} for rate of loss of dormancy was about 3.1.

Several chemical compounds with rather dissimilar biochemical actions can stimulate germination. The most important and potent are the plant hormones gibberellins. Only a few species of seed do not respond to treatment with those substances. In many cases they actually break dormancy; in others they enhance germination rate or final germination. It has also been shown, rather surprisingly, that several compounds that inhibit various metabolic processes can induce germination (Black, 1970). They include respiratory inhibitors (even though high concentrations of oxygen promote germination) and inhibitors of protein synthesis (such as chloramphenicol). The use of chemical treatments in the successful breaking of barley dormancy has involved lime water, hydrogen peroxide, thiourea, gibberellins, and kinetin.

According to a recent review (Anon., 1972), electricity may prove to be a key that unlocks seeds with tough, waterproof coatings which prevent germination. Cotton seeds with impermeable seed coats can be easily germinated when exposed to an electric glow-discharge. Germination also improved when three varieties of alfalfa seed were exposed to radio-frequency (RF) dielectric heating, microwave heating, and hot air. Once the seed coats became permeable, increased germination resulted. Additional study is needed before use recommendations can be made. At present, the methods are not economically feasible, nor is any one approach reliable for all kinds of seed.

As mentioned before, dormancy of most harvested cereal seeds is slowly lost in dry storage. In nature, however, temperature and light are most important in breaking dormancy. Alternating temperatures (e.g. several hours at 10° C. followed by several hours at 20° C.) are often effective, though the mechanism of the cyclic effect is not well understood. Often chilling imbibed seeds at 0° to 5° C. for several days helps to overcome dormancy and to germinate during later exposure at temperatures that are favorable to growth. This chilling requirement, apparently, prevents germination in late fall and regulates it in spring.

Many dormant seeds can be made to germinate by exposure to light. Light controls germination in all higher plants through the operation of a reversible pigment system. The effects of light in germination may be inhibitory, promotive, or nonpromotive, varying with species and light. The response to light may be affected by environmental conditions (oxygen tension or ambient temperature) and may change during storage (Borthwick et al., 1952).

It has been shown that light and temperature interact in the germination response. Genetic differences in response to controlled light and temperature treatments among seeds from widely scattered sources suggest possible evolutionary adaptations to contrasting climates.

The photoreaction has been shown to be controlled by the pigment phytochrome, a chromoprotein that can be measured in many plant tissues, including seeds. The pigment has been extracted from some plant tissues but not yet from seeds. Phytochrome can exist in two forms. In darkness, P_{730} — the species of phytochrome which is formed on illumination — slowly decays to P_{660}; in far-red light that transformation is rapid. To initiate germination in lettuce seeds, the phytochrome must be in the P_{730}-red illuminated condition. In barley, the presence of the appropriate form of phytochrome is not synonymous with dormancy. Yet, even in barley, which is indifferent to prevailing light conditions after it emerged from dormancy, the germination of dormant grain may be influenced by the type of illumination.

F. Viability

Various theories have been proposed to account for loss of seed viability in storage (Roberts, 1960; Anderson, 1970). Basically, they can be divided into two groups: those which link loss of viability with an intrinsic factor resulting from seed metabolism and those which postulate that the causes are extrinsic to the seed and are elaborated by microorganisms which live in association with the seed. There is a large volume of work which attributes loss of viability to both factors. Usually it is difficult to distinguish between cause and effect.

Reviews concerned with the storage of seed for maintenance of viability were published by Crocker (1948), Porter (1949), and Owen (1956). Roberts (1972) is the editor of a recently published book which describes general principles involved in loss of viability and vigor of seeds, and provides guidance on producing viable seeds, developing systems for short- or long-term storage, and testing viability and vigor of seeds. Haferkamp et al. (1953) reported that some barley cultivars germinated 96% after 32 years of storage under dry conditions. Robertson et al. (1943) reported about 71% germination after 22 years' storage of 6-rowed hulled barley but only 14% for naked barley.

Viability of cereal seeds is conditioned by temperature and humidity of storage. Bakke and Noecker (1933) reported that viability was reduced to 6% after storage for 3 days of damp (26.4% moisture) oats at 40°C. Carter and Young (1945) placed wheat at 12.2 to 18.6% moisture in sealed containers. Damaged ("sick") wheat symptoms appeared at 12.2% at 40°C. after 279 days but not at lower temperatures. Tuite and Christensen (1955) stored barley at 10 to 18% moisture and found little germination loss at room temperature in 30 days, even at the high moisture level, if molds were absent. According to Meredith et al. (1962), susceptibility to germination damage of damp barley is enhanced if it is stored in bulk prior to drying.

Armolik et al. (1956) studied the contribution of storage molds to the loss of germinability of surface-sterilized barley stored at moisture contents of 8 and 25%. *Fusarium moniliforme* Sheld. reduced germinability more rapidly than did species of *Aspergillus* and *Penicillium*. Autoclaved filtrates from cultures of *F. moniliforme* and *A. niger* reduced germination of barley.

Barley cultivars grown at several locations in the United States differed in their behavior during storage. Small-kerneled, Manchurian type, actively germinating cultivars were damaged more than the large-kerneled, 2-rowed cultivars which germinated more slowly. Both variety and environment under which the barley was cultivated affected tolerance to poor storage conditions. Samples harvested under dry conditions were generally more tolerant than those from areas in which environmental conditions did not favor full development of kernel dormancy, especially of combine-harvested grain.

Shands et al. (1967) studied the effects of harvest date and aeration during storage on viability of barley. They observed rapid loss of viability during the storage of late-harvested, weathered grain. Varietal differences were small and inconsistent.

Houston et al. (1957) stored rough rice at 11.2 to 16.5% moisture in loosely covered cans for 7 months. Changes occurred more quickly and extensively as temperature or moisture increased.

Roberts (1960) critically evaluated studies on viability of cereal seeds and obtained a simple mathematical relation between temperature, moisture content, and viability. The relationship was apparently similar for wheat, barley, and oats. A plot of log half-viability (defined as period from harvest until germination has dropped to 50%) vs. moisture content gave a straight falling line, which could be expressed as:

$$\log p = K_t - C_1 m$$

where p = half viability period, m = moisture content, and K_t and C_1 constants.

For samples stored at various temperatures, the relationship was:

$$\log p = K_m - C_2 t$$

where K_m and C_2 are constants.

Combining both equations:

$$\log p = K_v - C_1 m - C_2 t$$

For wheat, $K_v = 4.222$, $C_1 = 0.108$, and $C_2 = 0.050$.

Based on those data, a diagram showing relation between moisture content, temperature, and half-viability in wheat was calculated. The Q_{10} for decrease in half-viability was 3.3. This means that the viability period increased about 3.3 times with each fall of 10°C. in storage temperature.

According to Trolle and Pedersen (1971), first-class seeding grain should be a pure cultivar with high germinative capacity. The characteristic microflora of a good malting barley is characterized by *Alternaria* spp. and has little storage fungi (*Penicillium* and *Aspergillus* spp.) or field fungi (*Fusarium* and *Helminthosporium*). Levels of reducing and nonreducing sugars are important indicators of possible enzymatic activity in the grain resulting from fungal growth or the beginning of germination. Reducing sugars in storage-damaged barley averaged 0.58% compared with 0.17 to 0.33% in sound samples. Nonreducing sugars in damaged barley averaged 0.58% and were 1.74 to 2.87% in normal lots.

Gushing of beer is the result of inferior stability of carbon dioxide in the bottle. We distinguish between biological and nonbiological causes of beer gushing. The latter results from faulty composition of raw materials or processing. Biological sources of gushing are related to the presence of *Fusarium*, a characteristic field fungus (Trolle and Pedersen, 1971).

Prentice and co-workers conducted a series of studies of barley microflora, all of them of possible importance to malting and brewing quality. Ninety-seven isolates of microorganisms, represented by bacteria, yeast, and fungi that commonly infect barley, were applied to barley during the malting process (Prentice and Sloey, 1960). Observed changes resulting from action of microorganisms were increased nitrogen levels in laboratory and brewery worts, increased alpha-amylase and diastatic power of malts, and decreased beer gas stability. *Fusarium* were usually the cause of those changes in malt and beer characteristics. Consequently, 30 isolates of *Fusarium*, representing at least 10 species, were applied to barley during steeping and malting (Sloey and Prentice, 1962). The treatment increased steep and respiration loss; decreased both rootlet growth and malt recovery; increased extract values, alpha-amylase, wort nitrogen, and formol nitrogen in wort and beer; and decreased beer gas stability. *Fusarium moniliforme* (Sheldon) is one of several mold species which cause "scab." Scabbed grain often contains compounds that cause emesis when consumed by animals with simple stomachs. Work with lightly infected wheat indicated that the emetic material is located in the bran and aleurone tissue of the kernel (Prentice and Dickson, 1964). When an isolate of *F. moniliforme* was grown on a synthetic medium, it produced material that inhibited utilization of oxygen by germinating barley (Prentice, 1962). The inhibitor was partially purified by a combination of column chromatography and liquid-liquid extraction. The most active preparation caused 50% inhibition of oxygen utilization when used at a concentration of 10 γ per ml. in a manometric assay procedure. The chemical nature of emetic material associated with Fusarium in cereal grains and artificial media was reported by Prentice and Dickson (1968). Substances that cause emesis in pigeons were extracted from corn, wheat, and barley and from inoculated liquid culture media. Combination of column and thin-layer chromatography showed the presence of two active materials from a liquid culture of *F. moniliforme* but only one from infected cereals. Emetic preparations from *F. moniliforme* and infected cereals contained a polypeptide as a minor component. Ultraviolet and infrared spectrums, elemental analyses, refractive indexes, and amino acid composition of the emetic from corn, and one of the emetics from a liquid culture were similar.

V. CHANGES IN BREADMAKING QUALITY

The breadmaking quality of freshly harvested wheat or freshly milled wheat flour normally tends to improve for a time depending on the nature of the product and storage conditions. Subsequently, a point is reached where further aging no longer improves baking potential, and longer storage is accompanied by a gradual decline in breadmaking quality (Pomeranz, 1971a, b, c).

According to Rohrlich and Bruckner (1966), wheat flour should be "matured" before baking 1 to 2 months, rye flour 1 month, and whole wheat should be baked as soon as possible after milling. The pneumatic transport in modern mills accelerates maturation.

Kozmin (1935, 1936) suggested that changes in physical properties of wet gluten as a result of flour aging were due to increasing amounts of free unsaturated fatty acids in the flour. These fatty acids are formed by enzymatic hydrolysis of the flour fat. As the flour-aging process progresses, washed gluten prepared from flour becomes less extensible and more springy or elastic. Finally it becomes granular and is easily torn. Removal of fat from aged flour returned gluten to its original condition. The addition of this extracted fat, or of oleic acid, to freshly milled flour caused flour to have gluten characteristics similar to those of aged flour. Saturated fatty acids, on the other hand, produced no such effects. The effects of free unsaturated fatty acids on gluten behavior reported by Kozmin were confirmed by Sullivan et al. (1936), Sinclair and McCalla (1937), Barton-Wright (1938), and Sullivan (1940). Although in all instances the presence of free unsaturated fatty acids in flour had a marked effect on the physical properties of wet gluten, the effects on actual bread-baking quality of flour were relatively small. It was shown by Sullivan et al. (1936) and Sullivan (1940), however, that bread-baking quality is adversely affected to a marked degree by the presence of oxidation products of unsaturated fatty acids.

Fisher et al. (1937) found that an improvement in the bread-baking quality of freshly milled flour, similar to the improvement produced by artificial aging agents, could be accomplished by addition of small quantities of very old flour which, because of its age, had become unfit for bread-baking purposes. According to Zeleny (1954) this improvement may have been due to the high content of free unsaturated fatty acid in the blend to the optimum level for gluten development and bread-baking performance. The old flour itself probably contained oxidation products of unsaturated fatty acids in sufficient concentration to render it unfit for bread-baking.

There are several reports on storage, without damage, of wheat and wheat flour for long periods under normal conditions. Greer et al. (1954) noted an instance of flour stored in a British lighthouse at 10° to 20° C. in gas-tight cans for periods up to 27 years without any appreciable damage of either breadmaking quality or organoleptic properties.

Larmour et al. (1961) conducted a 5-year practical experiment to determine the effect of various types of packaging on the keeping quality of wheat flour and farina stored outdoors under simple conditions that might be encountered in an emergency. Twelve packaging materials and packaging sizes (from small packages suited for individual family use to large drums or bags for bakeries), two moisture levels (as received from the mill and dried to about 8 to 10%), outdoor and indoor storage, and two particle sizes (flour and farina) were among the variables studied. For outdoor storage conditions, the samples were stacked in 100-lb. bags on a large rodent-proof platform, covered with a waterproof tarpaulin, and kept in an unsheltered area, the mean annual temperature of which was 45° to 50°F. (7° to 10°C.).

The packing material affected storability considerably. The presence of a packaging moisture barrier effectively stabilized the moisture content. Dried samples (with a moisture of about 9%) stored in barrier packages retained their baking strength. Actually, a small but consistent increase in loaf volume was observed in those samples. Flours and farina of normal moisture (with a moisture of about 15%) showed a marked and apparently linear decrease in loaf volume potential. Changes in farina were distinctly slower than changes in flour. Dried samples in barrier packages stored indoors (a mean temperature of about 75°F., 24°C.) retained their baking strength. Dried samples stored in standard packages or samples with original milling moisture deteriorated more rapidly than comparable samples stored outside. Throughout the 5 years of storage, bread from dried flour was acceptable organoleptically though it developed a foreign odor and taste. Bread from normal-moisture flour or farina developed objectionable off-odors.

During storage, extractable fat, lipoxygenase activity, pigment content, gassing power, diastatic activity, and wet gluten decreased; fat acidity and acidity of aqueous extracts increased; and rheological properties (as determined by the farinograph and extensigraph) changed. However, none of the changes in physical or chemical properties were suited to predict the onset of deterioration in baking strength.

The nature of maturation during storage of wheat flour was studied by Yoneyama et al. (1970a, b). White and dark, freshly milled flours were stored for 90 days at 30°C. in air and in nitrogen. Several parameters were measured. They included: pH, microorganism population, protease activity, thiol and organic-N contents of metaphosphoric acid solubles, ascorbic and dehydroascorbic acid contents, lipid peroxides, titratable acidity, and some rheological properties. The most significant changes occurred in the sulfhydryl content. Those changes were related to changes in rheological properties of the dough and to breadmaking quality. Small increases were observed in acidity and mold counts, but it was postulated that they were not involved in the natural maturing action. Freshly milled long-patent flour was stored for 60 days at −30°, 0°, and 30°C. and viscoelastic coefficients for one rheological model were calculated. There were changes in soluble sulfhydryl content and in rheological properties of flours stored at 30°C. but not in samples stored below 0°C. After storing flour for 30 days at 0° to 20°C. the amount of thiol groups was unchanged or slightly lower; disulfide bonds increased (Puckova et al., 1971). Removing free lipids increased thiol content little and disulfide bonds considerably.

The potential bread-baking quality of freshly harvested wheat appears to improve somewhat during storage in a manner similar to that of flour but at a much slower rate. Saunders (1909, 1910) showed increases in the baking strength of flour milled from wheat that had been stored for 1 year in comparison with flour milled from the same wheat when freshly harvested. The work of Fitz (1910) indicated that a considerable part of this change may occur in the very early stages of storage. Saunders et al. (1921) investigated the baking strength of flour milled periodically from various lots of wheat over a 5-year period, while other varieties reached their maximum baking strength after 4 years and then receded somewhat in baking quality. Shellenberger (1939) has shown that although the bread-baking quality of wheat improves during storage after harvest, the extent of the improvement is ordinarily quite small. Presumably, the bread-baking quality of wheat will deteriorate eventually if the wheat is stored for a long period, but under ideal storage conditions, this deterioration appears to proceed very slowly. Robertson et al. (1939a) and Fifield and Robertson (1945) reported that satisfactory bread was made from flour milled from wheat stored for 9 to 22 years under nearly ideal storage conditions at Fort Collins, Colorado, and that the baking quality did not change appreciably during the last 5 years of storage. No data were available, however, on the initial baking quality of these lots of wheat.

More recently, Fifield and Robertson (1959) studied functional properties of samples of a hard red spring wheat and a hard red winter wheat which were stored at Fort Collins, Colorado, in a dry, unheated room for up to 33 years. While the earliest samples failed to germinate, about 12% of some of the samples stored for 25 to 30 years germinated. Storage decreased protein content slightly in about one-third of the samples. Ash in the wheat was unaffected, but the flour milled from wheat stored for prolonged periods of time had higher ash. There was a fairly uniform increase in fat acidity during storage. That increase, however, was not consistently related to breadmaking quality. As storage length increased, there was a decrease in bread crumb grain and texture but not in volume of loaves. Oxidation requirements showed no consistent change during storage; gassing power decreased; and thiamine content decreased somewhat but the differences were not larger than might be expected between samples from different crop years.

Decreases in breadmaking quality of wheat stored at elevated moisture and temperature levels were reported by Pomeranz et al. (1956).

More recently, Daftary and Pomeranz (1965) have shown for the first time that deterioration of grain attacked by storage fungi is accompanied by rapid disappearance of polar lipids (glycolipids and phospholipids) which are essential components in breadmaking of sound wheat flour. The breakdown of polar lipids was more rapid and extensive than formation of free fatty acids or disappearance of triglycerides. In a subsequent study (Daftary et al., 1970b), it was shown that the breakdown of bound lipids increased as temperature of flour storage increased from 23° to 30° to 37° C. The breakdown of bound lipids was accompanied by transformation of polar- to nonpolar-like components. The ratio of nonpolar to polar components in residual-bound lipids increased as storage temperature of flours increased.

SOUND   DAMAGED

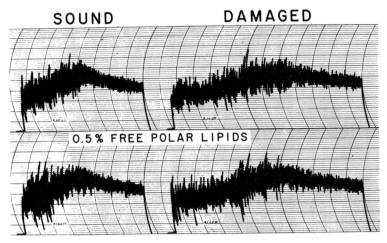

Figure 3. Mixograms of doughs from sound (left) and damaged (right) flours. Top row: unsupplemented flours; bottom row: flours mixed with 0.5% sound flour free polar lipids (from Pomeranz et al., 1968).

Gluten from damaged flours was difficult to wash out and had impaired rheological properties. In damaged flour, the yield of gluten was reduced and that of the starch fraction was increased. The starch fraction was rich in protein (Daftary et al., 1970a). Starch-gel electrophoretic patterns of gluten showed a decrease in glutenin and an increase in gliadin-like components. The water-soluble fraction contained an unusual component migrating to the cathode and showed almost complete destruction of fast-moving components.

Mixing times of doughs from damaged flours are consistently and substantially longer than those of doughs from sound flour (Figure 3). Adding

TABLE VII
Effects of lipids from sound flour on bread baked from sound and damaged Marquis flour with 3 grams of shortening per 100 grams of flour[a]

Lipid Description	Lipid Level g.	Sound Flour		Damaged Flour	
		Loaf volume cc.	Crumb grain	Loaf volume cc.	Crumb grain[b]
None	...	972	S	647	U
Total	0.5	...		650	U
Total	1.0	975	S	700	U
Total	1.5	950	S	870	Q-U
Free	0.8	...		685	Q-U
Free	1.5	950	S	850	Q-U
Nonpolar free	0.5	885	Q-U	635	U
Polar free	0.5	1043	S	835	Q-U
Polar free	1.0	1030	S	865	Q-U
Polar free	2.0	...		950	Q

[a]Data of Pomeranz et al. (1968).
[b]S = satisfactory, Q = questionable, U = unsatisfactory.

polar lipids from sound flour has little effect on mixing time or tolerance of sound or damaged flour (Pomeranz et al., 1968). The damaged flour has normal gas production as measured by pressure meters and by proof heights. Bread baked from damaged flour is substantially lower in loaf volume and poorer in crumb grain than bread baked from sound flour. In flours in which no damage to gluten proteins could be demonstrated, adding nonpolar lipids had a detrimental effect, and adding polar lipids had an improving effect (Table VII). Bread baked from damaged flour supplemented with total, free, or polar lipids still had impaired crumb color and flavor. Baking results of fractionated and reconstituted doughs indicated (Table VIII) that lipids from sound flours restored the loaf volume potential of damaged flour. Bread crumb grain of the damaged flour was nearly restored by the addition of lipids. Replacing gluten from damaged flour with that from sound flour simultaneously restored the lipids that were decomposed in storage-damaged flour, as 85 to 90% of flour lipids are found in the gluten during fractionation. Replacing starch and water-solubles from damaged flour with those from sound flour did not improve loaf volume or crumb grain. The crumb of damaged flour, with or without lipids, had a creamy-brown color. Color was improved to creamy by replacing the damaged gluten or damaged starch and water-solubles with the corresponding fraction from the sound flour.

In flours at more advanced stages of deterioration, starch-gel electrophoresis indicated damage to proteins in the gluten and in the water-soluble fractions (Daftary et al., 1970a). When 1.6% total free lipids from sound flour were added to mold-damaged flours, loaf volume was improved but not restored to that of the sound flour. Mixing times of damaged flours were substantially longer than mixing times of doughs from sound flours. Adding 1.6% total free lipids further increased mixing times. Mixing times increased as storage temperature increased, and as damage to breadmaking potentialities increased. The gluten, water-soluble, and starch fractions were tested by reconstituting and baking. The

TABLE VIII
Breadmaking characteristics of total and reconstituted
sound and damaged flours baked with 10-gram flour[a]

Composition	Total Lipids Added g.	Baking Absorption %	Mixing Requirement min.	Loaf Volume cc.
Sound flour (S)	...	65.6	3-3/4	83
Damaged flour (D)	...	69.0	9-1/8	66
Damaged flour (D)	0.12	68.5	9-3/8	82
Gluten (S) + starch[b] (S)	...	68.0	4	82
Gluten (D) + starch (D)	...	68.0	5-7/8	69
Gluten (D) + starch (D)	0.12	67.5	5-3/8	82
Gluten (D) + starch (S)	...	67.0	6	68
Gluten (D) + starch (S)	0.12	68.5	6	83
Gluten (S) + starch (D)	...	67.0	4-1/4	81

[a]Data of Pomeranz et al. (1968).
[b]Mixture of starch and water-solubles.

results indicated that both gluten and water-soluble fractions of damaged flours were impaired. Starch from damaged flour was not affected during storage. The impairment of the water-soluble fraction apparently resulted from enzymatic modifications of the water-soluble proteins.

The impairment of the breadmaking quality of gluten proteins does not appear to be primarily the result of enzymatic hydrolysis. Breakdown of gluten proteins would increase proteins of smaller molecular weight which presumably would have greater solubility and electrophoretic mobility. Instead, electrophoretic patterns showed no increase in fast-moving bands. In addition, when flour was extracted with 0.1N lactic acid, 92% of the proteins from sound flour and only 66% from damaged flour were solubilized. Thus, mold damage decreased solubility, thereby suggesting denaturation of gluten proteins (Daftary et al., 1970a).

Results of those studies indicated that wheat and flour lipids were most susceptible to mold damage and were apparently broken down before other wheat flour components. Damage to gluten and water-soluble components varied with storage conditions. At early stages of deterioration, gluten proteins were not damaged and adding lipids from sound flour practically restored loaf volume. At more advanced stages, proteins in water-solubles and in gluten were damaged. Starch seems to be the most resistant, and no damage to functional properties was recorded in any of the authors' investigations. Acker (1961) indicated that such damage was possible, though probably only at the most advanced stages of mold damage. While the results suggested a "sequence" of deterioration related to overall damage, different types of breakdown (depending on composition of fungal populations) of wheat macromolecules could take place under various storage conditions.

Relatively little has been published on the effects of insect infestation on the baking and taste qualities of bread baked from insect-damaged flour. According to Smith et al. (1971), insect-infested flour is generally rejected for aesthetic and assumed health reasons, and the effects of insect secretions and excretions on functional properties and organoleptic quality are seldom considered. The actual health hazard is generally implied but not well defined with the possible exception of quinone secretions of *Tribolium* spp. which may be important carcinogens. Chittenden observed as early as 1886 that strong infestation with *Tribolium* spp. converted cereal products into a gray, useless mass characterized by a persistent and disagreeable odor. Doane (1918) reported that while *Tribolium* spp. imparted a musty and disagreeable odor to bread made from infested flour, practically all the odor disappeared as the bread cooled. Payne (1925) found that secretions from *Tribolium confusum* (Duval) affected the viscosity of flour and the elasticity of dough.

Smith et al. (1971) reported that bread prepared from flour previously infested with insects showed changes in baking and organoleptic properties after 1-, 2-, and 3-month infestation periods. Bread made from flour infested with *Oryzaephilus surinamensis* (L.) and *Tenebrio molitor* (L.) revealed only minor changes in physical attributes but had a "chemo-phenolic" taste and odor. Bread prepared from flour infested with *Tribolium castaneum* (Herbst) and *Tribolium confusum* (Duval) had a reduced loaf volume, dark crumb, and a distinct offensive taste and odor. The objectionable odor decreased, but did not disappear, after baking. The deleterious effects intensified with increases in length of infestation and in population density levels. The authors concluded that quinone secretions adversely affect consumer acceptance of bread made from *Tribolium*-infested flour.

VI. MISCELLANEOUS FUNCTIONAL CHANGES

In the wet milling of corn it is more difficult to obtain a good separation of starch from other constituents of grain when corn has been stored under unfavorable conditions, even though no apparent damage to the corn can be observed, than when unquestionably sound corn is milled. Experimental wet-milling studies reported by Cox et al. (1947) showed that heat-damaged corn yields only about 45% as much starch as normal corn, that the viscosity of suspensions of the starch in water is very low, and that in many instances the starch granules appear to have split into wedge-shaped fragments.

Soybeans stored in glass jars for 1 year at moisture contents in excess of 15% were found by Ramstad and Geddes (1942) to show decreases in the iodine numbers of their oils. All soybeans stored at these high moisture levels showed considerable mold growth. These observations indicate that the oil from soybeans damaged by storage at high moisture content is likely to have inferior drying quality.

Rice is used as an adjunct in brewing to impart certain characteristics to wort and beer, but mainly for reasons of economy. There is a reluctance in industry to use milled rice products that were stored for long periods as they require higher temperatures of gelatinization and convert slowly (by the action of malt amylases) to fermentable sugars. Yasumatsu and Moritaka (1964) found that fatty acids were released during storage of rice from neutral fat in the same proportion as they were combined in the neutral fat. The increase in amounts of free fatty acids resulted in an increase in maximum viscosity of amylograms and impaired rheological properties of cooked rice (Yasumatsu et al., 1964). The mechanism of interaction was explained by the formation of helical structures of starch molecules with fatty acids.

Suzuki and Matsumoto (1971) found that rice stored at room temperature during the summer was less palatable after cooking than cooked rice from grain stored at 4°C. The amounts of n-hexanal in cooked rice increased with increasing storage time at room temperature, and the amounts of acetone or propionaldehyde increased with storage at the lower temperature.

The keeping quality of breakfast cereals depends to a large extent on the content and keeping quality of the fat which they contain. Thus, products made from cereal grains with low oil content (wheat, barley, rye-oil content of about 2%) have an advantage over products made from oats (oil content 4 to 11%, average 7%). Whole corn has a relatively high content (about 4.5%), but most of the oil is contained in the germ which is removed in the making of grits or flakes. The keeping quality of the fat depends on its degree of unsaturation, the presence of antioxidants or prooxidants, and length of storage and storage conditions (temperature, moisture content). Several heat treatments, such as toasting or puffing, may destroy antioxidants or induce formation of prooxidants. On the other hand, short temperature treatment at the surface may produce new antioxidants by the Maillard reaction. This may explain the improved antioxidant activity of steam-treated oat products.

Storage of breakfast cereals can cause bitter taste. In wheat and rye products, the bitter taste appears only after long storage. The bitterness is not noticeable in a freshly baked product. In oat products, and to some extent whole oat products, the danger of bitterness is noticeably higher. It can appear within a short time and render the product unpalatable. Bitter taste seldom develops in oat products that have been prepared by heat treatment, followed by kilning or dry heating. The delay or prevention of bitterness by such treatment suggests the involvement of enzymes in the formation of bitterness. In addition to inactivating the enzymes and removing some bitter substances, heat treatment also facilitates separation of groats. Inactivation of enzymes by heat treatment is more rapid at high than at low moisture content. Best results are obtained by treating raw oats with steam before kiln-drying, in the process known as stabilization. The stabilization process was introduced mainly to eliminate increase in free fatty acids in oatmeal from unsteamed oats (Kent, 1966).

Rolled oats do not normally develop free fatty acids because steaming the meal is generally adequate to inactivate oat lipase. In the stabilization process, the oats at 14 to 20% moisture are quickly raised to 205° to 212°F. (96° to 100°C.) by injection of live steam at atmospheric pressure, and maintained at that temperature for 2 to 3 min. The stabilization process, in addition to inactivating lipase and most of the other undesirable enzymes, improves flavor and resistance to onset of rancidity. Excessive steaming may result in oxidative rancidity. Sterilized oats are dried to 4 to 8% moisture by kilning. Purposes of kilning are: 1) to reduce the moisture content to a level satisfactory for the storage of milled products, 2) to facilitate the separation of groats by increasing the brittleness of the husk, and 3) to develop in the oats a characteristic nutty flavor (Kent, 1966). Before the introduction of stabilization (about 1950), the kilning process was also relied upon to reduce the lipolytic activity. It is improbable that complete lipase inactivation was obtained. The necessary temperature to inactivate 97% in oats increases from 148°F. (64°C.) at 12% moisture to 219°F. (104°C.) at 8% moisture. During kilning, the temperature of the oats exceeds 195°F. (91°C.), but by the time that temperature has been reached, the moisture content has fallen below 12% so that the necessary conditions for complete inactivation are not attained (Kent, 1966). Excessive heat treatment should be avoided as it reduces the thiamine content and damages the biological value of the proteins.

Involvement of enzymes in the formation of bitter substances has been postulated by several investigators. The participation of microorganisms seems excluded under normal storage conditions. Bitter taste is correlated with peroxidase activity. Peroxidase is apparently the most thermostable of any of the enzymes that could be involved in bitterness during storage, and has been suggested as the best index of effective heat treatment.

The picture is, however, much more complicated because apparently there are several bitter substances in oats (Acker, 1961). Bitter substances of the saponin type seem to form an adduct complex with other oat components that have no bitter taste. The formation of those bitter compounds cannot be traced to enzymatic action.

A second group of bitter substances is of the lipid type and is important in storage. Defatted oat products become less readily bitter than untreated oats. The difference is not due to lipase action, because free fatty acids produced by lipases have no bitter taste, and because lipase inactivation does not necessarily eliminate bitterness. However, formation of the bitter compounds is enhanced by the presence of free fatty acids, which are more susceptible to oxidation than triglycerides. Oils with a high peroxide value produce a bitter taste after mixing with defatted oats. Peroxides seem to act as precursors of the bitter substances, and the latter conversion seems to be very rapid. The extent to which the bitter compounds are formed is controlled by the concentration of peroxides. Peroxides could be produced by the enzyme lipoxygenase. That enzyme in oats, however, is low (about 10% of the lipoxygenase activity of rye, wheat, or barley). The low lipoxygenase activity seems to result from inhibition by natural antioxidants.

Effects of storage on dormancy and germinability and their relation to malting were discussed in detail elsewhere in this chapter.

Many physiological and biochemical changes occur during prolonged aging of nondormant seed. These changes include increased susceptibility to adverse germination conditions, reduced viability, lowered enzymatic activity, and leakage of seed components during imbibition. Anderson (1970) evaluated physiological and biochemical parameters in new and aged (differences of about 10 years) seed lots of four barley (*Hordeum vulgare* L.) varieties. Natural aging in a room without humidity control decreased percent germination in two varieties but caused no significant differences in the others. Only small differences were found in shoot length between the seed from new and old seeds. The older seeds were more sensitive to accelerated aging (100% relative humidity, at 45°C.) than newer seeds, even when no differences were found in percent germination or shoot growth. Oxygen uptake was not related to percent germination or age. Older seeds evolved up to 200% as much CO_2 as newer seeds, and had higher respiratory quotients. After 36 hr. germination, newer seeds showed 46 to 67% more total amylase activity than older seeds.

Both external and internal factors influence the process of aging in seeds, at various physiological, cytological, and genetical levels. Although external factors such as oxygen tension, temperature, humidity, and parasites may accelerate aging, it seems that metabolites elaborated during storage are the basic causes of the changes occurring in old seed. Experiments with extracts from old seeds indicated that such metabolites can effect germination and induce chromosome aberrations. Floris (1970) used the embryo transplantation technique to study the behavior of *Triticum* embryos and endosperm during the course of aging 1- to 5-year-old seeds. Aging was shown to be a progressive phenomenon. It affects both embryo and endosperm as shown by the behavior of old embryos transplanted on young endosperms, and the deleterious effects of aged endosperms on young embryos.

Anderson and Abdul-Baki (1971) followed changes in glucose utilization, into CO_2 and an ethanol-insoluble fraction, in whole seeds, embryos, and endosperms of wheat and barley which had reached different levels of deterioration through accelerated aging. Excised embryos from deteriorated wheat seeds had reduced respiration and glucose utilization into ethanol-insoluble material but not into CO_2. These treatments had no effect on respiration of excised embryos, though they reduced utilization of glucose. Incubation of excised tissues in glucose-^{14}C under N_2, as compared to air, affected utilization of glucose but not its uptake. Embryos produced more $^{14}CO_2$ and less labeled ethanol-insoluble material under N_2 than under air. Responses of endosperms to N_2 were much smaller than responses of embryos.

The authors concluded from these studies that the rapid decrease in glucose utilization, without loss of vigor or germinability, of freshly harvested seeds takes place in the endosperm. Work with intact cereal seeds indicated that as seeds aged, their ability to metabolize glucose decreased. However, a major reduction in glucose utilization took place before deterioration could be detected by germination and seedling growth tests (Abdul-Baki, 1969). This diminishes the usefulness of glucose utilization as a parameter of incipient seed deterioration. The reduction in capacity of embryos (rather than intact seeds) to incorporate ^{14}C glucose into ethanol-insoluble material appeared to be a promising index of deterioration in barley and wheat seeds (Anderson and Abdul-Baki, 1971).

Grzesiuk and Kulka (1971a) investigated RNA and DNA contents and nuclease activities in swelling and germinating oat and barley seeds that were previously stored for up to 5 years at 20° C. and relative humidity of 45 to 60%. With aging, RNA and DNA in the embryos of germinated seeds decreased. No RNA and DNA syntheses took place in seeds with a viability of 5%. Cessation of RNA transcription and DNA replication characterized biochemical mechanisms during seed aging. Nucleic acid synthesis in germinating embryos of young seeds occurred at the expense of nucleic acid disintegration in the endosperm and by the formation of those compounds *de novo* (^{32}P incorporation). The activity of the nucleases was several times greater in the younger than in the older seeds. In a subsequent study, changes in proteins were followed in the stored oat seeds (Grzesiuk and Kulka, 1971b). Aging of seeds was accompanied by decreased capacity to synthesize, during swelling and germination, high-molecular-weight albumins.

VII. INDEXES OF DETERIORATION

Storing grain for an "ever-normal granary" and the need to maintain strategic supplies make it important to recognize early stages of deterioration to prevent economic losses. Several tests may be used to determine the commercial condition of grain and to predict its future storage behavior. Those tests are based on the types of changes occurring in stored grain. Changes include: 1) visual observation, 2) increased fungal population, 3) weight loss, 4) decrease in germinability or viability, 5) heating, 6) production of toxins, and 7) various biochemical changes, including those that result in mustiness, souring, high fat acidity, or bitterness.

A. Visual Observations

When grain deteriorates in storage, especially when the deterioration is caused by spontaneous heating, the grain loses its natural luster and becomes rather dull and lifeless in appearance. This unnatural appearance is an indication that other physical indexes of deterioration may be present in the grain, and the grain should be examined closely to detect any of them. General appearance alone, as an index of deterioration, is considered as a quality factor in the routine inspection and grading of barley, oats, grain sorghums, and soybeans. The general appearance of any type of grain reflects to some extent the degree of soundness of the grain.

Abnormal odors, such as musty or sour odors, are usually associated with grain that is heating or that is badly deteriorated. Sour odors are present in grain that has undergone fermentation. Musty odors in grain are usually caused by the growth of certain molds. Grain may possess a musty or sour odor in early stages of deterioration, but these odors usually occur only when grain has reached a fairly advanced stage of deterioration. Musty odors in wheat frequently carry through into flour and bread or other baked products made from it.

Kernels with damaged germs, usually caused by mold growth or spontaneous heating, heat-damaged, and sprout-damaged kernels all indicate distinct deterioration in grain. These types of damaged kernels occur frequently in stored grain which contains excessive moisture and is not aerated and handled properly to prevent deterioration. Germ-damaged kernels can be identified by the brown to black discoloration of the germ or embryo of the affected kernels. Wheat damaged in this manner is frequently referred to as "sick" wheat. Kernels of grain that are damaged by heat to the extent that germs and portions of endosperms of kernels are materially discolored (dark red to mahogany) are considered by grain inspectors as heat-damaged kernels. Sprouted kernels can be easily identified by the presence of attached sprouts, or by evidence of the germ end of the kernels having been broken open from germination. This condition is distinguishable in the early stages of germination, and also after the sprout has emerged and has been broken off the kernel.

The large part of damage to grain that is caused by injurious insects occurs while the grain is in storage. Sufficient heat may be generated by their respiration to produce heating of the grain. Kernels of grain which contain dead insects, insect fragments, and insect refuse, and kernels of wheat, rye, barley, and grain sorghums which contain insect-bored holes are considered by grain inspectors as damaged kernels. The mere presence of injurious insects in stored grain is considered an index of deterioration.

B. Respiration

Respiration of cereal grains produces water, carbon dioxide, and heat. In cereals stored below 14% moisture at 20°C., respiration is slow but rises as water content and temperature increase. Losses resulting from damage are small and difficult to follow. Determination of either heat or carbon dioxide generated requires continuous control. Heat does not dissipate rapidly because cereals are poor conductors of heat. Several instruments are available for continuous recording and monitoring increases in grain temperature and interseed concentration of carbon dioxide.

C. Germination

Visual observations of discoloration are empirical and may fail to detect the early stages of deterioration which precede the actual appearance of coloration.

A positive germination test may be used as evidence that seeding and malting potentialities have not been impaired by damage in storage or by drying. The value of the rather time-consuming germination test in evaluating the condition of grain used in industrial processing (breadmaking, breakfast cereals, etc.) is more limited.

D. Biochemical Tests

Several attempts have been made to develop reliable and convenient biochemical indexes of storage behavior. Prolonged storage of cereals slightly decreases protein nitrogen and increases free amino nitrogen. Although the quantity of free amino acids increases only at advanced stages of deterioration, the qualitative pattern of changes in individual amino acids is more useful in detecting incipient damage. There are only trace amounts of gamma-amino butyric acid in sound, dry grain, but they increase strikingly after the grain is wet. At the same time, free glutamic acid decreases from activity of glutamic acid decarboxylase (GADA) (Linko, 1960).

Enzymatic assays. The activity of GADA decreases with increase in storage time, especially at moisture contents favorable to rapid deterioration. The enzyme appears to be present only in the embryo. The rate of decrease of its activity in storage depends on the moisture content of the cereal. Linko and Sogn (1960) found that in both wheat and corn, a logarithmic correlation exists between GADA and germination percentage (G%). With both cereal grains the correlation coefficients were significantly higher than with those involving free fatty acids (FFA).

Correlation	*Wheat*	*Corn*
G% vs. GADA	r = +0.920***	r = +0.949***
G% vs. FFA	r = –0.754***	r = –0.433***

During the early experiments, GADA was determined by means of Warburg manometric techniques. The rather elaborate method was not well suited for large-scale routine investigations. Later, a manometric technique employing standard Sandstedt-Blish pressure meters was developed (Linko, 1961). Ethyl lactate colored with crystal violet was used as manometer liquid instead of mercury. A 30-min. carbon dioxide evolution by 30 g. of ground (2 min. by Waring Blendor) grain, from 15 ml. of 0.1M glutamic acid in 0.067M phosphate buffer, pH 5.8, was measured. The figure obtained, added to one hundred, was used as a measure of GADA. Despite the high correlation between log GADA and G%, considerable variability was recorded. Composition (mainly protein level), genetic, and environmental factors affected the results. In addition, GADA would seem more useful as an index of soundness in grain that is to be germinated than in grain used for breadmaking or production of breakfast cereals (Rohrlich and Siebert, 1964). Those remarks on the limitations of the GADA test should not be interpreted as criticism or detract from the fact that the simple test can be used (provided its limitations are understood and correctly interpreted) to detect incipient damage, denaturation of proteins during drying damp grains at excessively high temperatures, and approximate the time that grain may be "safely" stored under certain conditions. Thus, for instance,

Bautista et al. (1964) found that the GADA test was a more reliable index than fat acidity of the viability of artificially dried and stored rice.

Tetrazolium tests. A decrease in viability is one of the first changes detected in grain storage. A biochemical test of grain viability is based on the reduction by germ dehydrogenases of 2,3,5-triphenyl tetrazolium chloride. The exposed surfaces of 100 cereal grains, bisected longitudinally, are soaked for 2 hr. in the dark in a 0.2% aqueous solution of tetrazolium. The appearance of a red coloration at the germ end indicates dehydrogenase activity; absence of a red color points to loss of viability. Alternatively, the red-colored compound (formazan) can be extracted from the grain and determined by measuring the absorbance of the extract. The relation between viability and concentration of formazan can be used to estimate deterioration.

Sorger-Domenigg et al. (1955) reported the following simple correlation coefficients between different indexes of deterioration in 68 commercial samples of wheat:

	Fat acidity	Formazan value	Germ damage
Viability	−0.92	−0.60	−0.49
Fat acidity		−0.56	+0.46
Formazan value			−0.69

Linko and Sogn (1960) reported the following correlation coefficients in 25 samples of hard red winter wheat at various stages of deterioration.

	Germination	GADA	Fluores-cence	Formazan value	Fat acidity
Germ damage	−0.969	−0.878	+0.804	−0.859	+0.837
Germination		+0.921	−0.758	+0.902	−0.906
GADA			−0.637	+0.873	−0.864
Fluorescence				+0.590	

Belderok (1963) reported that the tetrazolium method was useful in following changes during drying of wheat, and damage during sprouting in the field or prolonged storage accompanied by fungal attack. In wheat suitable for breadmaking at least 80% kernels showed viability by the tetrazolium method; below 60%, the wheat was invariably damaged. The author of this review believes, however, that the relation between viability and breadmaking is casual rather than causative. Admittedly, high formazan values indicate sound wheat. Wheat stored under adverse conditions or dried at excessively high temperatures shows low formazan values. However, if wheat is stored under normal conditions, formazan values may decrease without decreases in breadmaking values. In addition, the type of damage as shown by Geddes (1958) and Belderok (1963) may affect to varying degrees breadmaking and formazan values resulting in a rather wide spread around the regression line that correlates the two variables.

Fluorescence. Cole and Milner (1953) and McDonald and Milner (1954) have shown that dilute hydrochloric acid extracts of damaged wheat embryos exhibited an increase in fluorescence, which preceded the respiratory increase indicative of mold growth. On the other hand, fluorescence of sound wheat samples of widely varying source, variety, and class was low and fairly uniform. It was postulated that the increased fluorescence resulted from a Maillard-type nonenzymatic browning reaction. Linko and Sogn (1960) determined fluorescence in extracts of whole wheat kernels and isolated germ ends. The correlation coefficient between germination and fluorescence was as high as −0.957, but if few extreme samples of very high germ damage were excluded from the calculations, the correlation coefficient dropped to −0.412. There was generally little change in fluorescence in samples of 20 to 100% germination.

Cooks et al. (1970) determined the identity of the fluorescent fungal metabolites that were described previously by Daftary and Pomeranz (1965). The main fluorescent compound in the petroleum ether extract of moldy wheat flour was isolated, purified, and crystallized.

The major component, molecular weight 392, was 4, 6, 8(14), 22-ergostatetraen-3-one. The minor component was the C_{24}-ethyl analog, a finding of biosynthetic interest since C_{29} steroids are almost exclusively synthesized by plants rather than by microorganisms.

The fluorescent material showed no toxicity to 1-day-old ducks. Its strong fluorescence and formation during the early stages of mold damage in all wheat and flour samples, thus far tested, combined with relative ease of detection by thin-layer chromatography make it attractive using the method for establishing incipient deterioration in mold-damaged cereals. It must be emphasized, however, that the presence and amount of fluorescent compounds may vary widely with storage conditions, history of the cereals, and microbial population.

Acidity. Deterioration in grain and milled products of grain in storage is accompanied by an increase in acidity. Hydrogen-ion concentration tends to increase with age, but because of the buffer action of the proteins and other grain constituents, marked changes in hydrogen-ion concentration ordinarily do not occur until deterioration is fairly well advanced. Titratable acidity, on the other hand, is likely to increase significantly even in the very early stages of deterioration.

Zeleny and Coleman (1938) showed that the acids present in grain consist primarily of: a) free fatty acids produced by the action of lipases on fats; b) acid phosphates produced by the action of phytase on phytin; and c) amino acids produced by the action of proteolytic enzymes on protein. Acidity values and other indexes of deterioration were determined periodically in wheat stored in two experimental bins. Fat acidity, phosphate acidity, and total titratable acidity increased as the wheat deteriorated in storage. Viability of the wheat decreased in a somewhat parallel manner. The amino acid acidity showed no increase during the periods of storage studied. The rate of increase in fat acidity was greater than that of the phosphate acidity, particularly during the early stages of deterioration.

Studies were also made of the acids present in 245 samples of corn classified according to the percentage of "damaged kernels" and of 209 samples of corn classified according to viability. The correlation coefficient between fat acidity and percentage of damaged kernels (as determined for grading purposes) was +0.90, and the correlation coefficient between fat acidity and the logarithm of the percentage germination was −0.85.

Fat acidity is defined as the number of milligrams of potassium hydroxide required to neutralize the free fatty acids from 100 g. of grain (moisture-free basis). The test is performed by extracting the fats and fatty acids from a weighed portion of freshly ground grain with petroleum ether or benzene, and determining the free fatty acid content by titration of the extract dissolved in equal parts by volume of benzene and ethyl alcohol. According to AACC Approved Methods (formerly Cereal Laboratory Methods, 7th ed.), fat acidity in cereals can be determined by titration of extracts from one of the following three procedures: 1) after extraction for approximately 16 hr. in a Soxhlet (or similar type) with petroleum ether (b. p. 35° to 60° C.), 2) by a rapid method for grain, involving grinding-extraction with benzene for 4 min. in a Stein Mill, or 3) by a rapid method for corn, in which the ground material is shaken for 30 min. on a mechanical device or for 45 min. at frequent intervals by hand. In any of the above three methods, fat acidity is determined by titration with a standardized solution of potassium hydroxide in the presence of phenolphthalein dissolved in a mixture of benzene and 95% ethanol. The end point is determined by comparison with a color standard.

In addition, fat acidity can be determined by a colorimetric method in which the extracted fat dissolved in benzene is reacted with an aqueous solution of cupric acetate, and the transmittance at 640 nm. of the solution is compared with that of standard graph with purified oleic acid (Baker, 1961).

Baker et al. (1957) compared the rapid and simple grinder-extractor method with the general procedure (extraction times were 10 min. vs. 16 hr.). The rapid method gave slightly lower values; 0.3 units for wheat and 0.5 units for barley and rye. Fat acidity surveys of several hundred samples of sound and damaged grain indicated a maximum of 20 to 25 for cereal grains except oats. Damaged grains had higher values depending upon degree and type of damage. A curvilinear relation was found between fat acidity and moisture content of the grain at the time of extraction. Wheat and barley with 10 to 17% moisture showed a 1.0 to 1.5 unit increase in fat acidity for each percent increase in moisture. The authors suggested that samples should be analyzed at a moisture content not exceeding 10%, or that approximate correction factors should be applied. In a subsequent study, Baker et al. (1959) studied the relationship between fat acidity and types of damage in corn, wheat, grain sorghums, and soybeans. More than 500 samples of grain, officially graded as to type and percentage of damage which they contained, were tested. In general, storage damage of the type caused by molds and heating showed high positive correlation with fat acidity; field damage showed low correlation. Positive correlations between fat acidity values and percentage of damage for some principal types of damage were: "sick wheat," 0.847; heat damage (wheat), 0.651; heat damage (corn), 0.670; "rancid" damage (corn), 0.978; and "blue-eyed" mold (corn), 0.827.

Joffe and Small (1964) determined fat acidity in 100-g. samples of corn by the rapid method. Periodic determinations of acidity on the same samples of high-quality corn revealed large fluctuations with time when the corn was stored under well-controlled conditions. The fluctuations presumably resulted from sampling errors, actual variations in the metabolism of the grain, and elusive variations in storage conditions. Fat acidity values were affected by temperature during the extraction stage of the assay, particularly when the ambient temperature exceeded 26° C.

Fat acidity and breadmaking quality. Studies on the relation between formation of fatty acids during storage of cereals and breadmaking performance produced somewhat conflicting results. Fenton and Swanson (1930) observed that poor baking quality of wheat flour was associated with high fat rancidity. Storage deterioration was shown to harm milling properties of wheat. Sorger-Domenigg et al. (1955) and Pomeranz et al. (1956) confirmed that flour produced from wheat having high fat acidity had high ash content, poor color, and poor baking strength.

Development of fat acidity in wheat or in wheat flour has been considered an index of breadmaking quality. Decrease of loaf volume was reported when more than 30% of flour lipids was hydrolyzed (Geddes, in Greer et al., 1954). Other workers, however, found no such deterioration, even after complete hydrolysis. An examination of many white flours stored in British lighthouses is particularly interesting (Greer et al., 1954). Although the free fatty acid content of the fat increased considerably (up to about 70%, compared with 5 to 10% in freshly milled flours), the flours retained good baking quality long after extensive hydrolysis of fat had occurred. Neither oxidative rancidity nor fungal mustiness was related to free fatty acid content. Fifield and Robertson (1959) found that wheat stored up to 33 years failed to germinate. The baking quality of flour milled from the wheat so stored was not affected materially, despite a fairly regular increase in fat acidity. Shellenberger et al. (1958) found no correlation between bread quality and fat acidity of wheat flours stored at 40° F. (4° C.). The increase of fat acidity was related to the baking performance of flours stored at 100° F. (38° C.).

According to Hutchinson (1961), there are two main objections to using fat acidity as the sole criterion of damage. First, there is a large scatter of experimental points about the regression line between seed viability (probably the best direct index of grain soundness) and fat acidity. Second, storage for short periods under unsatisfactory conditions changes fat acidity little but has a marked effect on the storage potential of the grain. Linko and Sogn (1960) emphasized that fat acidity indicates lowered viability, though fat acidity is not necessarily associated with any of the known deteriorative processes.

Hutchinson (1961) concluded that fat acidity did not provide valid information for evaluation of the baking quality of stored wheat or flour. Wheat flour may maintain its baking quality for many years, despite a progressive increase in fat acidity. Actually, a certain improvement in baking quality may occur in the early stages of storage, as reported by Shellenberger (1939).

In damp wheat stored at ambient temperature and with ample air access, fat acidity is likely to increase. While acknowledging the value of fat acidity as an index of changes occurring in stored grain, we are not in a position to specify a meaningful limit for fat acidity, without considering the previous history of the grain. Neither is there any proof that an increase in fat acidity is identical with damage to grain. Rate of increase in fat acidity is generally an index of changes occurring in grain. Yet, two samples may have comparable fat acidity levels and differ substantially in breadmaking quality. In one, fat acidity may increase as a result of mold growth and concomitant damage to lipids, proteins, lipoproteins, and other flour components. In the other sample, fat acidity may increase slowly over a long period of storage at relatively low moisture. The second sample may have a higher fat acidity value than the first one, and (provided no damage was done to functional moieties governing breadmaking potentialities) still be well suited for breadmaking.

In light of this limitation, the author agrees with the statement of Zeleny (1954) in the first edition of this monograph. "Information obtained from practical studies of grain in commercial storage indicates that, although fat acidity values may be very helpful in predicting the storage behavior of grain, other factors, as yet unknown, also have a marked influence on the tendency of grain to heat and deteriorate. Different lots of sound grain of uniformly low fat acidity and of the same moisture content often show marked differences in their tendency to heat in storage. The types and quantities of fungi and bacteria present may account in part for these differences. Much more research needs to be done before it becomes possible to predict in advance the storage behavior of grain with a high degree of accuracy."

Recent studies from the author's laboratory (Daftary and Pomeranz, 1965; Pomeranz et al., 1968) indicated that decrease in polar wheat flour lipids preceded and was a better index of damage during storage than increase in free fatty acids. Determination of free fatty acids is a simple and rapid procedure that can be adapted to routine estimations and quality control. On the other hand, whereas increase in free fatty acids (unless they are oxidized) is only casually related to deterioration of wheat or wheat flour in storage, the decrease in glycolipids and phospholipids measures actual damage to breadmaking potentialities. Admittedly, at the time of writing this review, no simple and rapid tests are available to determine glycolipids in stored grain.

Nonreducing sugars. Bottomley et al. (1952) found that decreases in nonreducing sugars paralleled mold count more closely than did increases in fat acidity. However, neither of these two provided accurate information on the extent of damage to the grain. The authors concluded that a combination of the two methods, especially with identification of the molds present, would give a complete picture.

E. Summary

According to Geddes (1958), several tests may be used to determine the "commercial condition" of grain and to predict its future storage behavior. Whereas mold counts and viability tests are good indexes of incipient deterioration, fat acidity and nonreducing sugar content are useful as measures of the extent of the actual damage which has taken place.

In summary, high viability and germinability of grain are probably the best and most meaningful indexes of soundness, especially in grain to be used for seeding or malting. In grain and milled grain products, several biochemical tests can be used to estimate usefulness during processing into foods or feeds. None has been, and unlikely will be, found the "tell-all" test, as each measures changes in a certain parameter that is of greater significance in some applications than in others.

Both the biological and biochemical tests measure changes during storage and are necessary for quality control. Storage of dry grain is still the best and simplest safeguard against undesirable changes in stored cereals.

LITERATURE CITED

ABDUL-BAKI, A. A. 1969. Relationship of glucose metabolism to germinability and vigor in barley and wheat seeds. Crop Sci. 9: 732-737.

ACKER, L. W. 1961. Enzymic reactions in foods of low moisture content. Advan. Food Res. 11: 263-330.

AMEN, R. D. 1964. The concept of seed dormancy. Wallerstein Lab. Commun. 27(92): 7-18.

ANDERSON, J. D. 1970. Physiological and biochemical differences in deteriorating barley seed. Crop Sci. 10: 36-39.

ANDERSON, J. D., and ABDUL-BAKI, A. A. 1971. Glucose metabolism of embryos and endosperms from deteriorating barley and wheat seeds. Plant Physiol. 48: 270-272.

ANONYMOUS. 1972. Improving seed germination. Agr. Res. (U.S. Dep. Agr.) 20(7): 16.

ARMOLIK, N., DICKSON, J. G., and DICKSON, A. D. 1956. Deterioration of barley in storage by microorganisms. Phytopathology 46: 457-461.

AYERST, G. 1965. Determination of the water activity of some hygroscopic food materials by a dew-point method. J. Sci. Food Agr. 16: 71-78

BAILEY, C. H. 1921. Respiration of shelled corn. Minn. Univ. Agr. Exp. Sta. Tech. Bull. No. 3.

BAILEY, C. H. 1940. Respiration of cereal grains and flaxseed. Plant Physiol. 15: 257-274.

BAILEY, C. H., and GURJAR, A. M. 1918. Respiration of stored wheat. J. Agr. Res. 12: 685-713.

BAKER, D. 1961. A colorimetric method for determining fat acidity in grain. Cereal Chem. 38: 47-50.

BAKER, D., NEUSTADT, M. H., and ZELENY, L. 1957. Application of the fat-acidity test as an index of grain deterioration. Cereal Chem. 34: 226-233.

BAKER, D., NEUSTADT, M. H., and ZELENY, L. 1959. Relationships between fat acidity values and types of damage in grain. Cereal Chem. 36: 308-311.

BAKKE, A. L., and NOECKER, N. L. 1933.

The relation of moisture to respiration and heating in stored oats. Iowa Res. Bull. 165: 320-336.

BARTON-WRIGHT, E. C. 1938. Studies on the storage of wheaten flour. III. Changes in the flora and the fats, and the influence of these changes on gluten character. Cereal Chem. 15: 521-541.

BAUTISTA, G. M., LUGAY, J. C., CRUZ, L. J., and JULIANO, B. O. 1964. Glutamic acid decarboxylase activity as a viability index of artificially dried and stored rice. Cereal Chem. 41: 188-197.

BAYFIELD, E. G., and O'DONNELL, W. W. 1945. Observations on the thiamine content of stored wheat. Food Res. 10: 485-488.

BELDEROK, B. 1963. Untersuchungen über die Brauchbarkeit der Tetrazoliummethode bei der Bewertung der Backfähigkeit von Weizen. Getreide Mehl 13: 1-7.

BELDEROK, B. 1968a. Seed dormancy problems in cereals. Field Crop Abstr. 21: 203-211.

BELDEROK, B. 1968b. Changes in thiol and disulfide contents in barley embryos during dormancy and after-ripening. J. Inst. Brew. (London) 74: 333-340.

BLACK, M. 1970. Seed germination and dormancy. Sci. Prog. (London) 58: 379-393.

BORTHWICK, H. A., HENDRICKS, S. B., PARKER, M. W., TOOLE, E. H., and TOOLE, V. K. 1952. A reversible photoreaction controlling seed germination. Proc. Nat. Acad. Sci. U.S. 38: 662-666.

BOTTOMLEY, R. A., CHRISTENSEN, C. M., and GEDDES, W. F. 1950. Grain storage studies. IX. The influence of various temperatures, humidities, and oxygen concentrations on mold growth and biochemical changes in stored yellow corn. Cereal Chem. 27: 271-296.

BOTTOMLEY, R. A., CHRISTENSEN, C. M., and GEDDES, W. F. 1952. Grain storage studies. X. The influence of aeration, time, and moisture content on fat acidity, nonreducing sugars, and mold flora of stored yellow corn. Cereal Chem. 29: 53-64.

BROCKINGTON, S. F., DORIN, H. C., and HOWERTON, H. K. 1949. Hygroscopic equilibria of whole kernel corn. Cereal Chem. 26: 166-173.

BROWN, E., STANTON, T. R., WIEBE, G. A., and MARTIN, J. H. 1948. Dormancy and the effect of storage on oats, barley, and sorghum. U.S. Dep. Agr. Tech. Bull. 953.

CABELL, C. A., DAVIS, R. E., and SAUL, R. A. 1958. Some effects of variation in drying temperature, heating time, air flow rate, and moisture content on nutritive value of field shelled corn. J. Animal Sci. 17: 1204-1207.

CARTER, E. P., and YOUNG, G. Y. 1945. Effect of moisture content, temperature, and length of storage on the development of "sick" wheat in sealed containers. Cereal Chem. 22: 418-428.

CASHMORE, W. H. 1942. Temperature control of farm grain driers. Agriculture (London) 3: 144-149.

CHEN, S. S. C., and VARNER, J. E. 1969. Metabolism of ^{14}C maltose in *Avena fatua* seeds during germination. Plant Physiol. 44: 770-774.

CHEN, S. S. C., and VARNER, J. E. 1970. Respiration and protein synthesis in dormant and after-ripened seeds of *Avena fatua*. Plant Physiol. 46: 108-112.

CHENG, Y.-Y., LINKO, P., and MILNER, M. 1960. On the nature of glutamic acid decarboxylase in wheat. Plant Physiol. 35: 68-71.

CHITTENDEN, F. H. 1886. Insects affecting cereals and other dry vegetable foods. Bull. 4, New Series, U.S. Bur. Entomol., pp. 112-131.

CHOW, C. K., and DRAPER, H. H. 1969. Effect of artificial drying on tocopherols and fatty acids of corn. Agr. Food Chem. 17: 1316-1317.

CHRISTENSEN, C. M., and KAUFMANN, H. H. 1969. *Grain storage: the role of fungi in quality loss*. University of Minnesota Press: Minneapolis, Minn.

CLANTON, D. C., HEMSTROM, M. L., and MATSUSHIMA, J. 1960. Nutritive value of beef cattle rations containing artificially dried corn. J. Anim. Sci. 19: 376-380.

COLE, E. W., and MILNER, M. 1953. Colorimetric and fluorometric properties of wheat in relation to germ damage. Cereal Chem. 30: 378-391.

COLEMAN, D. A., and FELLOWS, H. C.

1925. Hygroscopic moisture of cereal grains and flaxseed exposed to atmospheres of different relative humidity. Cereal Chem. 2:275-287.

COLEMAN, D. A., ROTHGEB, B. E., and FELLOWS, H. C. 1928. Respiration of sorghum grains. U.S. Dep. Agr. Tech. Bull. No. 100.

COLVIN, R., CRAIG, B. M., and SALLANS, H. R. 1947. Hygroscopic equilibria for hulls and kernels of sunflower seed and oats. Can. J. Res. 25F: 111-118.

COOKS, R. G., DAFTARY, R. D., and POMERANZ, Y. 1970. Changes in mold-damaged wheat flours stored at various temperatures. Fluorescent compounds: 4, 6, 8(14), 22-ergostatetraen-3-one and its C_{24} ethyl analog. Agr. Food Chem. 18: 620-623.

COX, M. J., MacMASTERS, M. M., and RIST, C. E. 1947. Laboratory processing studies on soft corn. Paper presented at the 32nd AACC annual meeting, Abstracts Program.

CRABB, D. 1971. Changes in response to gibberellic acid of barley endosperm slices during storage. J. Inst. Brew. (London) 77: 522-528.

CREECH, G. T., and MADSEN, L. L. 1942. Generalized edema, or the so-called anasarca in cattle. Bureau Veterinarian 18(1): 1-3.

CROCKER, W. 1948. Life span of seeds. Bot. Rev. 4: 235-274.

DAFTARY, R. D., and POMERANZ, Y. 1965. Changes in lipid composition in wheat during storage deterioration. Agr. Food Chem. 13: 442-446.

DAFTARY, R. D., POMERANZ, Y., HOSENEY, R. C., SHOGREN, M. D., and FINNEY, K. F. 1970a. Changes in wheat flour damaged by mold during storage. Effects in breadmaking. Agr. Food Chem. 18: 617-619.

DAFTARY, R. D., POMERANZ, Y., and SAUER, D. B. 1970b. Changes in wheat flour damaged by mold during storage. Effects on lipid, lipoprotein, and protein. Agr. Food Chem. 18: 613-616.

DAVEY, P. M., and ELCOATE, S. 1965. Moisture content/relative humidity equilibria of tropical stored produce. I. Cereals. Tropical Stored Prod. Inf. 11: 439-467.

DAVIES, W. L. 1928. The cause of deterioration of maize and maize meal. Fertilizer, Feeding Stuffs, Farm Supplies J. 13: 784-785.

DeVAY, J. E. 1952. A note on the effect of mold growth and increased moisture content on the free amino acids in hard red spring wheat. Cereal Chem. 29: 309-311.

DOANE, R. W. 1918. Some problems in the control of insects in stored products in California. J. Econ. Entomol. 11: 313-319.

DOBCZYNSKA, D. 1966. Wplyw procesow suszenia i warunkow przechowania ziarna pszenicy na zawartosc przyswajalnej lizyny. Bull. Inform. 40(4): 73-83.

DUBOIS, M., GEDDES, W. F., and SMITH, F. 1960. The carbohydrates of the Gramineae. X. A quantitative study of the carbohydrates of wheat germ. Cereal Chem. 37: 557-568.

DUCHARTRE, M. P. 1852. Note sur la germination des cereales recoltes avant leur maturite. Acad. Sci. Compt. Rend. 35: 940-942.

EMERICK, R. J., CARLSON, C. W., and WINTERFELD, H. L. 1961. Effect of heat drying upon the nutritive value of corn. Poultry Sci. 40: 991-995.

FAIRBANKS, B. W., MITCHELL, H. H., and FARRAR, M. D. 1940. The feeding value of moldy corn from steel bins. Mimeo. Report, Ill. Ext. Serv.

FENTON, F. C., and SWANSON, C. O. 1930. Qualities of combined wheats as affected by type of bin, moisture, and temperature conditions. Cereal Chem. 7: 428-448.

FERREL, R. E., SHEPHERD, A. D., and GUADAGNI, G. 1970. Storage stability of lysine in lysine-fortified wheat. Cereal Chem. 47: 33-37.

FIFIELD, C. C., and ROBERTSON, D. W. 1945. Milling, baking, and chemical properties of Marquis and Kanred wheat grown in Colorado and stored 14 to 22 years. J. Amer. Soc. Agron. 37: 233-239.

FIFIELD, C. C., and ROBERTSON, D. W. 1959. Milling, baking, and chemical properties of Marquis and Kanred wheat grown in Colorado and stored 25 to 33 years. Cereal Sci. Today 4: 179-183.

FINNEY, K. F., SHOGREN, M. D., HOSENEY, R. C., BOLTE, L. C., and HEYNE, E. G. 1962. Chemical, physical, and baking properties of preripe wheat dried at varying temperatures. Agron. J. 54: 244-247.

FISHER, E. A., HALTON, P., and CARTER, R. H. 1937. Studies on the storage of wheaten flour. I. The influence of storage on the chemical composition and baking quality of flour. Cereal Chem. 14: 135-161.

FITZ, L. A. 1910. Handling wheat from field to mill. U.S. Bur. Plant Industry Circ. No. 68.

FLORIS, C. 1970. Ageing in *Triticum durum* seeds: Behaviour of embryos and endosperms from aged seeds as revealed by the embryo-transplantation technique. J. Exptl. Bot. 21: 462-468.

FOREMAN, F. W. 1920. Rapid volumetric methods for the estimation of amino acids, organic acids, and organic bases. Biochem. J. 14: 451-473.

FRAPS, G. S. 1931. Variations in vitamin A and chemical composition of corn. Texas Agr. Exp. Sta. Bull. 422.

FRAPS, G. S., and KEMMERER, A. R. 1941. Determination of carotene and cryptoxanthin in yellow corn. Ind. Eng. Chem. Anal. Ed. 13: 806-809.

FRAPS, G. S., and KEMMERER, A. R. 1937. Losses in vitamin A and carotene from feeds during storage. Texas Agr. Exp. Sta. Bull. 557.

GANE, R. 1941. The water content of wheats as a function of temperature and humidity. J. Soc. Chem. Ind. (London) 60: 44-46.

GAY, F. J. 1946. The effect of temperature on the moisture content-relative humidity equilibria of wheat. J. Council Sci. Ind. Res. (Australia) 19: 187-189.

GEDDES, W. F. 1935. Can. Grain Research Lab. Winnipeg 9th Ann. Rep., pp. 62-64.

GEDDES, W. F. 1958. The chemistry, microbiology and physics of grain storage. Food Technol. 12(11): 7-14.

GLASS, R. L., and GEDDES, W. F. 1960. Grain storage studies. XXXI. Changes occurring in low-molecular-weight compounds in deteriorating wheat. Cereal Chem. 37: 568-572.

GLASS, R. L., PONTE, J. G., Jr., CHRISTENSEN, C. M., and GEDDES, W. F. 1959. Grain storage studies. XXVIII. The influence of temperature and moisture level on the behavior of wheat stored in air or nitrogen. Cereal Chem. 36: 341-356.

GRACZA, R. 1965. Aging and storage studies in flours and air-classified flour fractions. Cereal Chem. 42: 333-358.

GREAVES, J. E., and HIRST, C. T. 1925. The influence of storage on the composition of flour. Utah Agr. Exp. Sta. Bull. 194.

GREER, E. N., JONES, C. R., and MORAN, T. 1954. The quality of flour stored for periods up to 27 years. Cereal Chem. 31: 439-450.

GROSS, E. 1919. Veränderungen der Getreidesamen bei 10-Jähriger Lagerung. Biedermanns Zent. 48: 395-400.

GRZESIUK, S., and KULKA, K. 1971a. Nucleic acids and nucleases in cereal seeds of various age. Bull. Acad. Polon. Sci. Cl. V. 19: 363-366.

GRZESIUK, S., and KULKA, K. 1971b. Proteins in ageing oat seeds. Bull. Acad. Polon. Sci. Cl. V. 19: 435-440.

HAFERKAMP, M. E., SMITH, L., and NILAN, R. A. 1953. Studies of age of seed. I. Relation of age of seed to germination and longevity. Agron. J. 45: 434-437.

HARRISON, D. C., and MELLANBY, E. 1939. Phytic acid and the rickets-producing action of cereals. Biochem. J. 33: 1660-1680.

HEYDECKER, W. 1969. The 'vigour' of seeds—a review. Proc. Int. Seed Testing Ass. 34: 201-219.

HOFFMAN, E. J. 1931. Das Getreidekorn, 2nd ed. K. Mohs, Parey, Berlin.

HOLLENBECK, C. M., and OBERMEYER, H. G. 1952. Relative stability of thiamine mononitrate and thiamine chloride hydrochloride in enriched flour. Cereal Chem. 29: 82-87.

HOUSTON, D. F., STRAKA, R. P., HUNTER, I. R., ROBERTS, R. L., and KESTER, E. B. 1957. Changes in rough rice at different moisture contents during storage at controlled temperatures. Cereal Chem. 34: 444-456.

HUMMEL, B. C. W., CUENDET, L. S., CHRISTENSEN, C. M., and GEDDES, W. F. 1954. Grain storage studies. XII. Comparative changes in respiration, viability, and chemical composition of mold-free and mold-contaminated wheat upon storage. Cereal Chem. 31: 143-150.

HUTCHINSON, J. B. 1961. Hydrolysis of lipids in cereals and cereal products. Soc. Chem. Ind. (London), Monograph No. 11: 137-148.

IWASAKI, T., and TANI, T. 1967. Effect of oxygen concentration on deteriorative mechanisms of rice during storage. Cereal Chem. 44: 233-237.

JENSEN, A. M., TERRILL, S. W., and BECKER, D. E. 1960. Nutritive value of corn dried at 140°, 180°, and 220° Fahrenheit for swine of different ages. J. Anim. Sci. 19: 629-638.

JOFFE, A., and SMALL, J. G. C. 1964. Studies on fat acidity of sound corn by the rapid method. Cereal Chem. 41: 230-242.

JONES, D. B., DIVINE, J. P., and GERSDORFF, C. E. F. 1942. Effect of storage of corn on the chemical properties of its proteins and on its growth-promoting

value. Cereal Chem. 19: 819-830.

JONES, D. B., FRAPS, G. S., THOMAS, B. H., and ZELENY, L. 1943. The effect of storage of grains on their nutritive value. Nat. Res. Council U.S., Reprint and Circ. Ser. No. 116.

JONES, D. B., and GERSDORFF, C. E. F. 1938. Changes that occur in the proteins of soybean meal as a result of storage. J. Amer. Chem. Soc. 60: 723-724.

JONES, D. B., and GERSDORFF, C. E. F. 1939. The effect of storage on the proteins of seeds and their flours. Soybeans and wheat. J. Biol. Chem. 128: XLIX-1.

JONES, D. B., and GERSDORFF, C. E. F. 1941. The effect of storage on the protein of wheat, white flour, and whole wheat flour. Cereal Chem. 18: 417-434.

KARON, M. L. 1947. Hygroscopic equilibrium of cottonseed. J. Amer. Oil Chem. Soc. 24: 56-58.

KARON, M. L., and ADAMS, M. E. 1949. Hygroscopic equilibrium of rice and rice fractions. Cereal Chem. 26: 1-12.

KARON, M. L., and HILLERY, B. E. 1949. Hygroscopic equilibrium of peanuts. J. Amer. Oil Chem. Soc. 26: 16-19.

KARP, D. 1959. Veranderungen und Schutz der Getreidefette. Getreide Mehl 9: 93-99.

KENT, N. L. 1966. *Technology of cereals with special reference to wheat*. Pergamon Press: Oxford, England.

KHAN, A. A., HEIT, C. E., WATERS, E. C., ANOJULU, C. C., and ANDERSON, L. 1971. Discovery of a new role for cytokinins in seed dormancy and germination. Search Agr. (Seed Inv. N.Y. Agr. Exp. Sta., Geneva) 1(9): 1-10.

KOCH, B. A., and MEYER, J. H. 1957. Effects of storage upon nutrient value of barley grains as a source of protein. J. Nutr. 61: 343-356.

KONDO, M., and OKAMURA, T. 1933a. Storage of rice. VI. Physical and biochemical studies of hulled rice stored in straw bags. Ber. Ohara Inst. Landw. Forsch. Kurashiki, Japan 5: 395-406 (Chem. Abstr. 27: 4284).

KONDO, M., and OKAMURA, T. 1933b. Storage of rice. VII. The influence of varying moisture content and germinating power upon the preservation of vitamin B in hulled rice. Ber. Ohara Inst. Landw. Forsch. Kurashiki, Japan 5: 407-412 (Chem. Abstr. 27: 4284).

KONDO, M., and OKAMURA, T. 1933c. Storage of rice. VIII. Hulled rice stored air-tight 26 and 28 years. Ber. Ohara Inst.

Landw. Forsch. Kurashiki, Japan 5: 413-420 (Chem. Abstr. 27: 4284).

KONDO, M., and OKAMURA, T. 1937. Storage of rice. XVI. Storage of rice in concrete silos for five years. Ber. Ohara Inst. Landw. Forsch. Kurashiki, Japan 7: 471-481 (Chem. Abstr. 32: 5087).

KOZLOVA, L. T., and NEKRASOV, B. P. 1956. Changes in wheat quality during prolonged storage. Trudy Tsentr. Nauch.-Issledovatel. Lab. Glavnoe Upravlenie Gosudarst. Material. No. 4: 60-80 (Chem. Abstr. 55: 9715a).

KOZMIN, N. P. 1935. The aging of wheat flour and the nature of this process. Cereal Chem. 12: 165-171.

KOZMIN, N. P. 1936. Das Problem der Bäckfahigkeit. Schafer Verlag, Leipzig.

KRIEGER, C. H., BUNKFELDT, R., THOMPSON, C. R., and STEENBOCK, H. 1941. Cereals and rickets. XIII. Phytic acid, nucleic acid, soybean phosphatides and inorganic salts as sources of phosphorus for bone calcification. J. Nutr. 21: 213-220.

LARMOUR, R. K., HULSE, J. H., ANDERSON, J. A., and DEMPSTER, C. J. 1961. Effect of package type on stored flour and farina. Cereal Sci. Today 6: 158, 160-164.

LARMOUR, R. K., SALLANS, H. R., and CRAIG, B. M. 1944. Hygroscopic equilibrium of sunflower, flaxseed, and soybeans. Can. J. Research 22F: 1-8.

LEACH, W. 1932. Further experimental methods in connection with the use of the Katharometer for the measurement of respiration. Ann. Botany 46: 583-596.

LEAVITT, S., and LeCLERC, J. A. 1909. Change in the composition of unground cereals during storage. Ind. Eng. Chem. 1: 299-302.

LINKO, P. 1960. Water content and metabolism of wheat during storage and germination. Ann. Acad. Sci. Fennicae, Series A, II. Chemica 98. Helsinki.

LINKO, P. 1961. Quality of stored wheat. Simple and rapid manometric method for determining glutamic acid decarboxylase activity as quality index of wheat. Agr. Food Chem. 9: 310-313.

LINKO, P. 1966. Beobachtungen über Hitzeschäden bei Getreide. Getreide Mehl 16: 86-90.

LINKO, P., CHENG, Y.-Y., and MILNER, M. 1960. Changes in the soluble carbohydrates during browning of wheat embryos. Cereal Chem. 37: 548-556.

LINKO, P., and MILNER, M. 1959a. Gas exchange induced in dry wheat embryos by wetting. Cereal Chem. 36: 274-279.

LINKO, P., and MILNER, M. 1959b. Free amino and keto acids of wheat grains and embryos in relation to water content and germination. Cereal Chem. 36: 280-294.

LINKO, P., and MILNER, M. 1959c. Enzyme activation in wheat grains in relation to water content. Glutamic acid-alanine transaminase and glutamic acid decarboxylase. Plant Physiol. 34: 392-396.

LINKO, P., and SOGN, L. 1960. Relation of viability and storage deterioration to glutamic acid decarboxylase in wheat. Cereal Chem. 37: 489-499.

LUND, A., PEDERSEN, H., and SIGSGAARD, P. 1971. Storage experiments with barley at different moisture contents. J. Sci. Food Agr. 22: 458-463.

LYNCH, B. T., GLASS, R. L., and GEDDES, W. F. 1962. Grain storage studies. XXXII. Quantitative changes occurring in the sugars of wheat deteriorating in the presence and absence of molds. Cereal Chem. 39: 256-262.

MACLEOD, A. M. 1967. The physiology of malting—a review. J. Inst. Brew. (London) 73: 146-162.

MADSEN, L. L., and EARLE, I. P. 1947. Some observations on beef cattle affected with generalized edema or anasarca due to vitamin A deficiency. J. Nutr. 34: 603-619.

MARCUS, A. 1969. Seed germination and the capacity for protein synthesis. Symp. Soc. Exp. Biol. 23: 143-160.

MAYER, A. M., and POLJAKOFF-MAYBER, A. 1963. *The germination of seeds.* MacMillan: New York.

McDONALD, C. E., and MILNER, M. 1954. The browning reaction in wheat germ in relation to "sick" wheat. Cereal Chem. 31: 279-295.

MEREDITH, W. O. S., ANDERSON, J. A., and HUDSON, L. E. 1962. Evaluation of malting barley, pp. 207-302. In: *Barley and malt,* A. H. Cook, ed. Academic Press: New York and London.

MILNER, C. K., and WOODFORDE, J. 1965. The effect of heat in drying on the nutritive value of wheat for animal feed. J. Sci. Food Agr. 16: 369-373.

MILNER, M., and GEDDES, W. F. 1945a. Grain storage studies. I. Influence of localized heating of soybeans on interseed air movements. Cereal Chem. 22: 477-483.

MILNER, M., and GEDDES, W. F. 1945b.

Grain storage studies. II. The effect of aeration, temperature, and time on the respiration of soybeans containing excessive moisture. Cereal Chem. 22: 484-501.

MILNER, M., and GEDDES, W. F. 1946. Grain storage studies. IV. Biological and chemical factors involved in the spontaneous heating of soybeans. Cereal Chem. 23: 449-470.

MILNER, M., and GEDDES, W. F. 1954. Respiration and heating, pp. 152-220. In: *Storage of cereal grains and their products*, J. A. Anderson and A. W. Alcock, eds. Monograph series, Vol. II. American Association of Cereal Chemists: St. Paul, Minn.

MITCHELL, H. H., and BEADLES, J. R. 1949. The effect of storage on the nutritional qualities of the proteins of wheat, corn, and soybeans. J. Nutr. 39: 463-484.

MONTGOMERY, R., and SMITH, F. 1956. A review of carbohydrates of wheat and other cereal grains. Agr. Food Chem. 4: 716-720.

MORRISON, W. R. 1963. The free fatty acid content of some wheat flours. J. Sci. Food Agr. 14: 870-873.

OWEN, E. B. 1956. The storage of seeds for maintenance and viability. Bull. No. 43. Commonwealth Bureau of Pasture and Field Crops: Hurley, Berks., England.

OXLEY, T. A. 1944. A simple gasometric apparatus for estimation of carbon dioxide. Chem. Ind. 1944: 24-25.

OXLEY, T. A. 1948. *The scientific principles of grain storage*. Northern Pub. Co.: Liverpool, England.

PAP, L. 1934. Water contents, relative humidity and the causes of deterioration in wheat (in Hungarian). Mezogayzdasagi Kutatasok 7: 177-180.

PAWLAK, M., and PION, R. 1970. Influence de la conservation sur la valeur nutritive des proteinés du ble. Ann. Biol. Anim. Biochim. Biophys. 10: 171-174.

PAYNE, N. M. 1925. Some effects of *Tribolium* on flour. J. Econ. Entomol. 18: 737-744.

PEDERSEN, H., NORGAARD-PEDERSEN, P. E., and GLAHN, P. E. 1971. Storage of grain in experimental silos: Functional principle and reproducibility of results in simultaneous experiments and in experiments separated in time. J. Sci. Food Agr. 22: 451-457.

PIXTON, S. W. 1968. The effect of heat treatment on the moisture content/relative humidity relationship of Manitoba wheat. J. Stored Products Res. 4: 267-270.

PIXTON, S. W., and HILL, S. T. 1967. Long-term storage of wheat. II. J. Sci. Food Agr. 18: 94-98.

PIXTON, S. W., and WARBURTON, SYLVIA. 1971. Moisture content/relative humidity equilibrium of some cereal grains at different temperatures. J. Stored Products Res. 6: 283-293.

POMERANZ, Y. 1971a. A review of some recent studies on biochemical and functional changes in mold-damaged wheat and wheat flour. Cereal Sci. Today 16: 119-122, 131.

POMERANZ, Y. 1971b. Biochemical and functional changes in stored cereal grains. Critical Rev. Food Technol. 2: 45-60.

POMERANZ, Y. (ed.). 1971c. *Wheat: Chemistry and technology*. Monograph series, Vol. III (rev.). American Association of Cereal Chemists: St. Paul, Minn.

POMERANZ, Y., DAFTARY, R. D., SHOGREN, M. D., HOSENEY, R. C., and FINNEY, K. F. 1968. Changes in biochemical and breadmaking properties of storage-damaged flour. Agr. Food Chem. 16: 92-96.

POMERANZ, Y., HALTON, P., and PEERS, F. G. 1956. The effects on flour dough and bread quality of molds grown in wheat and those added to flour in the form of specific cultures. Cereal Chem. 33: 157-169.

POPOV, N. F., and TIMOFEEV, L. I. 1933. Some data on the chemistry of wheat ripened after harvesting in storage, silos, or elevators. Sci. Inst. Cereal Res. (USSR) 11: 59-83 (Chem. Abstr. 29: 2607).

PORTER, R. H. 1949. Recent developments in seed technology. Bot. Rev. 15: 221-344.

PRENTICE, N. 1962. Partial purification of a metabolite produced by *Fusarium moniliforme* which inhibits the utilization of oxygen by germinating barley. Physiol. Plant. 15: 693-699.

PRENTICE, N., and DICKSON, A. D. 1964. Emetic material in scabbed wheat. Cereal Chem. 41: 548-550.

PRENTICE, N., and DICKSON, A. D. 1968. Emetic material associated with *Fusarium* species in cereal grains and artificial media. Biotechnol. Bioeng. 10: 413-427.

PRENTICE, N., and SLOEY, W. 1960. Studies on barley microflora of possible importance to malting and brewing quality. I. The treatment of barley during malting with selected microorganisms. Amer. Soc. Brew. Chem. Proc. 1960: 28-33.

PUCKOVA, L. I., TSYGANOVA, T. B., SOLOREVA, M. P., CHIRKOVA, S. R., and NECHAEV, A. P. 1971. Sulfhydryl groups and disulfide bonds in wheat flour gluten. Izv. Vyssh. Ucheb. Zaved. Pishch. Tekhnol. 2: 25-28 (Chem. Abstr. 75: 75052 a).

QUACKENBUSH, F. W. 1963. Corn carotenoids: Effects of temperature and moisture on losses during storage. Cereal Chem. 40: 266-269.

RAMSTAD, P. E., and GEDDES, W. F. 1942. The respiration and storage behavior of soybeans. Minn. Agr. Exp. Sta. Tech. Bull. 156.

ROBERTS, E. H. 1960. The viability of cereal seed in relation to temperature and moisture. Ann. Bot. N.S. 24: 12-31.

ROBERTS, E. H. 1969. Seed dormancy and oxidation processes. Symp. Soc. Exp. Biol. 23: 161-192.

ROBERTS, E. H. (ed.). 1972. *Viability of seeds*. Chapman & Hall: London.

ROBERTSON, D. W., FIFIELD, C. C., and ZELENY, L. 1939a. Milling, baking, and chemical properties of Colorado-grown Marquis and Kanred wheat stored 9 to 17 years. J. Amer. Soc. Agron. 31: 851-856.

ROBERTSON, D. W., LUTE, A. M., and GARDNER, R. 1939b. Effect of relative humidity on viability, moisture content, and respiration of wheat, oats, and barley seeds in storage. J. Agr. Res. 59: 281-291.

ROBERTSON, D. W., LUTE, A. M., and KROGER, H. 1943. Germination of 20-year-old wheat, oats, barley, corn, rye, sorghum, and soybeans. J. Amer. Soc. Agron. 35: 786-795.

ROCKLAND, L. B. 1969. Water activity and storage stability. Food Technol. 23: 1241-1246, 1248, 1251.

ROHRLICH, M., and BRUCKNER, G. 1966. *Das Getreide und seine Verarbeitung*. Vol. IV, part 1, 2nd ed. Verlag Paul Parey: Berlin.

ROHRLICH, M., and SIEBERT, K. 1964. Glutaminsäuredecarboxylase bei keimendem, reifendem, und lagerndem Getreide. Deutsch. Lebensm. Rundsch. 60: 369-373.

SALUN, I. P., and NADEZHNOVA, L. A. 1971. Changes in the *in vitro* digestibility of proteins contained in groats during storage. Voprosy Pitaniya 30(3): 70-73 (Food Sci. Technol. Abstr. 10M1116).

SATO, T., TACHIBANA, T., and ITO, K. 1971. Quality change of rice during storage. II. Changes of cooking characteristics and susceptibility of cooked and steamed rice to amylase action according to their drying conditions. Nippon Jozo Kyokai Zasshi 65(3): 266-268 (Chem. Abstr. 75: 150553v).

SAUNDERS, C. E. 1909. Effect of storage on wheat and flour. Can. Ann. Rep. Exptl. Farms 205-206.

SAUNDERS, C. E. 1910. Effect of storage on wheat and flour. Can. Ann. Rep. Exptl. Farms 168.

SAUNDERS, C. E., NICHOLS, R. W., and COWAN, P. R. 1921. Researches in regard to wheat, flour, and bread. Can. Dep. Agr. Cereal Div. Bull. 97.

SCHRICKER, J. A. 1948. The respiration and storage behavior of flaxseed. M.S. Thesis. University of Minnesota.

SHANDS, H. L., JANISCH, D. C., and DICKSON, A. D. 1967. Germination response of barley following different harvesting conditions and storage treatments. Crop Sci. 7: 444-446.

SHELLENBERGER, J. A. 1939. Variation in baking quality of wheat during storage. Cereal Chem. 16: 676-682.

SHELLENBERGER, J. A., MILLER, D., FARRELL, E. P., and MILNER, M. 1958. Effect of wheat age on storage properties of flour. Food Technol. 12: 213-221.

SHUTT, F. T. 1909. Influence of age on wheat and flour. Can. Ann. Rep. Exptl. Farms 144.

SHUTT, F. T. 1911. Influence of age on wheat and flour. Can. Ann. Rep. Exptl. Farms 168.

SIMPSON, G. M. 1965. Dormancy studies in seed of *Avena fatua*. 4. The role of gibberellin in embryo dormancy. Can. J. Bot. 43: 793-816.

SINCLAIR, A. T., and McCALLA, A. G. 1937. The influence of lipoids on the quality and keeping properties of flour. Can. J. Res. 15C: 187-203.

SLOEY, W., and PRENTICE, N. 1962. Effects of *Fusarium* isolates applied during malting on properties of malt. Amer. Soc. Brew. Chem. Proc. 1962: 24-29.

SMITH, L. W., Jr., PRATT, J. J., Jr., NII, I., and UMINA, A. P. 1971. Baking and taste properties of bread made from hard wheat flour infested with species of *Tribolium, Tenebrio, Trogoderma*, and *Oryzaephilus*. J. Stored Prod. Res. 6: 307-316.

SORGER-DOMENIGG, H., CUENDET, L.

S., and GEDDES, W. F. 1955. Grain storage studies. XX. Relation between viability, fat acidity, germ damage, fluorescence value, and formazan value of commercial wheat samples. Cereal Chem. 32: 499-506.

SREENIVASAN, A. 1939. Studies on quality in rice. IV. Storage changes in rice after harvest. Indian J. Agr. Sci. 9: 208-222.

STANSFIELD, E., and COOK, W. H. 1932. The drying of wheat (2nd report). Dominion Can. Natl. Res. Council Rep. No. 25.

STEFANOV, L., and GAVRILENKO, I. 1970. Reduction in the nutritive value of maize corn as a result of storage before processing and the preserving effect of carbon dioxide. Kharanitelna Promishlemost 19(6): 28-29 (Food Sci. Technol. Abstr. 10M1184, 1971).

STEVENSON, K. R. 1972. New treatment allows wet-grain storage without dryer or silo. Crops & Soils Mag. 24(5): 8-10.

STILES, W., and LEACH, W. 1931. On the use of the Katharometer for the measurement of respiration. Ann. Botany 45: 461-488.

SULLIVAN, B. 1940. The function of the lipids in milling and baking. Cereal Chem. 17: 661-668.

SULLIVAN, B., and HOWE, M. 1938. Lipids of wheat flours. I. The petroleum ether extract. Cereal Chem. 15: 716-720.

SULLIVAN, B., NEAR, C., and FOLEY, G. H. 1936. The role of lipids in relation to flour quality. Cereal Chem. 13: 318-331.

SUZUKI, Y., and MATSUMOTO, F. 1971. Storage temperature of rice and eating quality of cooked rice. Kaseigaku Zasshi 22(5): 288-295 (Chem. Abstr. 75: 150568 d).

SWANSON, C. O. 1935. Some factors which affect the diastatic activity in wheat. Cereal Chem. 12: 89-107.

TAUFEL, K., ROMMINGER, K., and HIRSCHFELD, W. 1959. Oligosaccharide von Getreide und Mehl. Z. Lebensm. Unters. Forsch. 109: 1-12.

TAUFEL, K., STEINBACH, K. J., and VOGEL, E. 1960. Mono- and oligosaccharides of some legume seed as well as their behavior on storage and germination. Z. Lebensm. Unters. Forsch. 112: 31-40 (Chem. Abstr. 54: 13288 d).

TROLLE, B., and PEDERSEN, H. 1971. Grain quality research committee under the Danish Academy of Technical Sciences. Summary of a report on the activities of the committee. J. Inst. Brew. (London) 77: 338-348.

TUITE, J. F., and CHRISTENSEN, C. M. 1955. Grain storage studies. XVI. Influence of storage conditions upon the fungus flora of barley seed. Cereal Chem. 32: 1-11.

YANNAI, S., and ZIMMERMANN, G. Influence of controlled storage of some staple foods on their protein nutritive value in lysine-limited diets. I. Protein nutritive value of defatted milk powder, wheat, and rice. J. Food Sci. Technol. 7: 179-184.

YASUMATSU, K., and MORITAKA, S. 1964. Fatty acid compositions of rice lipid and their changes during storage. Agr. Biol. Chem. 28: 257-264.

YONEYAMA, T., SUZUKI, I., and MUROHASHI, M. 1970a. Natural maturing of wheat flour. I. Changes in some chemical components and in farinograph and extensiograph properties. Cereal Chem. 47: 19-26.

YONEYAMA, T., SUZUKI, I., and MUROHASHI, M. 1970b. Natural maturing of wheat flour. II. Effect of temperature on changes in soluble SH content, and some rheological properties of doughs obtained from the flour. Cereal Chem. 47: 27-33.

ZELENY, L. 1954. Chemical, physical, and nutritive changes during storage, pp. 46-76. In: *Storage of cereal grains and their products,* J. A. Anderson and A. W. Alcock, eds. Monograph Series, Vol. II. American Association of Cereal Chemists: St. Paul, Minn.

ZELENY, L., and COLEMAN, D. A. 1938. Acidity in cereals and cereal products, its determination and significance. Cereal Chem. 15: 580-595.

ZELENY, L., and COLEMAN, D. A. 1939. The chemical determination of soundness in corn. U.S. Dep. Agr. Tech. Bull. 644.

CHAPTER 3

SAMPLING, INSPECTION, AND GRADING OF GRAIN[1]

G. R. BAUWIN,
Agricultural Marketing Specialist

H. L. RYAN,
Field Office Supervisor
Grain Division, Agricultural Marketing Service
U.S. Department of Agriculture, Chicago, Illinois

I. INTRODUCTION

Grains for which standards have been established are officially inspected under the U.S. Grain Standards Act (as amended) and the Regulations thereunder (Anon., 1968). Section 2 of the Act provides a policy "for the establishment of official United States Standards for Grain, to promote the uniform application thereof by official inspection personnel, and to provide for an official inspection system for grain; with the objectives that grain may be marketed in an orderly manner and that trading in grain may be facilitated."

The official inspection of grain by an authorized inspection agency is mandatory when grain is exported from the U.S. Grain moving in domestic commerce may be officially inspected at the request of any person interested.

Official inspection personnel are defined as employees of state or other governmental or commercial agencies or other persons licensed to perform all or specified functions involved in official inspection under the U.S. Grain Standards Act, or employees of the U.S. Department of Agriculture who are authorized to perform official inspection functions. Licensed or authorized personnel will issue grain-inspection certificates attesting to grades and other factors of the grain they inspect.

Grain inspection has a long history. Early methods of judging were based on such terms as "dry", "damp", "plump", "well-cleaned", "dirty", etc. Grain trade organizations began to evolve in the U.S. in the mid-1800's. Each developed its own "standards" for merchandising grain in the particular area. As time moved on and transportation improved, grain moved from one trade area to another. Persons

---

[1]Trade names are used in this publication solely for the purpose of providing specific information. Mention of a trade name does not constitute a guarantee or warranty of the product by the U.S. Department of Agriculture or an endorsement by the Department over other products not mentioned.

buying grain under a "standard" in one trade area had little assurance that the grain would, or could, receive the same grade designation in another trade area.

Complaints from domestic and foreign handlers about grading of grain mounted over the years, and in 1901 the U.S. Department of Agriculture initiated a project to study the many commercial grain standards then in effect and the methods used to apply them. As a result of this study, permissive federal standards for corn were established. Many of the existing grain inspection agencies adopted these standards for application in their market. There was, however, a notable lack of uniformity in the application of these permissive standards, and the problems were far from solved.

During the period 1903 to 1916, many bills were introduced in the U.S. Congress to establish standards and uniform grading procedures until, in 1916, the U.S. Grain Standards Act was finally passed. In subsequent years a number of minor amendments were passed, to make the Act and the Standards more meaningful, and in 1968 a major overhaul of the Act was passed by the Congress to bring the Act in keeping with modern times. Regulations to implement the modernized Act are in effect and materially increase the scope and efficiency of grain standards and grain inspection. U.S. Standards (Anon., 1970) are now in effect for wheat, corn, barley, oats, rye, grain sorghum, flaxseed, soybeans, and mixed grain. The Standards are constantly under study by the U.S. Department of Agriculture's Grain Division and, when considered necessary or desirable, changes are proposed and presented to the trade for consideration and comment.

Individual copies of the U.S. Grain Standards Act (as amended) and the Regulations thereunder, and the Official Grain Standards of the U.S. may be obtained from the Superintendent of Documents, U.S. Government Printing Office,

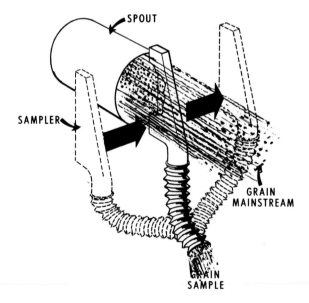

Figure 1. Operation principle of a diverter-type sampler.

**MATERIALS INLET FROM
PRIMARY SAMPLER**

DRIVE MOTOR

**ORIGINAL SAMPLE
DELIVERY SPOUT**

EXCESS SAMPLE SPOUT
(Back to main materials flow)

SECONDARY SAMPLES
(Four spouts of equally
divided sample)

Figure 2. Strand secondary-sample divider.

Washington, D.C., or from local offices of the U.S. Department of Agriculture's Grain Division, Agricultural Marketing Service. Volume orders should be directed to the U.S. Government Printing Office. Official inspection personnel sample and inspect grain, applying the procedures laid out in the Grain Inspection Manual (Anon., 1971). Because of the problems involved in distributing changes or adjustments in procedure to all manual holders, the general distribution of manuals and changes is limited to official inspection personnel. Offices of the U.S. Department of Agriculture's Grain Division and the official inspection agencies will make manual copies available for study or examination upon request.

II. SAMPLING

Obtaining a sample truly representative of the lot(s) of grain is an essential part of grain grading, for if the sample obtained is not representative, no amount of care in making the determination for grading factors will establish a true grade for the lot involved. This is achieved by a) proper sampling, b) correctly compositing the subsamples and reducing them to the proper size for grading, and c) preserving the samples through proper packaging until the time that grading can be completed.

A. Equipment

The following equipment is used for sampling grain under different

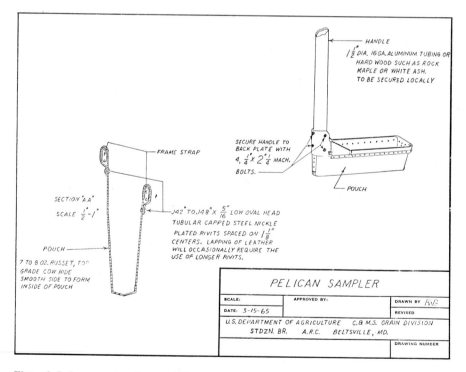

Figure 3. Pelican sampler, shape and dimensions.

circumstances, and for maintaining the representativeness of the sample until the time of grading. Each has its place.

DIVERTER-TYPE (PRIMARY) MECHANICAL GRAIN SAMPLER

This type of sampler (Figure 1) is mounted in a grain spout, at the end of a belt, or at the head of an elevating leg within a grain elevator. The principle is simple, and consists of a diverter (pelican) moving completely across the moving stream of grain. The movement of the pelican is electrically timed, and powered by an air cylinder or electric motor. This sampling method is considered the most accurate, because representative cross-sections of the grain stream are methodically withdrawn and composited for the final sample. The human sampling error is eliminated by this first step. A mechanical or gravity sampler (secondary sampler), to reduce the size of the sample to manageable proportions, is usually associated with this type of apparatus and is located somewhere between it and the collection point (Figure 2).

Figure 4. Pelican sampler being used.

Figure 5. Using a probe to sample a carlot.

PELICAN SAMPLER

The pelican sampler (Figures 3 and 4) is used for obtaining a representative sample from a free-falling stream of grain, particularly from one that is being spouted into holds of a vessel. It is also employed as the standard for determining the accuracy of diverter-type samplers.

PROBE OR TRIER

The standard probe (Figure 5) used for sampling bulk grain in boxcars is a double-tube, 12-compartment, brass or aluminum-alloy apparatus 6 ft. long and 1-3/8 in. in outer diameter. A 20-compartment, 12-ft. type is used for sampling grain in hopper cars and barges.

WOODSIDE-TYPE SAMPLER

This is a mechanical sampling device generally used for obtaining representative samples from bulk grain on a moving conveyor belt. Cross-sectional views and an operational view are shown in Figures 6, 7, and 8. The more common regular type is built as one unit and is installed directly over the conveyor belt. The top section is installed on the floor above, and directly over the bottom section. This type is used to avoid dusty, hazardous, or inadequate working conditions which often exist when a conveyor belt is located in a tunnel or basement. Regardless of the type employed, the number of chains (with sampling buckets) depends on the width of the conveyor belt. A three-chain sampler is satisfactory for use on conveyor belts as narrow as 30 in. If the conveyor belt is narrower than 30 in., only one chain should be used. The number of buckets per chain will depend on the size of the sample desired. However, each chain must carry the same number of sampling buckets. Furthermore, the sampling buckets must be evenly spaced on each chain and the buckets on any one chain must be alternately spaced with those on the other chains.

AUXILIARY EQUIPMENT

Ellis Cup. This hand scoop (Figures 9 and 10) is used for obtaining representative samples of bulk grain from a moving belt.

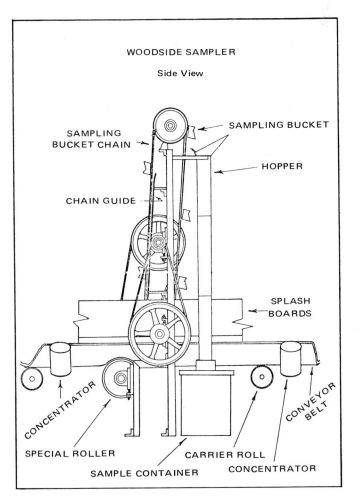

Figure 6. Woodside sampler.

Grain-Sampling Canvas. The grain-sampling canvas is used in conjunction with the probe. Sizes employed are 29.5 in. by 6 ft. and 29.5 in. by 12 ft. for the 6-ft. and 12-ft. triers, respectively. They are generally made of waterproof white flat duck.

Grain-Sampling Bag. These containers are used with all types of samplers and are 7.5 to 8 in. by 16 to 17 in. in size or larger. They will hold about 1,500 to 3,000 g. or more of grain and are made of waterproof white duck utilizing 34-in. three-ply drawstrings.

Boerner Divider (Cargo Model). The Boerner divider (Figure 11) is used in conjunction with the diverter-type, Woodside-type, and pelican samplers in elevators, ships, barges, and other places where portable equipment is required for reducing the size of a sample while maintaining its representativeness. It is usually constructed of brass and contains ten ducts and ten open spaces to divide the material that passes over the cone.

Sample Ticket. A form (Figure 12) used for identifying the sample, the sample ticket, contains such information as the date and time sampled, name of the

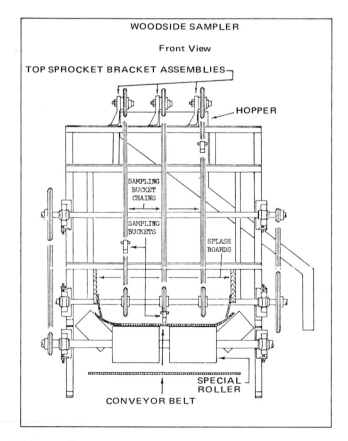

Figure 7. Woodside sampler, cross-sectional view.

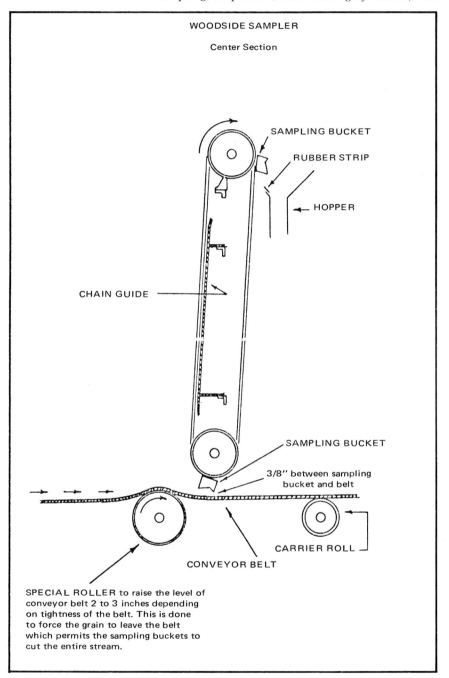

Figure 8. Woodside sampler, operational view.

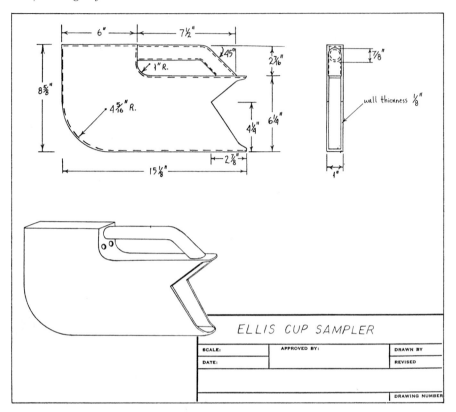

Figure 9. Ellis cup, the device.

sampler, type of grain sampled, identity of the carrier, grading factors, and other relevant information.

B. Methods

Before grain in a boxcar, truck, hopper car, or barge is moved into an elevator, it is usually sampled with a probe and then graded so that it can be stored in the proper bin. The compartmented portion of the probe is completely inserted in the grain at an angle of about 10 degrees from the vertical with the slots closed. Then, with the slots facing upward, it is opened, moved up and down in two short motions so that all of the compartments may be filled, then closed and withdrawn. The contents are then placed full length on a sampling canvas. This procedure is repeated until the required number of probes from the appropriate locations for that particular kind of conveyance (Figures 13, 14, 15, 16, and 17) have been obtained. The contents of each probe are examined carefully and the results of the examination, along with any sampling problems, are noted on the sampling ticket. The grain can be probed, at the discretion of the sampler, as many additional times as may be necessary to obtain a representative sample. In actual practice this

Figure 10. Using the Ellis cup to obtain a sample.

usually means that the same number of additional probes are added to the original sample, but are taken in a reverse pattern. Sometimes (usually in the case of compacted soybeans) one cannot obtain a representative sample, due to inability to get the probe completely down into the grain. In such cases, if possible, the sample is taken off the conveyor belt at the elevator with an Ellis cup during the time of unloading.

In the event that the sampler finds the grain in the conveyance to be out of condition (sour, musty, or heating—the heating owing to excessive respiration and not to natural heat), the boundaries of this inferior portion must be ascertained by repeated probing and examination of contents. Once this has been done, the sampler will take three separate samples: one from the whole car, one from the inferior portion, and one from the noninferior (remaining) portion. This is done so that the person who grades the grain will have the whole picture of the car in front of him. The amount of inferior grain must be estimated and noted on the front of the sample ticket and the location noted via a diagram on the reverse side.

Grain within an elevator is generally moved up into and from storage bins by belts. Outbound lots are dropped from the storage bins onto a belt and carried to the top of the headhouse. As a general rule, in subterminal and terminal elevators, several bins, each containing different grades of grain, are used simultaneously to give a blended product. Upon arrival at the top of the headhouse, the grain is moved onto a scale, then into a shipping bin (absent in country elevators), and finally, by gravity, through a spout into a boxcar, hopper car, barge, or ship. In shipping grain by grade, the elevator has to abide by certain regulations. Some of the most important are as follows:

a) All blending and mixing has to be completed before the grain reaches the sampler.

b) The elevator system must not contain any provisions for adding material to, or removing material from, the grain after it has passed the sampler.

c) The mixture has to be relatively uniform at all times.

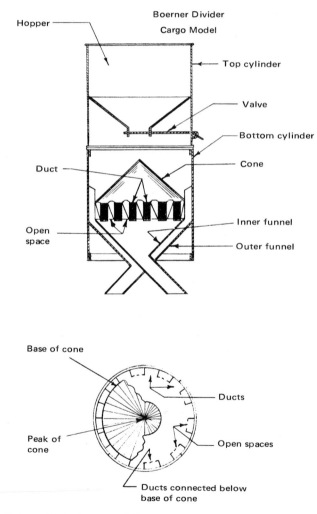

Figure 11. Boerner divider (cargo model).

B177198	APPEAL NO.	TO BOARD (Date)	STAT. SAMPLE	INSPECTION POINT CODE	FIELD OFFICE CODE
			01 ACG / 02 LI		

LOCATION | FIELD OFFICE | IDENTIFICATION

SEAL(S) BROKEN | MOVEMENT (Circle) | DESTINATION-ORIGIN (Cargo only)

| | 01 IN | 02 OUT | 03 LOCAL | 04 SUB |

SEAL(S) APPLIED | BUSHELS

| | 05 BOXCAR | 06 HOPPER CAR | 07 TRUCK | 08 EXPORT |

SAMPLED BY (Name or initials) | DATE(S) SAMPLED | AM / PM | TYPE SALE (Export only)

| | 09 LAKE AND INTER-COASTAL | 10 BARGE | 11 SEA VAN | 12 OTHER |

GRAIN (Circle)

| 01 WHEAT | 02 CORN | 03 BARLEY | 04 OATS | 05 RYE |
| 06 GRAIN SORGHUMS | 07 FLAX | 08 SOYBEANS | 09 MIXED AND NOT STANDARDIZED GRAIN | LIFT ROLL |

METHOD OF SAMPLING (Circle)

| MECH. | PELICAN | CUP | PROBE |

TYPE OF SAMPLE (Circle) | DEPTH PROBED

| 01 LI | 02 F | 03 F&LI |

REMARKS

FACTOR (Circle Factor Analyzed) If factor is not listed, write abbreviation on blank line at bottom.	INSPECTION RESULTS	SUPERVISION			
		GRAMS (PORTION / SEPARATION)	FIELD OFFICE RESULTS	GRADER(S) NAME OR INITIALS	BOARD RESULTS
01 CL					
02 DHY / 22 HVAC / 42 HARD					
03 DKG					
04 TW					
05 M					
06 ODOR					
07 HT / 27 HTF					
08 DKT / 28 DF					
09 FM / 29 HPFM					
10 SHBN / 30 MSFM / 50 THIN					
11 DEF / 31 BNFM / 51 BBB					
12 CCL / 32 BCFM / 52 SKBN					
13 WOCL / 33 MDKG / 53 SBLY					
14 OG / 34 HP / 54 BN					
15 FMOW / 35 CORN / 55 OCL					
16 SCO / 36 FINE					
17 WO / 37 SPL					

NAME OF INSPECTOR	LI CODE	GRADE U.S. NO.	CLASS AND SPECIAL GRADE	DATE INSPECTED
NAME OF SUPERVISOR	ACG CODE	GRADE U.S. NO.	CLASS AND SPECIAL GRADE	DATE SUPERVISED
BOARD OF APPEALS AND REVIEW (Name of Supervisor)	GRADE U.S. NO.	CLASS AND SPECIAL GRADE	DATE SUPERVISED

FORM GR-189 (4-1-69) | **GRAIN SAMPLE TICKET** | USDA-C&MS GRAIN DIVISION

B 177198

Figure 12. Sampling ticket, Form GR-189.

d) The person in charge of sampling should be able to see the carrier that is being loaded. If he cannot, a communication system has to be set up which will permit him to keep in touch with all aspects of the loading (identity of carrier, location in the carrier, etc.).

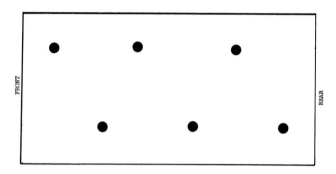

Figure 13. Sampling procedure for a truck.

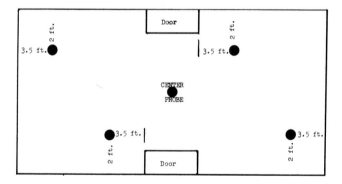

Figure 14. Sampling procedure for a boxcar (regular).

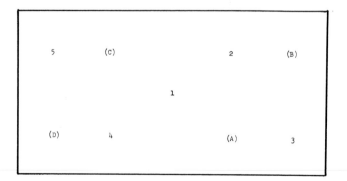

Figure 15. Sampling procedure for a boxcar (regular and reverse).

Diverter-type samplers are found in country elevators (those with a loading capacity of less than 10,000 bu. per hr.), subterminal elevators, and terminal elevators. They are used for sampling both in- and outbound grain. As a general rule, one can find them between the scale and the shipping bin on one of the top floors of the headhouse. The sample is collected either on the same floor as the sampler or on the floor below. These samplers can also be found above the scales in some country elevators.

The size of diverters used for grain, rice, and similar commodities can vary, but the width of the opening is constant: ¾-in. The frequency (sampling interval) with which the diverter cuts the stream of grain should be constant for that loading and such that there is at least one diverter cut for each 200 bu. of grain. These samplers, when operated at a standard speed and with a standard ¾-in. wide opening, should collect a standard quantity of grain per increment sample or diverter cut. Furthermore, this amount should be in proportion to the rate of flow of the grain past the diverter, approximately 175 and 150 g. per diverter cut per 1,000 bu. per hr. of flow rate for small grains and coarse grains (corn and soybeans), respectively.

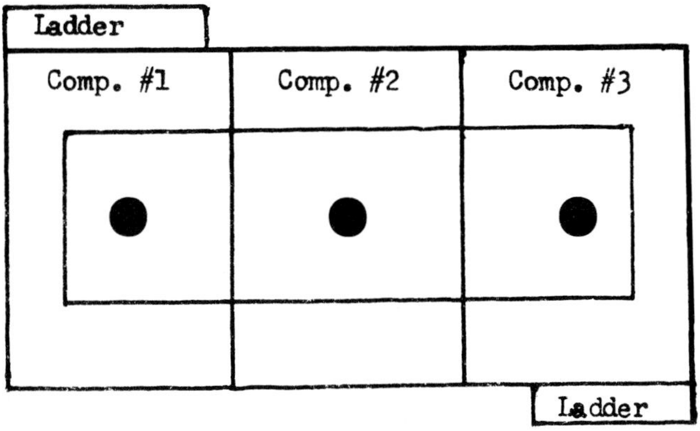

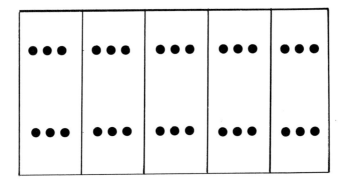

Figure 16. Sampling procedure for a hopper car.

Figure 17. Sampling procedure for a barge.

The final mechanical sample size will, of course, depend upon the setting used for the secondary sampler. This sample can then be divided with a Boerner divider (cargo model) to supply the required amount of grain for the grader, the applicant, the buyer, and the file.

The Woodside-type sampler is also found in country, subterminal, and terminal elevators, and is generally used only for outbound grain. The overall principles of sampling with this apparatus are similar to those for the diverter-type. However, a Boerner divider (cargo model), rather than a secondary sampler, is usually used to divide the sample further.

Regardless of the type of mechanical sampler used, the grain is inspected for condition (musty, sour, or heating) and for the presence of insects (Anon., 1963b, 1965c). This is done by taking at least one sample per 2,000 bu. off the belt with an Ellis cup; emptying the contents of the cup into a sieve; smelling the grain; and, finally, examining the material in the bottom pan.

The pelican sampler is used for sampling outbound grain, but it is rapidly being replaced by the diverter-type. In using the pelican, the individual should cut the stream of grain in the same way that a diverter-type does; that is, as one faces a slanted spout, the apparatus is swung from left to right completely through and perpendicular to the stream. The stream should never be cut from back to front or vice versa. Of course, there is no problem if the stream flow is vertical.

When the pelican is used for sampling grain moving into a hopper car or boxcar, the number of "cuts" to be taken must be sufficient to provide a representative sample of the grain. Each portion cut from the stream must be examined, with a sieve and bottom pan, to facilitate uniform quality in loading, before dumping its contents into the receptacle containing previous cuts. Upon completion of loading, the sample size is reduced to a working proportion with a Boerner divider (cargo model).

The same procedure is used in sampling grain going into a barge or ship, except that the number of "cuts" for the sample to be graded is usually limited to two per

TABLE I

Percentage of components of wheat, corn, and soybean samples drawn by a probe from hopper cars after loading and before unloading at Minneapolis, Denver, and Omaha

City and Sampling Frequency[a]	Components in						
	Wheat sample[b]			Corn sample[c]		Soybean sample[d]	
	Wheat	Corn	Screenings	Corn	Wheat	Soy-beans	Screenings
Minneapolis, out	88.48	4.94	6.58	94.81	5.19	90.18	9.82
Denver, in	87.40	5.48	7.12	95.36	4.64	91.05	8.59
Denver, out	91.03	3.96	5.01	94.37	5.63	97.07	2.93
Omaha, in	90.36	4.09	5.55	94.64	5.36	97.77	2.23
Omaha, out	90.75	4.12	5.13	94.00	6.00	95.36	4.64
Minneapolis, in	90.70	4.73	5.20	93.94	6.06	95.70	4.30

[a]Out = samples were drawn from loaded car before it was moved out of city named. In = samples were drawn before car was unloaded after arrival from another city.

[b]Components of lot: wheat, 90.27%; corn, 4.97%; screenings, 4.76%.

[c]Components of lot: corn, 95.01%; wheat, 4.99%.

[d]Components of lot: soybeans, 95.12%; screenings, 4.88%.

TABLE II

Average and range in percentage of foreign material in probe samples from 11 locations in each of ten boxcars from different elevators in different states

Car	Average %	Range %
1	2.56	1.67– 3.18
2	2.27	0.43– 4.22
3	4.15	2.40– 8.50
4	2.57	1.09– 3.93
5	2.10	1.50– 2.45
6	2.75	1.54– 3.73
7	3.73	1.45–11.52
8	1.80	1.15– 2.64
9	4.02	2.66– 6.28
10	3.82	1.31– 7.81

draft—one shortly after it starts, and one near the end. Each of these cuts is immediately preceded by a quality and uniformity check, especially for the presence of odor and insects.

Unless a "condition" situation prevails, there is one sample for a boxcar, hopper car, or barge. In the case of a ship or lake boat there will be one sample for each sublot and a composite of all sublots. Regardless of the type of apparatus used for obtaining the sample, the amount of grain required for grading purposes is about 2,500 g. This, along with the sample ticket, is placed in a sample bag immediately after being taken and transported as quickly as possible to the laboratory for grading. If considerable time is to elapse between its drawing and grading, the sample should be transferred from the sample bag to a moistureproof container.

C. Problems and Solutions

Factors that determine grade in grain (dockage, foreign material, damage, and the like) are seldom evenly distributed. Herein lies the basis for the main problems associated with sampling. This is borne out by the following statement taken from an article by Watson (1969): "Grain cycled between bins several times and tested for homogeneity (degree of mixedness) between cycles shows that, beyond a certain point of mixing, homogeneity of the grain does not increase. In our case, no increase in homogeneity occurred after three cycles of mixing. The data indicate that grain is probably never a homogeneous mixture and this contributes, significantly, to the problem of accurately sampling a grain lot."

The nonhomogeneous nature of grain is shown in Table I (Kramer, 1968a). Another good example is presented in Table II (unpublished Grain Division data) for the factor "broken corn and foreign material" (BCFM) in corn. Each range percentage is the average of 12 samples for a probe location (11 of them) in a boxcar. Each sample was taken with a 5-ft. probe in a different city (market) by a different individual. Unfortunately, the values that went into the average for each probe location are not available for showing this type of variation. The sampling pattern, and the average results for each probe location and probe combinations over all 50 cars, are shown in Figures 18 and 19, respectively. The maximum BCFM

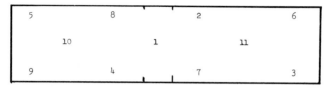

Figure 18. Sampling procedure for a "BCFM" experiment in corn.

values permitted in corn for U.S. grade Nos. 1,2,3,4, and 5 are 2.0, 3.0, 4.0, 5.0, and 7.0%, respectively. If the value exceeds 7.0%, the lot becomes U.S. Sample Grade. An analysis of the raw data indicated a variation in a) uniformity of loading, b) sampling procedure, and c) trimming procedure.

Grain in all "out-cars" or shipments must be correctly trimmed or leveled before official samples can be withdrawn. Incorrectly trimmed cars are the direct result of failure to pull down the grain humps that normally build up, one in each end of the car, during loading. It is essential that these humps be dropped so that the grain depth in any part of the car does not vary by more than 24 in.

Related to homogeneity is the fact that sampling of hopper cars with probes at different depths before and after transport showed no significant relocation (sifting of screenings to the bottom) of components in the car during transport (Kramer, 1968a). This is probably also true for grain transported in many other types of conveyances.

Accompanying grain homogeneity is the problem of performance and accuracy of various type samplers. This is discussed by Kramer (1968a, 1968b, 1968c), Watson (1969), and Watson et al. (1970).

Several diverter-type samplers were evaluated under conditions similar to those found in country elevators. Flow rates in such installations do not exceed 5,000 lb. per min., whereas terminal elevators have rates up to 40,000 lb. per min. Variables, in addition to type of grain, included spout angle (30 and 90 degrees), flow rate (2,000 and 4,000 lb. per min.), slot-width (0.50 and 0.75 in.), speed (100 and 200 ft. per min.), and grain velocity as a result of "free fall" (samplers located just below, 50 ft. below, and 80 ft. below the hopper bin). The factors tested were percent a) screenings in wheat, b) broken corn in whole-kernel corn, c) corn and screenings in soybeans, or d) corn and screenings in wheat.

Performance was not affected by spout angle or grain flow rate. However, regardless of the type of diverter, the ratio of sample weight to grain flow rate was significantly larger for the lower flow rate because the diverter could not take all of the grain subjected to it. Diverter slot widths and speeds also had, in general, no

2.99		2.86		2.82		2.80
	3.54		2.01		3.39	
2.87		2.95		2.88		2.89

Figure 19. Average percentages of "BCFM" by probe for 50 carlots of corn.

significant effect on sampling accuracy or variability. High grain velocity as a result of "free fall" did cause an overestimation of the amount of broken corn in corn owing to breakage occurring as the kernels hit the diverter, but had no effect on damage in "tough" wheat.

The diverter-type samplers were found to be generally more accurate than the belt-type mechanical (Woodside), belt-type manual (Ellis cup), pelican, and probe-type samplers, especially the latter. This was attributed to the fact that the diverters removed nearly a complete cross-section of the grain stream during each traverse of the stream. However, it may also be, in part, that more increments per unit volume were taken.

The belt-type mechanical manual samplers were found to have about the same accuracy and variability as the diverter-type, except when sampling screenings in soybeans. In the latter case there was a sifting of the screenings to the bottom of the belt and subsequent failure of the sampling cups to pick them up. Kramer (1968c) feels that these types of samplers sample only a part of the grain stream, and therefore may be biased by stratification of components of the grain stream flowing past the sampler.

Research work with mechanical- and gravity-type secondary sample dividers was reported by Watson et al. (1970).

The Boerner divider (cargo model), a gravity-type device, performed well in these tests. Since the composite primary samples are nearly always larger than desired for analysis, mechanical secondary dividers are used to reduce the size of the sample. This smaller sample, however, is usually less representative of the lot than the entire sample. It is believed that a mixer between the two types of samplers could bring about an improvement in this situation.

The pelican sampler was found to have about the same degree of accuracy and variability as the diverter-type, but there were indications that at high grain flow rates it began to overflow before traversing the entire grain stream. This could cause a bias in the sample if the components of the grain stream were stratified. The latter is generally the case for foreign material and can easily be seen by examining handfuls of grain at various locations at the end of a spout.

Studies with various types of probes (especially the 12-ft.) showed them to be unsatisfactory for estimating screenings in the case of soybeans, and to cause overestimates of screenings in the case of wheat. However, the estimate of screenings in corn was found to be good. These results, of course, could be interpolated to include the 6-ft. instrument. The results also showed that probe sampling of hopper cars is not as accurate a method of sampling foreign material as mechanical diverter-type sampling because, unless the grain is uniformly mixed, it is almost impossible to obtain a representative sample. There is a tendency for the foreign material to concentrate in the center of each hopper owing to stratification as the grain leaves the shipping bin and emerges from the spout used to fill the cars. The same thing occurs in loading boxcars with a boxcar-type spout.

The sampling situation today is such that a given lot of grain can be sampled numerous times, starting when it is first loaded and ending with the time it reaches its final destination, each time by a different person with a different type of sampler. These variations can lead to differences in grade, and, therefore, variation in the price of that grain. The solution would be to always use the same type of sampler and sampling procedure. According to Watson (1969), research to date suggests that wherever feasible only mechanical samplers should be used to sample grain. Perhaps this should be further restricted to the diverter-type. A diverter-type (or similar) apparatus, rather than the pelican, is needed for standardizing these machines, to keep the variation between such samplers as low as possible.

III. GRADING

All lots of grain that are offered for sale by grade must be sampled, inspected, and graded either at point of origin, en route, or at destination by an individual who is licensed by the Grain Division, Agricultural Marketing Service, U.S. Department of Agriculture. This individual is usually a member of a Grain Inspection Agency. There are about 120 of these Agencies in the U.S., and about 20% of them are state operated. The remainder are operated by trade groups or as individually owned businesses. Grain Division Directory D-3 is published annually

TABLE III

An example of discounts by grading factor for yellow soybeans, in cents

Moisture		Damage		Splits		Test Weight	
%	Cents per bu.	%	Cents per bu.	%	Cents per bu.	lb.	Cents per bu.
13.1–13.5	2½	2.1– 3.0	1	20 or less	0	54 or less	...
13.6–14.0	5	3.1– 4.0	2	20–21	½	53.9–53.0	½
14.1–14.5	7½	4.1– 5.0	3	21–22	1	52.9–52.0	1
14.6–15.0	10	5.1– 6.0	5	22–23	1½	51.9–51.0	1½
15.1–15.5	12½	6.1– 7.0	7	23–24	2	50.9–50.0	2
15.6–16.0	15	7.1– 8.0	9	24–25	2½	49.9–49.0	2½
16.1–16.5	17½	8.1– 9.0	12	...[b]			
17.1–17.5	22½	10.1–11.0	18				
17.6–18.0	25	11.1–12.0	21				
...[a]							

[a]Over 18%, 3 cents for each 0.5% or fraction additional.

[b]Continues to 30% at ½ cent for each 1%; over 30%, 1 cent for each 1%.

Foreign material:	All foreign material in excess of 1% shall be deducted from the gross weight and will not be paid for.
	An additional discount of 1 cent per bu. will be made for each 1% or fraction thereof over 2.0%.
Other colors:	Excess 2% by agreement.
Mottled:	5 cents per bu.
Materially weathered:	3 cents per bu.
Sour:	10 cents per bu.
Musty:	5 cents per bu.
Weevily:	2 cents per bu.
Heating:	5 cents per bu.
Heat-damaged:	In addition to above damage discounts: 1 cent each 0.5% HD over 0.5% HD, up to 5.0% HD.

by the Grain Division, Grain Inspection Branch, Agricultural Marketing Service, U.S. Department of Agriculture, Hyattsville, Md. It shows the places in the U.S. where grain-inspection services are regularly provided, and the kinds of grain that can be inspected. The list also gives the places where grain-inspection services are provided on request of interested parties, but where no licensed inspector is regularly located. Inspection services at such places are usually limited to sampling activities.

To receive a sampler's license, the individual must be deemed competent by an Administrator of a Grain Division Field Office. To receive an inspector's license, the individual must have had experience as a sampler and must pass a written and practical examination given by a Grain Division Field Office Administrator. He can be licensed to inspect only those grains passed in the test.

Grain Division Directory D-2, also published annually by the Grain Division, Grain Inspection Branch, Agricultural Marketing Service, U.S. Department of Agriculture, Hyattsville, Md., gives the names of every person licensed to inspect grain, his inspection point (city and state), and the grains authorized to grade.

The sampler's and inspector's work is supervised by Agricultural Commodity Graders (ACG's) of the Grain Division. This is done in several ways: over-the-shoulder inspection, use of their file sample for grading, or obtaining a new sample and grading it. Where a sample is graded (which is usually the case), a U.S. Government Form, GR-189, becomes the official document and contains the results of both individuals. The Program Analysis Group, Grain Division, Agricultural Marketing Service, U.S. Department of Agriculture, Hyattsville, Md., receives and processes these forms. The data are summarized on a monthly and cumulative basis for each licensed inspector and ACG by grade of grain sustained, raised, or lowered, and by grading factor sustained, raised, or lowered. The results are used by Field Office personnel in their supervisory work.

TABLE IV

U.S. Department of Agriculture official standards for soybeans

Grade	Minimum Test Weight per Bushel lb.	Maximum Limits of:					
		Moisture %	Splits %	Damaged kernels		Foreign material %	Brown, black, or bicolored soybeans in yellow or green soybeans %
				Total %	Heat-damaged %		
U.S. No. 1	56	13.0	10	2.0	0.2	1.0	1.0
U.S. No. 2	54	14.0	20	3.0	0.5	2.0	2.0
U.S. No. 3[a]	52	16.0	30	5.0	1.0	3.0	5.0
U.S. No. 4[b]	49	18.0	40	8.0	3.0	5.0	10.0
U.S. Sample Grade	U.S. Sample Grade shall be soybeans which do not meet the requirements for any of the grades from No. 1 to No. 4, inclusive; or which are musty, sour, or heating; or which have any commercial objectionable foreign odor; or which contain stones; or which are otherwise of distinctly low quality.						

[a]Soybeans which are purple mottled or stained shall be graded not higher than No. 3.

[b]Soybeans which are materially weathered shall be graded not higher than No. 4.

After a lot has been sampled and graded, the Agency issues a grade certificate to the seller. This certificate is usually attached to the invoice and to other documents. The seller, in turn, sends them to the buyer. The certificate conveys direct evidence of the official grade of the grain delivered. This practice is a protection to both the buyer and seller and tends to prevent controversy. The Inspection Agency charges a nominal fee for this service.

If the seller or buyer is not satisfied with the grade designated by the licensed inspector, he can appeal the finding to the nearest Federal Grain Division office. A new sample will be taken, graded, and a U.S. Department of Agriculture certificate issued. If the appellant is still not satisfied with the result, he can take his case to the Board of Appeals and Review, Grain Division, Agricultural Marketing Service, U.S. Department of Agriculture, Beltsville, Md. The decision of the Board would be based on a study of a new sample drawn by the Field Office, or on the file and the work sample obtained from the appropriate Federal Field Office. If, as a result of any appeal, there is a change in the grade, the appellant is not charged a fee for the service. However, if the inspector's grade is sustained, a fee is levied as provided by Title 7, Chapter 1, Part 26 of the Federal Register dated June 18, 1970.

In actually grading a lot of grain, a quantitative value for each of various specific factors (such as moisture, test weight, heat damage) is ascertained and, based on these and other criteria, a grade is designated, for example, U.S. No. 1 Soft Red

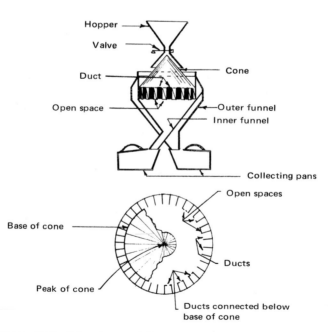

Figure 20. Boerner divider (laboratory model).

Winter Wheat (Anon., 1965b, 1970, 1971). Accuracy in sampling and grading becomes necessary not only because of a price differential between designated grades, but also because, in addition to this differential, there are price discounts by grade factors. A typical example of discounts (not necessarily for all buyers nor prevailing at the present time) for yellow soybeans is shown in Table III. The U.S. grades and grade requirements for soybeans are given in Table IV.

A. Equipment

Equipment used in grading grain, and normally found in both Agency and Federal laboratories, would include most of the following apparatus.

BOERNER DIVIDER (LABORATORY MODEL)

The Boerner divider is a device (Figure 20) used to reduce the size of a sample of grain while maintaining the representativeness of the original sample. This is the original Boerner divider and has been described by Boerner (1915).

MOTOMCO MOISTURE METER

The Motomco moisture meter (Figure 21) is prescribed by the U.S. Department of Agriculture for determining the moisture content of any grain for which standards have been established. The meter measures the electrical resistance of the grain. This value is then converted to percent moisture through use of moisture conversion charts (Figure 22). Pertinent literature dealing with the measurement of moisture in grain has been provided by Hunt and Neustadt (1966), Zeleny and Hunt (1962), Hunt (1965, 1969, 1970), and the U. S. Department of Agriculture (Anon., 1957, 1968).

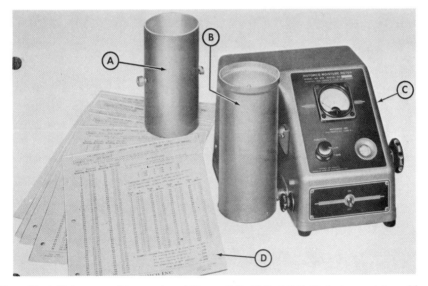

Figure 21. A Motomco moisture meter, A)Dump Cell, B) Test Cell, C) Instrument Assembly, D) Calibration Charts.

TEST WEIGHT PER BUSHEL APPARATUS

The official apparatus (Figure 23) is the one described by the U.S. Department of Agriculture (Anon., 1953). Test weight per bushel is the weight of the volume of grain required to fill, level full, a Winchester bushel measure of 2,150.42 cu. in.

MOTOMCO MOISTURE METER CONVERSION CHART

| Sample Size 250 Grams | CALIBRATE AT 33 | CORN - HIGH MOISTURE |

Meter Reading	Percent Moisture	Meter Reading	Percent Moisture
1		51	
2		52	
3		53	
4		54	
5		55	
6		56	
7		57	
8		58	
9		59	
10		60	20.94
11		61	21.17
12		62	21.40
13		63	21.62
14		64	21.85
15		65	22.08
16		66	22.31
17		67	22.54
18		68	22.77
19		69	22.99
20		70	23.22
21		71	23.45
22		72	23.68
23		73	23.91
24		74	24.14
25		75	24.36
26		76	24.59
27		77	24.82
28		78	25.05
29		79	25.28
30		80	25.51
31		81	25.74
32		82	25.96
33		83	26.19
34		84	26.42
35		85	26.65
36		86	26.88
37		87	27.10
38		88	27.33
39		89	27.56
40		90	27.79
41		91	28.02
42		92	28.25
43		93	28.47
44		94	28.70
45		95	28.93
46		96	29.15
47		97	
48		98	
49		99	
50		100	

INSTRUCTIONS

1. To obtain percent moisture to tenths of a dial division, see values below and add to percent moisture.

FRACTIONAL METER READING VALUES

.1	.02%	.4	.09%	.7	.16%
.2	.04%	.5	.11%	.8	.18%
.3	.07%	.6	.14%	.9	.20%

2. TEMPERATURE CORRECTION (Add or Subtract to % Moisture)
(a) If sample temperature is below 77°F., add correction.
(b) If sample temperature is above 77°F., subtract correction.

Temp. °F	% Moist.	Temp. °F	% Moist.	Temp. °F	% Moist.	Temp. °F	% Moist.
2	+ 3.55	28	+ 2.32	54	+ 1.09	80	− .14
3	+ 3.51	29	+ 2.27	55	+ 1.04	81	− .19
4	+ 3.46	30	+ 2.23	56	+ .99	82	− .24
5	+ 3.41	31	+ 2.18	57	+ .95	83	− .28
6	+ 3.36	32	+ 2.13	58	+ .90	84	− .33
7	+ 3.32	33	+ 2.08	59	+ .85	85	− .38
8	+ 3.27	34	+ 2.04	60	+ .81	86	− .43
9	+ 3.22	35	+ 1.99	61	+ .76	87	− .47
10	+ 3.17	36	+ 1.94	62	+ .71	88	− .52
11	+ 3.13	37	+ 1.90	63	+ .66	89	− .57
12	+ 3.08	38	+ 1.85	64	+ .62	90	− .62
13	+ 3.03	39	+ 1.80	65	+ .57	91	− .66
14	+ 2.98	40	+ 1.75	66	+ .52	92	− .71
15	+ 2.94	41	+ 1.71	67	+ .47	93	− .76
16	+ 2.89	42	+ 1.66	68	+ .43	94	− .81
17	+ 2.84	43	+ 1.61	69	+ .38	95	− .85
18	+ 2.80	44	+ 1.56	70	+ .33	96	− .90
19	+ 2.75	45	+ 1.52	71	+ .28	97	− .95
20	+ 2.70	46	+ 1.47	72	+ .24	98	− .99
21	+ 2.65	47	+ 1.42	73	+ .19	99	−1.04
22	+ 2.61	48	+ 1.37	74	+ .14	100	−1.09
23	+ 2.56	49	1.33	75	+ .09	101	−1.14
24	+ 2.51	50	+ 1.28	76	+ .05	102	−1.18
25	+ 2.46	51	1.23	77	---	103	−1.23
26	+ 2.42	52	+ 1.18	78	− .05	104	−1.28
27	+ 2.37	53	+ 1.14	79	− .09	105	1.33

EXAMPLE:
(Assume dial reading of 66.7 and temperature of 82°F.)
For dial reading of 66.0 moisture is 22.31%
Fractional meter value for .7 is 16%

Thus dial reading of 66.7 is 22.47%
For temperature of 82°F, subtract 24%
Final moisture is 22.23%

USDA C&MS
GRAIN DIVISION

Chart No. C-2-C
EFFECTIVE September 27, 1968

Figure 22. A Motomco moisture meter conversion chart for corn.

capacity. It is a quality determination and is not the same as legal weight per bushel. The latter is the number of pounds of grain required for a bushel without regard to volume and is the basis on which grain is bought and sold. For customs purposes, the legal weight per bushel has been fixed by federal law in the U.S. at 60 lb. per bu. for wheat and soybeans; 56 lb. for corn, rye, and flaxseed; 48 lb. for barley; and 32 lb. for oats. Test weight per bushel tends to increase as moisture content decreases, so the test should be taken as quickly as possible after the grain has been delivered to the laboratory.

SCALES

Toledo Scale. This device (Figure 24) is used for weighing all portions of grain in excess of 50 g.

Figure 23. The test weight per bushel apparatus.

Torsion Balance. This type of scale (Figure 25) is used for weighing all small portions of a sample.

CARTER DOCKAGE TESTER
The Carter dockage tester (Figures 26 and 27) is used for removing dockage material from wheat, rye, barley, grain sorghum, and flaxseed, and for the removal of cracked kernels and foreign material from corn and grain sorghum. It comes equipped with specially constructed sieves or riddles.

BARLEY PEARLER
This pearler (Figure 28) removes the outer hull and bran layers from the kernels, thereby permitting the inspector to determine whether a) the grade is Malting under the subclass Barley, b) the grade is Choice Malting Two-rowed Western or Malting Two-rowed Western Barley, and c) the lot contains heat-damaged kernels (Anon., 1965a).

SIEVES
Corn Sieve. The corn sieve (Figure 29) is perforated with round holes 12/64 in.

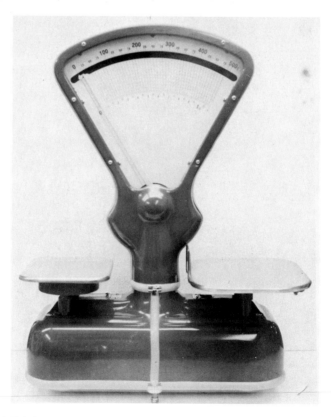

Figure 24. A Toledo scale.

in diameter and is used for removing a) cracked corn and foreign material from corn, and b) coarse foreign matter from wheat and rye in the dockage determination of these grains when a Carter dockage machine is not available.

Soybean Foreign-Material Sieve. This sieve is perforated with round holes 8/64 in. in diameter and is used in the foreign-material determination in soybeans.

Soybean Split Sieve. This sieve has 3/4 × 10/64-in. perforations and is used to facilitate the determination of splits in soybeans (the determination of splits in soybeans is not considered a sieving operation).

Fine-Seed Sieve. The fine-seed sieve (Figure 29) is perforated with round holes 1/12 in. in diameter and is used for removing fine seeds (such as mustard) in dockage determinations in wheat and rye.

Grain Sorghums Dockage Sieve. This sieve is perforated with round holes 2-1/2/64-in. in diameter and is used in making dockage determinations in grain sorghums.

Small Buckwheat Sieve. The small buckwheat sieve (Figure 29) has equilateral triangular perforations, the inscribed circles of which are 5/64 in. in diameter. This sieve is used a) for removing such seeds as wild buckwheat, pigeongrass, and seed of similar size in dockage determinations in wheat and rye; b) as part of the equipment for determining dockage in barley; and c) for removing "fine seeds" in connection with the sizing test for thin oats.

Small Chess Sieve. The small chess sieve (Figure 29) has 0.064 × 3/8-in. perforations and is used for: a) removing large-seeded flaxseed from wheat, b) determining the factor "thin oats" in the grading of oats, and c) determining "shrunken and/or broken kernels" in wheat and "thin or undersized kernels" in rye.

Large Chess Sieve. The large chess sieve (Figure 29) has 4-1/2/64 × 1/2-in. perforations and is used for removing chess seeds, quackgrass, and similarly shaped seeds from wheat.

Figure 25. A Torsion balance.

Figure 26. The Carter dockage tester, whole view.

Barley-Sizing Sieve. One sieve model has 5/64 × 3/4-in. perforations and is used for removing thin barley in grading "Eastern" barley (class Barley).

Another barley sizing sieve has 5-1/2/64 × 3/4-in. perforations and is used for removing thin barley in grading "Western" barley (class Western Barley).

Flaxseed Dockage Sieve. This sieve is perforated with round holes 4-1/2/64-in. in diameter and is used to facilitate the removal of small seeds from flaxseed in the determination of dockage in flaxseed.

Flaxseed Sieve. This sieve has 3/64 × 3/8-in perforations and is useful for separating cereal grains and other coarse material from flaxseed. It can also be used for removing flaxseed from wheat when determining dockage in wheat.

MISCELLANEOUS EQUIPMENT

Bottom Pan. To accompany the above-mentioned sieves.

Thermometers. These thermometers are mercury filled, with a range from $-10°$ to $110°$F. in $1°$ divisions. They are used for determining the temperature of the grain in the moisture evaluation.

Grain Cans. Plastic containers having a volume of 1-1/8 pints are used in the moisture determination.

Rubber Stoppers. Number 10 stoppers with a 3/16-in. hole size are used for the above-mentioned cans and thermometers.

Triangular Grain Pans. Used to hold work samples.

Buff-Colored Mat. Grain grading is carried out on this type of surface.

Lighting Booth. This fixture is centered above the grading table and consists of Glasser Lamps and Corning #70 or equal diffusion glass.

Black Light. A fluorescent lamp is used to trace additives and to look for objectionable foreign matter.

The master Motomco moisture meter, Carter dockage tester, barley pearler, small chess sieve, and barley-sizing sieves are located in the Equipment Section of The Board of Appeals and Review (Grain), Grain Division, Agricultural Marketing Service, U.S. Department of Agriculture, Beltsville, Md. These are used in standardizing their standard units. Barley, of course, is the test grain for the barley devices and Hard Red Winter Wheat for all of the others.

The standard machines are used in making up standard samples whose values are known only to Board personnel. A set of these samples is then sent, periodically, to each Federal Field Office for use in "checktesting" their equipment. Their results are sent back to the Board and, if these are found to be within tolerated limits, permission is given for continued use of the apparatus. The Field Office will then use their equipment as a base for "checktesting" equipment in the various non-Federal laboratories.

The Board has established tolerances for both the cargo and laboratory models of the Boerner divider and for the Toledo scale. The dividers are checked periodically by Field Office personnel with clean wheat. Each office also has a set of standard weights for "checktesting" its Toledo scale.

All equipment used in the sampling and grading of grain is continuously being scrutinized for possible improvement by the Equipment Section of the

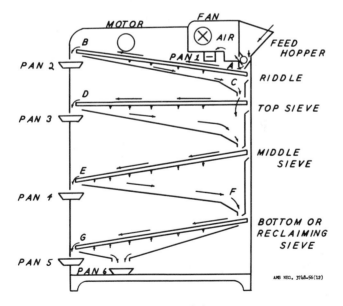

Figure 27. The Carter dockage tester, cross-sectional view.

Figure 28. The barley pearler.

Standardization Branch, Grain Division, Agricultural Marketing Service, U.S. Department of Agriculture, Beltsville, Md. This section is also constantly studying the possibility of using other devices to take as much of the human error as possible out of the grading process. An example of this would be an apparatus to detect commercially objectionable odors in grain.

B. Methods

Most of the factors and other criteria used in grading grain, and the amounts of grain required for each determination, are given in Table V (Anon., 1957). An example of grades and grade requirements for soybeans is presented in Table IV. The numerical grade is ascertained by the lowest grading factor as determined in the

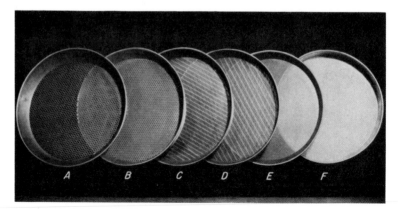

Figure 29. Some of the sieves used to supplement the dockage tester in determining dockage and for removing certain kinds of foreign material from grain.

TABLE V

Minimum quantity of grain in analytical portions recommended for inspection work
(quantities in g. unless otherwise stated)

Determination for	Wheat	Corn	Oats	Rye	Barley	Grain Sorghums	Flaxseed	Soybeans
Blight	...	...	...	...	30	...	...	...
Class	25	250	25	...	30	25	...	125
Color and texture	25	...	...	...	...	...	...	...
Cracked corn and foreign material[a]	1-1/8[b]	1-1/8[b]	...	1-1/8[b]	...	1-1/8[b,c]	1-1/8[b,e]	...
Dockage[d]	250	...	...	250	1-1/8[b]	1-1/8[b]	...	...
Ergot	50	...	250	50	250	...	...	125
Foreign material	1,000	...	30	...	30	...	...	1,000
Garlic	50	...	500	30	500	...	20	125
Heat damage	1,000	250	30	30	50[f]	30	25	125
Kind of grain	...	250	30	...	30	30	...	...
Mellow	...	...	...	...	50[f]	...	...	...
Moisture[i]	230	250	200	250	225	250	270	250
Nongrain sorghums	...	...	...	...	...	30	...	...
Shrunken or broken kernels								
All classes (except durum and red durum)	250	...	...	...	...	...	...	...
Durum and red durum	50[g]	...	...	...	...	...	...	...
Sizing	...	...	1-1/8[b]	...[h]	...[h]	...	...	...
Skinned and broken	...	...	...	...	30	...	...	...
Smut	250	...	500	250	500	250	...	...
Smut dockage	500	...	500	250	...	...	...	...
Sound	...	...	30	...	30	...	...	...
Splits	...	...	...	...	...	...	...	125
Stones and cinders	1-1/8[b]	1-1/8[b]	1-1/8[b]	1-1/8[b]	1-1/8[b]	1-1/8[b]	20	1-1/8[b]
Total damaged	50	250	30	30	30	30	...	125
Two-rowed	...	...	...	...	30	...	...	...
Weevil	1-1/8[b]	1-1/8[b]	1-1/8[b]	1-1/8[b]	1-1/8[b]	1-1/8[b]	...	1-1/8[b]
Wild bromegrass	...	...	1-1/8[b]	...	1-1/8[b]	...	...	...
Wild oats	...	...	...	...	30	...	...	...

[a] Refers to "total cracked kernels, foreign material, and other grains" for grain sorghums. [b] Quarts.
[c] 30 g. of sieve-cleaned grain is also hand-picked for additional foreign material and other grains.
[d] A sufficient quantity is used for every grain to provide at least 1-1/8 qt. of grain for the weight-per-bushel test.
[e] At least 15 g. of sieve-cleaned grain is also hand-picked for additional dockage material. [f] Weight before pearling.
[g] In Durum Wheat and Red Durum Wheat the sieving operation is supplemented by hand picking of the broken kernels that do not pass through the sieve. [h] One-fourth of dockage-free sample. [i] Exact weights.

TABLE VI

Special grade designations in the standards for the various grains

Special Grade Designation	Grain and Basis of Determination[a]									
	Wheat	Corn	Barley	Oats	Feed oats and mixed feed oats	Rye	Grain sorghums	Flaxseed	Soybeans	Mixed grain
Appearance										
Bleached	...	...	D	W	W	...	...	...	...	...
Bright	...	...	D[b]	W	...	...	W	...	...	...
Discolored	...	...	...	...	...	...	W	...	...	...
Stained	...	...	D[b]	...	...	...	...	...	...	...
Treated	D	...	...	...	...	...	...	...	...	W
Garlic bulblets										
Light garlicky	W	...	...	...	...	W	...	...	...	...
Garlicky	W	...	W	W	...	W	...	...	W	W
Smut										
Light smutty	D[c]	...	D	...	...	D[c]	D	...	...	...
Smutty	D[c]	...	D	W	W	D[c]	...	...	...	W
Smut dockage (optional method)	D	...	...	...	...	...	...	...	...	...
Test weight										
Extra heavy	...	...	...	W	...	...	...	...	...	...
Heavy	...	...	...	W	...	...	...	...	...	...
Medium heavy	...	...	...	W	...	...	...	...	...	...
Test weight of Western Barley	...	...	D[b]	...	...	...	...	...	...	...
Other factors										
Blighted	...	...	D	...	...	...	...	...	...	W
Choice Malting Two-rowed Western Barley	...	...	D[b]	...	...	...	...	...	...	...
Ergoty	D	...	D	W	W	D	...	...	...	W
Flint and dent	...	F	...	...	...	...	...	...	...	...
Flint	...	F	...	...	...	...	...	...	...	W
Malting Two-rowed Western Barley	...	...	D[b]	...	...	...	...	...	...	...
Plump	...	...	...	...	D	...	...	...	...	...
Special Red	...	...	...	W	...	...	...	...	...	...
Thin	...	...	...	W	W	...	...	...	...	...
Tough	D	...	D	W	W	D	...	...	...	W
Two-rowed	...	...	D	...	...	...	...	...	...	...
Weevily	W	W	D	W	W	W	W	...	W	W
Dockage system applied[d]	W	...	W	...	...	...	...	...	...	...

[a] W = the special grade is determined upon the grain as a whole. D = the special grade is determined upon the basis of the grain when free from dockage. F = special grade is determined upon the basis of the grain after the removal of the cracked corn and foreign material.
[b] The special grade in barley applies to Western Barley only.
[c] The odor of smut is determined upon the grain as a whole.
[d] Not considered a special grade although part of the grade designation.

TABLE VII

Minimum and maximum moisture limits for tough grain

Grain	Moisture Content of Tough Grain	
	In excess of %	Not to exceed %
Wheat	13.5	...
Barley		
Barley	14.5	16.0
Western Barley	13.5	15.0
Oats, feed oats, and mixed feed oats	14.0	16.0
Rye	14.0	16.0
Mixed grain	14.0	16.0

analysis. The lowest grade designation is Sample Grade. Special grade designations in the Standards for the various grains appear in Table VI, and the minimum and maximum levels for tough grain are shown in Table VII. A detailed discussion of the relationship between each grading factor and commercial grain use can be found in the Grain Grading Primer (Anon., 1957).

The grading process actually commences when the sample is drawn. At this time, the sampler identifies the lot and determines whether it is uniform, i.e., that portions do not vary widely in kind, quality, or condition, and that layers or pockets of screenings or other materials are nonexistent. This inspection is on a continuing basis during the loading of a ship or barge and any deviations are brought to the inspector's attention immediately. In the case of a loaded boxcar, hopper car, or barge, any lack of uniformity is noted on the sampling ticket (a Form GR-189 in the case of a Federal sampler) and the conveyance sampled accordingly. Once obtained, the sample is transported to the laboratory as quickly as possible.

Upon arrival at the laboratory, the sample, which ranges in weight from about 2,500 g. for corn and soybeans to approximately 1,500 g. for oats, is cut down into a file sample and a work sample. The former is placed in a moistureproof container and the latter in an open pan. The work sample is used for determination of most of the grading factors. Regardless of the factor involved, the Boerner divider (laboratory model) must always be used to provide the fractional part of the sample needed for the determination. All percentages, except moisture, are based on weight. In the event that the grade of a lot is determined by a narrow margin on only one factor, another determination is made on an additional portion of the work sample, and the grade is based on the average of the two determinations. This, of course, implies that no two portions of the same sample are exactly alike.

One of the first things the grader must do with the sample is make sure he is dealing with the grain in question or with a mixed grain; that is, he must check for *purity of type.* For example, corn can be any grain which consists of 50% or more of the whole kernels of shelled dent corn, or shelled flint corn (*Zea mays*), or both, and may contain not more than 10.0% of other grains for which standards have

TABLE VIII

Classes and subclasses of grain

Grain and Class	Subclass
Wheat	
Hard Red Spring Wheat	Dark Northern Spring
	Northern Spring
	Red Spring
Durum Wheat	Hard Amber Durum
	Durum
Red Durum Wheat	
Hard Red Winter Wheat	Dark Hard Winter
	Hard Winter
	Yellow Hard Winter
Soft Red Winter Wheat	
White Wheat	Hard White
	Soft White
	White Club
	Western White
Mixed Wheat	
Corn	
Yellow Corn	
White Corn	
Mixed Corn	
Barley	
Barley	Malting
	Blue Malting
	Barley
Western Barley	
Mixed Barley	
Oats	
White Oats	
Red Oats	
Gray Oats	
Black Oats	
Mixed Oats	
Rye	
Grain Sorghum	
Yellow Grain Sorghum	
White Grain Sorghum	
Brown Grain Sorghum	
Mixed Grain Sorghum	
Flaxseed	
Soybeans	
Yellow Soybeans	
Green Soybeans	
Brown Soybeans	
Black Soybeans	
Mixed Soybeans	
Mixed Grain	

been established under the U.S. Grain Standards Act. If it contains 10.1% of other grains, it is not corn, but mixed grain.

A subsequent step in testing for purity of type, when required by the Standards, is to determine the class and then the subclass of the grain. These are shown in Table VIII.

In the case of wheat, a class is a group of varieties of a specific species. The Official Grain Standards of the U.S. describe seven "classes" of wheat — hard red spring, durum, red durum, hard red winter, soft red winter, white, and mixed wheat — and each of four of these classes is divided, for grading purposes, into several subclasses. The seven classes are also grouped into four "contrasting classes". The percentage of other classes, subclasses, or contrasting classes of wheat permitted in a given grade of a given class or subclass is specified in the grading rules.

The subclass division is based on texture (hardness or softness of the kernels) or on variety characteristics, depending upon the class with which one is working. Certain classes of wheat can be mixed, but only to a certain extent, to qualify for a specific grade. In other words, contrasting classes is a grading factor. Another grading factor in wheat related to class is the total percentage of wheat of other classes, regardless of class, in a given class. The higher the percentage, except for mixed wheat, the lower the grade.

The three classes of corn and the five classes of grain sorghums, soybeans, and oats are based on color only.

The three classes of barley (Barley, Western Barley, and Mixed Barley) are based on color of hull (white or black) and area of production. Barley is divided into three subclasses (Malting Barley, Blue Malting Barley, and Barley), depending on such factors as species, color of the aleurone layer, percent damaged kernels, foreign material, skinned and broken kernels, thin barley, black barley, and presence of other grains. The barley pearling machine is used to dehull the kernels to facilitate the determination of heat-damaged kernels and aleurone color.

There are no classes in rye and flaxseed.

Mixed grain is any mixture of those grains for which standards have been established that does not fall within the requirements of any of the standards for such grains and that does not contain more than 50% foreign material. Wild oats in mixed grain are classed as a grain.

Test weight per bushel is usually the first analytical test made by use of instruments, and is a factor in all grains except Western Barley. It is expressed in whole and half pounds for soybeans, corn, oats, barley (classes Barley and Mixed Barley), flaxseed, grain sorghum, and mixed grain, and in terms of pounds and tenths of a pound for wheat and rye. In the case of wheat, rye, and barley, the dockage must be removed from the sample before test weight is determined; the flaxseed sample must be mechanically cleaned. The original sample is used with corn, oats, and soybeans. This statistic, along with sizing for some grains (rye, oats, barley), is a measure of *plumpness*.

Moisture content is measured by the Motomco moisture meter using a specified weight of grain, which usually is taken from the file sample and then returned to it immediately upon completion of the test.

Percent moisture is a factor in determination of the numerical grades of corn, soybeans, and grain sorghums. All numerical grades of wheat, barley, oats, rye, and flaxseed have the same maximum moisture percentage. However, these percentages differ from one of these grains to another and even between some classes of Barley. If the moisture percentage in each of these grains (except flaxseed) lies between a certain minimum and maximum value, the word "tough" is added to the designated grade. When the moisture percentage exceeds a certain value, *all* grains (*except wheat*) are designated "Sample Grade".

The next step in the analysis for all grains except corn, soybeans, oats, and mixed grain is generally a determination of percent dockage. The Carter dockage machine is used, supplemented in some cases by hand sieves.

Dockage in wheat, rye, and barley consists of a) the foreign material that can be readily removed by appropriate sieves and cleaning devices, and b) underdeveloped, shriveled, and small pieces of grain which cannot be recovered by proper rescreening or recleaning. In flaxseed, this portion is made up of the sieved dockage plus all foreign material remaining in the sample. Dockage in grain sorghums consists only of the material that will pass through the prescribed sieve.

Dockage is expressed in whole percents with fractions of 1% disregarded—except for wheat, in which it is stated in whole and half percents. This factor is the only item in grading for which tolerances have been established. It is noted as part of the grade designation, but does not lower the grade. However, when grain is sold, the percentage of dockage is deducted from the gross weight and payment is made only for the amount of dockage-free grain.

Foreign material and some other closely related items, in contrast with dockage, are grading factors. They also differ from dockage in that they (except thin rye) cannot be readily removed from the grain by appropriate cleaning machinery. These factors are a measure of cleanliness and include:

a) Corn: broken corn and foreign material.
b) Grain sorghums: broken kernels, foreign material, and other grains.
c) Oats: foreign material and wild oats.
d) Soybeans: foreign material and split kernels.
e) Wheat: foreign material.
f) Rye: total foreign material, foreign material other than wheat, and thin rye.

They are separated from the grain in the laboratory by the Carter dockage machine, hand sieves, "hand-picking", or various combinations of these methods.

An extremely important grading factor is grain damage (Anon., 1963b, 1966a, 1966b, 1966c, 1969, 1970, 1971). This causes most of the problems in grading, because very few people interpret some types of damage exactly alike. The proportion of damaged kernels in the grain—along with the absence of musty, sour, or commercially objectionable foreign odors—is a measure of *soundness*. Damaged wheat, corn, barley, rye, grain sorghum, flaxseed, and soybeans consist of the grain and pieces of grain that are heat-damaged, sprouted, frosted, badly ground-damaged, badly weather-damaged, moldy, and diseased. Malting and stinkbug are other types of damage, but are associated only with barley and soybeans, respectively. In determining (or "picking") damage, the entire surface of every kernel is inspected, exposing doubtful areas, if necessary, with a razor blade.

A serious defect and grading factor in wheat is "shrunken and broken kernels". These are separated from the grain with a sieve, but are not considered to be dockage, foreign material, or damaged grain. Although this defect can be found in all classes of wheat, it is most prevalent in the class Hard Amber Durum because of its extremely hard kernels. Thin barley in the class Barley also falls in this category.

"Skinned and broken kernels" is a serious defect (not considered damage) and grading factor in barley intended for malting purposes, because such kernels do not germinate satisfactorily.

The only two grading factors determined in an indirect manner are sound oats and sound barley. The percentage would be equal to 100 minus the sum of the percentages (if any) of heat-damaged kernels, other damaged kernels, foreign material and wild oats in oats, and total damaged kernels and foreign material in barley. The determination for barley, as compared with that for oats, is made after the dockage has been removed.

Appearance of the sample is also a factor in the grading of some grains. A few examples are:

a) Barley, for the subclass Barley of the class Barley, that is badly stained or materially weathered cannot be graded higher than U.S. No. 4.

b) Oats that are slightly weathered cannot be graded higher than U.S. No. 3.

c) Soybeans which are purple mottled or stained cannot be graded higher than U.S. No. 3.

There are four numerical grades for wheat, five for corn, five for the subclass Barley of the class Barley, three for the subclasses Malting Barley and Blue Malting Barley of the class Barley, five for Western Barley, four for oats, four for rye, four for grain sorghum, two for flaxseed, four for soybeans, one for mixed grain, and two for mixed feed oats under the category mixed grain. Each of these grains also has a grade designation called Sample Grade.

Sample Grade is made up of grain which does not come within the grade requirements of any of the numerical grades; or which is musty, sour, or heating; or which has any commercially objectionable foreign odor; or which is otherwise of distinctly low quality.

Distinctly low quality grain would be that which contains large stones, broken glass, animal filth, unknown foreign substance(s) or commonly recognized harmful or toxic substance(s). Some examples of some other factors that would be the basis for designating a lot of grain U.S. Sample Grade are as follows:

a) More than two crotalaria seeds in 1,000 g. of wheat, corn, barley, oats, rye, grain sorghum, soybeans, mixed grain, or flaxseed.

b) Castor beans in each of the above-mentioned grains.

c) "Seeds" of cockle burrs in corn, barley, oats, and grain sorghum.

d) Excessive moisture in the subclass Barley of the class Barley (more than 16%), Western Barley (more than 15%), rye (more than 16%), and flaxseed (more than 9.5%).

Because the commercial value of grain is not always reflected by its numerical grade alone, the Official Grain Standards provide for special grade designations for each of the grains except flaxseed. These are shown in Table VI.

The special-grade terms that denote grain of superior quality, such as "Heavy" and "Bright", appear in the complete grade designation immediately following the numerical grade, as U.S. No. 1 Extra Heavy Bright White Oats. Special grades denoting adverse qualities are added to the grade designation following the class or subclass name, as U.S. No. 1 Amber Durum Wheat, Tough, Smutty, Ergoty.

Some examples of special grade factors and the value required for each factor are as follows:

a) Blighted (barley): more than 4% blight-damaged.

b) Ergoty (wheat): more than 0.3% ergot.
c) Flint (corn): 95% or more flint corn.
d) Garlicky (wheat): more than 6 green garlic bulblets or an equivalent of dry or partly dry bulblets in 1,000 g.
e) Extra Heavy (oats): a test weight of 38 lb. or more per bu.
f) Plump (rye): 5% or less of the rye and other matter in the sample (by weight) passes through a small chess sieve.
g) Weevily (grain sorghum): 2 or more live weevils in 1,000 g.
h) Tough (wheat): more than 13.5% moisture.

An important responsibility of a licensed inspector and an ACG of Grain is the examination of a conveyance (especially export types) for cleanliness (moisture, rust, insects, rodents, oil) before loading. The inspection is made where the grain is to be loaded, and immediately before loading. If it appears that the receptacle is in such a condition as to contaminate the grain after being put aboard, the grain is not inspected.

During the grading of a lot in a Federal Laboratory, each fraction is placed in an envelope. The front of each envelope bears the name of the separation and the percentage that it makes up of the whole. When grading has been completed, these envelopes, along with the remainder of the work sample, are placed in a moistureproof box. Form GR-189 is then completed and used as the basis for issuing an official Grain Inspection certificate. The work sample (with separations) and the corresponding file sample are then stored. Appeal carlot and barge or ship samples are kept in storage 15 and 90 days, respectively. Nonappeal inbound carlots, outbound carlots, barge, and ship samples are kept 7, 15, 30, and 90 days, respectively. It is unfortunate that licensed inspectors are not required to keep their

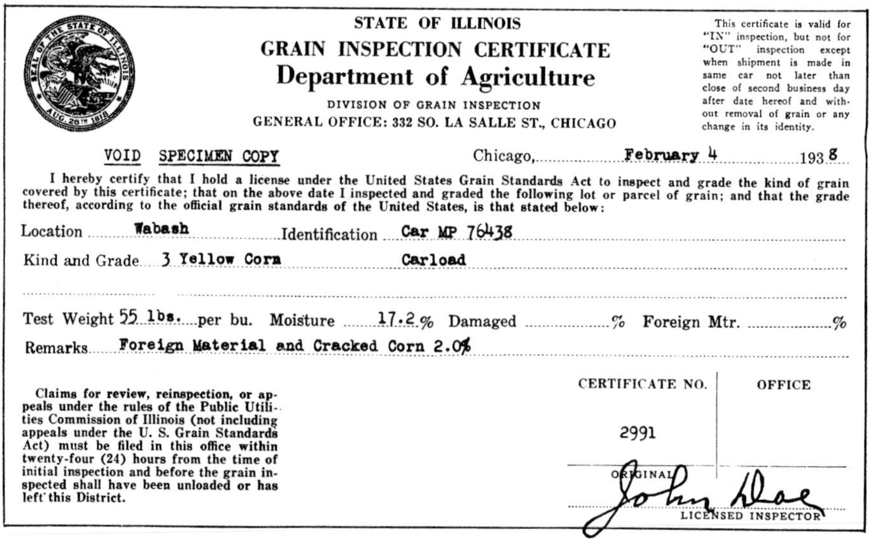
SEAL OF THE STATE OF ILLINOIS AUG. 26th 1818

STATE OF ILLINOIS
GRAIN INSPECTION CERTIFICATE
Department of Agriculture
DIVISION OF GRAIN INSPECTION
GENERAL OFFICE: 332 SO. LA SALLE ST., CHICAGO

This certificate is valid for "IN" inspection, but not for "OUT" inspection except when shipment is made in same car not later than close of second business day after date hereof and without removal of grain or any change in its identity.

VOID SPECIMEN COPY Chicago, February 4 1938

I hereby certify that I hold a license under the United States Grain Standards Act to inspect and grade the kind of grain covered by this certificate; that on the above date I inspected and graded the following lot or parcel of grain; and that the grade thereof, according to the official grain standards of the United States, is that stated below:

Location Wabash Identification Car MP 76438

Kind and Grade 3 Yellow Corn Carload

Test Weight 55 lbs. per bu. Moisture 17.2 % Damaged % Foreign Mtr. %

Remarks Foreign Material and Cracked Corn 2.0%

Claims for review, reinspection, or appeals under the rules of the Public Utilities Commission of Illinois (not including appeals under the U. S. Grain Standards Act) must be filed in this office within twenty-four (24) hours from the time of initial inspection and before the grain inspected shall have been unloaded or has left this District.

CERTIFICATE NO. 2991 OFFICE

ORIGINAL

John Doe
LICENSED INSPECTOR

Figure 30. A speciman State of Illinois grain inspection certificate for an "in" inspection of carlot grain.

work sample and separations on file. However, they must hold their file samples for the same length of time that the Federal Laboratory keeps theirs.

An official Grain Inspection certificate must be issued for each inspection and grading. A U.S. Department of Agriculture certificate is issued only for appeal lots, and supersedes the previously issued Agency certificate. An example of an Agency (in this case, the State of Illinois) and a U.S. Department of Agriculture certificate are shown in Figures 30 and 31, respectively (Anon., 1938).

Whereas the ACG-Grain supervises the work of the licensed inspector, the Board of Appeals and Review-Grain (BAR-Grain) supervises the work of the former. This is done through the use of board appeal, supervision ("S"), opinion, and referee samples.

Where a buyer or seller appeals a finding to the BAR-Grain, all available samples (the inspector's file sample, the ACG's work and file sample, and, if possible, a newly drawn sample) are submitted and used. In the case of "S" samples, all accumulated Form 189's for a given period of time within a Field Office, are separated into two groups: a grade-changed stack and a grade-sustained stack. Forms from each group are chosen by a random number and selection procedure prescribed by the Board. The corresponding work sample (together with separations) and file sample are shipped to the Board for review. Any ACG-Grain can submit a work sample (along with separations) to the Board for an opinion. In such a case, the Board will check his separations and return them to him. In the case of referee samples, the Board will send out unknown samples for the ACG-Grain to grade, and then will correct his work.

FORM GR-414 (7-1-71)	UNITED STATES DEPARTMENT OF AGRICULTURE CONSUMER AND MARKETING SERVICE GRAIN DIVISION **OFFICIAL GRAIN INSPECTION CERTIFICATE** OFFICIAL SAMPLE - LOT INSPECTION	COPY **US-** 126

Please refer to this certificate by the lettered prefix, number, and date. VOID SPECIMEN COPY

CHICAGO, ILLINOIS   **JULY 27, 1972**

(ISSUED AT)   (DATE OF INSPECTION)

I hereby certify that I am authorized under the U.S. Grain Standards Act to inspect the kind of grain covered by this certificate, and that on the above date the following-identified grain was inspected under the Act, with the following results.

[X] IN	[ ] OUT	[ ] LOCAL	[X] APPEAL INSPECTION	[ ] BOARD APPEAL INSPECTION

QUANTITY (This Is Not A Weight Certificate) [ ] Carload [X] **COVERED HOPPER**	METHOD OF SAMPLING **PROBE**	DATE SAMPLED **7/26/72**

LOCATION **IC MARKHAM YARDS**	IDENTIFICATION OF GRAIN **IC 56416**

GRADE AND KIND

U.S. NO. 1 SOFT RED WINTER WHEAT, TOUGH

TW **61.3** LBS.	M **13.7** %	HT	DKT **0.2** %	FM **0.5** %	SHBN **1.5** %	DEF **2.2** %	CCL %
WOCL %	BCFM %	SBLY %	BN %	THIN %	BB %	SKBN %	OG %
WO %	SCO %	FMOW %	BNFM %	SPL %	BBB %		

REMARKS   This certificate supersedes certificate No. **CG 51757** , dated **7/26/72** .

(See reverse side for abbreviations)

FEE: $15.00 APPEAL NO. 27	NAME AND SIGNATURE *Melvin Smith* TITLE MELVIN SMITH, **GRAIN SUPERVISOR**

This certificate is issued under the authority of the U.S. Grain Standards Act, as amended (7 U.S.C. 71 et seq.), and the regulations thereunder (7 CFR 26.1 et seq.). It is issued to show the kind, class, grade, quality, condition, quantity of sacks of grain, or other facts relating to grain as specified herein, at the time and place of inspection. It may not represent the grade, quality, or condition at a subsequent date or place. If it is not canceled by a superseding certificate, it is receivable by all officers and all courts of the United States as prima facie evidence of the truth of the facts stated herein. This certificate does not excuse failure to comply with the provisions of the Federal Food, Drug, and Cosmetic Act, or other Federal law.

WARNING: Any person who shall knowingly falsely make, issue, alter, forge, or counterfeit this certificate, or participate in any of such actions, is subject to a fine of not more than $5,000 or imprisonment for not more than 1 year, or both.

Figure 31. A specimen United States Department of Agriculture grain inspection certificate for an "in" inspection of carlot grain.

Field Offices may send samples to the Board for information on unusual grading problems (frost-damaged kernels, red-striped corn, etc.), new crops (seasonal differences), large intermarket movements (where there is a recognized difficult grading problem), and new varieties. On the other hand, the Board may call for submission of samples for review in cases where there may have been possible violations of the U.S. Grain Standards Act.

Any change in the grading standards is handled by the Standardization Section of the Standardization Branch, Grain Division, Agricultural Marketing Service, U.S. Department of Agriculture, Beltsville, Md. The first step in the process is a discussion—with *all* interested parties— of the proposed change. If a majority do not concur, the matter is dropped. If they approve, the proposed change and effective date of the change are printed in the appropriate section of the Federal Register of the U.S. Government. The Register may or may not provide for public hearings on the proposed revision, but persons who wish to submit written data, views, or arguments can file them with the Hearing Clerk, U.S. Department of Agriculture, Washington, D.C. Consideration is given to all written comments, and if there are no serious valid objections, the revision is printed again in the Federal Register as a change. An historical review of all changes up to 1960 has been published by the U.S. Department of Agriculture (Anon., 1963a).

C. Problems and Solutions

The major problems in grading grain are accuracy (closeness with which the measurement approaches the true value) and precision (repeatability of the measurement) of the values obtained for the various grading factors and for the grade designation. Accuracy and precision are affected mainly by the following sources of variation:

a) Type of sampling device.
b) Sampling procedure.
c) Grading factors: Machine-determined values, and manual-determined values (human judgment).
d) Sample homogeneity (inherent).

The sources are highly interrelated − each is involved, to some extent, in the final value ascribed to each grading factor of a lot and to the grade designation of that lot. It becomes essential, therefore, that variation within each category be kept to a minimum so that the interaction variation (product mix) will be kept within a normal tolerance range.

Types of sampling devices were discussed under sampling. It was suggested that variation in grading factors among newly drawn samples of the same lot could be *minimized* by having everyone use the same type of sampler. This type of variation could also be *further reduced* by having everyone use exactly the same sampling procedures.

Even if everyone used the same type of sampler and the same sampling procedures, the value of a factor for a sample drawn from a lot by one organization could be different from that for a sample drawn from the same lot by another organization (assuming a homogeneous mix) due to machine differences and to differences in human judgment.

Variability within a factor that is ascertained by the use of a machine, and which is due to the machine, can be *minimized* by continuous standardization of the unit with the master unit located in the Grain Division Laboratory, Beltsville, Md.

Variation due to differences in interpretation occurs most often in regard to damage, primarily with that type of damage involving differences in shades of color. Some examples are heat damage in soybeans and brown germ in corn. As a result, many questions arise as to whether an inspector or an ACG is rigid or lenient enough in the way he "picked" damage in a sample. Variability can be minimized through the use of interpretive line samples, i.e, samples with extremely stable colors. These should be on the grading desk of every grader each time he is grading a lot of that particular type of grain.

Finally, one is faced with the fact that grain, even after mixing, is rarely homogeneous. In other words, if a sample were divided by a Boerner divider (ignoring the slight error due to this apparatus) into X portions, the amount of factor Y in each portion could be different even if there were absolutely no human or machine error in each determination. The nonhomogeneous nature of grain was ascertained through studies involving the use of foreign material (screenings and other grains) as the testing factor. However, this can be extrapolated to include any of the grading factors. The nonhomogeneous nature of grain with respect to damage, for example, can be easily demonstrated in the laboratory, using a sample of corn with a known percentage of dyed kernels to represent this factor. In such an exercise, of course, there is no difficulty in determining what is and what is not a damaged kernel. The range of variation can be ascertained by repeating the analysis many times with the same sample. The dyed kernels are returned to and thoroughly mixed with the sample after each determination. It appears that the best way to handle this type of variation is through the establishment of tolerances.

Both Inspectors and ACG's Grain should have, for each numerical grading factor of each grain, the range (plus and minus) over which any reasonable finding (value) for each factor could be expected to vary at a given probability level (5% or 1%) when the sample has been drawn and graded in a *specific* manner. The availability and use of a table of such values would tend to take much of the existing bias and feeling of uncertainty out of sampling and grading. Fortunately, the Program Analysis Group, Agricultural Marketing Service, U.S. Department of Agriculture, Hyattsville, Md., is devoting considerable time to this problem, using hypergeometric distribution as the basis for the development of such tolerance tables.

Most certainly, the use of tolerances along with good interpretive line samples will make grain grading (via grading factors) about as exact as possible.

A problem that has come to the fore in recent years is the identification of pure or mixed samples of the red wheats: Hard Red Winter, Hard Red Spring, and Soft Red Winter. The division of these into classes is based on varietal or kernel characteristics. Two of the classes, Hard Red Spring and Hard Red Winter, are divided into subclasses on the basis of texture or kernel hardness. As long as the grain trade was dealing with the older established varieties, these separations were not too much of a problem. However, in recent years, new varieties of red "semidwarfs" have been developed from classes of wheat with parents from two or more of the classes. As these have varietal or kernel characteristics of all their parents, use of this factor in the grading process is made difficult. The solution to this problem is still under investigation. Meanwhile, it appears that the sedimentation procedure will have to be used as a stop-gap measure.

Since, in the merchandising of grain, we are actually selling or buying protein of different amounts and kinds, starch of different kinds, oil, minerals, vitamins, etc., it appears that, sometime in the future, a combination of physical and chemical factors will have to be used in grading. How quickly this will come about will depend, primarily, on the development of rapid and accurate analytical chemical procedures.

LITERATURE CITED

ANONYMOUS. 1938. The service of Federal grain standards. U.S. Dep. Agr. Misc. Publ. 328.

ANONYMOUS. 1953. The test weight per bushel of grain: Methods of use and calibration of the apparatus. U.S. Dep. Agr. Circ. No. 921.

ANONYMOUS. 1957. Grain grading primer. U.S. Dep. Agr. Misc. Publ. 740.

ANONYMOUS. 1963a. Historical review of changes in the grain standards of the United States. U.S. Dep. Agr., Agr. Mkt. Serv., Grain Div., Spec. Rep. AMS-513.

ANONYMOUS. 1963b. Principal stored grain insects. Agr. Ext. Serv. Folder 233, Univ. Minn., St. Paul, Minn.

ANONYMOUS. 1965a. Malting barley grade factors. Agr. Ext. Serv. Pamph., N. Dak. State Univ., Bismarck, N. Dak.

ANONYMOUS. 1965b. Spring wheat grade factors. Agr. Ext. Serv. Folder 231, Univ. Minn., St. Paul, Minn.

ANONYMOUS. 1965c. Stored-grain pests. U.S. Dep. Agr. Farmer's Bull. No. 1260.

ANONYMOUS. 1966a. Corn kernel damage. Agr. Ext. Serv. Pamph., Univ. Minn., St. Paul, Minn.

ANONYMOUS. 1966b. Oat kernel damage. Agr. Ext. Serv. Pamph., Univ. Minn., St. Paul, Minn.

ANONYMOUS. 1966c. Soybean kernel damage. Agr. Ext. Serv. Pamph., Univ. Minn., St. Paul, Minn.

ANONYMOUS. 1968. United States grain standards act as amended. U.S. Dep. Agr., Consumer and Mkt. Serv., Grain Div.

ANONYMOUS. 1969. Grain sorghum kernel damage. Agr. Ext. Serv. Pamph., Kans. State Univ., Manhattan, Kans.

ANONYMOUS. 1970. Official grain standards of the United States. U.S. Dep. Agr., and Consumer and Mkt. Serv., Grain Div.

ANONYMOUS. 1971. The grain inspection manual, Instruction No. 918 (GR)-6. U.S. Dep. Agr., Consumer and Mkt. Serv., Grain Div.

BOERNER, E. G. 1915. A device for sampling grain seeds, and other material. U.S. Dep. Agr. Bull. No. 287.

HUNT, W. H. 1965. Problems associated with moisture determination in grain and related crops. p. 123–5 in *Humidity and moisture, measurement and control in science and industry* (A. Wexler, ed.), vol. 2, Van Nostrand, New York, N.Y.

HUNT, W. H. 1969. Recommended procedure for state inspection of moisture measuring devices. U.S. Dep. Agr., Consumer and Mkt. Serv., Grain Div. A speech presented at the 1969 National Conference on Weights and Measures.

HUNT, W. H. 1970. Determination of moisture content of agricultural commodities by oven drying procedures. U.S. Dep. Agr., Consumer and Mkt. Serv., Grain Div. In speech presented at the 1970 Annual Convention of the Amer. Ass. Agr. Eng.

HUNT, W. H., and M. H. NEUSTADT. 1966. Factors affecting the precision of moisture measurement in grain and related crops. J. Ass. Offic. Anal. Chem. 49: 757–761.

KRAMER, H. A. 1968a. Sampling of wheat, soybeans and corn transported in covered hopper cars. U.S. Dep. Agr., Agr. Res. Serv. Spec. Rep., ARS 51-20.

KRAMER, H. A. 1968b. Effect of grain

velocity and flow rate upon the performance of a diverter-type sampler. U.S. Dep. Agr., Agr. Res. Serv. Spec. Rep., ARS 51-25.

KRAMER, H. A. 1968c. Performance of three diverter-type mechanical grain samplers and the pelican. U.S. Dep. Agr., Agr. Res. Serv. Spec. Rep., ARS 51-16.

WATSON, C. A. 1969. Summary of grain sampling research. U.S. Dep. Agr., Agr. Res. Serv. Spec. Rep. for the U.S. Dep. Agr. Consumer and Mkt. Serv., Grain Div.

WATSON, C. A., A. L. HAWK, P. NEFFENEGGER, and D. DUNCAN. 1970. Performance evaluation of grain sample dividers. U.S. Dep. Agr., Agr. Res. Serv. Spec. Rep., ARS 51-38.

ZELENY, L., and W. H. HUNT. 1962. Moisture measurement in grain. U.S. Dep. Agr., Consumer and Mkt. Serv., Grain Div. Presented at the 1962 Meeting of the Amer. Soc. Agr. Eng.

CHAPTER 4

MICROFLORA

CLYDE M. CHRISTENSEN

Department of Plant Pathology
University of Minnesota, St. Paul, Minnesota

HENRY H. KAUFMANN

Cargill, Inc.
Cargill Bldg., Minneapolis, Minnesota

I. INTRODUCTION

Fungi are a major cause of spoilage in stored grains and seeds, and probably rank second only to insects as a cause of deterioration and loss in all kinds of stored products throughout the world. Indeed, in commercial storage in the technologically advanced countries, where insects and rodents are effectively controlled, fungi probably cause more spoilage than any other single agent.

That fungi are a principal cause of disease in living plants, and of decay of dead plants and plant remains, was established well over a century ago; and that they might invade and kill seeds was recognized by some at least a hundred years ago, as indicated by the following quotation from the Annual Report of the Commissioner of Patents for 1863, p. 360: "Seeds that were of excellent quality originally, are frequently impaired by being brought on shipboard from foreign countries. It is found almost impossible to prevent a slight dampness, and this, together with the warmth of the place in which they are kept, induces the first stage of germination or mould, *either of which is sufficient to destroy the vitality of the seed.*" (Italics mine.) That is, he recognized that "the first stage of germination" was something different from "mould", and that either might reduce the viability of the seeds.

That fungi until recently were not recognized by many cereal chemists as well as practical grain men as a cause of discoloration, heating, and decay (and by some still are not so recognized) probably is due as much to the inconspicuous nature of the fungi concerned as to the biological, or at least mycological, innocence of the men. This inconspicuousness or invisibility of the fungi that cause spoilage and heating of stored grains is typical of fungi in general. Wood, for example, is decayed by fungi, and by fungi only, primarily by a special group — loosely termed 'wood-rotting fungi' — that are adapted to feeding on wood. Among these are many specialists that decay only a given kind of wood, or dead branches of a given size of a given kind of tree, and so on. Very commonly wood is decayed to the point of almost total consumption, so that it can be crumbled between the fingers, without any fungus being visible at any time. Fruits, vegetables, and other plant parts, including seeds, are decayed by fungi that may be invisible to the naked eye – or invisible even by microscopic examination. In the final stages of decay the causal fungus may produce a mass of visible spores, the first intimation to the layman that a fungus was involved. This invisibility of the physiologically active, decay-causing mycelium has given rise to the myth that "spoilage produces mold". Special techniques are required to detect the presence of fungus mycelium in decaying plant tissues, including seeds, especially in the early stages of decay. Such techniques, intended especially to reveal the presence and increase of storage fungi in stored grains and seeds have been developed (actually they were developed in the early 1950's), and will be described later. By means of these techniques the early stages of deterioration can be detected long before any loss in grade or in processing quality occurs. Anyone who stores grains and seeds stores fungi also; he should know something of the fungi involved, and of the conditions under which the fungi that he stores may damage his grain.

One often hears it stated that spoilage of stored grains, especially of wheat and corn, has become much more of a problem since the advent of the combine, which results in threshing grain of a higher moisture content than was the case with the old methods of binding and shocking wheat and of hand-picking corn. Unquestionably the problem has increased some, but it always has been with us. Alsberg and Black (1913) cite many papers by Italian workers from the early 1870's on dealing with corn imported from the U.S. and supposedly made toxic by fungi. There was a considerable international trade in grains more than a hundred years ago: in 1846 the U.S. exported 16,326,050 bu. of corn; and in 1880, 98,169,877 bu. of corn and 153,252,795 bu. of wheat[1]. Black and Alsberg (1910) recognized that fungi were a major cause of spoilage in grains, and stated, "The tests for micro-organisms and the tendency to become moldy involves the quantitative determination of the number of organisms in the suspicious sample compared with a sound sample". They were especially interested in possible toxic products produced by *Penicillium puberulum* isolated from stored corn – in other words, mycotoxins. Shanahan et al. (1910) investigated corn shipped from the U.S. to Europe. They took samples from 141 ships as these arrived at European ports, and stated that of a total of more than 15,000,000 bu. of corn in those ships, nearly 2,000,000 bu., or about 13%, "arrived in a heating or hot condition". They correctly attributed the trouble to excessively high moisture content in the grain. Sixty-four of the cargoes had moisture contents of 16.1 to 18.0% when loaded, and 73.4% of these were heating or hot when they arrived in Europe. One cargo had a moisture content of 28% when loaded. Even their figures did not tell the whole story, since the moisture contents given were presumably only those of "representative" samples, and were determined by methods not specified. It seems highly probable that portions of some cargoes had moisture contents from 5 to 10% above the figures given. Only recently have we come to realize that the

---

[1] Annual Report of the Commissioner of Patents for the year 1847; Annual Report of the Commissioner of Agriculture for 1880, 672 p., Government Printing Office, 1881, p. 204.

moisture-content figure of a representative or average sample is of very limited value in judging storability. Shanahan et al. pointed out that corn did not have an "urge to heat and germinate in the spring", a bit of whimsical and nonsensical folklore developed by practical men to put the blame on the corn instead of on those in charge of it. This belief still persists, probably handed down from one generation of grain handlers to another; truth is difficult to establish, but errors and false doctrine flourish as the green bay tree, and persist forever. Seeds of corn and of other grains germinate, of course, when they are moist enough and warm enough. Regarding this, Christensen (1965) stated: "Many practical grain men once believed, and a lot of them still believe, that grain has 'an urge to heat and germinate in the spring'. That is, about the time that corn and wheat are being planted in the fields the grain in its dark storage bin feels the eternal call of spring, begins to breath heavily, like an ardent bull, and sweats and heats. Granted that stored grain often heats and spoils in the spring, this romantic explanation of the process is complete nonsense; the same heating occurs in bins of turkey feed, in baled cotton, in wood, and in manure piles, materials that by no possible stretch of imagination could feed the mysterious call of spring, or respond to it if they did feel it".

This heavy traffic in unstorable corn persisted up to very recent times. In 1965–66, for example, a situation very similar to that described in 1910 by Shanahan et al. prevailed in corn shipped to European ports from Argentina and Brazil. The condition of corn exported from the U.S. evidently has improved greatly since the time of Shanahan's study. Sauer and Christensen (1968) tested 375 samples of grade No. 2 yellow corn being loaded onto ships for export. Germination of these lots averaged 57%, 16% of the surface-disinfected kernels yielded storage fungi, the fat-acidity values averaged 28, and in none did the moisture contents exceed 15.5%. Portions of these samples were stored at different moisture contents and temperatures, and tested periodically, with the results that "...if kept at the moisture content they had when loaded into the ships, and at a temperature of 10°C., [they] could be expected to maintain their quality for at least a year."

II. BACTERIA

Included in the microflora harbored by seeds and by other plant parts are a multitude of bacteria. Some of these affect the quality of some kinds of products made from cereal seeds; none of them, however, can grow at moisture contents below those where free water is available — that is, a moisture content in equilibrium with a relative humidity of about 100%. After fungi have raised the temperature of spoiling grain to about 55°C. and, in the process, have raised the moisture content to the point where free water is available, thermophilic bacteria may raise the temperature to about 70° to 75°C. and they, along with an assortment of thermophilic fungi, may carry the spoilage to its final stage. But by the time that thermophilic bacteria become involved in the heating process, the grain already is spoiled far beyond any use for food. Since bacteria are not involved in storage losses other than in the final stages of heating, they will not be discussed further in this chapter.

III. FUNGI

More than 150 species of fungi have been reported from cereal grains (Christensen and Kaufmann, 1969). Most of these have been isolated from seeds or kernels that first were shaken in a disinfectant to kill all surface-borne inoculum, then were placed on an agar medium and incubated for a few days to a week; so presumably the great majority of these fungi came from mycelium or spores within, or at least beneath the surface of, the seeds. Any agar medium is selective to a certain extent, and most students of seed microflora have been interested in seed-borne fungi that might cause disease of the plant that developed from the seed after planting – fungi that cause seedling blights, root rots, kernel smudge, and so on – and have used agar media designed to detect those fungi. Other techniques might detect other fungi. On seeds or kernels exposed to the air during their development, as are most kinds of cereal seeds except those of maize, one would expect to find representatives of all kinds of microflora that are disseminated by wind-borne inoculum, which would include many thousands of species of fungi, bacteria, algae, and protozoa. Slime molds and protozoa have, in fact, been reported from "weathered" malting barley (Kotheimer and Christensen, 1961). Fungi are the primary agents of decay of many kinds of plant materials, especially those made up in part or all of cellulose, and of many kinds of animal materials; they grow in and consume almost everything but metals – paper, twine and fabrics, wood, plant remains of all kinds, and animal products such as meats, hides, leather and glue. They thrive in materials within warehouses, elevators, mills, processing plants, and homes, as well as out of doors. Some of them, especially those that cause deterioration of stored materials, are found primarily in warehouses, mills, and homes, and are relatively rare outside. Many fungi, including those that cause deterioration of stored seeds and grains, produce spores in astronomical numbers, and these are carried everywhere by air currents. Whenever the environmental conditions are such as permit these fungi to grow, they will grow. They are omnipresent.

This is gone into in some detail because we often are asked, with some apparent puzzlement on the part of the asker, "But where do these fungi come from?" – as if the fungi were somehow intruders into an otherwise pure and orderly world. As stated by Christensen (1965), "There are close to a hundred thousand different kinds of fungi. They are not rare, chancy plants growing just here and there, but are present everywhere throughout the world, growing on all conceivable kinds of things. Their size is small, their structure simple, but they have many of the characteristics that make for survival, and on the basis of numbers and prevalence they must be counted among the successful and dominant organisms on the earth." Those who need and want an introduction to the fungi are referred to this book.

In general, the fungi that grown on and in seeds have been divided into two groups: 1) field fungi, and 2) storage fungi. This division is not taxonomically valid, but is based upon ecology of the fungi concerned, primarily the moisture-content requirements.

A. Field Fungi

There are a multitude of field fungi, of which *Alternaria, Cladosporium, Fusarium,* and *Helminthosporium* are representative genera. They are called field fungi because they invade the kernels of seeds before harvest, while the plants are growing in the field, or after the grain is cut and swathed but before it is threshed. One common exception to this is corn stored moist on-the-cob in cribs, where it may be attacked and decayed by typical field fungi. All field fungi require a high moisture content in order to grow — a moisture content in equilibrium with relative humidities of 90 to 100% (Koehler, 1938), which in cereal seeds means a moisture content of 22 to 23%, wet-weight basis, or 30 to 33% on a dry-weight basis. These fungi may discolor the seeds or kernels[2]; weaken or kill the embryo; or cause shriveling of the seed, and seedling blight, root rot, or other disease in the plants that develop from such seeds. A few may produce toxins. They may also affect the quality of the seeds of grains for various uses. With the exception mentioned above, that of corn stored with high moisture on-the-cob in cribs, the damage resulting from invasion by field fungi is caused before harvest, can be detected by routine inspection, and does not continue to increase in storage. The field fungi may survive for years in dry grain (Christensen, 1963), but die rapidly in grains held at moisture contents in equilibrium with relative humidities of 70 to 75% (Lutey and Christensen, 1963).

Very commonly, in fact almost without exception, *Alternaria* will grow from 100% of freshly harvested seeds of wheat, barley, oats, sorghum, and sunflower when these are surface-disinfected and plated on agar. If samples are taken of a given lot of seed from a warehouse, and *Alternaria* grows on from close to 100% of the surface-disinfected kernels placed on agar, it is conclusive biological evidence that the seeds are in the same condition as when harvested: there have been no deteriorative changes. If, during storage, the percentage of seeds yielding *Alternaria* gradually decreases with time, it is evident that trouble may be in the offing. Periodic sampling, plus testing of the samples for moisture and fungi, gives us information on storage conditions that cannot be obtained from warehouse records.

Some species of *Fusarium*, when growing in developing seeds, cause "scab" of barley and wheat or cob rot of corn. Depending on the species of *Fusarium* and on the conditions under which invasion has occurred, the invaded grain may be unattractive to animals, or toxic. Toxins produced by fungi will be discussed later in the chapter.

B. Storage Fungi

The storage fungi comprise only about 10 to 15 group species of *Aspergillus*, of which only five or six are at all common until deterioration is fairly well advanced, plus several species of *Penicillium*. Some species of *Penicillium* are field fungi; others are storage fungi (Mislivec and Tuite, 1970).

All of the storage fungi have the ability to grow in materials whose moisture contents are in equilibrium with relative humidities of 70 to 90% — relative humidities at which no free water is present. Some of them in fact *require* a high osmotic pressure to grow. Christensen et al. (1959) described a new species of *Aspergillus, A. halophilicus*, from wheat; the fungus required a concentration of at least 10 to 15% sodium chloride, or 55% sucrose, in agar in order to grow. It grew on agar in which an excess of sodium chloride or sucrose was present, growing over

---

[2]In the trade this usually is referred to as "weathering", but this is a misnomer because the discoloration is caused by fungi, or sometimes by bacteria, not by the weather.

salt or sugar crystals themselves. This fungus was later isolated from beans and sorghum seeds stored at moisture contents in equilibrium with a relative humidity of about 70%, and probably is common.

All of these fungi are common on a great variety of plant and animal materials that are exposed constantly or intermittently to relative humidities of 70 to 90%. Some of them grow in furniture stuffing, mattresses, and pillow stuffing (including foam rubber) in homes (where they may cause respiratory allergy), and their spores may occur in relatively tremendous numbers in the air within homes [Swaebly and Christensen (1952) reported up to 3,000,000 colonies of fungi, mainly *Aspergillus* and *Penicillium*, per gram of housedust]. They also are common in grain warehouses. Tuite and Christensen (1957) reported, "Inoculum of storage fungi was uncommon in the air in ripe wheat fields, moderately abundant in the air in country elevators where freshly harvested grain was being handled, and much more abundant in the air in a terminal elevator." We have found spores of storage fungi in amounts of millions per gram of dust collected in terminal elevators. There is no mystery as to where these molds come from: the primary source of inoculum is moldy material within the elevator or warehouse itself.

Over the past 20 years we have tested thousands of samples of cereal grains — wheat, barley, oats, rice, sorghum, and maize — from commercial bins in the U.S.; Mexico; Colombia, South America; and several European countries. The two group species consistently associated with beginning or incipient deterioration have been *A. restrictus* and *A. glaucus*. In grains where moisture contents in equilibrium are less than about 78 to 80%, these are the only species that can grow; in lots with moisture contents higher than this, these two species almost invariably appear first, and may be followed by *A. candidus, A. ochraceus, A. versicolor, A. flavus,* and *Penicillium*. There is a more or less regular ecological succession: first a slow or moderately rapid increase in *A. restrictus* and *A. glaucus*, in the first stages of deterioration, followed by *A. candidus* and *A. flavus*. By the time more than 5 to 10% of the kernels have been invaded by *A. candidus* or *A. flavus*, spoilage is well under way, and if the grain is not heating it shortly will be. Each of the species listed above has its own rather sharply delimited lower limit of moisture content, below which it cannot grow. All of these fungi invade the germ or embryo of the seeds preferentially, and sometimes exclusively. The embryos of cereal seeds contain much more oil than does the endosperm, and therefore at a given relative humidity will have a lower equilibrium-moisture content than does the endosperm. When we speak of a moisture content of 14.0% in these grains we are speaking of the moisture content of the whole kernels — we do not know what the moisture content of the embryo is.

The salient characteristics of each of the major group species of storage fungi are described below.

C. Characteristics and Significance of Major Storage Fungi

Aspergillus restrictus

Lower Limit of Moisture for Growth.

Corn and wheat	13.5–14.5%
Sorghum	14.0–14.5%
Soybeans	12.0–12.5%

Effects. *A. restrictus* kills and discolors germs; causes "sick" or germ-damaged wheat, and blue-eye in stored corn with a moisture content of 14.0 to 14.5% for some months; it does not cause heating (because it grows too slowly).

Possible Toxicity. Not known to produce compounds toxic to animals. We have grown a number of isolates in autoclaved moist grain and fed these to rats; also we have fed to rats samples of wheat very heavily invaded with different strains of *A. restrictus* and *A. glaucus*, and no illness and no lesions were observed in any of the rats so fed.

Other comments. *A. restrictus* is likely to be of significance as a cause of germ damage and mustiness in grains stored for several months to a year or more with moisture contents as listed above; at higher moisture contents it is unable to compete with other storage fungi.

Aspergillus glaucus

Lower Limit of Moisture for Growth.

Corn and wheat	14.0–14.5%
Sorghum	14.5–15.0%
Soybeans	12.5–13.0%

Effects. *A. glaucus* kills and discolors germs—very slowly at moisture contents near the lower limit for growth, more rapidly at higher moisture contents—causes blue-eye in corn stored with 14.5 to 15.0% moisture content; and also causes mustiness and caking. Normally it does not cause a large rise in temperature, and so its increase is not detected by temperature-sensing systems, but it may gradually increase the moisture content of the grain in which it is growing; and if the moisture increases to where *A. candidus* can grow rapidly, heating and spoilage may follow within a few days. That is, the increase in *A. glaucus* in itself may not be highly damaging, but such increase indicates that trouble might occur in the future.

Possible Toxicity. Some isolates of individual species within the *A. glaucus* group when grown in pure culture in the laboratory produce compounds toxic to experimental animals; and there is some circumstantial evidence to implicate feed ingredients invaded by one or more species of the *A. glaucus* group in cases of toxicity in the field. However, we have fed to rats and chicks rations containing grain heavily invaded by a mixture of *A. glaucus* species, and did not observe any ill effects.

Other comments. Increase of *A. glaucus* in early stages, and up to when incipient spoilage may be under way, is not detectable by inspection with the unaided eye; microscopic examination or culturing of surface-disinfected kernels, or both, is necessary to detect this. Many lots of wheat, corn, and sorghum that have been stored for several months will yield *A. glaucus* in from 10 to 20% of the surface-disinfected kernels. If a lot yields *A. glaucus* from 20 to 50% of the surface-disinfected kernels it should be regarded as of questionable storability, especially if the moisture content is near or at the level where *A. glaucus* or *A. restrictus* can continue to grow. If the lot yields *A. glaucus* from 50 to 100% of the surface-disinfected kernels when cultured on agar, the lot is partly deteriorated, whether this is or is not visible by inspection. If in a given bin the percentage of surface-disinfected kernels of grain that yield *A. glaucus* increases from one sampling period to the next, incipient spoilage is under way, and may lead eventually to rapid heating and spoilage. Samples should be withdrawn from such lots at intervals of a few weeks and tested for number and kinds of fungi, for moisture content, and for damage. In this way any condition likely to result in serious damage can be detected before it becomes of any practical significance, and the grain can be either aerated, turned, dried, or processed before it can heat or spoil.

Aspergillus candidus

Lower Limit of Moisture for Growth.

Corn and wheat	15.0–15.5%
Sorghum	16.0–16.5%
Soybeans	14.5–15.0%

Effects. A. candidus kills and discolors germs of seeds very rapidly; causes heating of up to 55°C. (130°F.), discoloration of entire kernels, and total decay. In commercial storage bins *A. candidus* and *A. flavus* are the major causes of heating in all cases that we have investigated, in all kinds of grains and seeds. Once *A. candidus* has begun to grow in a given lot of grain, heating and spoilage are likely to follow within a few days to a few weeks; its presence in surface-disinfected kernels is evidence of poor storage conditions in the past, and its increase is an indicator that an emergency exists NOW.

Possible Toxicity. As with *A. glaucus*, mentioned above, some isolates of *A. candidus*, when grown under the right conditions in the laboratory, produce compounds toxic to experimental animals (most isolates do not), but this might be a laboratory phenomenon of little or no practical significance. In some of our tests, samples of severely heat-damaged corn that had been decayed by a variety of fungi, including *A. candidus*, when fed to rats and to chicks as 10% of an otherwise balanced ration, resulted in about the same weight gain as a ration containing sound, food-grade corn.

Other Comments. Any increase in *A. candidus* between successive sampling periods of grain in a given bin is cause for alarm; it means that some of the grain may be spoiling, and the location and size of that portion should be determined by removing samples by probe and testing them for fungi.

Aspergillus ochraceus

Lower Limit of Moisture for Growth (same as for A. candidus).

Corn and wheat	15.0–15.5%
Sorghum	16.0–16.5%
Soybeans	14.5–15.0%

Effects. A. ochraceus kills and discolors germs.

Possible Toxicity. Some isolates of *A. ochraceus* produce a toxin, *ochratoxin*, similar to and just as toxic as *aflatoxin*. In tests of 164 samples of corn at the USDA Northern Regional Research Laboratory at Peoria, Ill., *only one sample* was found to contain ochratoxin, and this one was of sample grade, damaged, and musty. It seems unlikely that *ochratoxin* is likely to be of much significance in the numerical grades of grain in the U.S.

Other Comments. A. ochraceus, in our experience, never predominates in a given lot of grain, even one that is undergoing or has undergone spoilage. We seldom have recovered it from more than 5% of surface-disinfected kernels of wheat or corn undergoing spoilage in the U.S.; in Mexico we have recovered *A. ochraceus* from 20 to 40% of some lots of partially spoiled corn from commercial storage. If it were recovered from more than 5 to 10% of surface-disinfected kernels of a given lot, either that amount of partly deteriorated grain was added to or mixed with the lot at some time in the past, or deterioration is under way at present.

Aspergillus flavus

Lower Limit of Moisture for Growth.

Corn and wheat	18.0–18.5%
Sorghum	19.0–19.5%
Soybeans	17.0–17.5%

Effects. A. flavus kills and discolors germs and decays and discolors whole kernels, causes rapid heating up to 130°F. *A. flavus* and *A. candidus* are the chief causes of heating of stored grains up to 130°F.

Possible Toxicity. Some isolates, under some conditions of growth, produce aflatoxins. According to the evidence of the USDA workers at the Northern Regional Research Laboratory, aflatoxins are not likely to be present in significant amounts in grains such as wheat, corn, and sorghum, or in soybeans. Peanuts and peanut meal, cottonseed and cottonseed meal, and fishmeal are more likely to contain aflatoxin than the cereal grains or soybeans. Aflatoxin and other mycotoxins are discussed more fully later in the chapter.

Other Comments. The presence of *A. flavus* in surface-disinfected kernels is evidence of poor storage in the past, or of spoilage underway at present, in the bin from which samples were taken. If *A. flavus* increases between sampling periods from a given bin, it is evidence of spoilage somewhere in the bin, with heating and more spoilage likely to develop rapidly. As with *A. candidus*, any increase in *A. flavus* in the grain in a given bin is cause for immediate action – aeration, turning, drying, or utilization of the grain. If the moisture content of the grain is high enough to permit growth of *A. flavus*, aeration with air of low temperature may be required to prevent aflatoxin production.

Penicillium

Lower Limit of Moisture for Growth.

Corn and wheat	16.5–19.0%
Sorghum	17.0–19.5%
Soybeans	16.0–18.5%

Effects. Penicillium kills and discolors germs and whole kernels of seeds, causes mustiness and caking, and may be involved in early stages of heating, but does not cause such heating as rapidly or to so high a temperature as *A. candidus* and *A.*

flavus. It causes blue-eye in corn stored with a moisture content above 18.5% and at low temperature (*A. restrictus* and *A. glaucus* cause blue-eye in corn stored with moisture contents of 14.0 to 15.5%).

Possible Toxicity. Isolates of several different species of *Penicillium*, when grown as pure cultures in the laboratory, produce compounds toxic to various kinds of animals; how much of this is a laboratory phenomenon only is not known at present. The hemorrhagic syndrome in chicks, and an occasionally severe disease of turkey poults involving liver lesions, are suspected to be due to consumption of feeds heavily invaded by certain species of *Penicillium*, but this has not been proven beyond question. Feeds invaded by *Penicillium* and by some other fungi may result in less efficient weight gains than sound feeds.

Other Comments. Some common seed-invading species of *Penicillium* are able to grow at temperatures of 34° to 40°F., and some can grow slowly at a temperature below freezing. In spite of this, low temperature often is a very effective preservative of quality for stored grains with high moisture contents.

IV. WHEN STORAGE FUNGI INVADE SEEDS

It has been supposed by many of those in charge of and responsible for maintenance of quality in stored grains and seeds that, if loss in quality caused by storage fungi occurred in the seeds under their care, it must have resulted from damaging invasion of the seeds by storage fungi before harvest. They insist, often with vehemence, that the condition of the grain in question when under their care was such that storage fungi could not possibly have grown in it. This point is an important one, and for this reason considerable research has been devoted to determining whether seeds are invaded by storage fungi before harvest or after. The evidence from all of this is consistent: There is no significant invasion of seeds by storage fungi before harvest. The kinds of seeds studied have included wheat, barley, oats, rice, sorghum, maize, common beans, soybeans, and seeds of various kinds of vegetables; and the regions where this work has been done, or from where seeds were collected, included North and South America, Europe, Africa, and Southeast Asia. Many thousands of samples have been tested, over a period of more than 20 years. It is, of course, theoretically possible that some kinds of seeds under some circumstance may be heavily invaded by storage fungi before harvest – all we can say is that up to now, no such lots have been found. Some of the work concerning this is worth looking at more closely.

Tuite and Christensen (1957) collected ripe heads from plants of different varieties and classes of wheat in several states over a period of three harvest seasons. Some of the plants had been left standing in the field for as long as a month after normal harvest time, or were in shocks or in windrows, at times exposed to frequent rains. From 50 to 100 kernels of each sample were surface-disinfected and put on an agar medium favorable to the growth of storage fungi. Storage fungi grew from less than 5% of the kernels. About 3,000 kernels of wheat were collected from the field at harvest time and from combines and, *without being subjected to any surface disinfection*, were similarly put on an agar medium favorable to the growth of storage fungi. *Aspergillus glaucus* grew from about 5% on these, and other storage fungi grew from less than slightly less than 7% – and probably most of these were contaminants from laboratory air. Tuite (1959) cultured 73,000 surface-disinfected kernels of soft red winter wheat from 732 samples collected in Indiana, some from fields that remained unharvested for several weeks after the grain had ripened, because of heavy rains. Storage fungi grew from only 25 kernels, or 1 in 3,000. Tuite and Christensen (1955) collected many samples of mature barley kernels from plants in fields in Minnesota during moist weather, with frequent showers, when relative humidities above 75% sometimes prevailed for several days at a time. Some of the plants from which the samples were taken were lodged, and many kernels were severely discolored by field fungi. Kernels were lightly surface-disinfected and put on malt-salt agar for the detection of storage fungi. Some colonies of *Aspergillus flavus* developed in one of the dishes, almost certainly from contamination by airborne spores during the culturing process, and not from the grain itself. No storage fungi, other than those contaminants, grew from seeds. Both Tuite (1961) and Qasem and Christensen (1958) reported that very few surface-disinfected kernels of corn from plants in the field yielded storage fungi, even when the plants from which the kernels were collected had stood for some time in the field after normal harvest time and had been exposed to frequent rains. Kaufmann (1959) tested many hundreds of samples of wheat from lots arriving at terminal elevators in different sections of the U.S. over a period of 3 years. *Alternaria*, a common field fungi in wheat and in other small grains, grew from 48 to 83% of the surface-disinfected kernels; *A. glaucus*, from 1.4 to 10.9%; *A. flavus*, from 0.0 to 3.7%; *A. candidus*, from 0 to 0.5%; and *Penicillium*, from 0.0 to 0.8%. Some of these lots from which the samples were taken had passed through country elevators on their way to terminals, and it is highly probable that they contained at least some grain from a previous year's crop, since such "mixing off" is a common practice. It is possible that the different amounts of infection by storage fungi in these samples reflected the different amounts of such mixing in of old grain in the lots from which the samples came. In any case, very few of the thousands of samples examined were extensively invaded by storage fungi, and it is highly probable that those few had been in storage for some time before they arrived at the terminals. Thus, in many thousands of different kinds of grains taken from plants at or immediately after harvest, and over a period of 20 years, we have yet to find a single sample with more than a very light invasion of storage fungi in more than a small percentage of the seeds.

Under the conditions favorable to the growth of storage fungi, however, such invasion can occur within a few days. As an example, some years ago county elevator men in several locations in the winter-wheat growing area of the U.S. collected maturing wheat heads and sent them to us. We removed the kernels and incubated them on agar to determine whether they were invaded by storage fungi. The results of this study are included in the data given above. No storage fungi ever were isolated from these samples, with one exception. In that exception the green heads of wheat had been wrapped in waxed paper before they were mailed to us. The waxed paper served as a moist chamber, and in the 3 days that elapsed between the time the heads were collected in the field and the time they arrived at the laboratory, 100% of the surface-disinfected kernels that were put on agar yielded *Aspergillus glaucus*; when the heads were removed from the envelope in which they were sent, in fact, *A. glaucus* could be seen sporulating heavily on the glumes that

TABLE I

Storage fungi from wheat collected at various places from field to terminal, cultured without surface disinfection on malt-salt agar[a]

Sources of Samples	No. of Samples	No. of Kernels	Percentage of Kernels Yielding Fungi	
			A. glaucus	Other storage fungi
Heads of standing, shocked, and windrowed wheat	27	2,050	4.8	2.7
Combines	7	1,000	4.8	6.8
Country elevators, new crop	16	800	50.0	8.0
Trucks from country elevators unloading at terminal	12	575	64.0	6.0

[a]Tuite and Christensen (1957).

covered the kernels. Some of the data from work on this problem are summarized in Tables I and II.

V. CONDITIONS REQUIRED FOR GROWTH OF STORAGE FUNGI

Like other living things, storage fungi require food, water, a favorable temperature, a suitable atmosphere, and time. In practice, in farm or commercial storage, the critical factor usually is moisture, but temperature and time may be important too. Also, the rate at which storage fungi develop on the grain in a given bin, and the amount of damage they cause, will be influenced by the degree or extent to which the grain already has been invaded by these fungi (in different lots of grade No. 2 corn or wheat, invasion by storage fungi may range from 0 to 100%); by the amount of cracked and broken kernels and debris; and by the presence, numbers, and kinds of insects and mites. Each of these factors will be discussed separately, but in practice they are interrelated and interacting.

TABLE II

Percentage of surface-disinfected kernels of wheat yielding Alternaria and storage fungi in crop years 1953-54, 1954-55, and 1955-56 as the grain arrived at terminal elevators[a]

Region of U.S.	Alternaria	Storage Fungi			
		A. glaucus	*A. flavus*	*A. candidus*	*Penicillium*
East	71.2	6.6	0.8	0.3	0.8
Southeast	66.6	8.0	3.7	0.5	0.4
Northwest	60.5	10.9	1.1	0.3	0.3
Central	83.4	10.0	1.6	0.1	0.3
South	58.2	9.2	1.8	0.4	0.3
Southwest	67.8	7.5	0.7	0.2	0.1
Pacific Northwest[b]	48.4	1.4	0.0	0.0	0.0

[a]Kaufmann (1959).
[b]One year only.

A. Moisture

The lower limits of relative humidity that permit the different common storage fungi to grow, assuming a favorable temperature, are summarized in Table III, and the moisture contents of common grains and seeds in equilibrium with these relative humidities are summarized in Table IV. The lower moisture-content limits that permit invasion by the individual fungi are given in the previous section, in which the individual species are described. Actually, the data on lower limits of moisture content that permit invasion by the different fungi are only approximate, because the moisture content of a given kind of grain in equilibrium with a given relative humidity can vary considerably. Fairbrother (1929) mixed wheats of different moisture contents and allowed the mixture to reach equilibrium. The originally moister lot retained a moisture content 1 to 2% higher than the originally drier lot. The same has been shown in corn by Hubbard et al. (1957) and by Tuite and Foster (1963), and in rice by Schroeder and Sorenson (1961).

Most corn or maize in commercial channels in the U.S. has been artificially dried. A common practice is to dry a portion of a given lot to a moisture content below the limit of 15.5% specified for grade No. 2 corn, then to mix this with another portion, or several other portions, of higher moisture content to achieve an average of 15.5%. During a storage period of 3 to 6 months, a given lot may undergo numerous mixes. Depending on how long and at what temperatures these lots were stored before they were dried and mixed, one, both, or all may have been invaded to a moderate extent by storage fungi and may be of high storage risk. That is, among a hundred lots of corn, all of grade No. 2, there may be a tremendous range in degree of invasion by storage fungi and therefore in storability or deterioration risk. This will be discussed more fully below.

The Official Grain Standards of the United States (USDA, 1964) specify the maximum moisture content permitted in each of the numerical grades of grains and seeds. As emphasized by Christensen and Kaufmann (1969), these specifications were developed to promote orderly marketing; they do not indicate safe moisture contents for storage. The upper moisture limits for grades No. 2 or 3 corn (15.5 and 17.5%, respectively) or for grades No. 2 or 3 soybeans (14.0 and 16.0%, respectively) are too high for safe storage for more than a short time unless the temperature is so low that storage fungi cannot grow.

Moisture content may vary considerably from place to place in a given bulk or bin. Christensen and Drescher (1954) reported a range in moisture contents from a

TABLE III

Minimum relative humidity for the growth of common storage fungi at their optimum temperature for growth (26°-30° C.)

Fungus	Minimum Relative Humidity
Aspergillus halophilicus	68
A. restrictus, Sporedonema	70
A. glaucus	73
A. candidus, A. ochraceus	80
A. flavus	85
Penicillium, depending on species	80–90

TABLE IV

Moisture contents of various grains and seeds in equilibrium with different relative humidities at 25°-30°C.

Relative Humidity	Wheat, Corn, Sorghum	Rice		Soybeans	Sunflower	
		Rough	Polished		Seeds	Meats
65	12.5–13.5	12.5	14.0	12.5	8.5	5.0
70	13.5–14.5	13.5	15.0	13.0	9.5	6.0
75	14.5–15.5	14.5	15.5	14.0	10.5	7.0
80	15.5–16.5	15.0	16.5	16.0	11.5	8.0
85	18.0–18.5	16.5	17.5	18.0	13.5	9.0

low of 10% to a high of 18% in a bin of wheat in which the moisture content of a representative sample was 13.2%. Christensen and Kaufmann (1969) cite a case in which a bin of wheat in a terminal elevator began to heat, although according to the warehouse records it had a moisture content of only 12.2%. As the bin was emptied, samples were taken from the belt near the hopper. Some of these samples had moisture contents over 16%; some mixing had inevitably occurred as the grain flowed out, so that some of the grain in the bin probably had an even higher moisture content. Some of the damaged kernels, when surface-disinfected and plated on agar, yielded the storage fungus *Aspergillus flavus*. This fungus cannot grow in wheat with a moisture content below 18.5%, and it furnished positive biological evidence that some of the grain had a moisture content of 18.5%, not 12.2% as indicated on the warehouse records. Ramstad and Geddes (1943) found samples of soybeans with a moisture content of 28% in a bin where the average moisture content of the beans was 15%. In our experience, such differences in moisture contents from place to place are common, not rare, and they explain the cases of "mysterious" heating in which grain supposedly too dry to support the growth of storage fungi still was heated and spoiled by fungi. The only way to determine the range of moisture contents within a given bin is to take samples from different places and test each one separately.

Differences in temperature between different portions of a grain bulk can result in fairly rapid transfer of moisture — the higher the moisture content of the grain and the greater the temperature differences, the greater the transfer. Johnson (1957) calculated that in a large bin of corn with 14.5% moisture, a temperature differential of about 22°C. between the interior and the surface of the bulk would result, in 20 days, in sufficient transfer of moisture to raise the moisture content of a layer 6 in. deep on the surface of the bulk to 20%. Holman (1950) reported that soybeans stored in November, 1942, with an average moisture content of 12 to 13%, had, by February, 1943, a moisture content of 16 to 17% in the center of the upper surface of the bulk. By February, 1944, after 15 months of storage, the moisture content of the beans in the center of the upper surface of the bulk ranged from 20 to 24%. Christensen (1970) stored sorghum seeds of 14.3% moisture in a gallon glass jug and maintained a temperature of 10° to 15°C. higher in the grain near one side than in the grain near the opposite side. After only 3 days, the moisture content of the grain on the cool side was 1.4% higher than that of the grain on the warm side; and after 6 days the difference was 2.0%. Additional tests have confirmed the fact that relatively small differences in temperature, if constantly maintained, will result in relatively rapid transfer of moisture from the warmer to the cooler portion of a grain bulk. Localized infestations of insects, mites, or storage fungi within a bulk may result in even more rapid transfer, since the rise in temperature owing to the activity of the organisms is accompanied by production of metabolic water. One of the functions of aeration is to maintain a uniform temperature throughout a given bulk and reduce moisture transfer to a minimum. Absolute, or even approximate, uniformity in moisture content throughout a bulk of thousands, tens of thousands, or hundreds of thousands of bushels of grain in a given bin probably is impossible to achieve. Good storage practices require that the man in charge of the grain know the range of moisture contents in the grain under his charge, and this can be done only by periodically withdrawing samples and testing each separately. Concerning moisture content, Christensen and Kaufmann (1968) stated, "Sometimes the moisture content indicated on warehouse records differs from the moisture content of grain in the bin." To quote from them further:

The usual practice is to take an average sample from each lot of grain going into a bin and determine its moisture content. The overall average, or the weighted average, of these samples is considered by many warehousemen to be the average moisture content of the grain throughout its storage life. There are several sources of error:

1. An average sample from a given lot does not indicate the range of moisture content in that lot. A range of plus or minus 1 to 2 percent can be expected in the moisture content of grain in any carload or truckload. For safe storage it is essential that the highest moisture content in any portion of a given lot be known.

2. The meter or the operator may not be functioning properly. The accuracy of the meter should be tested occasionally, either by measuring moisture content of samples by oven drying or by submitting samples to state or federal grain inspection offices. With machines such as the Motomco, the quantity of grain must be weighed accurately and its temperature measured accurately. No moisture meter is infallible, and occasionally a meter may err by plus or minus 0.5 percent or more. For this reason, if the moisture content of a given lot of grain is near or within the range where deterioration might occur, several samples should be taken and their moisture contents determined. This also should be done with lots that are to be mixed to achieve an average moisture content considered safe for storage.

3. Moisture may shift from place to place in a bulk of stored grain. We have found the moisture content of some samples of grain taken from a bin of wheat to be 6 percent above the average given on the warehouse records. This transfer of moisture usually is greatest in winter in cool regions such as the northern United States. In winter the upper layers of corn in bins may accumulate a moisture content of 20-25 percent. When the temperature rises in the spring, some of this moist corn may germinate and storage fungi may invade the rest rapidly enough to cause heating. This has given rise to the old superstition that grain, especially corn, has an urge to heat and germinate in the spring. Corn and other grains germinate when they are moist enough and warm enough; they heat when they are invaded by insects or storage fungi.

4. Mixing grain lots of different moisture content to get an average presumed to be safe for storage or to meet a given grade may result in trouble. The moisture content in such mixes may never equalize, and many mixes have a very high storage risk.

5. In a supposedly uniform lot of grain there may be differences of as much as 1 percent in the moisture content of individual kernels.

6. Activities of insects and mites can increase the moisture content of grain rapidly – in some tests as much as 2 percent per month and a total of 5-10 percent in a few months. Fumigation may rid the grain of insects (some fumigants that kill insects do not kill mites) but the storage fungi continue to grow.

B. Temperature

Within certain limits, low temperature can be as effective as low moisture in preventing damage to stored grain by fungi and in preserving quality. This is

TABLE V

Approximate minimum, optimum, and maximum temperatures for growth of common storage fungi on grains

Fungus	Temperature for Growth, °C.		
	Minimum	Optimum	Maximum
Aspergillus restrictus	5–10	30–35	40–45
A. glaucus	0– 5	30–35	40–45
A. candidus	10–15	45–50	50–55
A. flavus	10–15	40–45	45–50
Penicillium	–5– 0	20–25	35–40

illustrated in Figure 1 from Qasem and Christensen (1958). Papavizas and Christensen (1958) stated that in white wheat stored at 15.0 to 15.5% moisture and 5° and 10°C. there was no invasion by storage fungi and no reduction in germinability in 12 months, but at 16.0 to 16.5% moisture and at 5° and 10°C. there was considerable reduction in germinability in 12 months. The approximate minimum, optimum, and maximum temperatures for growth of common storage fungi are summarized in Table V. Refrigerated storage, a comparatively recent development, is discussed in Chapter 11. Christensen and Kaufmann (1969) state, "The effect of temperature on the growth of storage fungi and on the damage they do has some complexities too. Corn or wheat that has not been invaded by storage fungi to any serious degree or extent, and is otherwise sound and in good condition, can be stored at a moisture content of 15.0% for nine months to a year without damage even if the temperature is 45°–50°F. If, on the other hand, the grain already has been moderately to heavily invaded by storage fungi, and is stored at a moisture content of 15.0% and a temperature of 45°–50°F., the fungi may continue to grow, and within six months may cause extensive spoilage. This is another case where information on the number and kinds of fungi on grain going into long-time storage greatly aids a warehouseman in evaluating grain condition and storability."

C. Oxygen-Carbon Dioxide

There are statements in the literature to the effect that all fungi are strictly aerobic, and this has been repeated so often that it has become part of the credo of even professional mycologists. It is false. Tabak and Cooke (1968) incubated a number of fungi, isolated from sewage sludges, in microaerophilic and anaerobic conditions in the laboratory. All of the fungi they tested, including *Fusarium*, grew to some extent under conditions as anaerobic as could be maintained in the laboratory. As judged by the weight of cell-mass produced, the rate of growth under strictly anaerobic conditions ranged from 20 to 50% of that which occurred under aerobic conditions. Yeasts, including *Candida* (or *Pullularia*), are common on maize silage and on some lots of moist grain in which near-anaerobic conditions have prevailed. It is possible that the lack of obvious development of filamentous fungi on corn (maize) silage is the result of competition with the acid-forming bacteria that usually predominate, rather than to inability to grow under high carbon dixoide and low oxygen concentration. Peterson et al. (1956), working with wheat at 18% moisture and 30°C., found that growth of storage fungi was reduced with decreasing oxygen concentration, but some growth occurred even at 0.2% oxygen; mold growth also decreased with increasing concentration of carbon dioxide above about 14%. Anaerobic or sealed storage of high-moisture grain is discussed in Chapter 10.

D. Degree of Invasion by Storage Fungi

Seeds invaded to some extent by storage fungi will, if kept under conditions that permit the fungi to increase, be invaded further, and will lose quality faster, than sound seeds stored under the same conditions. Table VI illustrates this. Christensen and Kaufmann (1969) state: "In Grade No. 2 yellow corn, there may be a very wide range in storability. We have sampled some bins of 100,000 bushels each of No. 2 yellow corn in which none of the samples taken from the bin had a moisture content over 14.2%, there was no germ damage, none of the kernels were invaded by storage fungi, and even germination (not considered in grade) exceeded 95%. This corn was essentially of seed grade and, by the way, it was kept in storage for four years without any damage or any decrease in grade.

"We have sampled other lots of No. 2 yellow corn in which the moisture content was 15.2%, slightly below the allowable maximum, 80 – 90% of the surface-disinfected kernels yielded storage fungi, germ damage was 5% (the maximum allowable in grade No. 2), and another 20 – 30% of the kernels had slightly discolored (and dead) germs which, at any temperature over 60 F and at a moisture content as high as this corn had, would soon become brown, and the germination was 40%. Kept at 25 C (77 F) for several months, this lot developed very heavy damage from fungi, especially "blue-eye" from masses of spores of *Aspergullis glaucus* produced on the surface of the germ under the pericarp. Samples stored at 20 C (68 F) developed somewhat less, but still extensive, damage.

"That is, one of the lots described above was sound, the other was partly deteriorated. Both were No. 2 yellow corn and commanded the same price. One could be stored without risk of deterioration, the other could not be. Simple laboratory tests would serve to distinguish such lots easily."

E. Foreign Material

This consists of seed fragments plus extraneous material such as weed seeds and assorted debris. The Official Grain Standards of the United States (USDA, 1964), for example, has the following definition for foreign material in corn: "(g) *Broken corn and foreign material*. Broken corn and foreign material shall be kernels and pieces of kernels of corn and all matter other than corn which will pass readily through a 12/64 sieve, and all matter other than corn which remains in the sieved sample." This debris is likely to be contaminated with some kinds of insects, mites, and storage fungi, and furnishes a good breeding ground for them. Also, when bulk grain is loaded into a bin from an overhead spout, this fine material accumulates as a column in the grain below the spout – the so-called "spout-line." By actual test, corn containing only 2 to 3% of foreign material when loaded into a bin had over 50% foreign material in the spout line. If air is forced through the grain in such a bin, it will channel around the central column of tightly packed material and in that portion of the grain the beneficial effects of aeration will be reduced or nullified.

TABLE VI

Germination, germ discoloration, and fungus invasion of three commercial samples of Grade No. 2 yellow dent corn and one sample of seed-grade yellow dent corn stored 2 and 4 months at 16% moisture content and 25° C.[a]

Sample	Months Stored	Germination %	% Germs Discolored		% Surface-Disinfected Kernels Yielding *A. glaucus*	Mold Count (thousands)
			Brown	Ochre		
Commercial, A.	0	50	1	16	40	7.5
	2	12	2	14	80	60
	4	0	16	26	100	442
Commercial, B.	0	62	2	11	55	11.5
	2	1	6	28	100	350
	4	0	18	46	100	960
Commercial, C.	0	48	5	22	46	81
	2	6	10	36	100	700
	4	0	28	58	100	1,200
Seed-Grade	0	98	0	0	4	4
	2	98	0	2	48	48
	4	69	4	14	100	92

[a]From Qasem and Christensen (1960).

F. Insects and Mites

Some kinds of grain-infesting insects such as the weevils, in which the larvae and pupae develop within the infested kernels, carry large numbers of spores of storage fungi, and a developing infestation will provide both the temperature and moisture to promote rapid growth of storage fungi. Agrawal et al. (1957) reported that in wheat originally of 14.6 to 14.8% moisture, an infestation by granary weevils, *Sitophilus granarius*, resulted in 3 months in an increase of moisture to 17.6 to 23%, whereas in the samples not infested with weevils the moisture did not increase. They stated that "—rather forceful aeration was required (with air at a relative humidity of 75%) to maintain a uniform moisture content when the insects were increasing." Christensen and Hodson (1960), and Misra et al. (1961), reported similar increases in moisture content accompanied by rapid increase in storage fungi, of grain infested with weevils. Sinha (1961) found the moisture content in grain in hot spots engendered by insects, and in grain above the hot spots, to be considerably higher than that of noninfested grain in the same bin. Amos (1948) reported that an infestation of mites in flour raised the moisture content from an original figure of 15.4 to 28.10% in 18 months. Grain-infesting mites also are associated with storage fungi. Griffiths et al. (1959) stated: "Grain-infesting mites *Acarus siro* and *Tyrophagus castellanii* were found in some abundance in samples of commercially stored wheat, the moisture contents of which ranged from 13.5 to 15.0%, which is the range of moisture contents at which the fungi in the *Aspergillus glaucus* group are likely to predominate. These mites, when developing in moldy grain, picked up spores of the storage fungi and carried these spores on the outside of their bodies, in their digestive tract, and in their feces. As they entered clean grain they inoculated it heavily with spores of these fungi and later they fed to a considerable extent upon the fungi that developed."

VI. EFFECTS OF FUNGAL INVASION

Invasion of stored grains and seeds by storage fungi can result in: a) decrease in germinability; b) discoloration; c) production of mycotoxins; d) heating; e) mustiness; and, finally, f) total decay.

A. Decrease in Germinability

That invasion by storage fungi can result in loss of germinability of the seed is now so well established that it no longer can be questioned. Good examples are given in Figures 1 and 2 and in Table VI. The data of Fields and King (1962) with peas are especially impressive, since in their tests the samples of peas free of storage fungi retained a germination of 98% throughout the period of the tests, whereas all of those that had been inoculated with various storage fungi were reduced to zero germination. Many other agents and processes can result in loss of germinability of seeds also, but, under the conditions that prevail when storage fungi invade seeds, they can and do contribute significantly to reduced germinability.

B. Discoloration

Both field and storage fungi may cause discoloration of whole seeds or of portions of them, particularly the germ and embryo, the preferred site of invasion, as already mentioned. According to the Official Grain Standards of the United States (USDA, 1964), "Damaged kernels shall be kernels and pieces of kernels of corn which are heat damaged, sprouted, frosted, badly ground damaged, badly weather damaged, moldy, diseased, or otherwise materially damaged". Except for sprouted and frosted kernels, all of the above involve different degrees of discoloration of the kernels. The wording of the above description implies that an inspector can distinguish the cause of the discoloration, which probably is not true. Christensen et al. (1971) examined kernels from more than a hundred lots of 100% damaged corn obtained from USDA Grain Inspection Offices, and found that the embryos of all damaged kernels were decayed to some extent by fungi. Both field and storage fungi were involved. Schroeder and Sorenson (1961) stated that what is called heat damage in rough rice may develop without any detectable rise in temperature, the discoloration presumably being caused by storage fungi. They state, "There was no correlation between 'heat-damage' and the temperature of the rice. These data show that 'heat damage' did not occur in relation to heating of stored rough rice but instead was associated with a high level of invasion by storage molds." Lutey (1961) isolated a bacterium, tentatively identified as *Bacterium herbicola* Burri & Duggeli, from stained barley that, when inoculated onto barley kernels with 40 to 45% moisture, caused the kernels to become jet black in a few days. After these kernels were dried they became very friable; in both color and texture they resembled kernels partially carbonized by heat.

Wheat in storage sometimes develops dark-brown to black germs, and then is known as "germ-damaged" or "sick" wheat. These discolored germs are high in fatty acids and also are very friable (two characteristics of plant tissues that have been decayed by fungi). When milled, such germs fragment and end up on the flour, and contribute undesirable characteristics to it. In the laboratory, wheat germs can be made to turn brown by various treatments — exposure to heat, to a combination of high temperature and high moisture, to toxic vapors or liquids, invasion by fungi and bacteria, etc. According to the evidence of Christensen (1955) and of Papavizas and Christensen (1957) it is highly probably that invasion of the germs by storage fungi is a major cause of this degrading (in a quality sense) discoloration.

Christensen (1955) stated, "Germination of the seed, and number and kinds of molds present, were determined in 'sick' and sound seeds picked from 26

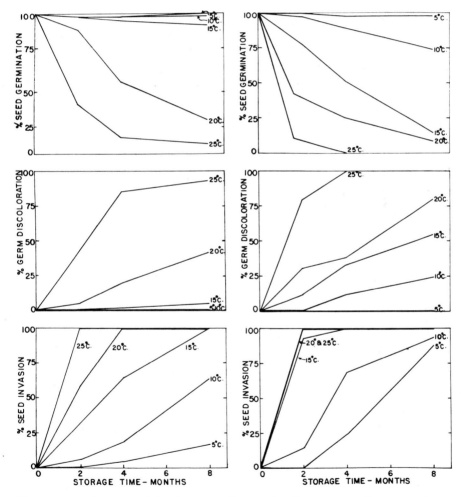

Figure 1. Percentage of seeds invaded, germs discolored, and germination of yellow dent corn inoculated with a mixture of fungi and stored 8 months at 5° to 25° C. and 16% (left) or 18% (right) moisture content.

commercial samples containing from 5 – 55% 'sick' wheat, and in sound wheat from bulks in which no deterioration had occurred. The germination of 'sick' seed always was zero; *molds were microscopically visible on the germs of 49% of the seeds* (italics mine); they had an average mold count of 402,000/g; and 94% of the surface-disinfected seeds yielded storage molds. The 'sound' seeds picked from the lots in which deterioration had occurred had an average germination of 43% and an average mold count of 32,000/g, and 84% of the surface-disinfected seeds yielded storage molds. The really sound seeds from bulks in which no deterioration had occurred had an average germination of 91%, an average mold count of less than 1,000/g, and 27% of the surface-disinfected seeds yielded storage molds. The major fungi present in the 'sick' seeds were *Aspergillus restrictus, A. repens, A. candidus,* and *A. flavus.* Judged by various microscopic and cultural technics, all samples of 'sick' wheat had been very heavily invaded by storage molds; all of the evidence indicated that invasion of the germs of the seeds by these molds had preceded decrease in germination and increase in 'sick' wheat. In commercial storage, it seems very probable that invasion of the germs of the seed by common species of *Aspergillus* is a common cause of 'sick' wheat." The evidence is even stronger now: No agent other than storage fungi has been shown to produce "sick" wheat in commercial storage.

Christensen and Kaufmann (1969) state, "However, neither in the laboratory of

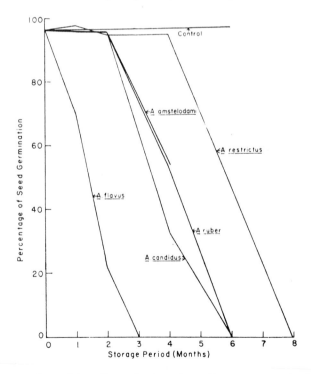

Figure 2. A comparison of the effects of various *Aspergillus* spp. on germination of pea seed stored at 30°C. and 85% relative humidity.

the Department of Plant Pathology of the University of Minnesota, where since about 1948 thousands of samples of wheat have been examined, including many hundreds with different amounts of germ damage, nor at the Grain Research Laboratory at Cargill, Inc., where since 1952 many thousands of samples of wheat from commercial storage throughout the United States have been examined, have we ever encountered a single case of germ damaged or sick wheat in which storage fungi were not involved."

C. Heating

At one time it was thought that the respiration of moist grain itself was chiefly responsible for the heating that sometimes accompanies spoilage. Actually, there is no evidence whatever that respiration of the seeds themselves, or of seed enzymes, is at all significantly involved in heating. Darsie et al. (1914) reported that germinating seeds in Dewar bottles, with moisture contents and respiration rates much higher than seeds in storage have, raised the temperature within the bottles only 1° to 3°C., whereas the lots of seeds overgrown with fungi increased 10°C. in temperature in 4 to 5 days, at which time the tests were ended. Hummel et al. (1954) found that respiration of wheat free of storage fungi, with moisture contents of 14 to 18%, and kept at 35°C., was so low that it was not detectable. There are no other reports on the respiration of grains, either free of or invaded by storage fungi, at moisture contents in equilibrium with relative humidities of 70 to 80%, the moisture contents at which, in actual storage, deterioration gets under way. By the time that metabolic water from the fungi, plus water from heat distillation resulting from fungus growth, has raised the moisture of the grain high enough so that seed respiration might come into play, the seeds are decayed and dead. Seed respiration could not possibly raise the temperature of the grain higher than the germinating seeds themselves can endure, which probably is not above 30°C. for the common cereal seeds at moisture contents high enough for respiration to occur. Dead seeds do not respire. The evidence by Ramstad and Geddes (1943), Milner and Geddes (1945, 1946), Carlyle and Norman (1941), Carter (1950), and Christensen and Gordon (1948) is consistent in showing that microflora are primarily, and often solely, responsible for the heating of moist grains and other moist plant materials. Walker (1967) revealed the vital role of water in spontaneous combustion of these materials. Briefly, the heating process of grain in farm and commercial bins is about as follows: Either some of the grain is moist enough when stored, or through moisture transfer later acquires a high enough moisture content, so that *Aspergillus restrictus* and *A. glaucus* can grow. *A. restrictus* grows so slowly that it probably does not increase either the temperature or moisture content of the grain appreciably (no one ever has attempted to measure the respiration of this important and ubiquitous storage fungus on grains in equilibrium with relative humidities of 70 to 75%). *A. glaucus*, however, if growing rapidly, can increase the temperature of the grain at least to 35° to 40°C. This results in some increase in moisture content in the grain where the fungus is growing, and a greater increase in the grain just above. Once the moisture content of the grain exceeds 15.0 to 15.5%, *A. candidus* can grow; and given optimum conditions, it can increase the moisture content and temperature of the grain rapidly. Once the moisture content of the grain reaches that in equilibrium with a relative humidity of 85% (18.5% moisture in the cereal seeds), *A. flavus* can grow. *A. candidus* and *A. flavus* together can increase the temperature of the grain to 55°C. and hold it there for weeks. Depending on whether the metabolic and distillation water from the activities of these fungi is carried off or whether it accumulates in the grain, the heating may gradually subside, or may pass into the next stage in which thermophilic bacteria plus perhaps a variety of thermophilic fungi may be involved — organisms which require free water. These free-water-requiring organisms are not likely to be involved in the earlier stages of heating because then no free water is available. They may carry the temperature up to 75°C., after which the purely chemical processes may take over and carry the temperature to the point of combustion. The question often comes up, in court cases involving settlement of losses of grain insured against fire, as to whether a given lot was "bin-burned" or "fire-burned". These cases are settled by the persuasiveness of the attorneys concerned, not by evidence.

D. Mustiness, Caking, and Total Decay

These are the final stages of spoilage caused by fungi, when the organisms involved become detectable by the unaided eye, and also by the unaided nose. By many warehousemen these are thought to be the first stages of decay, which of course is erroneous.

VII. CONTROL OF STORAGE FUNGI

A. Low Moisture and Temperature

By far the most generally used method of preserving quality in stored grains and seeds is storage at moisture contents too low for fungi to grow. Either a low temperature or a low moisture content is effective in prolonging viability and maintaining quality in most agricultural seeds. A combination of the two is even better. A low and uniform moisture content (in the grain in the bin, not merely on the warehouse records) and a low and uniform temperature also reduce the possibility of moisture transfer within the bulk or package, and add greatly to the storage life of the grain.

Sealed storage is discussed in Chapter 10, and refrigerated storage in Chapter 11.

B. Fungicides

It often is assumed that because many plant diseases, as well as decay and rot of many kinds of materials, can be prevented with suitable fungicides, the same should apply to storage fungi on seeds. There are several things to consider. The storage fungi grow in seeds and in other materials whose moisture contents are in equilibrium with relative humidities of 70 to 90%. No free water is available. Fungicides whose effectiveness depends on their being dissolved in water may, under those conditions, not be at all fungicidal. We have treated seeds with good seed-treatment fungicides that protect them against damping off when the seeds are planted in moist soil, have stored the seeds at a relative humidity of 75%, and have seen heads of *Aspergillus* grow out with a visible dab of fungicide on each of them. Milner et al. (1947) tested more than 100 supposedly fungicidal compounds for control of storage fungi on wheat; none of them greatly inhibited the fungi without also killing the seed. We have tested in recent years numerous compounds submitted by commercial firms as inhibitors of storage fungi on grains. All of these have had serious limitations of one sort or another, such as toxicity to animals, excessive cost, difficulty of application, undesirable effects on processing quality of the grain, and lack of toxicity to storage fungi. Many of them were effective at one combination of moisture content-temperature-time, but not at another. In practice, a whole range of moisture content-temperature combinations may occur within a given bin or tank at a given time, and unless protection can be assured under all of these conditions throughout the storage life of the grain, a fungicide is of little value.

Propionic acid and combinations of propionic and acetic acids are effective preservatives of high-moisture grains to be used for feeds (Sauer, 1972; Lane, 1972). Such high-moisture, acid-treated grain has a higher feed efficiency, for beef and dairy cattle, than dry grain or than grain dried and remoistened (Lane, 1972; Perry, 1972; Wilson, 1972). It is not suitable for nonfeed uses.

C. Evaluation of Condition and Storability

Biochemical methods of estimating degree of deterioration of stored grains are described in Chapter 2; so far as we are aware, none of these are used routinely to evaluate condition of grain in commercial storage. del Prado and Christensen (1952) suggested determining number and kinds of fungi in individual samples drawn from a bulk, as a measure of deterioration risk. Welty et al. (1963) used this, plus measurement of moisture content of the individual samples, to judge condition and storability of maize kept in commercial bins for 4 years. Christensen (1971b) used essentially the same methods to evaluate condition and storability of sunflower seeds. Both of us have had extensive experience with these methods since about 1952, and have found them to be useful and usable. They will be described briefly.

SAMPLING PROCEDURE

When a bin, tank, or ship is loaded with grain, several samples are taken. These are put in moistureproof containers and sent to the laboratory. Depending on the characteristics of these samples as determined by laboratory tests, and by knowledge of the conditions likely to prevail in storage, a future sampling time is chosen.

LABORATORY TESTS

As soon as the samples are received in the laboratory, they are tested for moisture content (usually by Motomco meter and by oven drying), for germinability, and for percent of surface-disinfected seeds or kernels yielding field and storage fungi. Sometimes accelerated storage tests are made in which samples of about 300 g. are stored in closed containers, at the moisture contents at which they were received and at moisture contents in equilibrium with a relative humidity of 75%, at 30°C., and are subsequently examined and tested.

Increase in storage fungi between successive sampling periods means that incipient deterioration is under way, and such an increase can be detected long before any damage of practical significance has developed. Increase in storage fungi is accompanied by decrease in field fungi and is followed by decrease in germination percentage and germination vigor of the seed. Some judgment is required, of course, in interpretation of the results, since an increase of 20% in surface-disinfected kernels yielding *Aspergillus glaucus* is cause for watchfulness, not necessarily for alarm (depending upon the use to which the grain is to be put), but an increase of 20% in surface-disinfected kernels yielding *A. candidus* very definitely is cause for alarm, since it means that deterioration already is in progress, and that heating, if not already under way, soon will be.

Use of this technique, or these techniques, requires a laboratory equipped with facilities for mycological work, plus a person capable of recognizing most of the relatively few kinds of fungi likely to be encountered, and with the judgment necessary to interpret the results. Proof of the effectiveness of these techniques is that they have been in use in our laboratories since about 1952, primarily to evaluate condition and storability, or deterioration risk, of samples of grain from commercial bins and warehouses, and have worked out very well.

VIII. MYCOTOXINS

Mycotoxins are toxic metabolic products produced by fungi. They have been of great concern since about 1961 when aflatoxin, the first mycotoxin of known economic importance to be identified chemically, was shown to have been responsible for the death of large numbers of poultry in England. Because of the many accounts of mycotoxins now available, the present one will consist mainly of a brief summary of some of the more important mycotoxin problems in cereal grains and their products. Much of what follows is condensed from a recent review (Christensen, 1971a).

A. Books and Reviews on Mycotoxins

Ciegler and Lillehoj (1968) list 15 reviews and symposia proceedings published on mycotoxins in the 6-year period from 1962 through 1967. Additional ones have been published since by Hesseltine (1969) and Christensen (1971a). Meyer (1970) lists more than 1,200 papers dealing with aflatoxin alone in the decade from 1960 to 1970. Of the books dealing with the subject, *Mycotoxins in Foodstuffs* (Wogan, 1965) is a compilation of papers presented at a symposium held at the Massachusetts Institute of Technology in 1964. The major emphasis is on aflatoxin, but chapters are devoted to alimentary toxic aleukia in man, facial eczema in ruminants, toxic moldy rice, Stachybotryotoxicosis, toxins produced by *Penicillium islandicum*, and to various aspects of fungi on stored grains and on other foods. *Moisissures Toxiques dans l'Alimentation* by Moreau (1968) summarizes the information on the mycology, pathology, and chemistry of all the major and minor mycotoxins and mycotoxicoses; it has 1,403 references. *Aflatoxin, Scientific Background, Control, and Implications* (Goldblatt, 1969) consists of thorough monographs by outstanding authorities on the major aspects of aflatoxins and aflatoxicoses, with one chapter devoted to other mycotoxins; it is required reading for anyone interested in the subject. *Toxic Micro-Organisms: Mycotoxins – Botulism* (Herzberg, 1970) is the proceedings of the U.S.-Japan conference on these subjects in 1968; 221 pages are devoted to mycotoxins, and the book is especially valuable both for the overall view of mycotoxins in general, and for the summaries of research on specific problems.

B. Major Mycotoxins and Mycotoxicoses

Aspergillus flavus AND AFLATOXINS

   A. flavus is a group species, sometimes designated *A. flavus-oryzae*. Raper and Fennell (1965) include 11 species in the group, most of which are not sharply delimited from one another and each of which probably contains an almost infinite number of varieties or races that differ from one another physiologically. Actually, *A. parasiticus* Spear, within the *A. flavus* or *A. flavus-oryzae* group, probably is a more common and more potent producer of aflatoxin than is *A. flavus* Link.

   Occurrence of A. flavus in Nature. *A. flavus*, like many other kinds of microbes, is almost ubiquitous. It occurs commonly in decaying vegetation of all kinds throughout the world. If grains, seeds, or other plant materials are stored at moisture contents and temperatures that favor the growth of *A. flavus*, it almost inevitably will develop from inoculum naturally present.

   Materials in which Aflatoxins Have Been Found. Borker et al. (1966) list the following in which aflatoxins have been found: cassava, cocoa, coconut, corn, cottonseed meal, fish meal, peanuts and peanut meal, peas, potatoes, rice, sake, soybeans, and wheat. Large concentrations of aflatoxin have been found in Brazil nuts and copra; one would expect to find aflatoxin occasionally in almost anything on which *A. flavus* grows, and, as indicated above, that includes well-nigh all plant parts and plant products. It also includes many animal products. Bullerman et al. (1969a, 1969b) inoculated various kinds of meats with aflatoxin-producing strains of *A. flavus* and *A. parasiticus*, incubated them under conditions favorable to the growth of *A. flavus*, and detected considerable amounts of aflatoxin in the meat. Some meat products are aged under conditions that permit rather profuse development of various fungi, especially species of *Aspergillus* and *Penicillium*.

   Since about 1965 investigators at the Northern Utilization and Development Laboratory, United States Department of Agriculture, Agricultural Research Service, at Peoria, Ill., have carried on a program of testing samples of grains and seeds from commercial channels for aflatoxin. The following quotations from Shotwell et al. (1969a, 1969b) summarize some of their results; "Very low levels of what appeared to be aflatoxin (2 to 19 p.p.b.) were detected by TLC in a total of 9 out of 1,368 assayed samples of wheat, grain sorghum, and oats. Samples that were positive by TLC were in the poorest grades. None of the results obtained by TLC was definitely confirmed by the duckling test, the sensitivity of which was 1 to 2 p.p.b." And, "Of the 1,311 corn samples assayed, 35 contained aflatoxins, primarily B-1, by TLC. Tests in ducklings confirmed the presence of aflatoxin in 30 of these positive samples. The 30 definitely positive samples contained aflatoxins at very low levels and were in the poorest grades (5 and SG). Levels of aflatoxin B-1 were 3 to 19 p.p.b., and the levels of G-1 in the five samples in which it was detected were 2 to 8 p.p.b. Our results indicate that the factors used to grade these corn samples would probably exclude from food markets samples likely to contain aflatoxin." And, "According to recent publications, the levels at which we detected aflatoxin in corn and soybeans would not be injurious to swine or cattle." There is always the chance, of course, that conditions in a given bin or tank of grain will become favorable for vigorous development of *A. flavus*, with resulting production of large amounts of aflatoxin.

   Krogh and Hald (1969) found aflatoxin in 86.5% of 52 samples of peanuts and peanut products (whole nuts, meal, and cake) imported into Denmark from ten countries. One sample contained 3,465 p.p.b. They stated, "As a direct consequence of these results the Danish Ministry of Agriculture in the fall [of] 1968 for use in feed manufacturing prohibited import of groundnut products which contain more than 100 μg aflatoxin per kg."

Conditions that Favor Growth of A. flavus and Production of Aflatoxin. A moisture content in equilibrium with a relative humidity of 85% is the minimum required for growth of *A. flavus* and for production of aflatoxin (Davis and Diener, 1970; Diener and Davis, 1969; Sanders et al., 1968). This is a moisture content of about 18.5%, wet-weight basis, in starchy cereal seeds such as maize, wheat, sorghum, and rice, and with a moisture content of about 8% in peanuts and in sunflower seed "meats". The optimum temperature for aflatoxin production is about 27°C., with 12°C. the lower limit and 40°C. the upper limit. Under optimum conditions some aflatoxin may be produced within 24 hr., with maximum production in 4 to 10 days. Not all strains of the *A. flavus* group produce aflatoxin, but strains which are capable of producing the toxin are common. Boller and Schroeder (1966) tested 284 isolates of *A. flavus* from rice, mainly from Texas, and 268 of these, or about 94%, produced some aflatoxin; 86 isolates, or 33%, under the conditions of their tests produced more than 10,000 p.p.b.

Effects of Aflatoxins on Animals. Aflatoxin B-1 is said to be the most potent hepatocarcinogen known (Butler, 1965). If consumed in amounts too small to cause obvious lesions it may result in slower than normal growth rate; in larger amounts it may cause various lesions, especially in the liver; and consumed in still larger amounts it may cause death.

Amounts of Aflatoxin Needed to Cause Injury. Different kinds of animals differ in their sensitivity to injury by aflatoxin. Rainbow trout and ducklings are very sensitive, and a ration containing less than 50 p.p.b. of aflatoxin, when consumed by them, will result in liver cancers (Halver, 1965; Carnaghan, 1965). Rats are relatively resistant to injury by aflatoxin, yet a diet containing only 15 p.p.b. of aflatoxin B-1 fed constantly resulted in a high incidence of liver cancer (Wogan and Newberne, 1967). Muller et al. (1970) fed 0.5, 1, 2, and 4 γ (mcg.) of aflatoxin B-1 to chicks, ducklings, pheasants, goslings, and turkey poults and stated, "The order of sensitivity from greatest to least was ducklings, turkey poults, goslings, young pheasants, and chicks. Chicks proved relatively resistant to aflatoxin injury." And, "All ducklings and turkey poults receiving the 1, 2, and 4 mcg/g diets died by the time of the termination of the trial and therefore they were the most severely affected species." There is other evidence that different breeds of chicks differ greatly in susceptibility to injury by aflatoxin, and so the place of chicks in the above order of sensitivity probably would depend on the breed used in the tests. Keyl et al. (1970) fed different amounts of aflatoxin to swine for 120 days and to Hereford beef steers for 4.5 months and found no evidence or any toxic effects in swine fed less than 233 p.p.b., or in beef fed less than 300 p.p.b. They also fed diets containing aflatoxin to dairy cattle, and found that within 72 hr. after feeding of aflatoxin had ceased, no more aflatoxin was excreted in the milk.

Methods of Detection of Aflatoxin. Positive detection of aflatoxin in any material requires chemical extraction by suitable solvent systems, purification by silica-gel column, isolation by thin-layer chromatography, and confirmation by infrared spectrometry plus, preferably, additional confirmation by duckling, fertile-egg, or other biological test. Modern chemical tests and procedures are described by Campbell (1970), Pons and Goldblatt (1969), and in the Official Methods of Analysis for the Association of Official Analytical Chemists (1970). Biological confirmatory tests are described by Legator (1969) and Brown (1970).

Control of Aflatoxin. Aflatoxins are not destroyed by the temperatures of ordinary cooking or the heat processing of home or commercial canning. They can be inactivated or detoxified microbiologically (Ciegler et al., 1966) or chemically (Dollear and Gardner, 1966), but the processes are not commercially feasible for most materials, and it is generally agreed that the best control is to harvest, store, handle, and process the raw materials and finished products of foods and feeds in ways that will prevent invasion by *A. flavus*. Theoretically this should not be difficult, but it is much easier said than done. Even in the U.S., for example, where long experience has been accumulated in the storage and handling of grains and seeds, and where facilities are available for monitoring of temperatures throughout stored bulks of grain, for maintenance of uniform and low temperatures by aeration, and for accurate measurement of moisture content, spoilage from invasion of grain by storage fungi, including *A. flavus*, is relatively common. As indicated in the previous section dealing with storage, many practical grain men still are unaware that fungi cause spoilage. In the less developed countries, with few facilities for protective storage and handling and little knowledge of the processes of spoilage or of the hazards involved, and especially in regions of high rainfall and intermittent or regular high relative humidity, the aflatoxin problem is likely to be much greater than it is in the U.S. Along with careful storage, of course, must go more or less constant surveillance to make sure that aflatoxin contamination in foodstuffs and feedstuffs is kept as low as possible. It seems likely that eventually materials will be routinely assayed for aflatoxin by sampling and testing programs such as have been developed to detect *Salmonella*. With relatively high-risk materials such as peanut products, cottonseed meal, copra, and fishmeal, it would seem only sensible to test shipments before they are accepted or before they are processed.

Aspergillus ochraceus AND OCHRATOXIN

Some strains of *A. ochraceus* produce ochratoxins (Theron et al., 1966), which are about as toxic as aflatoxins. *A. ochraceus* seldom is found in more than a small percentage of kernels even in lots of grain that are undergoing deterioration (Christensen, 1971a), although isolates of it capable of producing ochratoxin were common in black pepper (Christensen et al., 1967). In a recent survey, only one sample of corn, out of 283 tested, contained ochratoxin in the amount of 110 to 150 p.p.b., and that one was of Sample Grade (Shotwell et al., 1970). There are no other published reports of ochratoxin having been found in food or feedstuffs, but relatively few samples have been tested for it, especially samples of products that have undergone some incipient deterioration and that might be expected to contain it.

A number of other species of *Aspergillus* have been found to produce toxins in the laboratory (Austwick, 1965; Feuell, 1969; Reiss, 1968) and according to one of these authors (Feuell) there have been occasional outbreaks of disease in animals associated with the consumption of feeds heavily invaded by one or another of these species (and most probably by a number of other species as well), but there is no hard evidence to enable us to state conclusively that a given syndrome in a given kind of animal is the product of consumption of feed invaded by a given species or combination of species of these fungi. Production of toxins by combinations of species of fungi either growing together or following one another in the succession that occurs frequently in nature has not been much investigated, but it probably should be. It could be terrifically complex.

Penicillium TOXINS AND TOXICOSES

Many workers from before 1900 on have shown that several species of *Penicillium*, when grown in pure culture in the laboratory, produce materials that are extremely toxic to animals. Uraguchi (1969) presents strong circumstantial evidence that acute cardiac beriberi in man may result from ingestion of the toxin citreo-viridin produced by *P. toxicarium* Miyake (=*P. citreo-viride* Biorge) growing in rice. He states that the high incidence of this disease in Japan decreased abruptly in 1910, a year before the discovery of vitamins and nearly 10 years before their use in preventive medicine; in that year a program of rice inspection was widely adopted in Japan and, as a result, moldy rice was fairly well excluded from commercial channels. Recent papers concerning toxins produced by species of *Penicillium*, by means of which those interested can trace back the older literature, are those by Carlton et al. (1970) and Uraguchi (1969). Burnside et al. (1957) and Krogh and Hasselager (1968) established with a high degree of probability the cause and effect relationship between feed invaded by a given species of *Penicillium* and a disease in swine – in the latter case, "fungus nephrosis", which has been recognized for some decades in Denmark as being widely distributed and of high incidence in swine herds after wet harvest. *Penicillium* is common in many samples of feeds, and is predominant in some, and occasionally it occurs as a practically pure culture in the germs or embryos of damaged (decayed) kernels of corn.

Fusarium TOXINS AND TOXICOSES

Several species of *Fusarium* are common in grains and in other plant products and are known to produce potent toxins. At least two of these species have been associated with disease syndromes in man or in domestic animals.

F. tricinctum Toxins and Toxicoses. Joffe (1965) reported outbreaks of alimentary toxic aleukia in the Orenburg District of Russia, in the U.S.S.R., from 1942 to 1947, that of 1944 being especially severe, with more than 10% of the population affected, and many deaths. The cause was traced to consumption of grain, especially millet, that had overwintered in the field and had become infected with a variety of potentially toxigenic fungi. Joffe provided strong circumstantial evidence that the specific fungus primarily responsible for the toxicosis was *F. sporotrichioides* [in the Snyder and Hansen system of classification of species of *Fusarium* this is synonymous with *F. tricinctum* (see Snyder and Hansen, 1945)]. Smalley et al. (1970) reported that *F. tricinctum* was one of the most frequently isolated fungi from corn associated with toxicity in domestic animals in Wisconsin. Of 29 isolates of *F. tricinctum* that they tested for toxicity to rats, 22 caused severe reactions or death. From one strain of the fungus grown in the laboratory they isolated and purified a compound which, when given orally, had an LD_{50} of 3.8 mg. per kg. (=3.8 p.p.m.) for rats. This compound has not been detected in field samples at present writing (its most likely place and time of occurrence would be in corn stored on the cob in cribs, in winter) but there is every reason to suppose that it is involved in field cases of illness in domestic animals.

F. roseum and the Estrogenic Syndrome. F. roseum growing in corn may produce toxic compounds that, when consumed by swine, result in development of the estrogenic syndrome. This is characterized, in the female pigs, by swollen, inflamed vulva; prolapsed rectum; infertility; and abortion; and in the males by atrophied testes and enlarged mammary glands. In both males and females, consumption of corn invaded by F-2-producing strains of the fungus may result in greatly reduced weight gain (Nelson et al., 1965). A specific toxin, designated F-2, has been implicated (Mirocha et al., 1969) but it seems highly probable that several other and as yet unidentified toxins are produced by the fungus at the same time that F-2 is produced. Conditions for the production of the F-2 toxin are outlined by Eugenio et al., 1970.

C. Other Mycotoxicoses

The additional known mycotoxicoses are: Facial eczema in sheep (and to a lesser extent in cattle) in portions of New Zealand (and to a lesser extent in portions of Australia), due to consumption of dead forage containing large numbers of spores of the fungus *Pithomyces chartarum* (see Brook, 1969); the slobber syndrome, primarily in cattle, resulting from ingestion of red clover forage infected with *Rhizoctonia leguminicola* (see Ciegler and Lillehoj, 1968); and Stachybotryotoxicosis, resulting from consumption of straw invaded by *Stachybotrys atra*, and which occurs primarily in horses in the U.S.S.R. and in eastern Europe (see Forgacs and Carll, 1962). These are of no concern in stored cereal products, and so are outside the limits of this discussion.

LITERATURE CITED

AGRAWAL, N. S., C. M. CHRISTENSEN, and A. C. HODSON. 1957. Grain storage fungi associated with the granary weevil. J. Econ. Entomol. 50: 659-663.

ALSBERG, C. L., and O. F. BLACK. 1913. Contributions to the study of maize deterioration. Biochemical and toxicological investigations of Penicillium puberlum and Penicillium stoloniferum. U.S. Dep. Agr. Bureau of Plant Industry Bull. 270.

AMOS, A. J. 1948. Moisture content of mite-infested foodstuffs. Analyst (London) 73: 678.

ASSOCIATION OF OFFICIAL ANALYTICAL CHEMISTS. 1970. *Methods of analysis* (11th ed.), 1015 p. Publ. by the Association, P.O. Box 540, Benjamin Franklin Station, Washington, D.C. 20044.

AUSTWICK, P. K. C. 1965. Pathogenicity.

In: *The genus Aspergillus* by K. B. Raper and Dorothy I. Fennell, 686 p. Williams and Wilkins: Baltimore, Md. 21202.

BLACK, O. F., and C. L. ALSBERG. 1910. The determination of deterioration of maize, with incidental reference to pellagra. U.S. Dep. Agr. Bureau of Plant Industry Bull. 199.

BOLLER, R. A., and H. W. SCHROEDER. 1966. Aflatoxin producing potential of *Aspergillus flavus-oryzae* isolates from rice. Cereal Sci. Today 11: 342-344.

BORKER, E., N. F. INSALATA, C. P. LEVI, and J. S. WITZEMAN. 1966. Mycotoxins in feeds and foods. Advan. Appl. Microbiol. 8: 315-351.

BROOK, P. J. 1969. *Pithomyces chartarum* in pasture, and measures for prevention of facial eczema. J. Stored Prod. Res. 5: 203-209.

BROWN, R. F. 1970. Some bioassay

methods for mycotoxins. p. 12-18 in *Toxic micro-organisms: mycotoxins - botulism* (M. Herzberg, ed.). Proc. 1st U.S.-Japan Conf. on Toxic Micro-organisms, U.S.-Japan Cooperative Program in Natural Resources and U.S. Dep. of the Interior. Gov. Printing Office, Washington, D.C. 20402.

BULLERMAN, L. B., P. A. HARTMAN, and J. C. AYRES. 1969a. Aflatoxin production in meats. 1. Stored meats. Appl. Microbiol. 18: 714-717.

BULLERMAN, L. B., P. A. HARTMAN, and J. C. AYRES. 1969b. Aflatoxin production in meats. 2. Aged dry salamis and aged country cured hams. Appl. Microbiol. 18: 718-722.

BURNSIDE, J. E., W. L. SIPPEL, J. FORGACS, W. T. CARLL, M. B. ATWOOD, and E. R. DOLL. 1957. A disease of swine and cattle caused by eating moldy corn. II: Experimental production with pure cultures of molds. Amer. J. Vet. Res. 18: 817-824.

BUTLER, W. H. 1965. Liver injury and aflatoxin. p. 175-186 in *Mycotoxins in foodstuffs* (G. Wogan, ed.). Massachusetts Institute of Technology Press, Cambridge, Mass. 02142.

CAMPBELL, A. D. 1970. Chemical methods for mycotoxins. p. 36-42 in *Toxic micro-organisms: mycotoxins - botulism* (M. Herzberg, ed.). Proc. 1st U.S.-Japan Conf. on Toxic Micro-organisms, U.S.-Japan Cooperative Program in Natural Resources and U.S. Dep. of the Interior. Gov. Printing Office, Washington, D.C. 20402.

CARLTON, W. W., J. TUITE, and P. MISLIVEC. 1970. Pathology of the toxicosis produced in mice by corn cultures of *Penicillium viridicatum*. p. 94-106 in *Toxic micro-organisms: mycotoxins - botulism* (M. Herzberg, ed.). Proc. 1st U.S.-Japan Conf. on Toxic Micro-organisms, U.S.-Japan Cooperative Program in Natural Resources and U.S. Dep. of the Interior. Gov. Printing Office, Washington, D.C. 20402.

CARLYLE, R. E., and A. G. NORMAN. 1941. Microbial thermogenesis in the decomposition of plant materials. J. Bacteriol. 41: 699-724.

CARNAGHAN, R. B. A. 1965. Hepatic tumours in ducks fed a low level of toxic groundnut meal. Nature (London) 208: 308.

CARTER, E. P. 1950. The role of fungi in the heating of moist wheat. U.S. Dep. Agr. Circ. 838. 26 p.

CHRISTENSEN, C. M. 1955. Grain storage studies. XXI. Viability and moldiness of commercial wheat in relation to the incidence of germ damage. Cereal Chem. 32: 507-518.

CHRISTENSEN, C. M. 1965. *The molds and man* (3rd ed.), 284 p. University of Minnesota Press, Minneapolis, Minn. 55455.

CHRISTENSEN, C. M. 1970. Moisture content, moisture transfer, and invasion of stored sorghum seeds by fungi. Phytopathology 60: 280-283.

CHRISTENSEN, C. M. 1971a. Mycotoxins. Crit. Reviews in Environmental Control 2: 57-80.

CHRISTENSEN, C. M. 1971b. Evaluating condition and storability of sunflower seeds. J. Stored Prod. Res. 7: 163-169.

CHRISTENSEN, C. M., and R. F. DRESCHER. 1954. Grain storage studies. XIV. Changes in moisture content, germination percentage, and moldiness of wheat samples stored in different portions of bulk wheat in commercial bins. Cereal Chem. 31: 206-216.

CHRISTENSEN, C. M., H. A. FANSE, G. H. NELSON, FERN BATES, and C. J. MIROCHA. 1967. Microflora of black and red pepper. Appl. Microbiol. 15: 622-626.

CHRISTENSEN, C. M., and DOROTHY R. GORDON. 1948. The mold flora of stored wheat and corn and its relation to heating of moist grain. Cereal Chem. 25: 42-51.

CHRISTENSEN, C. M., and A. C. HODSON. 1960. Development of granary weevils and storage fungi in columns of wheat. II. J. Econ. Entomol. 53:375-380.

CHRISTENSEN, C. M., and H. H. KAUFMANN. 1968. Maintenance of quality in stored grains and seeds. Univ. Minn. Agr. Ext. Folder 226.

CHRISTENSEN, C. M., and H. H. KAUFMANN. 1969. *Grain storage: the role of fungi in quality loss*, 153 p. University of Minnesota Press, Minneapolis, Minn. 55455.

CHRISTENSEN, C. M., C. J. MIROCHA, and R. A. MERONUCK. 1971. Some biological and chemical characteristics of damaged corn. J. Stored Prod. Res. 7: 287-291.

CHRISTENSEN, C. M., G. C. PAPAVIZAS, and C. R. BENJAMIN. 1959. A new halophilic species of *Eurotium*. Mycologia 51: 636-640.

CHRISTENSEN, J. J. 1963. Longevity of fungi in barley kernels. Plant Dis. Rep. 47: 639-642.

CIEGLER, A., and E. B. LILLEHOJ. 1968. Mycotoxins. Advan. in Appl. Microbiol. 10: 155-219.

CIEGLER, A., E. B. LILLEHOJ, R. E. PETERSON, and H. H. HALL. 1966. Microbial detoxification of aflatoxin. Appl. Microbiol. 14: 934-939.

DARSIE, M. L., C. ELLIOTT, and G. J. PEIRCE. 1914. A study of the germinating power of seeds. Bot. Gaz. (Chicago) 58: 101-136.

DAVIS, N. D., and U. L. DIENER. 1970. Environmental factors affecting the production of aflatoxin. p. 43-47 in *Toxic micro-organisms: mycotoxins - botulism* (M. Herzberg, ed.). Proc. 1st U.S.-Japan Conf. on Toxic Micro-organisms, U.S.-Japan Cooperative Program in Natural Resources and U.S. Dep. of the Interior. Gov. Printing Office, Washington, D.C. 20402.

del PRADO, F. A., and C. M. CHRISTENSEN. 1952. Grain storage studies. XII. The fungus flora of stored rice seed. Cereal Chem. 29: 456-462.

DIENER, U. L., and N. D. DAVIS. 1969. Production of aflatoxin on peanuts under controlled environments. J. Stored Prod. Res. 5: 251-258.

DOLLEAR, F. G., and H. K. GARDNER, Jr. 1966. Inactivation and removal of aflatoxin. Proc. 4th National Peanut Research Conference, p. 72-81. Tifton, Georgia, July 14-15.

EUGENIO, CAESARIA P., C. M. CHRISTENSEN, and C. J. MIROCHA. 1970. Factors affecting production of the mycotoxin F-2 by *Fusarium roseum*. Phytopathology 60: 1055-1057.

FAIRBROTHER, T. H. 1929. The influence of environment on the moisture content of flour and wheat. Cereal Chem. 6: 379-395.

FEUELL, A. J. 1969. Types of mycotoxins in foods and feeds. p. 187-221 in *Aflatoxin, scientific background, control and implications* (L. A. Goldblatt, ed.). Academic Press, New York, N.Y. 10003.

FIELDS, R. W., and T. H. KING. 1962. Influence of storage fungi on deterioration of stored pea seed. Phytopathology 52: 336-339.

FORGACS, J., and W. T. CARLL. 1962. Mycotoxicoses. Advan. Vet. Sci. 7: 273-382.

GOLDBLATT, L. A. (ed.). 1969. *Aflatoxin, scientific background, control, and implications*. 472 p. Academic Press, New York, N.Y. 10003.

GRIFFITH, D. A., A. C. HODSON, and C. M. CHRISTENSEN. 1959. Grain storage fungi associated with mites. J. Econ. Entomol. 52: 514-518.

HALVER, J. E. 1965. Aflatoxicosis and rainbow trout hepatoma. p. 209-234 in *Mycotoxins in foodstuffs* (G. Wogan, ed.). Massachusetts Institute of Technology Press, Cambridge, Mass. 02142.

HERZBERG, M. (ed.). 1970. *Toxic micro-organisms: mycotoxins - botulism*. Proc. 1st U.S.-Japan Conf. on Toxic Micro-organisms, U.S.-Japan Cooperative Program in Natural Resources and U.S. Dep. of the Interior. For sale by the Superintendent of Documents, U.S. Gov. Printing Office, Washington, D.C. 20402.

HESSELTINE, C. W. 1969. Mycotoxins. Mycopath. Myc. Appl. 39: 371-383.

HOLMAN, L. H. 1950. Handling and storage of soybeans. p. 455-482 in *Soybeans and soybean products* (K. S. Markley, ed.), vol. 1. Interscience Publishers, Inc., New York, N.Y. 10016.

HUBBARD, J. E., F. R. EARLE, and F. R. SENTI. 1957. Moisture relations in wheat and corn. Cereal Chem. 34: 422-433.

HUMMEL, B. C. W., L. S. CUENDET, C. M. CHRISTENSEN, and W. F. GEDDES. 1954. Grain storage studies. XIII. Comparative changes in respiration, viability, and chemical composition of mold-free and mold-contaminated wheat upon storage. Cereal Chem. 31: 143-150.

JOFFE, A. Z. 1965. Toxin production by cereal fungi causing toxic alimentary aleukia in man. p. 77 in *Mycotoxins in foodstuffs* (G. N. Wogan, ed.). Massachusetts Institute of Technology Press, Cambridge, Mass. 02142.

JOHNSON, H. E. 1957. Cooling stored grain by aeration. Agr. Eng. 38: 597-601.

KAUFMANN, H. H. 1959. Fungus infection of grain upon arrival at terminal elevators. Cereal Sci. Today 4: 13-15.

KEYL, A. C., A. N. BOOTH, M. S. MASRI, M. R. GUMBMANN, and W. E. GAGNE. 1970. Chronic effects of aflatoxin in farm animal feeding studies. p. 72-75 in *Toxic micro-organisms: mycotoxins - botulism* (M. Herzberg, ed.). Proc. 1st U.S.-Japan Conf. on Toxic Micro-organisms, U.S.-Japan Cooperative Program in Natural Resources and U.S. Dep. of the Interior. Gov. Printing Office, Washington, D.C. 20402.

KOEHLER, B. 1938. Fungus growth in shelled corn as affected by moisture. J. Agr. Res. 56: 291-307.

KOTHEIMER, J. B., and C. M. CHRISTENSEN. 1961. Microflora of barley kernels. Wallerstein Lab. Commun. 24: (83) 1-7.

KROGH, P., and B. HALD. 1969. Forekomst af aflatoksin i importerede jordnøprodukter. Nord. Vet. Med. 21: 398-407.

KROGH, P., and E. HASSELAGER. 1968. Studies on fungal nephrotoxicity. p. 198-214 in *Yearbook of the Royal veterinary and agricultural college*, Copenhagen, Denmark.

LANE, G. T. 1972. Preventing mold growth in high moisture grain. Master Manual on Molds and Mycotoxins, ed. by G. L. Berg. Farm Technol. and Agri-Fieldman 28(5): 34a-41a.

LEGATOR, M. S. 1969. Biological assay for aflatoxins. p. 107-149 in *Aflatoxin, scientific background, control, and implications* (L. A. Goldblatt, ed.). Academic Press, New York, N.Y. 10003.

LUTEY, R. W. 1961. Staining of barley kernels by bacteria. Proc. Minn. Acad. Sci. 29: 174-179.

LUTEY, R. W., and C. M. CHRISTENSEN. 1963. Influence of moisture content, temperature, and length of storage upon survival of fungi in barley kernels. Phytopathology 53: 713-717.

MEYER, H. Bibliographie der Aflatoxine. 1970. Aus dem Institut fur Bakteriologie und Histologie der Bundesanstalt fur Fleischforschung, Kulmbach, West Germany. (Mimeographed.)

MILNER, M., C. M. CHRISTENSEN, and W. F. GEDDES. 1947. Grain storage studies. VII. Influence of certain mold inhibitors on respiration of moist wheat. Cereal Chem. 24: 507-517.

MILNER, M., and W. F. GEDDES. 1945. Grain storage studies. II. The effect of aeration, temperature, and time on the respiration of soybeans containing excessive moisture. Cereal Chem. 22: 484-501.

MILNER, M., and W. F. GEDDES. 1946. Grain storage studies. III. The relation between moisture content, mold growth, and respiration of soybeans. Cereal Chem. 23: 225-247.

MIROCHA, C. J., C. M. CHRISTENSEN, and G. H. NELSON. 1969. Biosynthesis of the fungal estrogen F-2 and a naturally occurring derivative (F-3) by *Fusarium moniliforme*. Appl. Microbiol. 17: 482-483.

MISLIVEC, P. B., and J. TUITE. 1970. Species of Penicillium occurring in freshly-harvested and in stored dent corn kernels. Mycologia 62: 67-74.

MISRA, C. P., C. M. CHRISTENSEN, and A. C. HODSON. 1961. The angoumois grain moth *Sitotroga cerealella* and storage fungi. J. Econ. Entomol. 54: 1032-1033.

MOREAU, C. 1968. *Moisissures Toxiques dans l'Alimentation*, 371 p. Editions P. Lechavalier, Paris.

MULLER, R. D., C. W. CARLSON, G. SEMENIUK, and G. S. HARSHFIELD. 1970. The response of chicks, ducklings, goslings, pheasants, and poults to graded levels of aflatoxins. Poultry Sci. 49: 1346-1350.

NELSON, G. H., C. M. CHRISTENSEN, and C. J. MIROCHA. 1965. A veterinarian looks at moldy corn. p. 86-91 in Proc. 20th ann. hybrid corn industry-research conf. American Seed Trade Association, Executive Building, Suite 964, Washington, D.C. 20005.

PAPAVIZAS, G. C., and C. M. CHRISTENSEN. 1957. Grain storage studies. XXV. Effect of invasion by storage fungi upon germination of wheat seed and upon development of sick wheat. Cereal Chem. 34: 350-359.

PAPAVIZAS, G. C., and C. M. CHRISTENSEN. 1958. Grain storage studies. XXVI. Fungus invasion and deterioration of wheats stored at low temperatures and moisture contents of 15 to 18 per cent. Cereal Chem. 35: 27-34.

PERRY, T. W. 1972. Improving feed efficiency with organic acids. Master Manual on Molds and Mycotoxins, ed.

by G. L. Berg. Farm Technol. and Agri-Fieldman 28(5): 42a–45a.

PETERSON, ANNE, VERA SCHLEGEL, B. HUMMEL, L. S. CUENDET, W. F. GEDDES, and C. M. CHRISTENSEN. 1956. Grain storage studies. XXII. Influence of oxygen and carbon dioxide concentrations on mold growth and grain deterioration. Cereal Chem. 33: 53-66.

PONS, W. A., Jr., and L. A. GOLDBLATT. 1969. Physicochemical assay of aflatoxins. p. 77-105 in *Aflatoxin, scientific background, control, and implications* (L. A. Goldblatt, ed.). Academic Press, New York, N.Y. 10003.

QASEM, S. A., and C. M. CHRISTENSEN. 1958. Influence of moisture content, temperature, and time on the deterioration of stored corn by fungi. Phytopathology 48: 544-549.

RAMSTAD, P. E., and W. F. GEDDES. 1943. The respiration and storage behavior of soybeans. Minn. Agr. Exp. Sta. Tech. Bull. 156. 54 p.

RAPER, K. B., and DOROTHY I. FENNELL. 1965. *The genus Aspergillus*, 686 p. Williams and Wilkens Co., Baltimore, Md. 21202.

REISS, J. 1968. Mycotoxine. I. Mycotoxine von *Aspergillus* Arten. Z. Allg. Mikrobiologie 8: 303-330.

SANDERS, T. H., N. D. DAVIS, and U. L. DIENER. 1968. Effect of carbon dioxide, temperature, and relative humidity on production of aflatoxin in peanuts. J. Amer. Oil Chem. Soc. 45: 683-685.

SAUER, D. B. 1972. How to use organic acids for best results. Master Manual on Molds and Mycotoxins, ed. by G. L. Berg. Farm Technol. and Agri-Fieldman 28(5): 46a–49a.

SAUER, D. B., and C. M. CHRISTENSEN. 1968. Germination percentage, storage fungi isolated from, and fat acidity values of export corn. Phytopathology 58: 1356-1359.

SCHROEDER, H. W., and J. W. SORENSON, Jr. 1961. Mold development of rough rice as affected by aeration during storage. Rice J. 64: 8-10, 12, 21-23.

SHANAHAN, J. D., C. E. LEIGHLY, and E. G. BOERNER. 1910. American export corn (maize) in Europe. U.S. Dep. Agr. Bureau of Plant Ind. Circ. 55.

SHOTWELL, ODETTE L., C. W. HESSELTINE, H. R. BURMEISTER, W. F. KWOLEK, GAIL M. SHANNON, and H. H. HALL. 1969a. Survey of cereal grains and soybeans for the presence of aflatoxin. I. Wheat, grain sorghum, and oats. Cereal Chem. 46: 446-454.

SHOTWELL, ODETTE L., C. W. HESSELTINE, H. R. BURMEISTER, W. F. KWOLEK, GAIL M. SHANNON, and H. H. HALL. 1969b. Survey of cereal grains and soybeans for the presence of aflatoxin. II. Corn and soybeans. Cereal Chem. 46: 454-463.

SHOTWELL, ODETTE L., C. W. HESSELTINE, MARION L. GOULDEN, and ELSIE E. VANDEGRAFT. 1970. Survey of corn for aflatoxin, zearalenone, and ochratoxin. Cereal Chem. 47: 700-707.

SINHA, R. N. 1961. Insects and mites associated with hot spots in farm stored grain. Can. Entomol. 93: 609-621.

SMALLEY, E. B., W. F. O. MARASAS, F. M. STRONG, J. R. BAMBURG, R. E. NICHOLS, and N. R. KOSURI. 1970. Mycotoxicoses associated with moldy corn. p. 163-173 in *Toxic micro-organisms: mycotoxins - botulism*. Proc. 1st U.S.-Japan Conf. on Toxic Micro-organisms, U.S.-Japan Cooperative Program in Natural Resources and U.S. Dep. of the Interior. Gov. Printing Office, Washington, D.C. 20402.

SNYDER, W. C., and H. N. HANSEN. 1945. The species concept in *Fusarium* with reference to discolor and other sections. Amer. J. Bot. 32: 657-666.

SWAEBLY, MARY ANN, and C. M. CHRISTENSEN. 1952. Molds in home dust, furniture stuffing and in the air within homes. J. Allergy 23: 370-374.

TABAK, H. A., and W. B. COOKE. 1968. Growth and metabolism of fungi in an atmosphere of nitrogen. Mycologia 60: 115-140.

THERON, J. J., R. J. Van der MERWE, N. LIEBENBERG, H. J. B. JOUBERT, and W. NEL. 1966. Acute liver injury in ducklings and rats as a result of ochratoxin poisoning. J. Path. Bacteriol. 91: 521-529.

TUITE, J. F. 1959. Low incidence of storage molds in freshly harvested seed of soft red winter wheat. Plant Dis. Rep. 43: 470.

TUITE, J. F. 1961. Fungi isolated from unstored corn seed in Indiana in 1956-1958. Plant Dis. Rep. 45: 212-215.

TUITE, J. F., and C. M. CHRISTENSEN. 1955. Grain storage studies. XVI. Influence of storage conditions upon the fungus flora of barley seed. Cereal Chem. 32: 1-11.

TUITE, J. F., and C. M. CHRISTENSEN. 1957. Grain storage studies. XXIII. Time of invasion of wheat seed by various species of Aspergillus responsible for deterioration of stored grain, and source of inoculum of these fungi. Phytopathology 47: 265-268.

TUITE, J., and G. H. FOSTER. 1963. Effect of artificial drying on the hygroscopic properties of corn. Cereal Chem. 40: 630-637.

U.S. DEPARTMENT OF AGRICULTURE. 1964. Official grain standards of the United States. Supt. of Documents, U.S. Govt. Printing Office, Washington, D.C.

URAGUCHI, K. 1969. Mycotoxic origin of cardiac beriberi. J. Stored Prod. Res. 5: 227-236.

WALKER, I. K. 1967. The role of water in spontaneous combustion of solids. Fire Res. Abstr. Rev. 9: 5-22.

WELTY, R. E., QASEM, S. A., and C. M. CHRISTENSEN. 1963. Tests of corn stored four years in a commercial bin. Cereal Chem. 40: 277-282.

WILSON, L. L. 1972. What is the nutritional value of organic acids? Master Manual on Molds and Mycotoxins, ed. by G. L. Berg. Farm Technol. and Agri-Fieldman 28(5): 50a–53a.

WOGAN, G. N. (ed.). 1965. *Mycotoxins in foodstuffs*, 291 p. Massachusetts Institute of Technology Press, Cambridge, Mass. 02142.

WOGAN, G. N., and P. M. NEWBERNE. 1967. Dose-response characteristics of aflatoxin B_1 carcinogenesis in the rat. Cancer Res. 27: 2370-2376.

CHAPTER 5

INSECTS

RICHARD T. COTTON

Stored-Product Insects Division
U.S. Department of Agriculture, Washington, D.C.

DONALD A. WILBUR

Department of Entomology
Kansas State University, Manhattan, Kansas

I. INTRODUCTION

That insects are a major cause of loss in stored grains and seeds, as well as in many other kinds of stored food products, is too well recognized to need emphasis here. They not only consume these materials but also contaminate them with insect fragments, feces, webbing, ill-smelling metabolic products, and with a variety of microflora; they therefore constitute a major sanitation and quality-control problem.

Arthur N. Hibbs (1968), a former president of the Association of Operative Millers, in an address before a conference sponsored by his organization, sharply defined the sanitation problems of the grain-storage and cereal-processing industries:

> We all have as our common goal, regardless of our affiliation, to do the best possible job in the field of sanitation. Today, as never before, the citizens of this nation, as well as foreign countries, are keenly aware of proper sanitation and pest control. Not only are they aware of it, but they demand it. And this is true no matter what industry we serve or service. Because of the enormous publicity given to sanitation standards and the use of certain chemicals to control pests, we are faced with a far more sophisticated and educated customer for our end products. And, I might add, a much more critical customer, too.

The Agricultural Research Service of the U.S. Department of Agriculture (1965a) estimated that storage losses from insects in the U.S. averaged $471,417,000 for each of the years 1951 to 1960.

If the information now available were utilized, most of these losses could be prevented. This chapter is designed to serve this end. In it are described the insects that prey upon our stored raw and processed cereal foods, the conditions under which they thrive and multiply, and the most effective and economical methods for preventing their depredations.

II. THE IMPORTANT SPECIES

The insects most destructive to our stored cereal grains originated or first became problems in those parts of the world where wheat, barley, and rice were grown.

Before crops were cultivated by man, the weevils and Angoumois grain moths occurred naturally in seeds on wild plants or in seeds gathered by rodents, ants, and other seed-harvesting animals (Linsley, 1944). Certain species were fungus feeders or scavengers; several were wood borers or lived under loose, dead bark; others inhabited nests of social insects and birds. When man began to store grain, these insects readily moved from their original native habitat to man-made stores. These pests have been carried by commerce to all parts of the world. In the days of the sailing vessels, grain and other dry foods swarmed with insects at the end of long voyages.

Today, several hundred different species of insects are associated in one way or another with stored grains and their products. Fortunately, only a few cause serious damage to seeds or cereal products in good condition. Some feed on the fungi growing on spoiled grain or on other dried vegetable materials. Others are predators or parasites that attack the true grain pests.

Environmental conditions in various parts of the world are not equally favorable for the development of all insect species, and those species that are injurious in some areas barely exist in others. In the discussion that follows, emphasis will be on those species of stored-product insects that are of greatest economic importance in North America, but some species in other parts of the world will also be mentioned.

A. Illustrated Publications to Aid in Identifications

Identification characteristics such as size; color; morphological structures, including wings and wing covers; and behavioral habits are sufficiently specific in most cases to enable relatively untrained persons to positively identify the more common pests. However, certain important species do not have prominent specific characteristics and should be referred to specialists for proper identification; these include rice and maize weevils, flat and rusty grain beetles and flour mill beetles, and saw-toothed and merchant grain beetles.

Many of the stored-product insects can be readily identified by referring to one or more of the following publications:

a) U.S. Department of Agriculture, Market Quality Research Division, Stored-Product Insects Research Branch. 1965. *Stored-Grain Pests*. Farmers' Bull. 1260.

b) Kansas State University Extension Service. 1961. *Stored Grain Insects*. Leaflet L-30, Extension Service, Kansas State University, Manhattan.

c) R. G. Strong and G. T. Okumura. 1958. "Insects and Mites Associated with Stored Foods and Seeds in California." The Bulletin, California Department of Agriculture, Vol. 47(3): 233-249.

d) Harry D. Pratt and Harold George Scott. 1962. "A Key to Some Beetles Commonly Found in Stored Foods." Proceedings of the Entomological Society of Washington (D.C.) 64(1): 43- 50.

e) H. E. Hinton and A. Steven Corbet. 1955. *Common Insect Pests of Stored*

Products, a Guide to their Identification. British Museum (Natural History) Economics Series 5, London.

f) Richard T. Cotton. 1963. *Pests of Stored Grain and Grain Products* (rev. ed.). Burgess Publishing Co.: Minneapolis, Minn.

B. Groups of Stored-Product Insects

Cotton and Good (1937) listed the insects found in stored grain and processed cereal products in four categories:

a) *Major pests* comprise those species responsible for most of the insect damage to stored grain and cereal products. They are particularly well adapted to life in the stringent environment imposed by a bin of grain.

b) *Minor pests* include an appreciably larger group that may become damaging locally and occasionally may approach the status of major pests. Frequently, large populations develop in grain or in cereal products going out of condition because of high moisture and poor sanitation. Certain species, such as hairy fungus beetles and foreign grain beetles, are indicators of high-moisture grain; when they occur in abundance in a grain mass, spoilage from molds probably has occurred.

c) *Incidental pests* are those insects that stray into an unscreened or open-doored processing plant or into open-doored boxcars being loaded or standing in the railroad yards. They include houseflies, roaches, moths, or other insects that might have been attracted to lights, odors, or shelter—in fact, any insect that happens to alight on or crawl into grain or grain products. Usually, these insects are ignored by grain handlers and food processors, but when a moth or beetle accidentally gets into a package of cake mix or breakfast food, it suddenly becomes a major pest to the housewife who opens the package.

d) *Parasites and predators* of grain-infesting insects frequently are found in bins of infested grain, where they are as unwanted by grain handlers as are the major pests.

Lists of stored-product insects are given in Tables I and II.

C. Insects That Develop Inside the Kernels

There are five species of grain-infesting insects that develop inside of kernels and comprise the "hidden infestation" in a grain mass. Weevils deposit their eggs inside the kernels; lesser grain borers and Angoumois grain moths deposit eggs outside of, and their newly hatched larvae promptly tunnel into, the kernels. There is little telltale evidence of their presence inside the kernels until they emerge as beetles or moths. Kernels appear to be sound and undamaged even though germ, endosperm, or both, may have been consumed. Whereas weevils, lesser grain borers, and Angoumois grain moths comprise the major internal feeders, insects such as the flat and rusty grain beetles, that normally live outside the kernels, occasionally will develop under the pericarps that cover the germ.

True grain weevils include granary weevils, rice weevils, and maize weevils. They are the most widely distributed and frequently the most destructive of all the insects that attack grain in farm and commercial storage. They can easily be distinguished from other major stored-grain insects because their head capsule is

TABLE 1

Alphabetical list of the major insect pests of stored grain

Scientific Name	Common Name	Family
Acarus siro L.	Grain mite	Acaridae
Anagasta kuhniella (Zeller)	Mediterranean flour moth	Phycitidae
Cadra cautella (Walker)	Almond moth	Phycitidae
Cryptolestes ferrugineus (Stephens)	Rusty grain beetle	Cucujidae
Cryptolestes pusillus (Schönherr)	Flat grain beetle	Cucujidae
Cryptolestes turcicus (Grouv.)	Flour-mill beetle	Cucujidae
Ephestia elutella (Hübner)	Tobacco moth	Phycitidae
Oryzaephilus surinamensis (L.)	Saw-toothed grain beetle	Cucujidae
Oryzaephilus mercator (Fauv.)	Merchant grain beetle	Cucujidae
Plodia interpunctella (Hübner)	Indian-meal moth	Phycitidae
Rhyzopertha dominica (F.)	Lesser grain borer	Bostrichidae
Sitophilus granarius (L.)	Granary weevil	Curculionidae
Sitophilus oryzae (L.)	Rice weevil	Curculionidae
Sitophilus zeamais Motschulsky	Maize weevil	Curculionidae
Sitotroga cerealella (Olivier)	Angoumois grain moth	Gelechiidae
Tenebroides mauritanicus (L.)	Cadelle	Ostomatidae
Tribolium castaneum (Herbst)	Red flour beetle	Tenebrionidae
Tribolium confusum Duval	Confused flour beetle	Tenebrionidae
Trogoderma granarium Everts	Khapra beetle	Dermestidae

elongated into a snout, on the tip of which are located tiny but powerful mouthparts. Their grub-like larvae are legless.

Unfortunately, the term weevil means different things to different people. Some grain handlers call all grain-infesting insects weevils. Others reserve the term for those insects, whether beetles or moths, that live inside the kernels. Some call all kernels with insect-emergence holes "weevil-cut kernels", whether the damage was done by true weevils, lesser grain borers, or Angoumois grain moths. The term weevils should be reserved for those insects whose head capsule is elongated into a snout and whose immature forms are legless grubs. If progress is to be made in insect sanitation, a proper and consistent terminology should be used in discussing the problems.

GRANARY WEEVILS

Granary weevils are uniformly blackish to reddish insects (Figure 1, C). The pits on the pronotum (the large plate behind the head) are oval-shaped, larger, and less compacted than those on rice and maize weevils. Granary weevils usually are larger than the other weevils and they do not have functional wings.

RICE AND MAIZE WEEVILS

Like granary weevils, the body color of rice and maize weevils (Figure 1, E) is blackish to reddish, but they have two light-yellowish spots on each of the two hardened front wings (elytra) that cover and protect the membranous flight wings. The pits on the pronotum are rounded and closely compacted. Usually rice and maize weevils are smaller than granary weevils.

Until a few years ago, rice and maize weevils were thought to be a single species known as the rice weevil. Today, specialists can distinguish the two species by the shape of their genital organs and by minor differences in the arrangement or patterns made by the pronotal pits (Boudreaux, 1969; Halstead, 1964; Kuschel, 1961). There may be considerable variation in the biology and behaviors of these weevils living in different geographical areas (Soderstrom and Wilbur, 1966).

DEVELOPMENT AND BEHAVIOR OF WEEVILS

A female weevil chews a hole through the tough seed coat and prepares a cavity in the endosperm in which to deposit an egg. Then she inserts a long ovipositor protruding from the tip of her abdomen into the hole and deposits a small, soft, whitish egg. As the ovipositor is withdrawn, glands associated with it secrete a gelatinous material that fills the remainder of the oviposition hole not occupied by the egg. The naked eye can scarcely detect an infested kernel after the gelatinous plug has filled the cavity. However, it has been discovered that certain stains will color the egg plug, thus disclosing the sites of egg disposition. These will be discussed later.

The newly hatched larva usually tunnels towards the center of a wheat kernel until it reaches the crease; then it tunnels back and forth along the crease. However, at times a newly hatched larva will feed just under the outer coat and make a pale scar that provides external evidence that a larva occupies the kernel. Rice and maize weevils rarely cross the crease, so that two weevil larvae may develop within a single

TABLE II

Alphabetical list of minor pests most frequently encountered in stored grain

Scientific Name	Common Name	Family
Ahasverus advena (Waltl.)	Foreign grain beetle	Cucujidae
Alphitobius diaperinus (Panzer)	Lesser mealworm	Tenebrionidae
Araecerus fasciculatus (DeGeer)	Coffee-bean weevil	Platystomidae
Attagenus piceus (Olivier)	Black carpet beetle	Dermestidae
Carpophilus dimidiatus (F.)	Corn sap beetle	Nitidulidae
Carpophilus hemipterus (L.)	Dried fruit beetle	Nitidulidae
Caulophilus oryzae (Gyllenhal)	Broad-nosed grain beetle	Curculionidae
Corcyra cephalonica (Staint.)	Rice moth	Galleriidae
Cynaeus angustus (LeConte)	Larger black flour beetle	Tenebrionidae
Gnathocerus cornutus (F.)	Broad-horned flour beetle	Tenebrionidae
Lasioderma serricorne (F.)	Cigarette beetle	Anobiidae
Latheticus oryzae (Waterhouse)	Long-headed flour beetle	Tenebrionidae
Liposcelis spp.	Psocids	Psocoptera
Palorus ratzeburgi (Wissmann)	Small-eyed flour beetle	Tenebrionidae
Palorus subdepressus (Wollaston)	Depressed flour beetle	Tenebrionidae
Ptinus claviceps (Panzer)	Brown spider beetle	Ptinidae
Ptinus villiger (Reitter)	Hairy spider beetle	Ptinidae
Prostephanus truncatus (Horn)	Larger grain borer	Bostrichidae
Stegobium paniceum (L.)	Drugstore beetle	Anobiidae
Tenebrio molitor (L.)	Yellow mealworm	Tenebrionidae
Tenebrio obscurus (F.)	Dark mealworm	Tenebrionidae
Tribolium audax (Halstead)	Black flour beetle	Tenebrionidae
Trogoderma spp.	Grain-feeding dermestids	Dermestidae
Typhaea stercorea (L.)	Hairy fungus beetle	Mycetophagidae

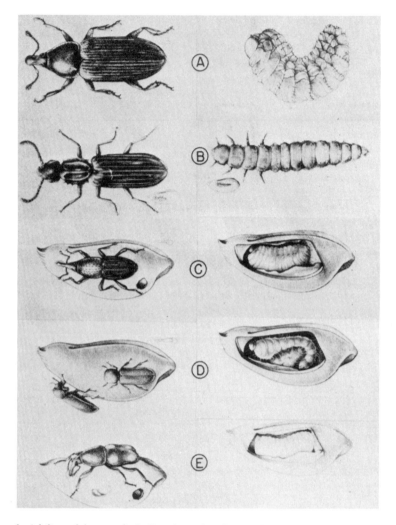

Figure 1. Adults and larvae of: A, Broad-nosed grain weevil; B, Saw-toothed grain beetle; C, Granary weevil; D, Lesser grain borer; and E, Rice weevil.

wheat kernel provided their tunnels are on opposite sides of the crease. Using radiographic techniques, Sharifi and Mills (1971) found seven kernels containing two maize weevils each among 2,000 infested wheat kernels, and 22 kernels containing two rice weevils each among 1,700 infested wheat kernels. The ratios were 3.5 per 1,000 and 13 per 1,000, respectively. When two or more eggs are deposited on the same side of the crease, the larvae will fight until one is destroyed. When granary-weevil larvae are about half grown, they cut a passage through the crease and occupy the center of a wheat kernel. Rarely will more than one granary weevil develop in a kernel.

During its development, a weevil larva sheds its exoskeleton (skin) four times. The grub greatly increases in size after each molt, except the fourth. The width of its tunnel is indicative of the larval instar (Kirkpatrick and Wilbur, 1965). The grubs eat ravenously of the endosperm and convert this starch into fatty tissue, which they store throughout their bodies. After the fourth molt, the grubs undergo a transformation stage known as pupa, during which the stored fat is broken down into simpler materials which are used by the pupa to build beetle tissues. Weevils and most other insects that damage grain and cereal products have four distinct stages: egg, larva, pupa, and adult. However, larvae of all the species are not necessarily restricted to four molts; some may have 3, 5, 6, 7, or more molts, while others have a variable number depending on the type of available nutrients or on the environmental conditions, especially temperature. Normally, the adults remain inside their kernels for a few days after pupation before chewing an escape hole through the seed coat and emerging. By passing their developmental life inside a kernel, the defenseless larvae are protected from most enemies as well as from sudden changes in temperature and moisture while, at the same time, they are surrounded by an abundance of nutritious endosperm.

Under favorable conditions of moisture and temperature, rice and maize weevils may complete their development from egg to adult in about 4 weeks, but granary weevils require an additional 5 to 10 days. Under less favorable conditions, however, this developmental period may be extended to several months. As each female weevil is capable of laying several hundred eggs, an enormous increase in population is possible within a few weeks.

The size of the weevil depends somewhat on the size of the grain kernel as well as on the species. In small grains such as millet or grain sorghum, the weevil will be small; but in corn, a particularly favorable food, it will attain its maximum size. When granary weevils and rice weevils feed on corn, the granary weevils will be the larger; but if rice weevils feed on corn and granary weevils on wheat, they may become of equal size.

Granary, rice, and maize weevils rarely develop in anything except seeds. However, occasionally they develop in solid-milled cereal products such as macaroni, and they have been found breeding in tightly packed flour.

Since granary weevils cannot fly, they are confined to grain stores that can be reached by walking or to which they are transported by man. Maize and rice weevils can fly from one site to another and commonly infest corn in the field in southern and southeastern U.S.

LESSER GRAIN BORERS

Lesser grain borers (Figure 1, D) are about 1/10 in. long; they are somewhat smaller than weevils and much smaller than their nearest grain-infesting relative, the larger grain borer *Prostephanus truncatus*. Their brownish, cylindrical bodies appear to be divided into two distinct parts. When viewed from above, the head is completely covered by the pronotum, the front margin of which has numerous tubercules or projections. Unlike the legless weevil grubs, lesser grain borer larvae have three pairs of legs attached to the body behind the head.

Of recent years, this cosmopolitan species has become one of the most destructive pests of wheat in the U.S. (Potter, 1935). It differs from weevils in that the eggs are deposited outside of the kernels. Upon hatching, most of the tiny larvae chew their way into kernels where they pass through four or more molts, or instars, and a pupal state, after which they emerge as beetles (Howe, 1949). Some larvae, however, will develop in available flour or nutritious dusts outside of the kernels. Feeding by larvae and beetles frequently reduces grain kernels to thin bran shells.

Both larvae and beetles produce an inordinate quantity of fecal pellets. Larvae inside kernels push their pellets along with some particles of starchy endosperm out of the kernels through their entrance holes so that, in heavy infestations, large quantities of fecal-pellet dust accumulates in the grain mass. The pellets have a sweetish, musty odor that characterizes lesser grain-borer infestations.

Lesser grain borers have well-developed flight wings which enable them to migrate readily from one granary to another and, on occasion, to swarm.

Other beetles that spend their immature lives concealed within the kernels of grain are the broad-nosed grain weevil (Figure 1, A) and the coffee-bean weevil (Figure 2, D). Both are minor pests.

ANGOUMOIS GRAIN MOTHS

Angoumois grain moths (Figure 2, C) are small, delicate moths with light buff-colored front wings. The hind wings are margined with long hairs; their tips are elongated and point like an "accusing finger". The larvae are whitish caterpillars with three pairs of legs just behind the head and five inconspicuous, stumpy pairs of legs on the abdomen. This cosmopolitan species is second in importance only to the weevils and the lesser grain borer as a pest of stored grain. The moth lays its eggs on grain in storage; in some regions in the U.S. it infests grain in the field. The caterpillars, which hatch from the eggs, burrow into the kernels and complete their development hidden from view. From four to eight or more instars are required before development is completed. The number of instars and the length of the life cycle are influenced by the type of food utilized. When germ feeding occurs early in larval development, fewer instars and shorter developmental periods result (Mills, 1965). Under favorable conditions the mean length of the developmental periods is 38 days on wheat, 35 on corn, and 33 on grain sorghums (Mills and Wilbur, 1967). Before pupating, each caterpillar makes an escape tunnel to the outside of the seed, leaving only a thin layer of the seed coat intact, like a glassine window, for the moth to burst through as it leaves the kernel. Frequently the silken cocoon, in which the pupa developed and from which the moth has escaped, fills the escape opening. The soft-bodied moths are unable to penetrate below the surface of binned grain, except for cob corn in cribs. In early times, the most damage to wheat occurred in shock or stack before threshing. Where wheat is combined, this species is relatively unimportant. In the southern part of the commercial corn area and throughout the southeastern states, severe field infestations of corn occur annually, so prompt shelling is desirable.

D. Insects That Develop Outside the Kernels

For the most part, insects that comprise this group feed on broken kernels, on the germ portion of grain kernels, on grain dust, or on flour or other cereal products. These insects are commonly known as "flour beetles", "bran beetles", or "bran bugs". Their eggs usually are laid indiscriminately among the kernels or throughout the product. For the most part the larvae are free-living, though several species tunnel under the germ covering where the larvae develop as "hidden infestation".

CONFUSED AND RED FLOUR BEETLES

Confused and red flour beetles of the genus *Tribolium* (Figure 2, E) are cosmopolitan insects that once lived under bark, feeding on living and dead plant and animal materials. Now they feed on grain, flour, dried fruits, nuts, and

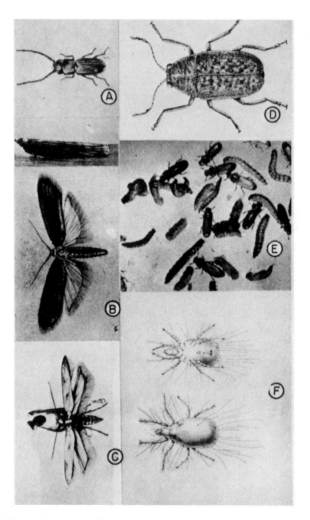

Figure 2. A, Flat grain beetle, adult; B, Rice moth, adult; C, Angoumois grain moth, adult; D, Coffee-bean weevil, adult; E, Confused flour beetle, adults, larvae, and pupae; and F, Grain mites.

numerous other stored-food products. They closely resemble one another in appearance, behavior, and life cycle. They are flat, reddish-brown beetles, approximately 3 to 4 mm. long, and are identifiable by the following characteristics:

Confused flour beetle (T. confusum)	Red flour beetle (T. castaneum)
a) Slightly larger, 3.5 mm.	a) Slightly smaller, 3.3 mm.
b) Antennae gradually enlarged toward the tip	b) Antennae with the last three segments abruptly enlarged
c) Eyes smaller	c) Eyes larger
d) Underneath, the width of each eye is about 1/3 the distance separating them	d) Underneath, the width of each eye is equal to the distance separating them
e) Wings not functional	e) Wings functional

These species are by far the most abundant and destructive insects infesting flour and other prepared cereal products (Good, 1936). They live in grain in storage, especially corn, and are particularly abundant in dead flour stock and other nutritious foods in protected places throughout mills and cereal processing plants. Their populations increase rapidly because the females deposit large numbers of eggs and the larvae have short developmental periods. Under favorable environmental conditions, females will deposit 400 or more eggs at the rate of from 6 to 12 eggs daily over several months; and the progeny of a single pair could, if unrestricted, reach the staggering total of over one million in 150 days (Gray, 1948). Eggs are covered with a sticky fluid that soon accumulates flour or dust particles, so that the eggs rarely are seen by millers. For this reason, many millers formerly thought that flour beetles occurred in flour as a result of spontaneous generation.

The larvae undergo from 5 to 12 molts, and under favorable conditions the life cycle from egg to adult requires approximately 30 days. The length of the developmental period varies widely, depending on temperatures, type of food, available moisture, and other factors. Howe (1956b) found that the optimum conditions for the rapid development of red flour beetles from egg to adult (20 days) lie between 35° and 37.5°C. and above 70% relative humidity. At 70% relative humidity and 22°C., a similar development took 75 days. With both species, the extent of egg deposition and the length of the life cycle decrease as the temperature rises (Park and Frank, 1948). The red flour beetle develops more rapidly than the confused flour beetle and has a higher fecundity. The number of larval molts for these species varies widely, but probably averages seven or eight.

Flour beetles generally limit their populations by their cannibalistic behavior, since both adults and larvae consume eggs and pupae. Chapman (1928) was of the opinion that the number of eggs eaten varied directly with the population of adults per gram of flour.

Both species damage grain and cereal products by eating them and by contaminating them with their dead bodies, cast skins, and fecal pellets. In addition, both species have odoriferous glands on the thoracic and abdominal segments that secrete a pungent, irritating liquid containing quinones (Roth, 1943). When large populations occur in flour, the flour turns pink from contamination by these secretions. Loconti and Roth (1953) determined that the secretion from the red flour beetle contained from 80 to 90% 2-ethyl-1,4-benzoquinone, 10 to 20% 2-methyl-1,4-benzoquinone, and a trace of 2-methoxy-1,4-benzoquinone. The first two repelled starving beetles when flour mixed with ground-up insects was offered them; the methoxyquinone was not repellent. Flour-beetle populations also contaminate flour with their fecal pellets, which contain uric acid.

Near relatives of the confused and red flour beetles, occasionally damaging in the U.S. and Canada, include the black flour beetle, *Tribolium audax* Halstead, and the large flour beetle, *Tribolium destructor* Uytten.

Flour beetles are widely used by biologists, especially in basic studies of genetics, nutrition, and population behavior, since they are easily cultured, they have short life cycles, their food is readily available and can be manipulated, large populations can be maintained in small containers, and, when kept in glass jars, neither larvae nor adults can escape by crawling up the sides of the glass.

SAW-TOOTHED AND MERCHANT GRAIN BEETLES

Saw-toothed grain beetles and merchant grain beetles of the genus *Oryzaephilus* (Figure 1, B) are difficult to separate, as both are small (1/10 in. long), very flat, reddish-brown beetles with six sawtooth-like projections on each side of the pronotum (the large plate behind the head). The head of the saw-toothed grain beetle is longer behind the eye than that of the merchant grain beetle. Both species have wings, but use them rarely or not at all. They enter mills and other food-processing plants in infested grains or other raw products. They are among the first grain-damaging insects to enter bins of newly harvested wheat throughout the Central Wheat Belt. At times these insects become very abundant. Normally they feed outside the kernels, but the larvae will penetrate into the germ area and remain as "hidden infestation" during their developmental period. Both species feed on processed cereals, dried fruits, nuts, cookies,and crackers, and, in fact, on nearly all stored human and animal foods; thus, along with Indian-meal moths, they are foremost in numbers and importance as household pests. They enter most types of packaged foods.

Generally, the beetles live from 6 to 10 months, but they have been known to live for 3 years. The females lay from 50 to 300 eggs. The time required for development from egg to adult may vary from 20 to 75 days depending on temperature, relatively humidity, and food (Howe, 1956a). Lowering the temperature and humidity slows larval development. The number of larval molts varies from two to four, with by far the greatest number having three molts.

It is generally agreed that saw-toothed and merchant grain beetles do not attack the endosperm of sound kernels, though small larvae do penetrate the germ covering and develop on the embryo. Turney (1957) found that more progeny developed in rice when both the moisture content and the amount of cracked kernels were increased; this is undoubtedly true of other grains as well.

FLAT, RUSTY, AND FLOUR-MILL BEETLES

Flat grain beetles, rusty grain beetles, and flour-mill beetles of the genus *Cryptolestes* (Figure 2, A) are so much alike in appearance and behavior that a distinction is rarely made between them by personnel in the grain industry.

Figure 3. A, Dark mealworm, adult; B, Indian-meal moth, larva; C, Indian-meal moth, adult; D, Hairy spider beetle, adult; E, Red flour beetle, adult; F, Cadelle, larvae; G, Cadelle, adult; and H, Black flour beetle, adult.

Generally all three species are called *flat grain beetles,* although this name belongs to *C. pusillus.* As with saw-toothed grain beetles, many grain-beetle larvae tunnel under the germ covering of wheat where they feed on the germ until they mature and pupate; thus they provide additional "hidden infestation". They are reddish-brown, flat beetles about 1/16 in. long, which makes them the smallest of the major grain-damaging insects. In Kansas, *Cryptolestes* beetles are among the first insects to infest newly harvested wheat in farm storage. They prefer grain of the upper limits of moisture for safe storage.

According to Ashby (1961), sound wheat is unsuitable for culturing the rusty grain beetle at 70% relative humidity but it becomes suitable with small additions of flour and damaged grain. All species herein discussed have four instars; they develop faster at higher relative humidities. The flat grain beetle, *C. pusillus,* and the flour-mill beetle, *C. turcicus,* make tough cocoons in which they pupate; other *Cryptolestes* make weaker cocoons (Currie, 1967). Currie found that rusty grain beetles are coldhardy, the flour-mill beetle fairly coldhardy, and the flat grain beetle not coldhardy.

CADELLES

Cadelles (Figure 3, G) are shining black or dark reddish-brown beetles about 1/2 in. long, which makes them the largest of the major stored-grain-damaging insects. Their larvae (Figure 3,F) range between 5/8 and 1 in. long; they are creamy white with a black head, two black or dark plates on the upper part of the segment just behind the head, and a dark plate with two stout dark projections on the tip of the abdomen.

The cadelle is a common destructive cosmopolitan pest of grain and cereal products (Back and Cotton, 1926). Farmers throughout the wheat belt call the larvae "flour worms" because they bin sound wheat kernels but, by the time the grain is moved to the elevators, the larvae and beetles have reduced much of it to a floury dust (Wilbur and Halazon, 1965). The germ is consumed first, but the endosperm may be eaten as well. Formerly cadelles were abundant in flour mills, where they cut holes in sifter bolting cloths and tunneled into wooden equipment and bins throughout the mill. Cadelles are predaceous on other insects as well as being consumers of grain and grain products.

Both larvae and adults bore deep into the woodwork of granaries, mills, ships, and warehouses, thus weakening the structures. Also, they gnaw holes through sacks, cardboard, and waxed and other paper containers.

Cadelles are true hibernating insects. Beetles and larvae survive long cold winters while hidden deep in the tunnels they have made in the woodwork. There may be one or two generations each year. Females have been known to deposit more than 3,400 eggs during their adult lifetime of 1 or 2 years (Bond and Monro, 1954). According to Bond and Monro, the larvae readily mature in 8 weeks when provided with favorable foods, temperature, and humidity. However, under normal field conditions, an appreciably longer developmental time is required. Most larvae molt three or four times, but under unfavorable conditions they may molt several more times. The larvae pupate within their tunnels in wood or other materials.

KHAPRA BEETLES

Khapra beetles of the genus *Trogoderma* are important pests in many hot, dry regions of the world. They have been widely distributed by commerce and sometimes become injurious in protected places such as heated buildings in England and other cooler countries. In 1953, khapra beetles were discovered to be widely distributed in California, and soon were found in Arizona, New Mexico, and Baja California. They became very destructive in stores of grain and seeds in this region until their eradication during the early 1960's.

The beetles are small, 1.8 to 3.0 mm. long, pale reddish-brown to black, oval-shaped beetles with unmarked wings or with indistinct red-brown markings. The yellowish-brown larvae are covered with long brown hairs. Both beetles and larvae closely resemble other species of the genus *Trogoderma*, so specimens should be referred to an expert *Trogoderma* taxonomist for positive identification.

The larvae feed on many kinds of grain, seeds, and other products of vegetable origin, but they can develop on products of animal origin as well. Normally, the beetles do not feed, though they may remain alive from a few days to several months.

Often, the discovery of khapra-beetle larvae and their cast skins provide the first indication of an infestation. Young larvae feed on damaged kernels; fourth-instar and older larvae attack whole grain or seeds (Lindgren et al., 1955). Activity is usually restricted to the top 12 in. of grain, but occasionally the larvae penetrate much deeper. They tend to congregate in cracks and crevices, and thus are difficult to remove by ordinary sanitary procedures.

The beetles do not fly. The species is disseminated naturally by crawling larvae, by birds and other animals, and by wind. However, the agencies of commerce provide their most important means for distribution.

The development of khapra-beetle larvae is frequently characterized by periods of arrested development, known as diapause, which may extend for more than 4 years (Burges, 1959). Diapause appears to be initiated by one of three means: low temperatures, very low or very high humidities, or accumulations of fecal pellets which taint the food media. The larvae normally molt from four to seven times, but under unfavorable conditions they may molt many times. Larvae in diapause and hidden in cracks and crevices provide conditions most favorable for their dispersal in commerce. Quarantine agents at all ports of entry into the U.S. are especially alert for khapra beetles.

Eradication of khapra beetles in southwestern U.S. resulted from the concerted efforts of inspectors who located the infestations, and fumigators who developed techniques for applying fumigants on a larger scale than ever before attempted.

There are several other species of *Trogoderma* in the U.S., but for the most part they have been minor pests.

SPIDER BEETLES

Spider beetles of the genus *Ptinus* and closely related genera (Figure 3, D) compose a curious group of insects whose globular body and long legs superficially resemble spiders. They occasionally damage stored grain and milled cereal products in the U.S. Smallman and Gray (1948) considered them to be the most important pests of flour-storage warehouses in Canada; in England, the Australian spider beetle, *P. tectus*, has become one of the most widespread of general warehouse pests (Howe, 1950).

Spider beetles attack most cereal products and animal foods. They consume foodstuffs; contaminate food with their excreta, silk, and body fragments; cut holes through fabrics, cellophane, and cardboard packages; and tunnel into woodwork.

INDIAN-MEAL MOTH

There are several general-feeding moth species, most important of which is the Indian-meal moth (Figure 3, B and C), whose larvae attack stored grain and stored foodstuffs. The adult is a small moth, 5 to 10 mm. long, with wings held close together when at rest. The basal one-third of the front wings is grayish; the outer two-thirds has a coppery luster, so that when the moth is resting, its wings appear to be marked with a prominent brown band. The hind wings are uniformly silver gray and fringed with hairs. The mature larvae are yellowish white—occasionally yellow, pinkish, or greenish white. They average 13 mm. in length, but vary widely with different foods and rearing conditions.

The larvae utilize many kinds of foods. They are injurious pests of all grains and cereal products; they are foremost among moth pests of the household; they are particularly damaging to nuts and dried fruits. Infestations in binned grain are confined to kernels at or near the surface. The larvae confine their feeding to the germ of wheat kernels, with the kernels otherwise appearing normal. Aitken (1943) found that the thiamine content of flours from wheat degermed by Indian-meal moths was lower than from normal wheat, and that the degermed wheat gave a definitely inferior loaf in volume, crumb texture, and crumb color. He ascribes this to the removal of the scutellum and epithelium layers along with the germ, as discovered by Ward (1943).

In addition to contamination by feces, cast skins, dead specimens, and parasite cocoons, the larvae always leave silken threads behind as they crawl over their food. Heavily infested bins of grain may become completely covered with a blanket of silk, underneath which the larvae live protected from changes in the weather and from parasites.

Larvae undergo five to seven molts and under favorable conditions require from 4 to 6 weeks to complete their development.

Several insect parasites attack the larvae, but they rarely bring about control; and the presence of the parasites in food products may be as objectionable as the Indian-meal moths themselves.

At times the tobacco moth is an important pest of bulk-stored wheat in England and Europe. The closely related almond moth is a serious pest in seed stores in southern U.S., where it attacks seed corn, small grains, beans, and cowpeas. It is also troublesome in bulk storages of rough rice and grain sorghum, and occasionally has been found infesting bulk wheat. The rice moth (Figure 2, B) is a common pest of rough rice in the U.S. The life cycle of these moths is similar to that of the Indian-meal moth.

MITES

Mites, which are almost microscopic, grayish-white, smooth, wingless, soft-bodied arthropods, frequently are abundant in stored grain in Canada and occasionally in the U.S. The adults have eight legs, as do spiders, daddy-long-legs, scorpions, and ticks.

Although several species of mites live in stored grain, not all are destructive. Some are predaceous on the mites that damage grain. The most destructive grain-infesting species is the grain mite, *Acarus siro* (Figure 2, F). It attacks the germ, although it will feed on other parts of the grain or on the molds growing on grain. Mites differ from grain-damaging insects in that under favorable conditions their life cycle from egg to adult may be completed within 9 to 11 days (Hughes, 1961). This enables an outbreak population to develop in a short time. Mites hatch from their eggs as six-legged larvae, but upon their first molt they become eight-legged nymphs, and they continue to have eight legs throughout the remainder of their immature and adult life. At one time in their development they may undergo a unique stage known as hypopus, in which the body wall hardens and suckers appear on the under side. These suckers enable the hypopus mite to attach itself to an insect or other animal and thus be provided with a convenient carrier to a new location. In the absence of food, or with other unfavorable conditions, mites may remain in the hypopus stage up to several months. When favorable conditions return, the hypopus transforms to a regular nymph and development continues until it becomes a sexually mature adult.

SCAVENGERS

Insects that feed on decaying or moldy grain constitute many of the species reported as grain-infesting insects. They are not beneficial in the sense that scavengers of carrion are useful in disposing of decaying material; on the other hand, they do not severely damage stored grain unless they are present in large numbers. In such cases, they promote the conditions that cause spoilage. Infestations by certain species provide warnings to handlers of high-moisture grain. Mealworms, hairy fungus beetles, foreign grain beetles, corn-sap beetles, and black-fungus beetles are among the common scavengers and fungus feeders.

E. Species most Destructive to Cereal Products

After the grain has been milled, the soft, starchy endosperm is exposed to the attack of insects. Many species—including the flour beetles that survive only at higher moistures in sound, unbroken grain—multiply rapidly in milled cereal products. The rate of reproduction of flour beetles in grain is much slower than in flour. Since the life cycle of flour beetles from egg to adult requires approximately 30 days under favorable conditions, certain preventive and control measures in the mill are commonly scheduled on a monthly basis.

Confused flour beetles and red flour beetles constitute more than 80% of the insect populations of flour mills in North America, and are easily the worst enemies of the miller. In the Central States the two species are believed to be about equally abundant in mills; in mills in the South, the red flour beetle is the more common; in the North and in Canada, the confused flour beetle is predominant. In addition to being found in grain stored at flour mills, they can survive and increase in many parts of the mill structure. Many pieces of equipment in the mill stream have niches or dead spaces where mill stock can accumulate and remain "dead stock" until removed by cleaning. This dead stock provides an ideal place for flour beetles to develop in large numbers and spread to other equipment in the mill. As indicated earlier, flour beetles cause the flour in which they live to discolor to a dirty gray and, when disturbed, they secrete a vile-smelling liquid into the flour. In addition, they contaminate the flour by their presence, their cast skins, and their fecal pellets, containing uric acid. The uric acid content of infested flour is proportional to the insect population, according to Venkatrao et al. (1960). These authors found a marked increase in fat acidity and a decrease in thiamine content in infested flour, and noted that the gluten became brittle after a time. In addition, the loaf volume of the bread gradually decreased as infestation progressed and the bread had an off-flavor and bitter taste.

Smallman and Loschiavo (1952) assessed the relative susceptibilities of certain mill stocks and found that tailings stocks and 3rd low-grade flours were four times more favorable for development and increase of confused flour beetles than 1st-break stock, and three times more favorable than 2nd middlings.

For many years, the Mediterranean flour moth was one of the most destructive pests in flour mills and cereal warehouses in North America. It is one of the few insects that thrives on a diet of pure endosperm. Today it is seldom seen, as it succumbed to the early practice of cyanide fumigation.

The Indian-meal moth prefers the germ and bran and will not grow on a diet of patent flour alone. Nevertheless, it is one of the most widely distributed of the insect pests of grain and cereal products, and it is found frequently in cake mixes, corn meal, and in products having fair amounts of fat or shortening.

Although most of the insect pests of stored grain also feed on milled cereals, there are a few that are especially destructive to these products. Owing to its habit of burrowing into woodwork, the cadelle often is found in wooden elevators and other apparatus in mills, and in the woodwork of railway cars and storage warehouses. Consequently, packages of milled cereals frequently are invaded by this insect during storage or transit. In the days when infested flour was reconditioned for blending, cadelle larvae were screened out by the thousands.

Saw-toothed grain beetles and flat grain beetles are common in warehoused cereal products. Because of their small size and flat shape, they can easily penetrate packages of most types. Although they do not actually consume much food, their presence renders it unfit for human consumption.

In countries with cool climates, spider beetles are very troublesome as pests of cereal products in storage. In England, the brown spider beetle is particularly destructive, whereas in Canada the hairy spider beetle is a serious pest of flour warehouses. According to Freeman and Turtle (1947), the brown spider beetle is the most widespread and common stored-product pest in England. The fully grown larvae may chew holes in sacks of flour. When infestations are severe, the entire inside of the flour sacks may be covered with cocoons, and the bag fabric so weakened as to tear easily.

Mites are particularly troublesome in milled cereal products in countries with cool, moist climates. Freeman and Turtle (1947) stated that the grain mite is the principal pest of stored wheat, flour, and wheat offals in England, except in warm, dry stores.

F. Species most Abundant in the U.S.

Although some of the insects that attack stored grain are general feeders and eat many kinds of grain, some have distinct preferences. Records over a 3-year period from the commercial corn area, including Illinois, Iowa, Nebraska, Minnesota, and South Dakota, showed that the following six species were more commonly found in stored shelled corn than any others, and constituted more than 98% of the insect population: saw-toothed grain beetle, flat grain beetle, red flour beetle, foreign grain beetle, larger black flour beetle, and hairy fungus beetle. The first three comprised the greater portion of the insect population. In the South, where field infestations are universal, the maize weevil is by far the most abundant species in stored corn.

In the Great Plains hard winter wheat region, seven species constitute over 90% of the insect population of wheat in farm storage. They are flat grain beetle, saw-toothed grain beetle, lesser grain borer, red flour beetle, cadelle, granary weevil, and rice weevil. Their abundance varies with climatic conditions. In the northern part of the region the hardier species, the flat and rusty grain beetles, and saw-toothed grain beetles, are predominant; whereas in the southern part, lesser grain borer and rice and maize weevils become increasingly abundant. Along the Eastern Seaboard the Angoumois grain moth is occasionally one of the common pests of stored wheat, although, ordinarily, the flat grain beetle and the rice weevil are the predominant species in that region. In rough rice in storage, the Angoumois grain moth, rice weevil, flat grain beetle, lesser grain borer, and red flour beetle are most abundant.

III. ECOLOGY

The insect pests of stored grain have certain temperature, moisture, and food requirements which directly affect their abundance, and hence their ability to cause damage (Cotton et al., 1960).

A. Temperature

As a group, grain-damaging insects are mostly of subtropical origin and do not hibernate. They have not developed resistance to low temperatures, so that in the northern parts of North America they are rarely abundant enough to cause serious damage to grain in storage. A thorough knowledge of the limiting effect of low temperatures is invaluable in formulating management programs for the safe storage of grain. Records of the relative susceptibilities of various stored-grain insects to low temperatures are given in Table III.

Temperatures that are not quickly lethal indirectly cause the death of many insect pests of stored grain by rendering them inactive and by preventing them from feeding. The life processes of insects that do not hibernate are not sufficiently retarded by low temperatures to enable the food reserves of their bodies to sustain them through an extended period of dormancy. As a result, they die from starvation. A few insects such as the cadelle are true hibernators and can survive exposure to low temperatures for a long time.

According to Robinson (1926), the rice weevil is dormant at temperatures of 45°F. or below, and the granary weevil at 35°F. or below. Anderson (1938) noted that neither species mated when the temperature fell below 53.6° to 55.4°F. Although Richards (1947) has placed the lower limit of oviposition at 49.1°F., most writers agree that few eggs are laid at temperatures below 60°F. Hatching and

TABLE III

Resistance of various insects that attack stored grain and grain products
(Cotton, 1950)

Insect	Days Exposure Required to Kill all Stages at						
	0°– 5°F.	5°– 10°F.	10°– 15°F.	15°– 20°F.	20°– 25°F.	25°– 30°F.	30°– 35°F.
Rice weevil	1	1	1	3	6	8	16
Granary weevil	1	3	...	14	33	46	73
Saw-toothed grain beetle	1	1	3	3	7	23	26
Confused flour beetle	1	1	1	1	5	12	17
Red flour beetle	1	1	1	1	5	8	17
Indian-meal moth	1	3	5	8	28	90	...
Mediterranean flour moth	1	3	4	7	24	116	...

development of larvae at temperatures between 55° and 60°F. are very slow. Red flour beetles and saw-toothed grain beetles do not lay eggs at 60°F., hence reproduction ceases at that temperature. Tyroglyphid mites are able to breed in stored wheat at temperatures between 40° and 50°F. if moisture conditions are favorable.

Subject to certain upper limits, the rate of development and reproduction of all grain-infesting insects increases with rising temperatures (Table IV). A grain temperature of 70°F. is considered to be favorable for the insects and constitutes the danger line. At 70°F. or higher temperatures, severe damage to stored grain from insects may be expected, whereas below this temperature serious damage is not likely to occur. With few exceptions, temperatures above 95°F. are unfavorable for the reproduction of most grain-infesting insects; oviposition ceases, and the adults are short-lived. The lesser grain borer is an exception, however, since reproduction by this species has been recorded by Gay and Ratcliffe (1941) at temperatures of 100°F.

Temperatures above 100°F. soon cause the death of most grain-infesting insects, although an extreme case of adaptation to high temperatures has been recorded by Von Wahl (1923), who observed the grain mite *Acarus siro* (L.) living in fermenting tobacco at 131°F. A temperature of 140° F. for 10 min. is considered effective for sterilizing milled cereals against all cereal-infesting insects.

The effect of temperature in limiting the regional abundance of various species

TABLE IV

Reproduction of red flour beetles (25 pairs) in clean wheat as affected by temperature and grain moisture, indicated by number of progeny after 5 months
(Cotton et al., 1960)

Percent Moisture	60°F.	75°F.	80°F.	85°F.	90°F.	95°F.
9	0	0	0	0	33	0
12	20	17	28	112	257	44
15	90	24	91	144	370	165

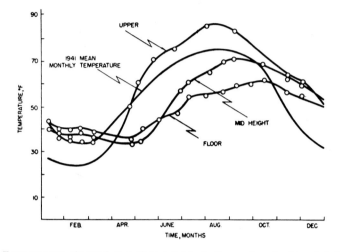

Figure 4. Temperatures observed at various heights in the center of a bin of shelled corn at Ogden, Iowa, from January 10, 1941, to January 27, 1942. (After Barre and Cotton, 1942.)

is quite pronounced. After a series of mild winters, the Angoumois grain moth may become troublesome in the soft winter wheat region of the Atlantic Seaboard as far north as New York and in the commercial corn area to a line passing through the southern half of Illinois and Indiana. On the other hand, it is never troublesome in these regions after a severe winter. The granary weevil is more abundant in the Northern States than in the South, whereas with the rice and maize weevils the reverse is true. Mites are seldom troublesome in stored grain in the U.S., but are common in the cooler climates of Canada, England, and Russia. In corn stored in the commercial corn area and wheat stored in regions with a similar climate, the flat

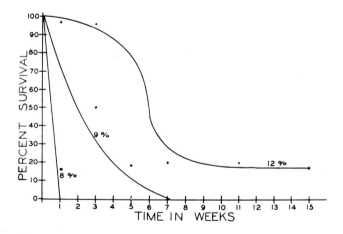

Figure 5. Survival of rice weevil adults at 85°F. in wheat of five different moisture contents (Cotton et al., 1960).

grain beetle complex and the saw-toothed grain beetle survive winter temperatures better than other grain-infesting species. Undoubtedly this accounts for their greater abundance in grain stored in this region. Grain temperatures typical for the commercial corn area throughout the year are presented in Figure 4.

B. Moisture

Grain moisture is an important factor in the life economy of insect pests of stored grain, because they depend on their food supply for the moisture needed to carry on their life processes. Up to a certain point, increasing the grain moisture favors a rapid increase in the numbers of insects. Beyond that point, microorganisms take over and destroy the insects, except the fungus feeders, along with the grain. If, on the other hand, the moisture content of the grain is low, the water required for carrying on vital life processes must be obtained by breaking down the food supply or the food reserves in the fatty tissues of the body.

The moisture requirements naturally differ with different species of insects, as does the ability of the insects to produce the water they need. Rice, maize, and granary weevils are unable to reproduce in grain with a moisture content below 9%, and the adults soon die in dry grain. Rice-weevil adults survived for only 1 week in 8% moisture wheat at 85°F.; at 9% moisture, about 70% were dead by 3 weeks, though a few lived for 7 weeks; at 12% moisture many lived for over 15 weeks (Figure 5). The critical moisture content in wheat for both rice- and granary-weevil development is between 11 and 12% (Figure 6, A).

Temperature directly influences a weevil's ability to reproduce in grain. Even when provided with a favorable 14% moisture wheat, few rice- and granary-weevil progeny were produced at 60°F.; but the progeny greatly increased at 70°F., peaked at 80°F., and fell off appreciably at 90°F. (Figure 6, B).

Flour beetles, on the other hand, produce progeny in flour or grain dust from which practically all moisture has been removed. Nevertheless, in whole-kernel

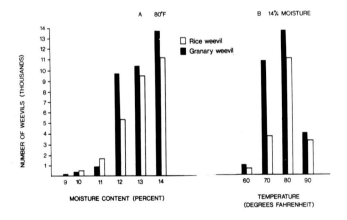

Figure 6. Reproduction of rice and granary weevils (50 pairs each) in wheat as affected by temperature and grain moisture, indicated by number of progeny after 5 months (from Table 10, Cotton et al., 1960).

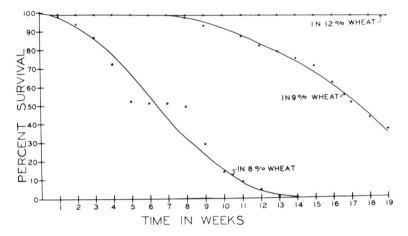

Figure 7. Survival of confused flour beetle adults at 80° F. in clean wheat of different moisture contents (Cotton et al., 1960).

grain, high moisture is essential for reproduction and survival. The presence of grain dockage or dust also is of vital importance; without it, dry grain is unfavorable for reproduction (Figures 7 and 8). McGregor (1964) found that dockage greatly enhances the ability of red flour beetles to develop in wheat, the number of insects present being directly proportional to the percentage of available dockage. The effect of grain moistures of 8, 9, and 12% on the survival of confused flour beetles in clean wheat is shown in Figure 7. The longevity of the insect is reduced as the

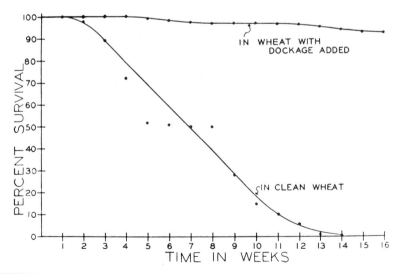

Figure 8. Survival of confused flour beetle adults in 8% moisture wheat as affected by dockage (Cotton et al., 1960).

grain moisture is lowered, although low moisture has less effect on this species than on the rice weevil (Figure 5). However, when dockage was added to the 8% moisture wheat, nearly 100% of the beetles were alive after 16 weeks (Figure 8).

The effects of the moisture content of wheat in farm storage on its attractiveness to grain-infesting insects and on the extent of their reproduction are shown in Figure 9. Uninfested lots of wheat of varying moisture contents that were placed in farm bins in June were examined in September to determine their attractiveness to insects and the extent of their population increase. Insect populations were never excessive in dry grain, whereas with more adequate moisture the insects multiplied rapidly. Grain with a moisture content above 15% was attractive to insects at first, but infestations died out later.

C. Heating of Grain by Insects

Bulk grain with a water content of from 11 to 14%, and in apparently good condition except for the presence of insects, often becomes hot. Heat resulting

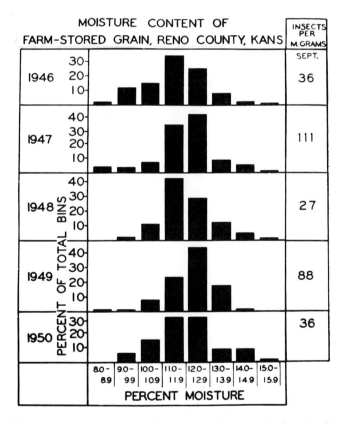

Figure 9. Effect of moisture content of untreated farm-stored wheat in Reno County, Kansas, 1946-1950, on the insect population, as shown by the average number of insects per 1,000 g. of wheat in September. (Cotton et al., 1960.)

from the metabolism of grain and microorganisms under such conditions is not sufficient to account for a pronounced rise in temperature. According to numerous investigators, the source of heat is the metabolism of the insects themselves.

Grain heating is of two types: a) "dry-grain heating" or "insect-caused heating", which may develop in grain with a moisture content of approximately 15% or less and results in temperature increases up to 108°F.; and b) "wet-grain heating" caused by microorganisms, and which occurs in grain with a moisture content of approximately 15% or more and produces temperatures as high as 144°F. These two types of heating may develop simultaneously in a bin of grain and "dry-grain heating" may be superseded by "wet-grain heating".

An "insect-caused" hot spot begins when the insects produce metabolic heat faster than the heat can escape. Howe (1962) pointed out that a small local rise of temperature accelerates the metabolism of each insect and speeds the rate of population increase; thus the amount of metabolic heat continuously increases until it reaches a level that is unfavorable to insects. At this point the adult insects move to the periphery of the hot spot, thereby increasing its size; often the immature insects within the kernels are killed.

In bins that are heating as a result of insect activity, surface grain may become damp and caked from the upward translocation of water within the bulk of grain under the influence of a temperature gradient. This is most obvious in the autumn when the surface grain cools rapidly. The water vapor moves upward from the heating areas and condenses on the cooler surface grain, thus causing molding and sprouting to a depth of 6 to 8 in.

The moisture that results from insect metabolism does not necessarily move upward and become deposited on surface grain. It may accumulate in pockets within the grain mass in amounts sufficient to create an environment highly favorable to storage fungi. Agrawal et al. (1957) relate a circumstance in which granary-weevil-infested grain attained a moisture content of from 17.6 to 23% within 3 months after the infestation began while noninfested grain developed a moisture content of only 14.6 to 14.8%, in equilibrium with a 75% relative humidity.

The factors that determine the amount of metabolic heat produced by insects include the insect species, the population size, and the grain temperature and moisture. Generally it is believed that any of the major stored-grain insects may cause dry-grain heating, but experiments by Eighme (1966) cast some doubt on this point. In his tests the saw-toothed grain beetles and red flour beetles neither initiated nor promoted the spread of hot spots.

"Wet-grain heating" may occur in insect-free grain with a moisture content above 15%. It results in much higher temperatures than heating caused by insects. The metabolism of the microflora on the kernels provides the chief sources of "wet-grain heating".

D. Sources of Infestation

Newly harvested, uninfested grain in farm storage may become infested from many sources, including holdover infested grain, especially that retained for animal feed; cracks, crevices, cadelle tunnels, and double-wall construction in bins or other parts of the granary, whether empty or occupied; accumulations of waste or spilled grain in or under the granary or in machinery and implements, or in empty grain and feed sacks; imported feeds or seeds from infested sources, especially elevator sweepings; migration by flight from nearby infested sources; and, in the South, field-infested grain.

In Southern regions, infestations are carried over from year to year in various buildings on the farmstead. In the more northerly regions, where temperatures are low for extended periods, most stored-grain insects succumb to the cold, except under special conditions. Stored-grain insects may survive long, cold winters in animal shelters, hay barns, and other protected places (Wilbur and Warren, 1958). The animals and their manures provide heat and moisture, and the everpresent feed spillage provides the necessary food. The stores of hay and straw give off accumulated heat and provide insulation from the winter's cold.

In commercial and government storage, uninfested grain becomes contaminated from infested grain or wastes on the premises unless exceptionally favorable sanitation procedures have been followed. Many of the older elevators, especially those of the wooden crib type, are difficult to disinfest. Much commercial grain received from farm storage is infested. Grain shipped in wooden boxcars during summer and fall months is almost certain to become infested during shipment. Insects capable of flight migrate in all directions from feed mills that process infested grain.

Field infestations of small grains, with the exception of rice, are of little consequence. However, many grain handlers are firmly convinced that small grains become infested in the field before harvest. Throughout the wheat belt, elevator personnel complain of wheat received directly from the field as "rolling with weevils". It is unlikely that this ever occurs in wheat harvested with a combine. The period from the milk stage of the kernels to harvest normally is too short to produce a generation of any of the major insect pests of stored grain. When newly

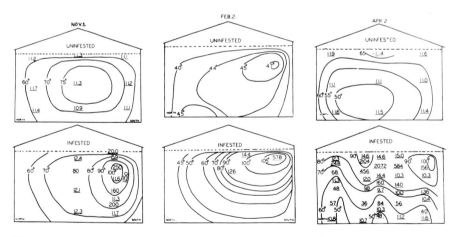

Figure 10. Grain temperatures, moisture levels, and insects in infested and uninfested wheat in steel bins in November, and in the following February and April. Figures underscored with solid lines are percent moisture; those with broken lines are number of insects per 1,000 g. of grain. (Cotton et al., 1960.)

harvested wheat arrives at a country elevator "rolling with weevils", the most logical explanation is that this new wheat has been intermingled with infested wheat at the farm. In the days when wheat was cut, bound, shocked, and stacked for weeks before being threshed, such infestations were possible.

There are, however, several types of insect injury done prior to harvest in the Central Wheat Belt that superficially resemble injury by storage pests (Wilbur, 1962). As the kernels ripen, small wheat-head armyworm larvae may eat into the kernels to feed on the soft, milky contents and make holes that look much like emergence holes of weevils or other internal-feeding insects. Other small cutworms, cowpea curculios, and even young grasshoppers make similar holes. When kernels damaged in this manner are cut into with a knife, it is apparent that the hole was made by an insect feeding from the outside of the kernel because the walls of the hole are parallel and the cavity is free of insect excrement.

In more northerly parts of the wheat belt, stink bugs of the family Pentatomidae (order Hemiptera), sometimes known as gluten bugs, stick their piercing, sucking mouthparts into the milky kernel and extract the contents. This results in shriveled kernels resembling drought or hessian-fly injury.

In the large corn-growing region of northern U.S., corn becomes infested in the same manner as small grains. Because of its comparatively short growing season, much corn is harvested while the moisture content is high and is stored on the ear in cribs or slat bins so that it will dry safely. Winter temperatures usually are low enough to destroy any field infestations, and normally this corn is fed or moved into commerce before it becomes reinfested. In the southern U.S., however, and in countries with similar or warmer climates and a longer growing season, corn may be left in the field to dry. Under these conditions it invariably becomes infested in the field. Rice is similarly subject to field infestation, which is augmented during warehouse storage of the bagged rice and during bulk storage in farm bins or in crib-bin elevators.

E. Distribution of Insects in Bulk Grain

The distribution of insects in bulk grain is influenced by many factors. Various species of moths that infest grain are fragile and weak and cannot force their way below the kernels on the surface to deposit eggs. For this reason, moth infestations are confined largely to surface grain. Grain-infesting insects of the weevil or flour-beetle types move freely through bulk grain; therefore their distribution is influenced largely by temperature, moisture, and accumulations of chaff.

Temperature is very important. Birch (1946) observed that in bulk wheat stored in piles, severe damage was confined to the surface four or five inches and to a depth of several inches on the floor. High temperatures in the middle of the bulk grain, generated by the metabolism of the insects, had killed the insects there or had driven them to the cooler surface grain.

Temperature has pronounced effects on insect distribution in wheat stored in small steel bins in the U.S. During spring, summer, and autumn most of the insects in a bin of bulk grain are in the upper half of the bin, whereas in midwinter they are likely to be in the lower half. In midsummer, the insects usually are uniformly distributed in the four quadrants, whereas in winter most of them will be found in the south quadrant (Figure 10).

In elevator bins, insects often are more abundant at the botto
surface grain, but may occur in any part of the bin. The location of in
may be due to chance distribution during binning. In bins eq
thermocouple cables, the presence of insect colonies usually is indicate
high temperature, or "hot spots".

Insects are attracted to damp grain. If leaks occur and portions of a
become damp, insects will be found there in greater abundance than ii
Surface grain that is cooler than the bulk of grain may become damp a
translocation of water from the interior of the grain mass. Whenever a b
has parts at different temperatures, moisture moves from the warmer to
parts. When heating by insects occurs beneath the surface grain ai
temperatures are low, the temperature gradient is very steep. Water move
be so excessive that considerable rotting of the surface grain will res
surface grain often attracts scavenger and fungus-feeding insects such as
fungus beetle and the foreign grain beetle, and their presence serves as a
indicator of high-moisture grain.

Pockets of dockage throughout a grain mass are not only attractive but are
essential to many insects. McGregor (1964) provided red flour beetles with
chambers containing clean wheat and wheat with various amounts of dockage. He
found that wheat containing dockage was preferred, and that the fecundity of the
insects increased rapidly as the amount of dockage was increased. McGregor
concluded that dirty wheat will become highly infested and go out of condition
more quickly than will clean wheat.

Feeding activities of Angoumois grain moths and weevils prepare the way for
flour beetles and for scavenger insects, some of which, because they have shorter
developmental periods, soon outnumber the original inhabitants of the grain. Grain
in storage in wooden farm bins may be quickly infested by saw-toothed grain
beetles, flat grain beetles, and cadelles; the latter sometimes migrate from the
woodwork of the bins in such large numbers that the surface of the grain appears to
be in motion. As the cool autumn weather approaches, cadelles leave the grain and
tunnel into the woodwork of the bin to hibernate. In the Great Plains, lesser grain
borers in wheat are often accompanied by large populations of long-headed flour
beetles. This may be because wheat attacked by the lesser grain borer becomes
quite floury from fecal pellets and endosperm. If grain is held in storage over the
winter in temperate zones, the hardier species such as the flat grain beetles and the
saw-toothed grain beetles survive the winter in greater numbers than the others.
During the spring months these two species, along with cadelles, are the first insects
to enter newly binned wheat in central U.S.

F. Considerations Relating to Cereal Products

The factors that influence the abundance of insects in stored grain also affect
their abundance in milled cereal products. In general, as temperatures and relative
humidities rise, the rates of reproduction and development increase, although there
are upper limits above which both temperature and moisture conditions are
unfavorable. Gray (1948) observed that the rate of oviposition by confused flour
beetles increased with the rise in temperature, from an occasional egg at 61°F. to an
average of 10.1 per day at 90°F. Hatching occurred up to 100°F., but at 105°F. all

eggs were dead in 60 hr. Holdaway (1932) noted that eggs of this insect did not hatch in a moisture-saturated atmosphere, owing to fungus growth. Biotic constants for confused flour beetles reared on whole-wheat flour at a constant relative humidity of 75% and for various temperatures were established by Chapman and Baird (1934). They found that at 22°C. (71.6°F.) the average duration of egg, larval, and pupal stages totaled 93 days, whereas at 32°C. (89.6°F.) it was only 27 days. At 17°C. (62.6°F.) the larvae died before pupating. Holdaway (1932) noted that under constant temperature conditions but with variable relative humidities, the rate of growth of a population of confused flour beetles increased with the rise in relative humidity from 25 to 75%. Furthermore, he observed that the population which a given unit of flour would maintain increased with the increase in relative humidity. An increase in population of 20% occurred with a rise in relative humidity from 25 to 50%; and an increase of 58% occurred as the relative humidity rose from 25 to 75%.

The factors of nutrition and the availability of food sometimes modify the effects of relative humidity and temperature. When grain is milled, the food content of the kernel is made available in a form that can be utilized by the immature stages of insects that are unable to develop in undamaged grain or in grain with a moisture content below an adequate level. Some insects are able to develop in flour from which most of the water has been removed. Fraenkel and Blewett (1943) found that confused flour beetles and saw-toothed grain beetles developed fairly well in flour at about 6% water content, and the Mediterranean flour moth developed in flour at 1% moisture. In another publication the same authors (1944) stated that confused flour beetles and Mediterranean flour moths, by utilizing metabolic water, could develop in food with very little free moisture. At lower humidities, more food is eaten to produce a given unit of body weight, the length of the larval period increases, and the weight of the pupae decreases. More food must be consumed at low humidities because part of the food is utilized to produce water. For every milligram of dry weight of pupae produced, confused flour beetles consumed an average of 5.17 mg. of food (dry weight) at 70% relative humidity, and an average of 7.25 mg. at 20% relative humidity. Some insects do not grow well in flour with a water content below 10%. With flour in equilibrium at a high relative humidity, molds prevent insect development.

The type of food greatly affects the ability of an insect to develop and to mature to the adult stage. Bell (1971) found considerable differences in extent of survival to the adult stage of Angoumois grain moths when the wheat kernel was fractioned to endosperm, germ, and bran and pelleted into two-fraction mixtures at different ratios. The greatest survival of larvae to the adult stage was obtained on whole-kernel diets and with endosperm-germ mixtures containing 1 to 50% germ and endosperm-bran mixtures containing 10 to 20% bran. The bran was beneficial when added to endosperm or germ up to a certain point, but in larger amounts it was detrimental to successful larval development. No larvae survived on endosperm-bran diets with more than 30% bran or on bran-germ diets containing more than 5% bran. Of the larvae that failed to survive, mortality usually occurred while they were very young. None of the pelleted diets gave a shorter developmental period than whole kernels. The longest larval periods resulted from 100% endosperm pellets, but the addition of small amounts of germ greatly reduced the larval period. Pellets with a high germ content or of pure germ extended larval development appreciably.

The food medium also affects the rate of reproduction as well as the rate of development of insects. Cotton et al. (1945) found that the enrichment of flour with riboflavin increased the rate of reproduction of confused flour beetles by 72.5% over that in nonenriched flour, and that the beetles reproduced faster and developed more rapidly in shorts, bran, and whole-wheat flour, which are naturally rich in this vitamin, than in clear, straight, or patent flours.

Considerable research has been done by Fraenkel and Blewett (1943) on the basic vitamin requirements of confused flour beetles and other insect pests of stored cereals. According to these writers, all insects require vitamins of the B group. At least seven of this group are essential for the proper growth and development of flour beetles: thiamine (B-1), riboflavin (B-2), nicotinic acid, pyridoxine, pantothenic acid, choline, and biotin, and possibly also inositol and p-amino-benzoic acid. These authors state that some stored-product insects have lower vitamin requirements than others, possibly owing to the presence in their bodies of intracellular microorganisms or symbionts that provide accessory food substances.

Insect infestations in bagged cereal products tend to concentrate near the outside layers. Similar observations have been reported for saw-toothed grain beetles and other beetles. The larvae of moths invariably come to the outside walls of bags to pupate.

Heating of cereal products as a result of insect infestation occurs at times, but is not as common as the heating of grain. The fundamental causes of heating and the reactions of the insects are much the same in both cases.

IV. DAMAGE CAUSED BY INSECTS

Damage and losses to stored grain may be as great as those sustained by growing crops. Damage to growing crops usually is visible; damage to stored grain frequently is concealed. The type and extent of damage to stored grain are difficult to estimate. In farm storage, where the greatest losses occur, the grain generally is not weighed when it is binned, so it is impossible to determine the extent of shrinkage due to insect feeding during storage. The presence of an insect infestation or contamination in milled cereal products intended for human consumption is much more serious than a similar infestation in stored grain. There are no practical methods for removing all insect contamination from such products, and in the U.S., infested cereal products entering interstate commerce are subject to seizure and destruction or to diversion into animal feed.

The following outline presents types of damage to grain and grain products and the nature of the losses that ensue.

A. Direct Insect Damage to Kernels, Grain Products, and Structural Containers

CONSUMPTION OF THE KERNEL

Some insects, including rice weevil, maize weevil, granary weevil, lesser grain borer, and Angoumois grain moth, feed largely on the endosperm, although the latter two also may consume the germ. Other pests such as Indian-meal moth larvae and mites restrict their feeding to the germ. Cadelles, dermestids, and flour beetles first eat the germ and then the endosperm, which may eventually be completely destroyed.

Feeding on the kernels results in loss in weight, loss of nutrients, conversion of the nutrients to inferior food materials, reduction of germination, reduced vigor of seeds, downgrading of market grains, and lowering of market values.

White (1953) found that 50% of the total loss in weight of wheat kernels from larval rice weevil feeding occurred during the last 9½ days of weevil development and 68% of the loss occurred when there was no outward evidence of infestation. Unpublished observations at Kansas State University indicate that a rice weevil consumes approximately 26% of the weight of the wheat kernel in which it lives during its development, whereas a granary weevil consumes 56% of its kernel.

CONTAMINATION OF GRAIN AND CEREAL PRODUCTS

Insect infestations result in contamination by entire insects or parts thereof. Infestations may include eggs, egg shells and egg cases, larvae and cast larval exoskeletons, pupae and pupal cases and cocoons, and mature insects. Internal-feeding weevils and Angoumois grain-moth larvae deposit their excreta or fecal pellets inside the kernels; lesser grain borers push excreta along with some starch particles out of the kernel through the entrance hole and leave excreta-starch accumulations as dockage in the infested area.

In addition to the flour consumed, the flour beetles secrete a pungent, irritating liquid consisting of ethylquinone, toluquinone, and methylquinone from certain abdominal and thoracic odoriferous glands. Contamination from large populations of flour beetles turns the flour pink.

Freeman and Turtle (1947) state that flour invested with mites has a particularly objectionable smell. When such flour is used for breadmaking, the bread has a sour taste, poor color, and may not rise adequately.

Larvae of Indian-meal moths, Mediterranean flour moths, and certain other moths spin silken webs over their foods, so that their presence in cereal products ruins much more than the amount of the products eaten. Frequently a thick carpet of webbing will cover the surface of stored grain infested by Indian-meal moths. Older millers will recall that, when Mediterranean flour moths infested their mills, their webbing would tie moving millparts so tightly during the weekend shutdown that it had to be removed to get the mill into operation again.

DAMAGE TO STRUCTURES AND CONTAINERS

Cadelle larvae, lesser grain borers, and dermestid larvae tunnel into wooden parts of granaries, boxcars, and ship holds to such an extent that the structures are weakened (Wilbur and Halazon, 1965). Their holes provide hibernation and hiding places for themselves and other insects, and lodging places for nutritious dusts and cracked kernels upon which these insects feed. Thorough cleaning of bins is difficult, if not impossible, under these circumstances. In wooden farm bins in the Central Wheat Belt, the granaries may be so weakened that the tunneled parts collapse. Wooden parts of elevator boots in old mills frequently are perforated by cadelle larvae.

These insects and others, including cigarette beetles, drugstore beetles, and spider beetles cut holes through sacks, packages, bolting cloth, or other cloth and paper materials. Millers used to refer to cadelles as bolting-cloth beetles.

B. Indirect Insect Damage to Grain and Grain Products

HEATING AND MOISTURE MIGRATION IN STORAGE

When insects feed on grain, the breakdown of the grain starches during insect metabolism results in heat, moisture, and energy as end products. The heat produced by insects in this manner and the damage that results are discussed under Ecology of this chapter, section C (p. 215). Lowering the grade of grain as a result of damaged kernels and of off-color and off-odors may cause a substantial price decrease.

DISTRIBUTION OF STORAGE FUNGI AND OTHER MICROORGANISMS THROUGHOUT THE GRAIN MASS

Storage fungi are recognized as a major cause of spoilage in stored grains and seeds. Insects and mites are frequently responsible for their distribution and development. Grain-infesting insects carry fungus spores into the grain and may increase the moisture content of the grain sufficiently so that the spores can develop. Christensen and Kaufmann (1969) summed up the situation by stating that at least some of the common grain-infesting insects regularly carry into the grain they infest a large load of inoculum of storage fungi, and, as they develop in the grain, provide conditions favorable for the development of these fungi. Christensen added that what appears to be an insect problem may be an insect-plus-storage-mold problem.

Of great significance is the possible distribution of such harmful bacteria as *Salmonella, Streptococcus*, and *Escherichia coli* by grain-infesting insects. Husted et al. (1969) found that *Sitophilus oryzae* retained *Salmonella montevideo* internally and externally after being in contaminated wheat for 7 days, and for at least 5 weeks after being in contaminated wheat for 14 and 21 days.

Aflatoxin, a poisonous substance produced by the fungus *Aspergillus flavus*, and other mold-producing toxins that grow in grain and in feedstuffs, possibly are distributed by grain-infesting insects, also.

HUMAN DISEASES TRANSMITTED OR CAUSED BY STORED-GRAIN OR STORED-PRODUCTS INSECTS

Tapeworm diseases, including dwarf tapeworm and rat tapeworm, are transmitted from rodents to man by cockroaches and mealworms as well as by fleas (Scott, 1962). Such enteric bacterial and protozoal diseases as typhoid, diarrhea, and dysentery are transmitted mechanically from man to man by cockroaches and other stored-food pests. Various intestinal infestations as intestinal acariasis, intestinal myiasis, and canthariasis result from ingestion of live stored-food mites, from cheese maggots and other stored-food flies, and from yellow mealworms and other stored-food beetles. A severe dermatitis known as grain itch, grocer's itch, vanillism, or other names is caused by bites of stored-food mites. In addition, some persons are allergic to mill dust containing fragments and fecal pellets of stored-food insects.

CONSUMER RESISTANCE TO UNSANITARY PRODUCTS

At the beginning of this chapter, Arthur Hibbs, a former president of AOM, was quoted as saying that the citizens of this nation are keenly aware of proper sanitation and pest control and they demand it. He added that cereal processors are faced with a far more sophisticated and educated, and a much more critical, customer than formerly.

Our grandmothers used their kitchen flour sifter to remove flour beetles and larvae from the flour before each baking. Today, when the housewife finds a single insect in the flour, the package is promptly destroyed and the milling company that manufactured the flour receives a letter sizzling with indignation. The housewife places full blame on the miller rather than on the railroad that carried the flour, or the wholesaler or retailer who stored the flour for various lengths of time before it was purchased.

All too frequently carloads of infested grain are purchased and rejected by several milling companies before the cars reach their final destination at an animal-feed mill.

Unfortunately, large shipments of flour are returned to the mill, at great expense to the millers, because the customers found insects in the load. In many instances, these insects were of a type that were neither injurious nor of economic concern. If persons in charge of receiving shipments would learn to identify the few major insect pests of grain and cereal products, much time, trouble, and expense would be saved.

INSECT FRAGMENTS AND EXCRETA IN GRAIN PRODUCTS

Insects render unfit for human consumption much more grain and grain products than they eat, because every infestation contaminates its host product with insect fragments and excreta. Insect fragments are minute particles of the bodies of dead insects or of their cast skins. Excreta of weevils and Angoumois grain moths are retained inside the kernels until grinding releases the pellets into the flour. On the other hand, lesser grain borers push their excreta out of the kernels into the grain mass and, for the most part, such excreta are removed as the grain is cleaned before milling. Excreta from flour beetles and most other major insect pests of cereal products are deposited directly into the product and cannot be removed.

Today, there are fewer insect fragments and excreta in cereal products produced in the U.S. than at any previous time; however, they have not been eliminated. Aside from the occasional transmission of toxic bacteria and other microorganisms, there appears to be no actual physical harm in the presence of fragments and feces in cereal products. As an elderly senator put it, "I have always eaten bread with insect fragments in it and I'm pretty healthy."

However, most persons have a natural revulsion to all forms of filth in their food. The thought that they may be eating insect fragments and excreta affects the esthetic sensitivities of most people, but when such filth is actually observed it may have serious effects. During a dinner party, an associate took a forkful of chef salad and noticed part of a cockroach with legs still kicking among the lettuce. Frantically he searched for the other part of the roach and when he couldn't find it, he became violently ill and remained in that condition for several days. The public wants to believe that the cereal products they are using are as free of insect filth as possible. If there were to be a statement on a package of flour to the effect that "this flour contains fewer than five insect fragments per 50 g.", it would have an adverse effect on the consumer, even though such a low count represents a major achievement over the past 20 years.

C. Insecticidal Treatment

COSTS

Important among the various types of insect damage, though sometimes considered to be unrelated, are the many costs associated with insecticidal treatment. These include the value of the insecticides used; labor required for the preparation of buildings for treatment, for insecticidal application, and for policing during treatment; losses in production involved in plant shutdown before, during, and after treatment; the special equipment and apparatus required for plant cleanup, insecticidal application, and aeration; and the various necessary pieces of safety equipment including gas masks and canisters.

INSECTICIDAL RESIDUES

Because of the danger of excessive chemical residues following application of fumigants and residual insecticides, considerable expenditures in time, labor, and apparatus are required to evaluate foodstuffs following insecticidal treatment. Because of the possibilities of danger to consumers, Food and Drug inspectors have adopted stringent regulations regarding such residues. Violations result in seizure of the products and in prosecution of the responsible companies. The publicity that invariably accompanies such procedures results in a wave of consumer reactions.

INSECTICIDAL RESISTANCE

At present (1971) only two residual insecticides are approved for application directly to grain or cereal products: malathion and pyrethrins. Resistance to these insecticides has developed among various strains of stored-product insects to such an extent that higher dosages are required for control, or that insecticidal treatment is no longer practical. In some cases resistant strains are larger, darker, and more resistant to heat, starvation, and desiccation than are susceptible strains.

V. DETECTION OF INSECT INFESTATION IN GRAIN

The value of grain for milling purposes and for human food is directly correlated with the quantity of insect contamination present (Cotton, 1962). Because the most important grain-infesting insects live inside the kernels during much of their lives, it is difficult for grain handlers to determine the extent of infestation in their grain. There are, however, various techniques and procedures that can be of great help in evaluating infestations. The simplest and most practical are discussed.

A. Visual

The emergence holes made by weevils, lesser grain borers, and Angoumois grain moths provide the best visual evidence of a "hidden" infestation. A rapid method of estimating the internal insect infestation in a grain sample is based on the assumption that for every kernel of wheat with a weevil emergence hole, there are five times that many kernels with internal infestation. To make detection easier, a seed-blowing device or laboratory aspirator for seed separation has been recommended for concentrating insect-emerged kernels into a fraction of their original sample (Milner et al., 1953).

White (1949) developed a box-like apparatus equipped with mirrors and lights that permits the viewer to see both sides of a small sample of grain without turning it.

Many granary-weevil larvae (and to a lesser extent, rice weevils) feed for a short time on the nutritious aleurone layer just under the seed coat before tunneling directly into the kernel. This activity results in a pale scar that is visible on the outside of the kernel.

As the internal-feeding insects mature, they slightly darken and appreciably soften the kernels, a condition which is apparent to careful observers.

The presence of small strands of silk or of fecal pellets or excessive starch particles is evidence of infestation.

B. Stains

Weevils chew a small hole through the seed coat into the endosperm, in which an egg is deposited. As the ovipositor is withdrawn, the female secretes a gelatinous plug that fills the egg channel so that the egg cavity is difficult to see without a microscope. Various stains have been discovered that will color the egg plug without staining the seed coat, unless it has been damaged mechanically.

A solution of acid fuchsin dye consisting of 0.5% acid fuchsin diluted in 50 cc. of glacial acetic acid and added to 950 cc. distilled water will stain egg plugs a cherry red (Frankenfeld, 1948). A convenient procedure is to place the sample of grain in a tea strainer and soak in warm water with a little detergent for 2 to 5 min., then cover the grain in the tea strainer with the acid fuchsin stain for about 3 min. The grain is then removed, washed under the tap, and examined by naked eyes or with a reading glass for the cherry-red spots that mark the egg plugs. Feeding punctures and other mechanical injuries may stain pink. The acid fuchsin stain solution may be used repeatedly.

Goossens (1949) stained egg plugs with gentian violet with favorable results. Milner et al. (1950a) used a water-soluble fluorescent dye, berberine sulfate. When stained egg plugs are examined under a 3660Å ultraviolet light, they fluoresce a greenish-yellow. Iodine will stain the egg plugs, but it also stains all exposed starch.

The chief disadvantage in the stain techniques is that they are strictly egg-plus stains, so that their use is restricted to weevil-infested grain; lesser grain borers and Angoumois grain moths do not fill their entrance holes with a gelatinous plug.

C. Specific Gravity

A simple, cheap, and effective qualitative test that is especially useful to operators of small line elevators was developed by White (1957). He adjusted a solution of sodium silicate (water glass) with water to a specific gravity of 1.190, added a handful of wheat kernels to the solution, and stirred to remove air bubbles. Noninfested kernels, along with some kernels containing eggs and early instars, sank to the bottom of the container, while kernels with intermediate and older insects floated to the top of the solution. The operator can check his results by splitting the kernels with his thumbnail and exposing the insects inside. This test is designed to determine the presence or absence of internally infesting insects, but not to determine the exact extent of the infestation.

D. Radiography (X-Ray)

Milner et al. (1950b) applied an X-ray technique to detect internal insect infestations in grain. They found that a Machlett cobalt-target X-ray diffraction tube with a beryllium window provided a satisfactory radiation source. Several companies, including General Electric and Westinghouse, manufacture X-ray Grain Inspection Units. To our knowledge, only the Field Emission Corporation of McMinnville, Oregon, is currently making an apparatus of this type—the Flaxitron.

Radiographs made with an X-ray Grain Inspection Unit provide excellent pictures of the insects inside the kernels, ranging from eggs to internal adults. Dennis (1953) found that when kernels to be radiographed were encased in soda straws, film was conserved and preparation and examination time reduced. Also, soda straws provided a convenient way for handling grain samples for storage, identification, and reexamination.

E. Ninhydrin-Impregnated Paper

Dennis and Decker (1962) developed a technique known as the ninhydrin process that met many of the requirements for an accurate and convenient detector of internal infestation. Ninhydrin is an organic dye that is a very sensitive indicator of free amino and keto acids, and produces a strong purple color in the presence of insect body fluids. Dennis and Decker constructed a prototype of an apparatus in which wheat kernels were crushed between folds of ninhydrin-treated filter paper; when insects were present, a purple stain appeared on the paper. At the Tropical Stored Product Centre at Slough, England, an apparatus known as the Ashman-Simon Infestation Detector was developed somewhat after the Dennis and Decker apparatus (Ashman et al., 1970; manufactured by Henry Simon, Ltd., of Stockport, England). When 50-g. samples are run through this instrument, it is said to detect a small proportion of eggs and young larvae, about half of the moderate sized larvae, and 80 to 90% of older larvae in small cereal grains. The machine is small and is designed for hand or electrical operation (or both).

F. Cracking-Flotation

A procedure for determining the extent of internal infestation long used in the cereal industries consists of coarse-grinding the kernels with a burr mill to release the confined insects and insect parts. Insect materials are separated and floated to the surface of an alcohol solution by mineral solvents. The floated material is trapped off and examined microscopically. A detailed procedure is given in the 11th edition of *Methods of Analysis* (Association of Official Analytical Chemists, 1970, p. 818).

G. Carbon Dioxide

Howe and Oxley (1952) considered the amount of carbon dioxide produced in a standard sample of grain over a 24-hr. period to be indicative of the extent of the hidden insect population. When the carbon dioxide content reached the 1% level as revealed by a simple gas analyzer, an infestation of approximately 25 larvae per lb. of grain was indicated.

H. Uric Acid

Since uric acid is an important constituent of insect excreta, Subrahmanyan et al. (1955) measured the uric acid content of a grain or cereal-food sample and correlated this measurement with the extent of insect infestation.

I. Aural

Adams et al. (1953) placed grain samples in a soundproof box, amplified the sounds made by insects while moving and feeding, and recorded the sounds on an oscilloscope.

The last three methods generally are not considered useful in the U.S. because of the time involved in analysis, the extent of infestation necessary to give measurable results, and the equipment necessary for analysis.

LITERATURE CITED

ADAMS, R. E., J. E. WOLFE, M. MILNER, and J. A. SHELLENBERGER. 1953. Aural detection of grain infested internally with insects. Science 118: 163-164.

AGRAWAL, N. S., C. M. CHRISTENSEN, and A. C. HODSON. 1957. Grain storage fungi associated with the granary weevil. J. Econ. Entomol. 50(5): 659-663.

AITKEN, R. T. 1943. A note on the damage to wheat caused by the Indian meal moth. Cereal Chem. 20(6): 700-703.

ANDERSON, K. T. 1938. Der Kornkäfer (*Calandra granaria* L.). Biologie und Bekämpfung. Monograph-angew. Ent. 13. P. Parey: Berlin.

ASHBY, K. R. 1961. The population dynamics of *Cryptolestes ferrugineus* (Stephens) (Col., Cucujidae) in flour and on Manitoba wheat. Bull. Entomol. Res. 52: 363-379.

ASHMAN, F., D. G. ELIAS, J. F. ELLISON, and R. SPRATLEY. 1970. Ashman-Simon infestation detector: An instrument for detecting insects within food grains. Trop. Stored Prod. Information, No. 19.

ASSOCIATION OF OFFICIAL ANALYTICAL CHEMISTS. 1970. *Methods of analysis* (11th ed.), W. Howitz, Ed. Publ. by The Association, P.O. Box 540, Benjamin Franklin Station, Washington, D.C. 20044.

BACK, E. A., and R. T. COTTON. 1926. The cadelle, 42 p. U.S. Dep. Agr. Bull. 1428.

BARRE, H. J., and R. T. COTTON. 1942. Recent developments in the farm storage of grain. Feedstuffs 14(43): 35-41.

BELL, K. O., Jr. 1971. Angoumois grain moth, *Sitotroga cerealella* (Olivier), reared on pellets and meals composed of various combinations of endosperm, germ, and bran of wheat. Ph.D. dissertation, Kansas State University.

BIRCH, L. C. 1946. The heating of wheat stored in bulk in Australia. J. Aust. Inst. Agr. Sci. 12(1-2): 27-31.

BOND, E. J., and H. A. U. MONRO. 1954.

Rearing the cadelle *Tenebroides mauritanicus* (L.) (Coleoptera: Ostomatidae) as a test insect for insecticidal research. Can. Entomol. 86(9): 402-408.

BOUDREAUX, H. B. 1969. The identity of *Sitophilus oryzae*. J. Econ. Entomol. 62(1): 169-172.

BURGES, H. D. 1959. Dormancy of the khapra beetle: quiescence or diapause. Nature (London) 184: 1741-1742.

CHAPMAN, R. N. 1928. The qualitative analysis of environmental factors. Ecology 9: 698-711.

CHAPMAN, R. N., and L. BAIRD. 1934. The biotic constants of *Tribolium confusum* Duval. J. Exp. Zool. 68: 293-304.

CHRISTENSEN, C. M., and H. H. KAUFMANN. 1969. *Grain storage: The role of fungi in quality loss*, 153 p. University of Minnesota Press: Minneapolis, Minn.

COTTON, R. T. 1950. *Insect pests of stored grain and grain products* (rev. ed.). Burgess Publ. Co.: Minneapolis, Minn.

COTTON, R. T. 1962. How to detect hidden infestation in grain. Northwest. Miller 266(1): 36-39.

COTTON, R. T. 1963. *Pests of stored grain and grain products* (rev. ed.), 318 p. Burgess Publ. Co.: Minneapolis, Minn.

COTTON, R. T., J. C. FRANKENFELD, and E. G. BAYFIELD. 1945. Relative susceptibility of enriched and non-enriched flours to insect attack. Northwest. Miller 221(7): 3a, 23a.

COTTON, R. T., and N. E. GOOD. 1937. Annotated list of the insects and mites associated with stored grain and cereal products, and of their arthropod parasites and predators, 81 p. U.S. Dep. Agr. Misc. Publ. 258.

COTTON, R. T., H. H. WALKDEN, G. D. WHITE, and D. A. WILBUR. 1960. Causes of outbreaks of stored grain insects, 35 p. Kans. Agr. Exp. Sta. Bull. 416.

CURRIE, JEAN E. 1967. Some effects of temperature and humidity on the rates of development, mortality and oviposition of *Cryptolestes pusillus* (Schonherr) (Coleoptera, Cucujidae). J. Stored Prod. Res. 3: 97-108.

DENNIS, N. M. 1953. A technique of grain orientation for radiographic analysis, 2 p. U.S. Dep. Agr., ARA, BEPQ, ET-310.

DENNIS, N. M., and R. W. DECKER. 1962. A method and machine for detecting living internal insect infestation in wheat. J. Econ. Entomol. 55(2): 199-203.

EIGHME, L. E. 1966. Relationships of insects to hot spots in stored wheat. J. Econ. Entomol. 59(3): 564-569.

FRAENKEL, G., and M. BLEWETT. 1943. The natural foods and the food requirements of several species of stored product insects. Trans. Roy. Entomol. Soc. (London) 93: 457-490.

FRAENKEL, G., and M. BLEWETT. 1944. The utilization of metabolic water in insects. Bull. Entomol. Res. 35(2): 127-139.

FRANKENFELD, J. C. 1948. Staining methods for detecting weevil infestation in grain, 4 p. U.S. Dep. Agr., ARA, BEPQ, ET-256.

FREEMAN, J. A., and E. E. TURTLE. 1947. Insect pests of food: the control of insects in flour mills. Her Majesty's Stationery Office: London.

GAY, F. J., and F. N. RATCLIFFE. 1941. The importance of *Rhizopertha dominica* as a pest of wheat under wartime storage conditions. J. Counc. Sci. Ind. Res. (Australia) 14: 173-180.

GOOD, N. E. 1936. The flour beetles of the genus *Tribolium*, 58 p. U.S. Dep. Agr. Tech. Bull. 498.

GOOSSENS, H. J. 1949. A method for staining insect egg plugs in wheat. Cereal Chem. 26(5): 419-420.

GRAY, H. E. 1948. The biology of flour beetles. Milling Production 13(12): 7, 18-22.

HALSTEAD, D. G. H. 1964. The separation of *Sitophilus oryzae* (L.) and *S. zeamais* Motschulsky (Col., Curculionidae) with a summary of their distribution. The Entomologist's Monthly Magazine 99: 72-74.

HIBBS, A. N. 1968. Proc. Sanitation Workshop, Grain and Cereal Products, Sept. 8-11, Kansas State University, Manhattan. Publ. by NPCA, Inc., P.O. Box 586, Elizabeth, N.J. 07207.

HINTON, H. E., and A. S. CORBET. 1955. Common insect pests of stored products, a guide to their identification,

61 p. British Museum (Natural History) Economic Series 5: London.

HOLDAWAY, F. G. 1932. An experimental study of the growth of populations of the flour beetle, *Tribolium confusum* Duval, as affected by atmospheric moisture. Ecol. Monogr. 2: 261-304.

HOWE, R. W. 1949. The development of *Rhizopertha dominica* (F.) (Col., Bostrichidae) under constant conditions. The Entomologist's Monthly Magazine 86: 1-5.

HOWE, R. W. 1950. Studies on beetles of the family Ptinidae. III. A two-year study of the distribution and abundance of *Ptinus tectus* Boield in a warehouse. Bull. Entomol. Res. 41(2): 371-394.

HOWE, R. W. 1956a. The biology of the two common storage species of *Oryzaephilus* (Coleoptera, Cucujidae). Ann. Appl. Biol. 44(2): 341-355.

HOWE, R. W. 1956b. The effect of temperature and humidity on the rate of development and mortality of *Tribolium castaneum* (Herbst) (Coleoptera, Tenebrionidae). Ann. Appl. Biol. 44(2): 356-368.

HOWE, R. W. 1962. A study of the heating of stored grain caused by insects. Ann. Appl. Biol. 50: 137-158.

HOWE, R. W., and T. A. OXLEY. 1952. Detection of insects by their carbon dioxide production. Gt. Brit. Dept. Sci. Ind. Res., Pest Infestation Res. Rep., 20 p.

HUGHES, A. M. 1961. The mites of stored food, 287 p. Gt. Brit. Min. Agr., Fish. Food, Tech. Bull. 9. Her Majesty's Stationery Office: London.

HUSTED, S. R., R. B. MILLS, V. D. FOLTZ, and M. H. CRUMRINE. 1969. Transmission of *Salmonella montevideo* from contaminated to clean wheat by the rice weevil. J. Econ. Entomol. 62(6): 1489-1491.

KANSAS STATE UNIVERSITY EXTENSION SERVICE. 1961. Stored grain insects, 6 p. Kans. State Univ., Ext. Serv. Leaflet L-30.

KIRKPATRICK, R. L., and D. A. WILBUR. 1965. The development and habits of the granary weevil, *Sitophilus granarius*, within the kernel of wheat. J. Econ. Entomol. 58(5): 979-985.

KUSCHEL, G. 1961. On problems of synonymy in the *Sitophilus oryzae* complex (30th contribution, Col. Curculionidea). Ann. Mag. Nat. Hist. 4(40): 241-244.

LINDGREN, D. L., L. E. VINCENT, and H. E. KROHNE. 1955. The khapra beetle, *Trogoderma granarium* Everts. Hilgardia 24(1): 1-36.

LINSLEY, E. G. 1944. Natural sources, habitats, and reservoirs of insects associated with stored food products. Hilgardia 16(4): 187-224.

LOCONTI, J. D., and L. M. ROTH. 1953. Composition of the odorous secretion of *Tribolium castaneum*. Ann. Entomol. Soc. Amer. 46(2): 281-289.

McGREGOR, H. E. 1964. Preference of *Tribolium castaneum* for wheat containing various percentages of dockage. J. Econ. Entomol. 57(4): 511-513.

MILLS, R. B. 1965. Early germ feeding and larval development of the Angoumois grain moth. J. Econ. Entomol. 58(2): 220-223.

MILLS, R. B., and D. A. WILBUR. 1967. Radiographic studies of Angoumois grain moth development in wheat, corn, and sorghum kernels. J. Econ. Entomol. 60(3): 671-677.

MILNER, M., D. L. BARNEY, and J. A. SHELLENBERGER. 1950. Use of selective fluorescent stains to detect insect egg plugs on grain kernels. Science 112: 791-792.

MILNER, M., E. P. FARRELL, and R. KATZ. 1953. Use of a simple blowing device to facilitate inspection of wheat for internal infestation. J. Ass. Offic. Agr. Chem. 36(4): 1065-1069.

MILNER, M., M. R. LEE, and R. KATZ. 1950. Application of X-ray technique to the detection of internal insect infestation of grain. J. Econ. Entomol. 43(6): 933-935.

PARK, T., and M. B. FRANK. 1948. The fecundity and development of the flour beetles, *Tribolium confusum* and *Tribolium castaneum* at three constant temperatures. Ecology 29(3): 368-394.

POTTER, C. 1935. The biology and distribution of *Rhizopertha dominica* (Fab.). Trans. Roy. Entomol. Soc. London 83(4): 449-479.

PRATT, H. D., and H. G. SCOTT. 1962. A key to some beetles commonly found in stored foods. Proc. Entomol. Soc. Wash. 64(1): 43-50.

RICHARDS, O. W. 1947. Observations on

grain weevils, *Calandra* (Col., Curculionidae) I. General biology and oviposition. Proc. Zool. Soc. London 117: 1-43.

ROBINSON, W. 1926. Low temperature and moisture as factors in the ecology of the rice weevil, *Sitophilus oryzae* (L.), and the granary weevil, *Sitophilus granarius* (L). Minn. Agr. Exp. Sta. Tech. Bull. 41.

ROTH, L. M. 1943. Studies on the gaseous secretion of *Tribolium confusum* Duval. II. The odoriferous glands of *Tribolium confusum*. Ann. Entomol. Soc. Amer. 36: 397-424.

SCOTT, H. G. 1962. How to control insects in stored foods, Part I. Pest Contr. 30(12): 24-34.

SHARIFI, S., and R. B. MILLS. 1971. Radiographic studies of *Sitophilus zeamais* Mots. in wheat kernels. J. Stored Prod. Res 7: 195-206.

SMALLMAN, B. N., and H. E. GRAY. 1948. The control of spider beetles in western Canada, 10 p. Canadian National Millers Ass.

SMALLMAN, B. N., and S. R. LOSCHIAVO. 1952. Mill sanitation studies. I. Relative susceptibilities of mill stocks to infestation by the confused flour beetle. Cereal Chem. 29: 431-440.

SODERSTROM, E. L., and D. A. WILBUR. 1966. Biological variations in three geographical populations of the rice weevil complex. J. Kans. Entomol. Soc. 39(1): 32-41.

STRONG, R. G., and G. T. OKUMURA. 1958. Insects and mites associated with stored foods and seeds in California. Calif. Bull. Dep. Agr. 47(3): 233-249.

SUBRAHMANYAN, V., M. SWAMINATHAN, S. V. PINGALE, and S. B. KADKOL. 1955. Uric acid as an index of insect filth in cereals and milled products. Bull. Cent. Food Technol. Research Inst. Mysore (India) 4: 86-87.

TURNEY, H. A. 1957. Some effects of cracked grain on the reproduction of the saw-toothed grain beetle. J. Kans. Entomol. Soc. 30(1): 6-8.

U.S. DEPARTMENT OF AGRICULTURE, Agricultural Research Service. 1965a. Losses in agriculture, 120 p. U.S. Dep. Agr. Agr. Handbook 291.

U.S. DEPARTMENT OF AGRICULTURE, Market Quality Research Division. 1965b. Stored-grain pests, 46 p. Farmers' Bull. 1260, Stored-Product Insects Research Branch.

VENKATRAO, S., R. N. NUGGEHALLI, S. V. PINGALE, M. SWAMINATHAN, and V. SUBRAHMANYAN. 1960. The effect of infestation by *Tribolium castaneum* Duv. on the quality of wheat flour. Cereal Chem. 37(1): 97-103.

Von WAHL, C. 1923. Milbeu m fermentierendem Tabak. Z. Angew. Entomol. 9: 416.

WARD, A. H. 1943. Location of vitamin B_1 in wheat. Chem. Ind. (London) 62: 11-14.

WHITE, G. D. 1949. An apparatus for rapidly inspecting both sides of small objects, 4 p. U.S. Dep. Agr., ARS, BEPQ, ET-265.

WHITE, G. D. 1953. Weight loss in stored wheat caused by insect feeding. J. Econ. Entomol. 46(4): 609-610.

WHITE, G. D. 1957. The practicability of flotation as a means for detecting infestation in wheat. Down to Earth (Dow Chemical Co.), Summer.

WILBUR, D. A. 1962. *Stored grain insects*. Chapter 16 in: *Fundamentals of applied entomology*, Robert E. Pfadt, ed. The Macmillan Co.: New York, N.Y.

WILBUR, D. A., and G. HALAZON. 1965. Pests of farm stored wheat and their control, 31 p. Kans. Agr. Exp. Sta. Bull. 481.

WILBUR, D. A., and L. O. WARREN. 1958. Grain sanitation on Kansas farms. Proc. 10th Int. Congr. Entomology, Vol. 4, 1956.

CHAPTER 6

CHEMICAL CONTROL OF STORED-GRAIN INSECTS AND ASSOCIATED MICRO- AND MACRO-ORGANISMS

PHILIP K. HAREIN

Professor and Extension Entomologist
University of Minnesota, St. Paul, Minnesota

ERNESTO DE LAS CASAS

Research Associate
University of Minnesota, St. Paul, Minnesota

I. INTRODUCTION

The Food and Agriculture Organization of the United Nations (FAO) estimated in 1973 that world supplies of food no longer provide an adequate buffer against crop failure and starvation; food supplies for millions of people depend almost entirely on each year's harvest. At least 10% of harvested food crops are destroyed by pests in storage, and current losses of 30% apparently are common in large areas of the world (Hall, 1970), especially in some of the tropical and subtropical areas where the need for increased food is greatest. In some of those regions a certain amount of insect infestation in grains and in other food products is accepted as normal, or even as desirable, as indicating "maturity" in the products. In the U.S., however, and some of the other developed countries, strict control of stored products insects is dictated not only by economic necessity but also by strict governmental standards concerning permissible contamination. The present review aims to summarize the principles and practices of control of insect pests of stored cereal grains and their products; the emphasis is on chemical control, as indicated by the title, since chemical pesticides will be essential for this control for a long time to come, but material on integrated control involving nonchemical means has also been mentioned.

II. PROTECTANTS

The natural habitats of stored-grain insects (Linsley, 1944, Woodroffe, 1961, Cutler and Hosie, 1966, and Strong, 1970a) are important sources of infestation for newly harvested grain. Insects that are natural infesters of seeds from wild plants, especially those gathered by other seed-harvesting animals, adapt with little trouble to grain harvested by man.

All static accumulations of grain are subject to infestation by stored-grain insects. A significant source of this infestation in some areas results from insect activity in the field, just before or following the initial steps of harvest. Some of the important biological characteristics responsible for the success of these insects include their wide range of foods and environmental tolerances, their ability to survive exceedingly long periods without food, and, of course, their reproductive capacity and relatively small size.

Thorough sanitation is the most effective means of preventing insect infestations. Although chemical controls are effective, they should be considered as a supplement to, rather than as a substitute for, sanitation. Storage areas should be clean and constructed tightly enough to keep out insects, rodents, and birds, and to keep in fumigant gases if such treatment becomes necessary. Loading and unloading docks should also be clean and constructed so that grain cannot accumulate under them.

All grain, dust, and chaff should be removed frequently from harvesting machinery, transport vehicles, and storage areas. The surface of equipment and storage areas that will be in contact with the grain should be sprayed about 2 weeks before harvest. The following insecticide formulations are suggested:

Insecticide Formulation	Amount of Insecticide per 7.56 liters of Water
Methoxychlor 50% WP[a]	353 ml.
or	
Methoxychlor 25% EC[a]	940 ml.
or	
Pyrethrins 6% EC combined with piperonyl butoxide 60%	646 ml.
or	
Malathion–premium grade	235 ml.
(Cythion) 57% EC	

[a]WP = wettable powder; EC = emulsifiable concentrate.

Spray to the point of runoff using 3.7 liters total formulation (one of the above) per 46.5 m.^{2} of surface. Allow the treated surfaces to dry before contacting grain. Also, if possible, spray the outside walls of the bins to a height of 1.8 m. and the ground around the bin to a distance of 1.8 m. out from the foundation. Applying residual insecticides to storage areas not only reduces existing insect populations, but also serves to protect the grain from migratory insects, some of which travel great distances. In subtropical areas farm machinery is generally treated with 2% malathion dust.

A program of constant surveillance of incoming grain is a necessary step to establish and maintain an effective insect prevention program. Stored grain should be inspected at 30-day intervals, especially during the summer and autumn months, to determine if some type of treatment is needed. No expensive equipment is needed for inspection to detect the insects; it is sufficient merely to sift samples of grain over a screen with 10 to 12 wires per in. Damaged kernels, abnormal odors, webbing, or hot spots are also important clues to insect infestation. Insect damage to grain in storage is reportedly related directly to the amount of infestation at the time of storage (Floyd, 1971).

A. Conventional Chemical Protectants

The major residual insecticides applied to stored grain for protection against insect infestation are malathion and the pyrethrins, although several new materials are being investigated. These grain protectants have several advantages: they persist for extended periods at concentrations lethal to the target insects; they are generally safer than fumigants to apply; and they require little special equipment or methodology (USDA, 1962). One application is usually sufficient during a single storage season. The protectants can also be used effectively in loosely constructed storage facilities that can not be fumigated successfully without extensive and expensive sealing efforts.

Unfortunately, only a few insecticides are approved for use on stored grain since they must meet certain standards. Approved insecticides must be effective against target pests over extended periods (Parkin, 1963), have a relatively low toxicity to nontarget organisms, including man, and provide little chance for toxic residues as prescribed by legal sources, without reducing seed viability.

Inert dusts have demonstrated some value for protecting stored grain, as they may be both toxic and repellent to some insects. Some that have been evaluated in the U.S. include diatomaceous earths, silica aerogels, magnesium oxide, aluminum oxide, and activated clays (La Hue, 1966, White et al., 1966, La Hue and Fifield, 1967, and McGaughey, 1971b). Research has also been conducted on inert dusts in India (Venugopal and Majumder, 1964, Majumder and Venugopal, 1968, and Bano and Majumder, 1968) and in Kenya (Ashman, 1966). These materials lose their effectiveness on moist grain, as they kill principally either by abrasive action or by absorption of lipids. The adsorptive action of dusts on insects must involve both physical and physiological phenomena, since the results obtained are not explained as simply a product of adsorption. Dusts with high surface area per gram and with particles exceeding 20 Å with low mineral sorptivity for water appear to be the most effective (Ebeling, 1969).

Inert dust has been rarely used for grain protection in the U.S. because it reduces the test weight and the commercial grade of the grain. Commercial interest in use of inert dusts is greater in other countries with less stringent grading standards, especially if effective pesticides are unavailable or too costly.

The application of inert dusts can produce disadvantages, i.e., dust contamination of the air, damage to machinery, increased risk of fire or explosion, or lung damage (silicosis) to workers.

The relative effectiveness of inert dusts as protectants for corn, sorghum, and wheat compared to malathion, diazinon, and synergized pyrethrins have been evaluated (La Hue, 1966, 1967, and 1970a).

Most protectants are applied to grain to prevent insect infestation, and are not expected to eradicate an existing population. Thus the grain should be treated before being placed in storage or at least during transfer from one site to another, before infestation. The protectants can be applied as dusts, wettable powders, solutions, emulsions, aerosols, or smokes.

Grain protectants may lose their biological activity rapidly if the grain temperature is excessively high (Rowlands, 1967). Strong and Sbur (1964a) reported this characteristic with malathion, naled, dichlorvos, Guthion, and diazinon.

Protectant dusts are diluted with inert ingredients such as clay, diatomaceous earth, grain flour, or talc and are either dispensed through applicators to the surface of the grain mass or are prorated onto the grain stream as it is being transferred to the next storage site. All other protectant formulations are generally applied as sprays, aerosols, or smokes, the primary purpose being to achieve a uniform application before an infestation.

Twelve dust and three aerosol formulations appeared to be feasible substitutes for various residual insecticides when applied as gas-propelled aerosols and micronized dusts into aircraft (Gillenwater et al., 1972). A dust formulation composed of 40% chlorpyrifos and another mixture containing 13.3% chlorpyrifos, 8.5% resmethrin, and 21.3% propoxur killed both the adult and larval stages of *Attagenus megatoma, Trogoderma inclusum,* and *T. glabrum.* The most promising aerosol was 7.5% resmethrin.

As mentioned earlier, there are few insecticides approved for use directly on grain after harvest, the primary residuals being malathion and pyrethrin. Their characteristics and usefulness are reviewed below.

MALATHION

Malathion (0,0-dimethyl phosphorodithioate of diethyl mercaptosuccinate) is an organophosphorus compound with relatively high toxicity to insects and low toxicity to man. Its chemistry, methods of analysis, and storage stability are adequately described by Miles et al. (1971).

Malathion is effective against many species of stored-grain insects, but there is evidence of increased insect resistance (Parkin et al., 1962b, Hayward, 1962, and La Hue, 1969a,b). Malathion applied as dust or sprays at 8 p.p.m. gave excellent control of *Sitophilus oryzae* for 5 months in stored polished rice (Bang and Floyd, 1962). Four parts per million also provided complete protection from *Cryptolestes turcicus* but was less effective against *Tribolium castaneum.* Parkin (1963) found it also provided the required protection at 10 p.p.m. for stored seeds from potential infestations of *Oryzaephilus* spp., *Tribolium* spp., and *Sitophilus* spp. He failed to get adequate control of moths at 10 p.p.m., although this was obtained by Moore and Decker (1961). McFarlane (1961) also reported malathion ineffective against *Cadra cautella* in Kenya.

Quinlan (1972) attempted to apply malathion uniformly as a thermally generated aerosol to insect-infested corn in storage. One-half of the formulation was introduced into the aeration system and the remainder was applied into the space over the grain mass. The aeration system was activated simultaneously to aid in distribution. However, most of the malathion was deposited in the center above the aeration outlet with only trace amounts found adjacent to the walls. A uniform application of malathion may not be necessary to achieve desirable results. Minett and Williams (1971) indicated that treatment of a small proportion of a wheat bulk with high concentrations of malathion may be more effective than uniform treatment of all kernels.

Malathion at 2 p.p.m. on 10% moisture wheat effectively controlled *Sitophilus* spp. and *Rhyzopertha dominica* (Lindgren et al., 1954), but it may be less effective on grain of higher moisture content. Both the residual stability and the subsequent effectiveness of malathion are generally reduced by increases in grain moisture as well as temperature. Watters (1959) obtained 99% mortality of *Laemophloeus ferrugineus* on 13.5% moisture wheat with 2 p.p.m. malathion, but 16 p.p.m. were needed to achieve comparable control in wheat with 15.5% moisture, and in wheat of 18.0% moisture the insects were not controlled. Malathion residues that degraded from 19.7 to 3.4 p.p.m. on grain sorghum during a 1-year storage period still provided excellent protection against mixed populations of stored-grain insects (La Hue, 1969a). The effectiveness of malathion may also depend on the kind of grain treated (La Hue, 1970b).

Malathion, ronnel, and silica gel provided effective control of stored-grain beetles (King et al., 1962). However, effective malathion residue did not persist on grain sorghum above 14% moisture. Heavy infestations of *Oryzaephilus surinamensis* were controlled by 10 p.p.m. malathion, 2 p.p.m. fenitrothion, or 4 p.p.m. dichlorvos (Green and Tyler, 1966). Both malathion and fenitrothion were effective for 8 months. The relative toxicity and residual effectiveness for malathion and diazinon were compared against 17 species of stored-product insects (Strong et al., 1967). Bromophos was persistent on concrete, fenitrothion moderately so, and malathion residues degraded rapidly (Lemon, 1967a). Tyler and Green (1968) reported the persistence of fenitrothion at 2 p.p.m. was similar to malathion at 10 p.p.m. on warm, damp grain.

Secreast and Cail (1970) published an improved procedure for determining malathion residues on stored agricultural products. Their percentage recovery from several commodities increased significantly compared to results using established procedures. Malathion and pyrethrins, as well as lindane and dichlorodiphenyltrichlorethane (DDT), if governmental restrictions allow, can be most helpful in protecting seed grain from insect damage. Even higher dosages than required for long-lasting protection can be applied without fear of reducing seed viability (Parkin, 1963).

Most countries allow direct application of malathion on grain and cereal products, provided certain tolerance levels are not exceeded. However, only premium grade deodorized malathion should be used. Malathion on grain degrades at a rate depending on the moisture content of the grain (Watters, 1959), temperature (Gunther et al., 1958), and the presence of enzymes (Rowland, 1964). Malathion residues are also unstable when applied to alkaline surfaces such as concrete. Hill and Thompson (1968) and Thompson and Hill (1969) have reported residues in various cereal grains imported into the United Kingdom. Malathion application of 0.47 liters per 1,000 bu. of rice resulted in residues exceeding 8 p.p.m. on the hull and bran fractions after a 30-day storage period (McGaughy, 1969). In 1971a McGaughy reported the degradation rate of malathion on rough rice, rice hulls, bran, and milled rice. Varieties of bran and milled rice differed in their retention of malathion, a difference that was dependent in part on the surface area and thickness of the kernel hulls. Apparently, moisture content and temperature also influenced the retention of malathion on grain sorghum, while natural foreign material on the sorghum at harvest had no effect (Kadoum and La Hue, 1969). The effect of the biological activity of sorghum grain on malathion degradation during 9 months of storage was evaluated in 1972 (Kadoum and La Hue). The malathion residue decreased to 34% of the initial deposit. However, greater quantities of malathion residue were detected on and within sterilized sorghum kernels than were found on viable kernels, as only 14% of the initial malathion deposit remained after 9 months' storage.

According to Bindra and Sidhu (1972), no insecticide is recommended as a protectant for grain in India because of the fear of toxicity hazards to consumers. However, benzene hexachloride (BHC) and DDT are being used illegally as grain protectants. Such contaminated cereals are the source of about 75% of the daily intake of these pesticides. To avoid such contamination, research was conducted on the residual life of malathion and pyrethrins. After 2 months' storage, malathion residues in maize grains had decreased from 20 p.p.m. to 4.66 p.p.m., below the 8-p.p.m. tolerance approved by the Codex Alimentarius Commission.

Off-odors may exist in dough and unleavened bread prepared from flour containing malathion residues (Godavaribai et al., 1960). However, no difference in the flavor of beer produced from malathion-treated grain was noted (Witt et al., 1960). In addition, the malting properties or germination of barley were not altered after a 32-p.p.m. malathion-dust application and a 9-month storage period (Parkin et al., 1962a).

PYRETHRINS

The insecticidal characteristics and safety qualities of pyrethrins (pyrethrolone esters of chrysanthemum carboxylic acid) have been established for a considerable period although the exact date marking their use as an insecticide is not known. Pyrethrum powder was introduced into the U.S. in the mid-nineteenth century.

An oil-base formulation of pyrethrins was used against many species of insects prior to World War II (Mallis, 1969). They knock down insects rapidly, though death may not occur immediately; in fact, insects may recover from their paralysis and escape. Generally pyrethrins are more effective against insects in adult stages than juvenile stages, especially the most active or free-flying species (Lloyd and Hewlett, 1958).

Several chemicals have been tested in different proportions as potential synergist for pyrethrins. The synthetic pyrethroid SBP-1382 ($\pm$) -*cis, trans*- (s-benzyl-3-furyl) methyl 2,2-dimethyl-3- (2-methyl propenyl) cycloproparrecarboxylate appears to be effective against a wide range of insects (Brooks et al., 1969). A related compound (+) -*trans*-chrysanthemic acid ester of ($\pm$) allethrolone (bioallethrin) also appears effective against four species of stored-product insects (Davies et al., 1970). The synergist piperonyl butoxide (2-(2 butoxyethoxy) ethoxy-4,5 (methylenedioxy) -2 propyltoluene) greatly increases its toxicity, especially if the ratio of piperonyl butoxide to pyrethrins and to the diluent are optimum for combating specific pest insects. The ratio of 1:10 pyrethrins:piperonyl butoxide is most widely accepted. In fact, this ratio is the primary formulation labeled for postharvest application to grains in the U.S. However, Brooke (1958) and Stevenson (1958) noted that piperonyl butoxide did not greatly alter the toxicity of pyrethrins to stored-product moths.

For stored-grain insects, pyrethrins are generally used as space treatments, as bulk grain applications, or as surface treatments on the walls and floors of the storage areas. As space treatments they are generally applied by thermal or mechanical generators to produce aerosols. Such applications are aimed to contact flying or crawling insects directly exposed to the aerosol particles. Thermal aerosol formulations usually consist of 0.2% pyrethrins and 2.0% piperonyl butoxide (percent by weight) plus the diluent. Formulations for mechanical aerosols frequently have 0.5% pyrethrins and 5.0% piperonyl butoxide. Whatever the formulation, the dosage of pyrethrins applied for stored-product insects should be about 0.3 g. per 1,000 ft.[3] of space.

The thermal generators reportedly decrease the effectiveness of pyrethrins as a result of degradation while exposed to high temperatures. Ultralow volume (ULV) application of synergized pyrethrins as a space treatment is a relatively new technique. The advantages are more effective distribution of particles with less range in size, resulting in greater insecticidal efficacy. Some insect resistance to pyrethrins has been noted but this potential problem fails to be of major concern currently.

The repellent properties of synergized pyrethrins are important in protecting stored commodities from insect infestation. A high level of repellency to *S. oryzae, T. confusum, T. castaneum, C. pusillus,* and *O. surinamensis* throughout a 12-month storage period was observed by La Hue (1966). Brooke (1961) reported both the toxicity and repellency of 1.17 p.p.m. pyrethrin with 27 p.p.m. piperonyl butoxide protected wheat from infestations of *S. granarius, S. oryzae,* and *R. dominica.* However, most researchers agree that the toxic effect of pyrethrins is lost rapidly when applied to stored grain, whereas the repellent action remains the primary factor for insect protection 6 to 12 months thereafter. Subsequently, insect-free commodities can be effectively protected against stored-grain insects by applying pyrethrins to their surfaces only. Application rate is 235 ml. of 6% pyrethrins combined with 60% piperonyl butoxide in 3.78 to 7.56 liters of water per 93 m.[2] of grain surface. This should be applied evenly over the surface of the grain immediately after the grain is leveled off upon reaching its storage site.

As with other insecticides, each species and stage of stored-grain insect differs in its susceptibility to synergized pyrethrins. Since most insect infestations of stored products involve more than one insect species or stage, the dosage applied should be effective against the least susceptible individuals to obtain the desirable results.

Pyrethrins and piperonyl butoxide residues on grain are persistent with the piperonyl butoxide outlasting the pyrethrins. Most is absorbed in the germ and bran (Strong et al., 1961). However, since pyrethrins have a relatively low toxicity to mammals, their residues are not considered with alarm. Of more concern may be off-odors in bread made from flour that had recently been in contact with treated surfaces (Watters, 1956).

In the U.S., the amount of residue cannot exceed 3 p.p.m. pyrethrins or 20 p.p.m. piperonyl butoxide, as established by the Environmental Protection Agency.

DIAZINON

Strong et al. (1967) reported diazinon (0,0-diethyl 0- (2-isopropyl-4-methyl-6 pyrimidinyl) to be more effective than malathion against 13 species of stored-grain insects. Results of residual protectant tests on wheat indicated diazinon to be slightly more effective than malathion in preventing infestation of six insect species. Test results obtained by La Hue (1970a) showed that diazinon protected wheat from extensive damage by *R. dominica* for 6 months.

Telford et al. (1964) noted considerable loss of diazinon residue after treatment. However, Roan and Srivastava (1965) reported that diazinon penetrated the interior of a wheat kernel and maintained a stable level in 45 days, after which diazinon residue dissipation was extremely slow. About 70% of the diazinon applied adhered to the grain. The cleaning, tempering, and milling process appeared to dissipate about one-half of the residue.

FENITROTHION

Out of 16 organophosphorus insecticides, fenitrothion (0,0-dimethyl 0- (3 methyl-4-nitrophenyl phosphorothionate) was one of the most effective against *T. confusum* and *T. castaneum* (Lemon, 1966) and it proved, in subsequent studies (Lemon, 1967a), to be the most toxic compound to *S. granarius* in wheat. Even heavy infestations of *O. surinamensis* were killed in farm-stored barley with 2 p.p.m. fenitrothion (Green and Tyler, 1966). Fenitrothion was also highly effective in protecting bagged wheat and barley from infestation by *O. surinamensis, S. granarius,* and *T. confusum* (Kane and Green, 1968). Dosages of 2 and 4 p.p.m. were effective for 6 and 10 months, respectively. The residues of fenitrothion disappeared gradually. Fenitrothion residual persistency was similar to malathion on damp, warm grain but was superior on dry, cool grain (Tyler and Green, 1968).

FENCHLORPHOS

Fenchlorphos (0,0-dimethyl 0-2,4,5-trichlorophenyl phosphorothionate) has potential for the control of *S. oryzae* on wheat (Harein, 1960). Wheat treated in a laboratory to provide a fenchlorphos residue of 4 p.p.m. resulted in a LD_{95} when the weevils were exposed 14 days. Although a dosage of 1 p.p.m. killed only 7% of the adult weevils, it decreased their reproductive potential 94%. Such a phenomenon is questioned by Lemon (1967b) as his research results were contrary to Harein's.

BROMODAN

Because bromodan (5- (bromomethyl) -1,2,3,4,7,7-hexachloro-2-norbornene) has a relatively low mammalian toxicity of 12,900 LD_{50}, it was tested as a protectant for wheat against infestations of three species of stored-grain insects (Harein and Gillenwater, 1966). Twenty parts per million killed all the *S. oryzae* and *Lasioderma serricorne* and prevented their reproduction. At 8, 16, or 24 p.p.m. on barley and wheat, bromodan provided some protection for grain in bags, but killed the insects in farm bulk grain.

BROMOPHOS

Bromophos (0,0 dimethyl 0-2,5 dichloro-4 bromophenyl phosphorothionate) is also another candidate protectant for stored grain (Green et al., 1970), especially if malathion resistance continues to increase. It has a relatively low mammalian toxicity and its residual life on high-moisture grain appears longer than that of malathion.

PHOXIM

Phoxim (phenylglyoxylonitrile oxime 0,0-diethyl phosphorothionate) appears promising as a protective treatment of bulk grain and other bulk-stored commodities (McDonald and Gillenwater, 1967). Later Strong (1969) suggested that its usefulness as a space application and as a residual treatment on storage facilities be studied further. Phoxim applied at 5 p.p.m. was superior to 10 p.p.m. malathion against several species of stored-product insects (La Hue and Dicke, 1971). Although its effectiveness against *S. oryzae* was excellent for 12 months, it had decreased toxicity to *T. confusum, T. castaneum,* and *R. dominica* after 9 months on stored hard winter wheat.

GARDONA

Gardona (2 chloro-1- (2,4,5-trichlorophenyl) vinyl dimethyl phosphate), an organophosphate insecticide similar to malathion, is effective as a residual for some species of stored-product insects, especially *T. confusum* and *T. castaneum* (Strong, 1970c). *S. granarius* mortalities of 95 to 100% were obtained after 20-day exposure to wheat with a residue of 8 p.p.m. (Harein and Rao, 1972) and Gardona at 15 p.p.m. reduced weevil reproduction significantly. Gardona at 10 p.p.m. generally was not as effective as 10 p.p.m. malathion in protecting wheat at 10, 12, and 13.5% moisture from damage by several species of stored-product insects (La Hue, 1973). Increases in moisture content also reduced the efficacy of Gardona.

Gardona persisted on corn and wheat for 8 months in farm storage (Hall et al., 1973). Ninety-four percent of the residue was in the bran, fine feed, and germ of the corn. The wheat bran had 90% of the Gardona.

LINDANE

Lindane (gamma isomer of benzene hexachloride) contains at least 99% of the gamma isomer of benzene hexachloride (BHC) and is one of the most toxic isomers to insects and mites. However, its use is becoming more limited because of a long residual life and its ability to migrate to untreated areas.

Since 1945, formulations of BHC and of its gamma isomer have been widely tested, recommended, and used as stored-product protectants with general success. Direct application to stored grains, residual applications in storage areas, and both discontinuous and continuous vaporization have been employed. Lindane residues have been found in rainwater in England, in air, liver and kidney fats, in many cereal foodstuffs, in milk, in butter, in eggs, and in human fat in several countries. However, the levels are well below those considered hazardous. The dietary intake of humans in the U.S. is less than one-six-hundredth FAO-WHO acceptable daily intake. Lindane is now banned in Sweden and in Finland. New legislation in Canada is limiting its field use, and no registrations for stored-product protection seem likely to be allowed. In the U.S., the situation is similar. England has not legislated against lindane and its use in storage areas will probably continue.

In addition, some stored-product insects have developed resistance to lindane (Champ and Cribb, 1965, Dyte and Blackman, 1970, and Parkin, 1965a,b).

DICHLORVOS

There is a need for an insecticide with a relatively high initial toxicity to insects and with short-lived residues for use as a grain protectant. This applies especially where grain fumigants are unsuitable because of excessive residues, because of poor insect control resulting from nonuniform distribution, or because of inadequate concentration resulting from loosely constructed storage areas. Dichlorvos (2,2-dichlorovinyl dimethyl phosphate) possesses some of these required characteristics to serve as a likely candidate (Mattson et al., 1955). Besides, many laboratory and field studies over the past several years have documented its ability to protect different grains against stored-product insects (Strong and Sbur, 1964a,b, Green and Tyler, 1966, Green and Wilkin, 1969, Kirkpatrick et al., 1968, McGaughey, 1970, La Hue, 1970b, and Harein and Rao, 1972).

Dichlorvos has little value as a commodity fumigant as it is unable to penetrate into materials. Dichlorvos residues do occur especially with relatively high moisture or temperature. Applying dichlorvos to wheat at 15 p.p.m. resulted in deposits ranging from 2.4 to 6.0 p.p.m. immediately after treatment (Vardell et al., 1973). Temperature was important as little loss of residue occurred at $-18°C$. Dichlorvos hydrolyzes in the presence of water or is metabolized by grain to produce dimethyl phosphate and phosphorylated protein derivatives. Lesser amounts of phosphoric acid, desmethyl dichlorvos, and monomethyl phosphate are also produced (Rowlands, 1970).

Rowlands (1970) noted that dichlorvos prolongs the residual life of certain other organophosphorus insecticides if present in the grain. This response may be reciprocal. It appears, however, that malathion residues in grain treated with dichlorvos would have little influence on the degradation of dichlorvos to acceptable residue levels (Elms et al., 1972).

Harvested grain, especially in tropical countries, is often stored in jute bags for extended periods. Conventional fumigation or residual insecticide applications are usually not feasible with small lots of produce stored in many places over wide areas. However, dichlorvos, dissolved in carbon tetrachloride and applied into the sacked grain with a motorized knapsack sprayer, produced high control of the infesting insects (Green and Wilkin, 1969).

The toxicological evaluation of dichlorvos for man indicates that 10 p.p.m. in the diet would be safe. The estimated acceptable daily intake is 0 to 0.004 mg. per kg. of body weight.

MINERAL OIL

Application of mineral oil to the surface of stored shelled corn is effective in preventing infestations of *Plodia interpunctella*. In the U.S. it is recommended that the mineral oil be unsulfonated, technically white, 100 to 200 sec. viscosity, and free of objectionable odors. Two quarts (1.88 liters) of this oil should be applied to each 9.3 m.² of corn surface. These surface treatments will not control insect infestations established within the grain bulk.

B. Potential Protectants

There is, and will continue to be, a need for evaluating new experimental compounds that have potential for use as direct contact, residue, or vapor toxicants to combat stored-grain insects. Most of this research is being conducted in the U.S. at the USDA Stored-Product Insects Research and Development Laboratory in Savannah, Georgia. Speirs and Lang (1970) reported the relative effectiveness of 68 candidate insecticides. An additional 22 had been covered in a similar publication in 1962 by Speirs. The effectiveness of 48 insecticides was compared against five species of stored-grain insects by Strong and Sbur in 1968. Strong followed up with laboratory evaluations of several organophosphorus insecticides on *A. alfierii* (1970b) and the flour beetles, *T. confusum* and *T. castaneum* (1970c). McDonald and Speirs (1972) reported three new chemicals with greater toxicity than malathion to larvae of *P. interpunctella.*

Any attempt to find components of natural foods with potential for inhibiting stored-grain insects is not new but it has gained interest with the increased restrictions on conventional insecticides. Preliminary studies in the U.S. indicate that natural oils extracted from the peels of various fruits are moderately toxic to *S. oryzae.* Lemon and grapefruit oil proved most effective. Studies should continue in an effort to isolate and identify the toxic components in these oils.

Capric acid occurs in triglycerides within many foods including milk. When mixed with stored foods and dehydrated foodstuffs, it has effectively controlled *T. confusum* at concentrations considered safe for mammals (House and Grahm, 1967). Lyophilized citrus oils from lemon, grapefruit, lime, kumquat, and tangerine were also highly toxic to *Callosobrunchus maculatus* (Su et al., 1972a) and moderately toxic to the rice weevil, *S. oryzae* (Su et al., 1972b). Sorbic acid, butylated hydroxyanisole, and butylated hydroxytoluene acted as ovicides to *T. confusum* when applied at 2 and 5% as additives in their diet (Baker and Mabie, 1973).

Plant and animal parts are also often used to protect stored crops from insect infestation in many parts of Africa. For instance, in Tanzania hot pepper, cypress and mahogany leaves, and some species of ferns are favored. Also ashes from specific plant species are mixed with grain to inhibit insect infestation. However, little has been done to investigate the claimed insecticidal properties of these plants. Worsley (1934) did report that the plants *Cassia didymotrya* and *Barringtonia racemosa* had toxic properties slightly less than nicotine sulfate. Many other plant materials have also been tested for insect control (Jacobson, 1958, and Lichtenstein, 1966).

The control of dermestids looks promising using sex pheromones to attract adults to areas treated with chemosterilants, insecticides, or disease agents (Burkholder and Dicke, 1966b).

The juvenile hormone analogue (methyl 3,7,11-trimethyl-7,11-dichloro-2-dodecenoate) was effective in controlling *Stegobium paniceum* (Bhatnagar-Thomas, 1973). Higher dosages were required for *R. dominica,* and it is to be expected that other stored-grain insects that develop within the grain kernels would require relatively high dosages for control.

It was considered unlikely that strains of insects resistant to pheromones would appear, but Dyte (1972) reported that a strain of *T. castaneum* that was resistant to many conventional insecticides was also resistant to the synthetic juvenile hormone identified as a *cis-trans* mixture of methyl 10,11-epoxy-7-ethyl-3,11-dimethyl-2,6-triecadienoate.

III. FUMIGANTS

A fumigant is a chemical which exists as a gas or produces a gas or vapor from solids or liquids. At available concentrations under practical conditions, it is lethal to specific stored-product pests. The word *fumigant* was derived from *fumus,* a Latin term for smoke. However, fumigants do not include smokes, because smokes are suspensions of particulate matter that probably will deposit on the outer layers of treated commodities. The same applies to mists and fogs. Fumigants must be in the gaseous state before they can be effective. As gases they diffuse through air and permeate products, and also can enter the respiratory system of insects. Compared to residual insecticides, fumigants have no lingering effectiveness, and as soon as they diffuse away from the target area, insect reinfestation may follow.

One reason for the wide acceptance of fumigants for control of stored-grain insects is the multiple methods by which they may be applied. Some modifications are usually possible to alter application methods required under different conditions of climate, storage, etc.

The bioactivity of fumigants is influenced by the method of application. Fumigants can be applied singly or mixed with others to improve their effectiveness or decrease their potential hazard. They may be applied as a gas, a liquid, or a solid in the form of tablets, pellets, or granules. The commodity or the space treated may be enclosed by structures composed of metal, concrete, wood, Fiberglas, or plastic and held at, above, or below atmospheric pressures with or without facilities for recirculating the gas to achieve homogenous gas concentrations.

An ideal fumigant should have the following characteristics:

1. Low cost per *effective* dosage, including application costs;
2. High acute toxicity to both immature and adult insects, but free from undue hazard to man;
3. High volatility and good penetration power but not excessively sorbed by grain;
4. Positive warning properties and easily detected;
5. Noncorrosive, nonflammable, nonexplosive under practical conditions, with good storage life;
6. Nonreactive with the commodity to produce residual odors;
7. Aerates readily and leaves no harmful residues;
8. Noninjurious to seed germination or to grain quality;
9. Noninjurious to milling or processing quality of grain or products; and
10. Ready availability plus simple and economical application.

A fumigant that meets all the above requirements has not been developed, especially when considering the wide variety of fumigation circumstances one may encounter.

The safe and effective use of fumigants depends, in part, on knowing their major physical, chemical, and biological properties. Whitney (1961) listed 17 fumigants and their properties, the group comprising about 99% of the stored-product insect fumigants in the U.S. Pertinent properties of the major fumigants are provided in Table I.

TABLE I

Fumigants for grain and cereal products[a]

Name and Synonym	Chem. Formula	Molecular Weight	Sp. Gravity as vapor (air = 1)	Explosive limits (% vol. in air)	General Comments
Acrylonitrile (vinyl cyanide)	CH_2CHCN	53.06	1.83	3–17	Spot fumigant
Carbon disulfide (carbon bisulfide)	CS_2	76.13	2.63	1–50	Mixed with nonflammable chemicals
Carbon tetrachloride (tetrachloromethane)	CCl_4	153.84	5.3	Nonflammable	Liquid fumigant aids in distribution and reducing fire hazard
Chloropicrin (trichloronitromethane)	CCl_3NO_2	164.39	5.7	Nonflammable	Intense odor. Used as a warning agent
Dichlorvos (DDVP, Vapona)	$CCl_2CHOPO(OCH_3)_2$	221.00	7.6	Nonflammable	Space fumigant effective against wide variety of exposed stored-product insects

Ethylene dibromide (ethylene bromide)	$C_2H_4Br_2$	187.88	6.48	Nonflammable	Spot fumigant
Ethylene dichloride (ethylene chloride)	$C_2H_2Cl_2$	98.97	3.35	6–16	Used with CCl_4 as grain fumigant
Ethylene oxide (oxiran)	$(CH_2)_2O$	44.05	1.52	3–80	Fumigant for microorganisms. Reduces seed germination
Hydrogen cyanide (hydrocyanic acid)	HCN	27.03	0.93	6–41	Space fumigant or recirculated through grain
Methyl bromide (bromoethane)	CH_3Br	94.95	3.27	Nonflammable	Space or commodity fumigant
Phosphine	PH_3	34.00	1.2	Spontaneously flammable	Highly toxic with excellent penetration properties

[a] Adapted from Whitney (1961) and Monro (1969a).

A. Concentration × Time

Most fumigations have, in the past, been recommended simply on the basis of dosage followed by an estimate of the required exposure or fumigation time. Such recommendations have some measure of success but they do not always take into consideration the multiple factors that can alter the anticipated fumigant concentration. Thus fumigation could be successful more often following the development, refinement, and use of analyzing techniques to monitor fumigant concentration in various areas during the fumigation, so that sublethal concentrations could be supplemented with additional amounts of fumigant. The addition of relatively small amounts or an extension of the exposure time to provide a suitable concentration × time factor (C×T product) may allow control of the pest without exposing the product to excessive dosages resulting from a follow-up fumigation. Savings of time and labor are also realized, an excellent example being the *T. granarium* fumigations in the U.S. (Armitage, 1955, 1956). Heseltine and Royce (1960) reported how integrated C×T products for ethylene oxide and methyl bromide could be used under practical situations. Time, temperature, and dosage relationships for carbon disulfide, sulfuryl fluoride, acrylonitrile, methyl bromide, ethylene dibromide, carbon tetrachloride, methyl chloroform, ethylene dichloride, and chloropicrin were determined for *T. confusum* (Kenaga, 1961). Other values and applications of C×T products have been investigated by Whitney and Walkden (1961), Harein and Krause (1964), Estes (1965), and Howe and Hole (1967).

Because of the multitude of variables to consider in determining C×T products for stored-product insects, Thompson (1970) developed dosage recommendations for methyl bromide, carbon tetrachloride mixed with ethylene dibromide, aluminum phosphide, and others. His C×T products were expressed as the weight of fumigant to be used per unit weight and volume of the commodity. Certain variables were also considered when estimating the dosage.

B. Fumigation Safety

The probability that a fumigant will harm nontarget organisms when used properly is often referred to as its *toxicity hazard*. However, fumigants with relatively low toxicity hazards may result in serious injuries if not used properly or if the fumigation procedure is relatively difficult. Any fumigant is potentially lethal to humans before, during, or after its application. Many commonly used grain fumigants have characteristic odors at concentrations safe to humans for a single exposure, but people become used to the odor quickly and may fail to detect harmful concentrations. Protective devices are available in certain countries that will prevent injury to the applicator even though he may be applying the fumigant while in the storage area. The use of remote techniques for application, such as the recirculation of methyl bromide or the use of fixed spray nozzles for applying liquid grain fumigants, is of value in limiting the applicator's contact with the fumigant.

Skin contact with any fumigant should be avoided. Both acrylonitrile and hydrogen cyanide can be absorbed through the skin in toxic amounts. Ethylene dibromide and methyl bromide can produce skin blisters if contaminated clothing is not removed immediately. Even vapor contact to the skin may be harmful. Suitable protection for the applicator's eyes is obtained with full-face gas masks, the same masks required for protection against vapor inhalation. Any person using fumigants, including those responsible for persons handling the fumigants, must be well acquainted with the hazards involved. The following safety checklist, adapted from a fumigation checklist prepared by Kansas State University, Manhattan, includes most of the important considerations which should receive attention before, during, and after a fumigation.

PRELIMINARY PLANNING AND PREPARATION
A. Understand fully the facility and commodity to be fumigated, including the:
　1. Design of the structure; adjacent as well as connecting structures both above and below ground.
　2. Number of persons or animals expected to be at or near the area to be fumigated.
　3. Commodity, its history and condition.
　4. Availability of and emergency shutoff stations for electricity, water, and gas.
　5. Nearest telephone with pertinent emergency numbers for fire or police departments, hospitals, and physicians.
B. Select and obtain a suitable fumigant.
C. Understand label directions, warnings, and antidotes.
D. If feasible, notify local medical, fire, and police authorities, and other security personnel as to the chemicals to be used, proposed date and time of use, type of gas mask required, and fire hazard rating.
E. Have available alternate application or protective equipment and replacement parts.
F. Inform all persons directly or indirectly involved of the fumigation potential hazards to life and property and the required safety measures and emergency procedures.
G. Display appropriate warning signs for posting treated areas, provide for security of buildings, and arrange for watchmen when required.
H. Have necessary first-aid equipment and antidotes available.
I. Apply the fumigant from outside the structure where possible.
J. Develop plans to ventilate the area when the required exposure is terminated *before* treatment is started.

PERSONNEL AND PROTECTIVE EQUIPMENT
A. Assign two persons to each fumigation, especially in circumstances where entry into a fumigated area is essential. If possible arrange for a two-way radio communication system.
B. All protective equipment should be stored so as to insure maximum life of the device and be readily accessible to employees at all times.
C. Canister type gas masks—
　1. Are ineffective when sufficient breathable oxygen is not available.
　2. Do not prevent sorption through the skin.
　3. Will not remove toxic gases if the concentration is above the level stated on the canister.
　4. Have operating conditions listed only for unused canisters.
　5. Require different types of canisters for different toxic gases.
　6. Should be mutilated when their effectiveness is exhausted to prevent reuse.

D. All fumigators and their personnel should be instructed in first aid and other emergency procedures including personal decontamination and antidotes.

E. Personnel handling fumigants should be cautioned to report all indications of illness or physical discomfort regardless of their apparent minor nature. These may include, but not be restricted to, any or all of the following: dizziness, nausea, headaches, and lack of coordination.

APPLICATION PROCEDURES AND FUMIGATION PERIOD

A. All applications should be made in accordance with the fumigant manufacturer's recommendations.

B. Consider prevailing winds and other pertinent weather factors in regard to fumigation effectiveness and safety.

C. Apply fumigants from outside the exposed areas where appropriate.

D. Provide watchmen, when required.

POST-APPLICATION PROCEDURES

A. Before re-entry, use a suitable gas detector to determine fumigant concentration. Do not depend on odors. Various methods to monitor field fumigant concentrations are described in detail by Monro (1969a).

B. Place guards at all entrances to prevent unauthorized entry.

C. Turn on all ventilating or aerating fans where appropriate.

D. Check for gas concentrations in areas that are expected to aerate slowly.

E. Remove warning signs when the gas concentration is within safe limits for human exposure.

F. Return unused chemicals in proper and clearly labeled containers to storage area. Dispose of empty containers.

C. Fumigant Toxicity to Humans

As was mentioned earlier, fumigants kill by preventing the assimilation of oxygen by the tissues in the target pest. Simple asphyxiants such as carbon dioxide and nitrogen have little or no poisonous effects upon the pests, but when they replace the oxygen of the atmosphere, the results can be lethal.

Carbon dioxide is a colorless, odorless, noncombustible gas with a faint acid taste. It is normally present in the atmosphere at a concentration of about 0.03%. Exposure to concentrations between 3 and 8% increase respiration and concentrations of about 15% may cause respiration to cease with paralysis developing. The patient must be removed to fresh air immediately. If respiration is impaired or has stopped, apply artificial respiration and get the patient to a physician.

Most other fumigants kill by preventing the tissues of the body from using oxygen by disrupting the normal enzymatic activities associated with cell respiration. This applies to humans as well as to most stored-grain pests.

One of the most toxic fumigants is hydrocyanic acid (HCN), a colorless gas or liquid with a bitter, almondlike odor. Human inhalation of low concentrations will result in headache, dizziness, loss of balance, and nausea. High concentrations increase the respiration initially but later cause breathing difficulty, unconsciousness and paralysis, convulsions, and respiratory arrest. Chronic exposure over prolonged periods of time can produce fatigue, weakness, skin irritation, gastrointestinal disturbances, speech difficulty, confusion, and death. Any person overexposed to hydrocyanic acid should be transferred to fresh air immediately and kept at rest. If breathing has stopped or is erratic, artificial respiration and oxygen should be administered until a physician arrives.

Another highly toxic fumigant is carbon disulfide. This is a faintly yellow, highly flammable, foul-smelling liquid. Moderate exposures cause fatigue, visual disturbances, nausea, vomiting, and headache. Exposure may also result in psychic changes that range from simple irritability to manic-depressive psychoses. Prolonged skin contact to carbon disulfide may lead to blisters that are extremely difficult to heal.

Several chlorinated hydrocarbons are also used as fumigants. Carbon tetrachloride is a good example. It is a colorless liquid. Its contact with the skin causes reddening and chafing and, if prolonged, produces blisters. There are many reports of carbon tetrachloride poisoning from accidental ingestion; however, one of the most important routes of absorption is by inhalation. The immediate effects of overexposure to its vapors include burning of the eyes, dizziness, headache, and occasionally ringing in the ears. Those overexposed to it are prone to accidents and may readily make mistakes in the performance of their duties.

Another fumigant in this group is chloroform. This is a colorless liquid of aromatic odor. As with carbon tetrachloride, its contact with the skin will cause reddening and, if exposure is continued, blisters will develop. The inhalation of chloroform vapors produces fatigue, dizziness, confusion, and loss of consciousness. Death usually results from respiratory paralysis and circulatory failure.

Methylene chloride is also a chlorinated hydrocarbon. It is a colorless liquid. Breathing methylene chloride vapors causes headache, giddiness, stupor, irritability, and numbness. Higher concentrations will cause loss of consciousness and death from respiratory paralysis. However, methylene chloride does not appear to be detrimental to liver and kidneys as observed with carbon tetrachloride and chloroform.

Ethylene chloride is a colorless liquid of aromatic odor. Contact of ethylene chloride with the skin will also cause reddening and burning. The inhalation of ethylene chloride results in fatigue, dizziness, headache, nervousness, and tremors. This may be associated or followed by nausea and vomiting. With severe exposure, the victim may become unconscious and die from paralysis of respiration.

All of the foregoing chlorinated hydrocarbons are decomposed by contact with an open flame or red-hot metal to form hydrochloric acid and phosgene. The former causes irritation of the eyes and the respiratory tract and the latter is a highly toxic gas.

Methyl bromide is a brominated hydrocarbon. It is highly toxic, being readily absorbed both through the lungs and through the skin. After exposure the skin may become red and itch, followed by development of blisters. The symptoms of poisoning from inhalation of methyl bromide vary considerably both in their degree and in their time of appearance. The most common early symptoms are the feeling of fatigue and complaints about blurred vision. This may be followed with temporary blindness, conjunctivitis, and swelling of the eyelids. Many applicators complain about ringing in the ears, dizziness, confusion, and fainting spells. Exposure to high concentrations may cause sudden death from respiratory paralysis and heart failure.

The last fumigant to be considered is phosphine (hydrogen phosphide). Phosphine is a colorless gas with an odor resembling garlic. Its inhalation causes restlessness that may be followed by tremors, fatigue, and sleepiness. The victim becomes nauseated and often suffers from vomiting and diarrhea, thirst, headache, dizziness, ringing in the ears, fainting spells, and a burning sensation in the chest. Eventually he or she may become sleepy, pass into rigor, and develop convulsions before death. Death may be delayed a few days but still may be sudden. Continued exposure to sublethal concentrations may lead to chronic poisoning characterized by bronchitis, gastrointestinal disturbances, destruction of the teeth, and disturbances of speech, vision, and motor functions.

Fumigants, as well as all insecticides, are poisons that should be handled with great care. Means to safeguard the applicator are varied. Protective clothing is available and must be used properly. Fumigants should be applied by remote control, as is done when recirculating methyl bromide or when applying liquid fumigants through a fixed-nozzle system.

D. Fumigant Characteristics

METHYL BROMIDE (CH_3Br)

Le Goupil (1932) was first to report the fumigation value of methyl bromide. It became popular during the 1930s as a fumigant for plants, vegetables, and some fruits, especially by quarantine officials. Methyl bromide has also been used extensively as a fumigant for stored products, mills, ships, and railway cars because of its ability to penetrate products at concentrations lethal to the insect pests under normal atmospheric pressures. It is highly toxic to most stages of stored-product insects. The pupal stage may be an exception (Howe and Hole, 1966, and Monro et al., 1952). Even the age of the pupal stage can alter the efficiency of methyl bromide (Godden and Howe, 1965, and Bennett, 1969), as young pupae were the most resistant.

Fisk and Shepard (1938) reviewed the early use of methyl bromide as a fumigant. Lethal concentrations of methyl bromide in five kinds of grains at various moisture contents to *S. oryzae* and *T. confusum* were determined by Whitney and Walkden (1961). Adult *S. oryzae* were the most susceptible, followed by immature *S. oryzae* and adult *T. confusum*. Higher concentrations for shorter periods were more effective than lower concentrations for longer periods. Mostafa et al. (1972) found the eggs of four species of stored-product insects became more susceptible to methyl bromide with age.

Methyl bromide and ethylene dibromide were included in fumigation studies conducted by Lindgren et al. (1954) as well as Krohne and Lindgren in 1958. Both were effective alone and, in 1959, Kazmaier and Fuller reported that mixtures of these two fumigants were more effective than methyl bromide against all life stages of *T. confusum*. This was also true for both fumigants early in the exposure period.

According to Brown and Heseltine (1949), the effectiveness of methyl bromide is limited as a fumigant in silo bins because of unsatisfactory distribution of the gas. However, when applied with carbon dioxide, methyl bromide penetrated to the bottom of the bins (Calderon and Carmi, 1973). Apparently, the carbon dioxide acted as a carrier.

Methyl bromide is available in steel cylinders varying from 5 to 1,800 lb. (2 to 816 kg.) and in cans containing 1 lb. (0.45 kg.). As methyl bromide is dispensed from its container some evaporative cooling takes place. One of several forms of heat exchange can be supplied (Hammer and Amstutz, 1955). A coil of copper pipe, immersed in a container of hot water, through which the methyl bromide must pass may suffice to vaporize the liquid, which is required because liquid methyl bromide should not contact such commodities as grain or cereal products. Even the release of a relatively low temperature methyl bromide gas may result in uneven distribution and uneven mortality. Liquid methyl bromide could be dispensed into shallow pans to allow evaporation before diffusion as a gas into the air or commodity.

Methyl bromide is nonflammable and nonexplosive. It has no corrosive action in its pure form on most metals except aluminum, but it reacts with many plastic and organic materials. Monro (1969a) provides a list of the materials that may be damaged by exposure to methyl bromide. Polyethylene and neoprene seem to be the least affected, although rubber is strongly attacked. It still may be used in conjunction with many synthetic rubber and plastic sheets that serve as tarpaulins for fumigations since the concentration of methyl bromide should not exceed 1%. Thompson (1966) reviewed the properties and usage of methyl bromide as a fumigant.

HYDROGEN CYANIDE (HYDROCYANIC ACID, HCN)

Although HCN was one of the first chemicals to be used for fumigating grain, dry cereal products, and empty storage areas, its use has decreased in recent years. It is relatively soluble in water, in which it forms a dilute acid and this has limited its acceptance. Also being sorbed extensively it does not penetrate as effectively as desired for a commodity fumigant, and it has been replaced by phosphine and other fumigants. Details on the physical, chemical, and biological activity of HCN plus methods of application and detection are covered by Monro (1969a).

PHOSPHINE (HYDROGEN PHOSPHIDE, PH₃)

The use of phosphine generated from aluminum phosphide as a fumigant for bulk grain was established in Germany about 1937. Originally, the method consisted of inserting packets of aluminum phosphide into grain. In the 1950s a new formulation, consisting of aluminum phosphide and ammonium carbonate in tablet form, became available. Phosphine is produced now in a formulation consisting of a compressed mixture of aluminum phosphide, ammonium carbonate, and paraffin. Phosphine, carbon dioxide, and ammonia are produced when this formulation comes in contact with humid intergranular air. The carbon dioxide and ammonia help to combat the flammability of phosphine. Only aluminum hydroxide remains as a residue. Decomposition of the tablet takes about 36 hr. at 25° C. if sufficient moisture is available during which time about one-third of its weight is diffused as phosphine. Phosphine smells somewhat like garlic, but this odor cannot be used for warning purposes since it disappears under some fumigation conditions (Bond and Dumas, 1967). The developmental history of phosphine for use on raw and processed agricultural products was reviewed by Hazleton (1968).

Phosphine is one of the most toxic fumigants to stored-product insects (Bond and Monro, 1961, Qureshi et al., 1965, Lindgren and Vincent, 1966, Sinha et al., 1967, and Vincent and Lindgren, 1972). Although highly toxic to many insects, phosphine is markedly less so to certain stages of some species (Lindgren et al., 1958, Anon., 1966). Heseltine and Thompson (1957) stated that "a concentration-time (C × T) product of 10 mg hr/l of phosphine is sufficient to control adult *Sitophilus* spp. but that young pupae of these species require a C × T product of 300 mg hr/l." Ozer (1961) conducted a detailed study of the toxicity of phosphine to both *S. granarius* and *S. oryzae*. His results show small effects on mortality with increases in concentration, a finding which is borne out by the difficulty experienced in some field trials. Reynolds et al. (1967) noted that all preadult stages of *S. granarius* reached a susceptible stage of development during a 10-day fumigation of wheat, a factor necessary to produce complete mortality. Exposure periods of 3 to 5 days or even longer are recommended.

The effectiveness of phosphine is increased by its low molecular weight and low boiling point, characteristics that promote its rapid diffusion and penetration into grain (Heseltine and Thompson, 1957, McGregor, 1961, and Rout and Mohanty, 1967), through cereal products in mills (Cogburn, 1967), in railway cars (Schesser, 1967c), into commodities under tarpaulins (Cogburn and Tilton, 1963, and McGregor and Davidson, 1966), or through bagged flour in plywood overpacks (Gillenwater, 1973).

Phosphine is applied by prorating the aluminum phosphide tablets or pellets on grain as it flows into storage or by injecting it into stored grain using a special metal probe. The probe is pushed to the bottom of the grain mass and the tablets are applied automatically as it is withdrawn. This also can be accomplished using ordinary metal piping and dropping the tablets manually. In warehouses or railway cars the formulation can be dispersed onto sheets of paper or in envelopes, which permits recovery of the aluminum hydroxide residue. Phosphine has no adverse effects on food materials and, under normal conditions, will not affect the germination of seeds (Strong and Lindgren, 1960, and Beratlief and Alexandrescu, 1964).

DICHLORVOS (0,0-DIMETHYL-2,2-DICHLOROVINYL PHOSPHATE)

This organophosphate insecticide has often been called a residual fumigant. It has potential as a residual or contact insecticide (Strong and Sbur, 1961, 1964a, 1964b; Jay et al., 1964; Kirkpatrick et al., 1968; La Hue, 1970b; and Harein and Rao, 1972) but it is short-lived as it hydrolyzes in contact with water and has limited fumigation characteristics. It is effective against houseflies and mosquitoes at very low concentrations. At higher concentrations, various household insects, such as cockroaches, and stored-product moths and beetles also succumb to dichlorvos. As always, there are exceptions, e.g., *Tenebroides mauritanicus* was not controlled even after extended exposures to dichlorvos (Bond et al., 1972), and *T. castaneum* escaped dichlorvos treatments in warehouses (McFarlane, 1970). A mixture of malathion and dichlorvos had an antagonistic effect on *S. oryzae* and *R. dominica* (Champ et al., 1969).

There are various methods to dispense dichlorvos as a gas. Strips of polyvinyl chloride (PVC), impregnated with dichlorvos, slowly release its vapors to provide lethal concentrations over several weeks. Adult *Anagasta kuhniella* were eliminated and 75 to 80% of the larvae were killed in empty metal bins using the PVC strips (Conway, 1966). Warehouse infestations of *Ephestia elutella* (Green et al., 1966) and *C. cautella* (McFarlane, 1970) were also controlled using this "strip" formulation. Excellent control of adult *P. interpunctella* was obtained during 24-hr. exposures to the vapors from a dosage of one strip per 28.3 m.^{3} of space over shelled corn (La Hue, 1971). Malathion-resistant *P. interpunctella* were no exception (La Hue, 1969b). Dichlorvos applied daily as an oil mist also was effective against *E. elutella* in a London warehouse (Green et al., 1968) and against *O. surinamensis* and *S. granarius* in bagged grain (Green and Wilkin, 1969). Chemical analysis of air concentration indicated that the dichlorvos diffused rapidly. A dichlorvos concentration of 3 γ per liter retarded the infestation of flour in cotton bags and prevented the infestation of flour in multiwall paper bags over a 5-month storage period (Harein et al., 1970).

Gillenwater and Harein (1964) developed a dispenser to accelerate the release of dichlorvos from impregnated resin pellets. Heated air is passed through an aggregate of the dichlorvos pellets using the apparatus shown diagrammatically in Figure 1. This dispenser provides an immediate buildup of an effective vapor concentration that would be distributed uniformly throughout the storage area (Gillenwater et al., 1970). Vaporization of dichlorvos from the vapor dispenser (Figure 1) or application as an aerosol from a pressure cylinder were both effective against *S. granarius* in empty cargo ships (Bond et al., 1972). Both a dichlorvos-malathion mixture (Schesser, 1967b) and a dichlorvos-Gardona mixture (unpublished research) have been evaluated for protecting commodities in transit.

Attfield and Webster (1966) described several formulations of dichlorvos including their bioactivity. Estimates of dichlorvos concentrations in air after different methods of dispensation and its relative toxicity to various species of stored-product insects were investigated by Harein et al. (1970).

POTENTIAL FUMIGANTS

There is a constant need to develop and evaluate new chemicals as potential fumigants for controlling stored-product insects. Of special interest is the possibility of finding new fumigants that are more specific for the target insects than current formulations and less hazardous to the applicator or the consumer. Many of the candidate chemicals that have been studied and reported on have never been marketed. Some deserve a reevaluation.

Soles and Harein (1962) reported the relatively high fumigant toxicity of *N*-(α-methylacetonitrile) morpholine and acetate of dimethyl 2,2-dichloro-1-hydroxyvinylphosphonate to four species of stored-product insects. The candidate fumigants 1,2,3-tribromo propene, ethylenimine, and crotyl bromide (86% 1-bromo-2-butene and 14% 3-bromo-1-butene) were more toxic at LD_{95} than carbon tetrachloride to stored-product insects (Harein and Soles, 1964). In 1966, Kirkpatrick reported three of seven test fumigants to be more toxic than methyl bromide at LD_{95}. Cooper and Gillenwater (1972) reported that five of the six candidate fumigants included in their testing program were more effective than methyl bromide against *T. confusum*, *L. serricorne*, and *A. megatoma*. The level of effectiveness of all six compounds indicated that further evaluation as potential grain and space fumigants was warranted.

E. Residues after Fumigation

The Environmental Protection Agency currently has charge of determining acceptable residues on foods and feeds in the U.S. These residues result from the application of fumigants or insecticides or from the formation of their metabolites as they degrade. The amount of the originally applied chemical or of their metabolites that persists as residues depends on a number of factors, including the dosage and application procedure, temperature and moisture of the target product, storage and handling characteristics, processing methods, and time between application and residue sampling.

Two major factors that determine the efficacy of fumigants are their rate of diffusion into and sorption by the commodity being treated. The penetration of a fumigant throughout the commodity proceeds by diffusion, a natural process of equalization following the release of one gas into another. Sorption encompasses adsorption (attachment of gas molecules to the commodity surface), adsorption (penetration of gas molecules into the commodity to form solid or liquid solutions), and chemisorption (chemical reaction to form new and relatively stable compounds).

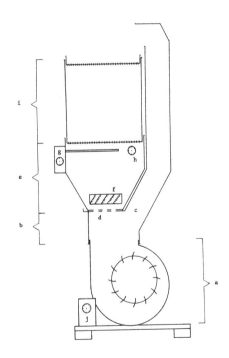

Figure 1. Schematic of the insecticide vapor dispenser. a, centrifugal blower; b, adapter; c, air duct; d, air-flow regulator; e, air-heating chamber; f, electric heater elements; g, thermostatic switch; h, dial thermometer; i, formulation cartridge; and j, automatic timer.

Fumigants containing bromine, such as methyl bromide, are especially subject to chemisorption. The tolerance for methyl bromide in the U.S. is 50 p.p.m. determined as inorganic bromide. This acceptable maximum level can be surpassed, especially if excessively high dosages are applied or if the grain receives numerous applications. It often is necessary to treat grain more than once, particularly in tropical climates.

Methyl bromide decomposes within grain to give inorganic bromide and methylated derivatives of -OH, -SH, and -NH groups. The proteins account for 80% of this reaction (Rowlands, 1970) and there appears to be a positive correlation between 1) protein and fat content of milled grain fractions and 2) level of bromide sorption due to fumigation (Gibich and Pedersen, 1963). These by-products are not known to be detrimental to the food value of the grain, and are nontoxic to humans (Winteringham, 1955; Rowlands, 1967, 1970; and Shuey et al., 1971). Still, there are possible disadvantages, as methyl bromide-treated flour may cause bread to bear off-odors, especially when it is still fresh from the oven or when the loaves are tightly wrapped (Brown and Heseltine, 1962). Off-flavors and odors are especially a problem in soybean flour fumigated with methyl bromide (Dow Chemical Co., 1957).

Fumigation at low temperatures and excessive dosages to maintain adequate insect control may result in less bromide residue (Lindgren et al., 1962). Wheat fumigated 48 hr. had eight times more residue than wheat fumigated 2 hr. About 65% additional bromide residue was added with a second fumigation within 24 hr. Certainly, another method to decrease fumigant residue is to dilute fumigated flour with nontreated flour, a method often practiced but not condoned by some regulatory agencies. Vacuum fumigation tends to result in greater amounts of residues than similar fumigation at atmospheric pressure (Whitney, 1963).

There are differences in the location and the amount of naturally occurring bromide in wheat compared to that resulting from methyl bromide fumigations (Gibich and Pedersen, 1963). It is unfortunate, therefore, that the several methods for determining amounts of bromide residues in food do not distinguish between the bromide ion and organically bound bromide, even though they may differ in their toxicity. By 1970, Heuser and Scudamore had described a method in which they could be determined separately. The same method is applicable for separating residues following fumigation with ethylene dibromide.

The affinity of ethylene dibromide for grain and the resulting comparatively high bromide residues have been researched many years. Free ethylene dibromide can usually be detected in grain for several weeks after treatment. The volatile dibromide is removed gradually with aeration (Olomucki and Bondi, 1955). Ethylene dibromide does not penetrate well into grain and its desorption rate is relatively slow. Wheat at 9% moisture contained more ethylene dibromide after 10 days' aeration than wheat with 15% moisture (Sinclair et al., 1962). Later Sinclair et al. (1964) fumigated wheat and corn kernels at 10° and 29°C. and noted that bromide residues were 40 and 30 p.p.m., respectively. These residues decreased to 5 p.p.m. within 5 days. Fumigation at reduced pressures caused a significant increase in residue. Various methods for identifying and quantitating bromides, as reaction products or unchanged fumigant, were revised and new methods were developed by Heuser (1969).

Although ethylene dibromide diffuses slowly through grain and is relatively difficult to remove, partly due to its sorption characteristics, it does not seem to affect the grains' nutritive value (Bridges, 1956). It will reduce the reproductive capacity of bulls (Malling, 1969) and the egg-laying of chickens (Bondi et al., 1955). Ethylene dibromide is frequently mixed with methyl bromide, ethylene dichloride, and carbon tetrachloride for use as a fumigant.

Ethylene dichloride is considered relatively inactive chemically when used as a fumigant (Rowlands, 1971). When soybeans were fumigated with ethylene dichloride-carbon tetrachloride (75:25), a residue of each remained in both the hull and interior of soybeans (Storey et al., 1972). Toasting the soybeans during processing removed the residues from the hulls, but steaming dehulled soybeans had no effect on the residues.

Aluminum phosphide, powdery remnants of aluminum hydroxide, and traces of phosphate are the three residual products following fumigation with Phostoxin®. Phosphine converts to innocuous phosphates in a short time (Robinson and Bond, 1970). The other two residual products are reduced to extremely low levels during grain processing (Liscombe, 1963). Bread made from phosphine-fumigated flour contained residues of 0.004 to 0.021 p.p.m. of phosphine (Bruce et al., 1962). Such residues do not affect the baking quality or nutritive value of flour. The Phostoxin tablets or pellets should be enclosed in a sachet or envelope when fumigating processed foods so they do not come in contact with the product. Dieterich et al. (1967) also list the several residues in prepared foods and dried fruits after fumigation with phosphine. The maximum was 0.017 p.p.m. in dried apples, but the majority had 0.01 p.p.m. or less. Rats showed no adverse symptoms following a 3-month diet of wheat fumigated with relatively high concentrations of phosphine. Tkachuk (1972) located non-PH_3 residues in wheat treated with phosphine; he noted that they could not be removed by aeration. Most were located in the bran. Some could be extracted with water and were identified as hypophosphite and pyrophosphate.

Berck and Gunther (1970) developed a rapid method of measuring the sorptive affinity of granular or powdered substrates for phosphine, and Berck et al. (1970) compared microcoulometric, thermionic, and flame-photometric detectors for determining minute amounts of phosphine in foodstuffs, air, and water. A tolerance of 0.1 p.p.m. PH_3 from Phostoxin fumigation of cereals in international trade is recommended.

A multidetection system using gas chromatography to determine fumigant residues in foods was developed by Heuser and Scudamore (1969). The sensitivity of their results was generally better than 0.1 p.p.m. for 20 compounds. Malone (1969) found that an acid-reflex method was the most promising for extracting fumigant residues from grain. He recommended that further refinement of the method and an aeration or dissipation study on both whole and ground grain be developed.

It is evident that the methods to determine fumigant residues range from complex, sophisticated techniques to simpler routine methods used only to determine if the original fumigant applied had been removed in sufficient quantities for subsequent safe use of the fumigated product. However, part of the fumigant applied may react with components of the product to produce reaction compounds. Here lies the need for the more selective analytical methods in quantitating these end products. New chemicals proposed for use as fumigants, especially if they have fluorine or silicon bases, must be fully investigated to determine potential food contamination from their metabolites.

F. Aeration

The primary purpose of aeration is to force air through bulk-stored grain to equalize grain temperatures and moisture content. However, fumigants can also be introduced and diffused satisfactorily with the same aeration system. In fact, such aeration systems, permanent or temporary, provide a practical method of applying fumigants to stored grain. The fumigant is usually more uniformly distributed and the dosage requirements somewhat less for aeration than for other methods.

Upright storage facilities can be fumigated by either a single-pass or a recirculation aeration technique. The aeration fans are operated just long enough for one complete air change for the single-pass method. Such can usually be obtained in 10 min. at 1/20 cfm./bu. or 20 min. at 1/40 cfm./bu. Single-pass applications, combined with gravity penetration, have been used in flat storage facilities, although the recirculation method is frequently the most effective. Storey (1967) compared gravity, penetration, single pass, and closed recirculation with methyl bromide in flat storages. The fumigant is moved through the grain several times using the recirculation method. There are aeration systems that can recirculate the fumigant by moving it down one bin and up through another. The recirculation method has been adapted for use in many different types of storage facilities (Kline and Converse, 1961). However, air-flow resistance varies depending on the type of grain, its moisture, and dockage content (Shedd, 1953). Most of the liquid fumigants are dispersed satisfactorily by aeration, although methyl bromide is the most widely used fumigant under such circumstances. Storey (1971) studied the distribution of methyl bromide and a combination of carbon disulfide and carbon tetrachloride through grain sorghum and wheat in silo-type elevator tanks using aeration systems. The type of grain, fumigant dosage, and air-flow rate affected the fumigation efficiency. Phosphine should not be used with aeration because of its degradation at reduced pressures.

G. Effect on Seed Germination

Although fumigants are useful in protecting stored seed grain from insect injury, some will reduce the viability of the seed.

The liquid fumigant mixtures such as carbon tetrachloride, carbon disulfide, carbon dichloride, as well as phosphine (Strong and Lindgren, 1960) are relatively safe regarding seed germination.

Little or no injury to germination occurred when fumigating seed with methyl bromide if the seed moisture was less than 12%, the dosage was less than 32 mg. per liter, the exposure period did not exceed 24 hr., and the temperature was 26.7°C. (Whitney et al., 1958). The overall relative order of tolerance of the seeds tested was oats, barley, grain sorghum, corn, and wheat. Strong and Lindgren (1959a,b,c, 1960) conducted a series of tests with methyl bromide and hydrogen cyanide on rice, oats, barley, sorghum, and small legume seeds. The hydrogen cyanide did not damage germination. Dosage, temperature, type of seed and its storage history, exposure time, and moisture content of the seeds were the major factors contributing to methyl bromide injury. The germination of corn seed at 13% or lower moisture was not seriously impaired by hydrogen cyanide if the seeds were aerated thoroughly before planting (Strong and Lindgren, 1961). Additional research on the effect of methyl bromide on seed germination was reviewed by Gostick (1970).

Bushnell (1972) fumigated barley seed with ethylene oxide, and reduced seed germination to less than 60%. Neither ethylene oxide nor propylene oxide is generally recommended because of these adverse effects on seed germination.

H. Monitoring Fumigant Concentrations

There is a marked advantage of knowing the concentration of a fumigant within a treated space or commodity compared to just having information on the fumigant dosage. Monitoring fumigant concentration throughout the desired exposure period allows use of C×T products and, if necessary, a change of dosage or exposure to obtain or at least approach the desired insect control in all areas. Equipment for measuring fumigant concentrations is also handy for detecting gas leaks and for measuring the progress of post-fumigation aeration, which is important for the safety of both operator and commodity.

The thermal conductivity method of measuring methyl bromide in air was developed for practical use by Phillips and Bulger (1953). Production models of the original unit were improved in subsequent years, thus improving a means to study the distribution, penetration, sorption, and C×T patterns within bulk lots of shelled corn, wheat, grain sorghum, barley, rice, seeds, and related commodities. Phillips (1957), Kenaga (1958), Heseltine (1961), and Koucherova and Lisitsyn (1962) are sources of information on the design, calibration, operation, and utilization of the thermal-conductivity gas analyzer.

Monro (1969a) explains the value, design, and operation of interference refractometers for measuring fumigant concentrations. These instruments are relatively simple to use and the gas concentration values obtained are not affected by voltage variations, a potential problem with most electrical units. In essence they consist of glass tubes containing specific chemicals that change color upon exposure to particular fumigants. Air plus the fumigant are drawn through the tubes using either a hand-operated pump or bellows. The length of color change within the tubes is proportional to the gas concentration, assuming the instrument has been properly calibrated. Heseltine and Royce (1960) describe the usefulness of color indicators that are placed within the fumigation area and react proportionately to the gas concentration and exposure period.

Halogenated hydrocarbon fumigants such as methyl bromide can be measured by use of halide leak detectors or halide lamps. Such lamps are generally available from refrigeration supply dealers and are sufficient for obtaining field estimates of gas concentrations. They work on the principle that a flame in contact with copper will be green to blue if an organic halide gas is present in the atmosphere surrounding the flame. As the gas concentration increases, the flame changes from greenish-blue to blue. Fuels used for the flame include kerosene, wood alcohol, acetylene, and propane. Naturally they cannot be used with any gas or in any area where there is a fire hazard. Halide meters are also available commercially and are designed primarily for measuring halogenated hydrocarbons in air at concentrations up to 500 p.p.m. with 10% accuracy.

Precise spectrophotometric and gas-chromatographic methods of measuring minute gas concentrations of many fumigants have also been developed for acrylonitrile (Brieger et al., 1952), carbon disulfide (Berck, 1965a, and Bielorai and Alumot, 1966), carbon tetrachloride (Berck, 1965b, and Bielorai and Alumot, 1966), chloropicrin (Kanazawa, 1963, and Berck, 1965a), dichlorvos (Webley and McKone, 1963, and Heuser and Scudamore, 1966), ethylene dibromide, ethylene dichloride, hydrogen cyanide, and methyl bromide (Berck, 1965a), and phosphine (Dumas, 1964, 1969, and Chakrabarti and Wainman, 1972). Various chemical methods for detection of many of the fumigants are also useful (Monro, 1969a, and Bond, 1973).

I. Fumigation under Tarpaulin

One common method of fumigating bagged grain or packaged cereal products is to enclose it under gasproof sheets that will retain the fumigant at concentrations and for periods lethal to stored-product insects. Polyethylene, vinyl films, and synthetic rubbers, or materials coated with one or more of these products are effective in retaining methyl bromide (Phillips and Nelson, 1957). Polyethylene or polyvinyl chloride sheets at least 12.7 mm. thick are suitable for indoor fumigations. Nylon or cotton fabrics laminated with neoprene, polyvinyl chloride, or butyl rubber should be used outside. Even accidental contact of such sheets with liquid methyl bromide does not produce weak areas unless the tarpaulin was stretched out and under stress.

Another advantage of tarpaulin fumigations is the possibility of treating the commodity in place assuming there is sufficient room above and around the stack to allow for laying and sealing the tarpaulin and applying the fumigant. The sheet-floor joint is sealed by laying tubular sacks containing sand (sand snakes) or lengths of chain on the edge of the fumigation sheet. Allowing the tarpaulins to remain in place after fumigation and aeration would help protect the product against reinfestation.

Brown (1959) describes fumigations with methyl bromide under gasproof sheets and with phosphine (Brown et al., 1968), and Bowen (1961) provides a formula for calculating the correct fumigant dosage. Methyl bromide or phosphine works best for fumigating large stacks because it must penetrate quickly and diffuse rapidly. Liquid fumigants are effective for small stacks. Empty gas or oil drums may also be used to fumigate very small quantities of a commodity. Recommended dosages are suggested in Table II. The fumigant can be introduced by pouring on a liquid fumigant or by inserting a packet of a solid-type fumigant on the surface of the commodity, after which the container or chamber could be sealed with a tarpaulin. A box composed of masonite panelwood or its equivalent painted with an asphalt-aluminum emulsion can serve as a fumigation chamber for methyl bromide (Simmons, 1960). Various tarpaulin application procedures and precautions are explained by Monro (1969a).

IV. VARIABLES THAT INFLUENCE THE EFFICIENCY OF FUMIGATION

The primary factors that decrease or increase the distribution and biological activity of fumigants into grain are temperature, moisture, fumigant formulation and dosage, storage structure, dockage, and characteristics of the insect population and of the grain kernels. The size, shape, and structure of the kernels determine the capacity of the grain to compact in storage and thus to retard the movement of gases through the grain mass. Also the kernels influence the kind, rate, and extent of sorption of the gases and of their release into the atmosphere.

A. Temperature and Moisture

Temperature and moisture of grain are two of the major factors producing the greatest variations in the efficiency of a fumigant. Temperature changes deep within bulk stored grain are slow unless spontaneous heating occurs from insect or microorganism activity, or forced aeration is utilized. When grain is fumigated, the gas comes into equilibrium with the temperature of the grain in a short time. An increase in temperature results in greater molecular activity of the gas. This in turn facilitates the diffusion and penetration of the fumigant within the grain mass by decreasing sorption. The opposite effect occurs as temperatures decrease. Sublethal gas concentrations may result if the grain temperature is excessively high or low. When the temperature of the grain is 46°C. or higher, the fumigant vaporizes rapidly and may escape before lethal gas concentrations can be obtained throughout the grain mass. However, most stored-grain insects cannot survive in grain at this relatively high temperature, thus reducing the need for fumigation. Stored grain with a temperature of 10°C. or below need not be fumigated, as most insect pests are relatively inactive at this temperature. Unfortunately, some stored-grain pests are able to survive low temperatures that prohibit the practical use of fumigants (Cunnington, 1965) and some develop concentrated populations to create a favorable environment within a cool grain mass (Monro, 1969a). In general, fumigants with a relatively low boiling point can be used more effectively at reduced temperatures than other fumigants because of the adequate vaporization of the liquid fumigants to produce a lethal gas concentration within a required period of time.

As mentioned earlier, temperatures may not be constant throughout a grain mass. Heating can occur in grain with a moisture content of 15% or below as the result of insect activity. These hot spots may reach 40°C. This increased temperature accelerates insect activity and the hot spots may spread throughout the grain mass. Such temperatures usually will not damage the grain but secondary effects resulting from translocation of water to the surface of the grain mass may be costly. Wet grain heating occurs in grain of more than 15% moisture due to the metabolism of microorganisms, especially storage molds. The kernels become discolored, develop a musty odor, and deteriorate in nutritive value. Fumigants are useful to reduce heating produced by insects but those available today do not control storage molds.

In the absence of insects and molds, temperatures within bulk-stored grains change slowly, the only exceptions being the layers of kernels next to the bin wall and at or near the surface. The lag between the wall and center temperatures is usually large. Even with a sharp and significant change in the outside temperatures, changes within the bin are small. For example, beginning in September in the U.S., the temperature in the center of binned bulk grain remains higher than that near the walls until late March. The reverse of this

TABLE II

Dosage table for fumigants used in smaller chambers[a,b]

	milliliters of liquid/100 ft.³[c]							
	1/16 lb./ 1,000 ft.³	1/4 lb./ 1,000 ft.³	1/2 lb./ 1,000 ft.³	3/4 lb./ 1,000 ft.³	1 lb./ 1,000 ft.³	2 lb./ 1,000 ft.³	3 lb./ 1,000 ft.³	4 lb./ 1,000 ft.³
Acrylonitrile 34% + carbon tetrachloride 66%	2.1	8.5	17.0	25.6	34.1	68.2	102.3	136.4
Carbon disulfide	2.2	9.0	17.9	26.9	35.9	71.7	107.6	143.5
Carbon tetrachloride	1.8	7.1	14.2	21.3	28.4	56.8	85.2	113.6
Chloropicrin	1.7	6.9	13.7	20.6	27.4	54.9	82.3	109.7
Ethylene chlorobromide	1.7	6.7	13.4	20.1	26.8	53.6	80.5	107.3
Ethylene dibromide	1.3	5.2	10.4	15.6	20.8	43.7	62.6	87.4
Ethylene dichloride 75% + carbon tetrachloride 25%	2.1	8.4	16.9	25.3	33.8	67.5	101.3	135.1
Ethylene oxide at 7°C.	3.2	12.7	25.5	38.2	51.0	102.0	153.0	204.0
Hydrocyanic acid	4.1	16.5	32.9	49.4	65.9	131.8	197.6	263.5
Methyl bromide[d] at 0°C.	1.6	6.5	13.0	19.5	26.1	52.2	78.3	104.4
Propylene oxide	3.4	13.6	27.3	40.9	54.5	109.1	163.6	218.2

[a]Source: Monro (1969a).

[b]Quantities of liquid in milliliters per 100 cu. ft. at 20°C. equivalent to dosages in pounds per 1,000 cu. ft. (to be used for measuring small quantities of liquids before evaporation in smaller chambers).

[c]Conversion factors: 100 ft.³ = 2.83 m.³; 1 lb. = 16 oz.; 1 oz./1,000 ft.³ = g./m.³ = mg./liter (approximately); 1 fl. oz. (Brit.) = 28.4 ml.; 1 ml. = 0.035 fl. oz. (Brit.); 1 fl. oz. (U.S.) = 29.6 ml.; 1 ml. = 0.034 fl. oz. (U.S.).

[d]Methyl bromide is often dispensed as a liquid held under pressure in a graduated measuring glass, such as a 280-ml. applicator.

process occurs throughout the spring and summer. Moisture migration, or movement, within the bin is a direct response to temperature variation. Temperature gradients create convection currents, causing cool air to move downward near the outside bin walls, then across toward the center where the air is warmed and rises toward the surface. The higher temperature at the center enhances the moisture loss from the grain to the warmer air and the moisture is carried by the convection air currents to the cooler area near the surface. Moisture is lost from the air by condensation, to be absorbed by the surface grain. Wet grain heating may result. The relationship of storage temperature and grain moisture content to insect heating, reduction in germination, and damp grain heating, established by Burges and Burrell (1964), has been used as a guideline for safe storage.

Increasing the moisture content of grain generally increases the sorptive capacity of the kernels with a resulting loss of fumigant concentration. In general a 25% increase in fumigant dosage is, or should be, allowed to compensate for absorption and penetration when the grain moisture content exceeds 14.5% (Lindgren and Vincent, 1960, Pedersen, 1960, Kunz et al., 1964, and Monro, 1969a). However, sufficient moisture is mandatory for fumigation with phosphine. With low amounts of moisture available, the rate of phosphine generation may be too little and too late to obtain adequate insect mortality.

B. Methods of Application

Liquid formulations, such as those containing carbon tetrachloride, carbon disulfide, and ethylene dichloride, are commonly used in farm and elevator storage. They are versatile in that they can be applied in several different ways, and they are formulated in various proportions to provide mixtures that will give the most uniform distribution throughout the grain mass. For instance, carbon disulfide and carbon tetrachloride will usually penetrate readily and reach most areas of a bin. The differential sorption of carbon tetrachloride and carbon disulfide in wheat may result in proportions of the two gases different from those applied; Harein and Krause (1961) noted increased proportions of carbon tetrachloride near the bottom of a column of wheat early in the exposure period.

Some fumigants may be applied directly to the grain stream as the bin is being filled. There is an advantage to this method of application since it disperses the fumigant more evenly throughout the grain mass. Gases such as methyl bromide and hydrogen cyanide are convenient to apply if the storage is equipped with an aeration system to distribute the gas. Calcium cyanide, Phostoxin, and other solid-type formulations are especially well adapted for application to grain as it is being moved, although they can also be probed into the grain. Gas is evolved from the solids when they are subjected to moisture in the grain or in the air.

Two standard methods of applying fumigants are gravity penetration and forced distribution. With gravity penetration, the fumigant is usually distributed over the surface grain or it is probed into the grain. The fumigant can also be introduced either continuously or intermittently. Sometimes, an extra amount is added for the first and last lots of grain where the greatest concentrations of insects usually occur and where the fumigant is most easily lost.

Another means of fumigating deep bins is the layering method. This is accomplished by placing a certain amount of grain in a bin, applying a prorated amount of the total dosage of fumigant to the surface of the grain, and introducing an additional amount of grain at each desired level until the bin is filled.

A guide for various fumigation application rates for bulk grain is covered in Table III.

C. Dockage

Dockage is also important as it reduces fumigation efficiency because of poorer penetration, greater sorption, and channeling of vapors through the grain mass. Mortalities of *S. sasakii* decreased significantly when fumigating wheat of 6% or more dockage (Harein, 1961). In addition, dockage generally favors insect survival and development and provides some protection for the insects from the toxic concentrations of the fumigants. Further research is needed to determine the effects of all types of dockages on fumigation efficiency in various grains.

D. Storage Facilities

Grain storage structures and materials vary widely in the U.S., in addition to the tropics and subtropics. In North America construction material includes metal, concrete, and wood. All types have to be sealed for successful fumigation. Gasproof tarpaulins have been used in the U.S. to ensure a lethal gas concentration for *T. granarium* (Armitage, 1955, 1956).

The most gastight storages are constructed of metal. For example, enclosures fashioned from sheet metal welded at the seams are the most effective. Such tanks may have been constructed originally for storing oil, and later converted into grain storages. Other storages in this general group are usually circular and constructed from corrugated metal strips that are bolted together at the joints. The gastight qualities of these circular metal bins are improved if the joints are caulked when the bins are assembled. Rectangular buildings constructed of corrugated and flat metal and bolted together at the seams are included in this same category.

Storage structures fashioned from concrete are popular. It is important that the walls be finished so that they are smooth and free of pockets, grooves, or any other irregularities. Such irregularities provide places where grain may remain static to provide a home for insects. Cracks and crevices in the walls or foundations also serve as hiding places for certain species of insects. Larvae of the dermestid beetles are particularly attracted to such areas, increasing the problem of fumigation since the fumigant vapors may not penetrate into the crevices in sufficient concentration to kill the insects. The concrete walls may also become porous in time and permit the escape of excessive amounts of fumigant vapors.

Grain stored in wooden facilities is difficult to fumigate because such structures are porous and permit an excessive amount of fumigant to escape. As a result of this leakage, fumigant dosage recommendations for wooden bins may be twice the amount recommended for metal and concrete bins (Monro, 1969a). It may even be necessary, in some instances, to cover the wooden structure with a gastight tarpaulin to retain the fumigant, but the cost of this can be prohibitive. Wood storages also provide cracks into which grain may lodge and where insects

TABLE III

Fumigants and dosage recommended for bulk fumigation of grain in upright and flat storages[a]

Fumigant	Dosage[b]		Minimum Exposure (days)	Remarks
	per m.³	per 1,000 bu.		
Direct mixing			Upright Storage	
Calcium cyanide	154.5 g.	12.0 lb.	7	May stain white maize and polished rice
Chloropicrin	25.7 g.	2.0 lb.	1	Should be removed by aeration after 24 hr.
Mixture EDC75:CT25	430.0 ml.	4.0 gal.	3	For maize × 1.5
Mixture CS₂ 16:CT84	269.0 ml.	2.5 gal.	3	Mixture may contain 2% SO₂
Mixture EDB7:EDC30:CT63	215.0 ml.	2.0 gal.	3	For maize × 1.5
Aluminium phosphide[c]	2.5 tablets	90 tablets	3	5 days at 10-15°C.
	9 pellets	300 pellets		4 days at 16-20°C.
				3 days at 21°C. or above
Surface application (gravity distribution)				
Mixture EDC75:CT25	430.0 ml.	4.0 gal.	7	For maize × 1.5
Mixture CS₂ 16:CT84	322.0 ml.	3.0 gal.	7	For maize × 1.5
Mixture EDB7:EDC30:CT63	269.0 ml.	2.5 gal.	7	For maize × 1.5
Carbon tetrachloride (CT)	537.0 ml.	5.0 gal.	14	More often used in combination
Recirculation				
Methyl bromide	25.7 g.	2.0 lb.	1	Should be removed by aeration after 24 hr.
Hydrocyanic acid	38.6 g.	3.0 lb.	1	Grain should be thoroughly aerated before removal
Mixture chloropicrin 85:methyl chloride 15	38.6 g.	3.0 lb.	1	Should be removed by aeration after 24 hr.
Mixture ETO10:CO₂ 90	386.1 g.	30.0 lb.	1	Do not use on seed
Mixture CH₃ Br70:EDB30	12.9 g.	1.0 lb.	1	Should be removed by aeration after 24 hr.

Flat Storage

Application by probe				
Aluminium phosphide[c]	2.5 tablets	90 tablets	3	5 days at 10°–15°C. 4 days at 15°–20°C. 3 days at 21°C. or above
Surface application (gravity distribution)				
Mixture EDC75:CT25	483.3 ml.	4.5 gal.	7	For maize × 1.5
Mixture $CS_2$16:CT84	537.0 ml.	5.0 gal.	7	For maize × 1.5
Mixture EDB7:EDC30:CT63	429.6 ml.	4.0 gal.	3	For maize × 1.5
Methyl bromide	32.2 g.	2.5 lb.	1	Applied under gastight sheet in South Africa; must be removed by aeration after 24 hr.
Recirculation				
Methyl bromide	38.6 g.	3.0 lb.	1	Should be removed by aeration after 24 hr.
Hydrocyanic acid	38.6 g.	3.0 lb.	1	Should be thoroughly aerated before grain is moved
Mixture chloropicrin 85:methyl chloride 15	38.6 g.	3.0 lb.	1	Should be removed by aeration after 24 hr.
Mixture CH_3Br70:EDB30	19.3 g.	1.5 lb.	1	Should be removed by aeration after 24 hr.

[a]Source: Bond (1973).

[b]All dosages, unless otherwise stated, are given for grain temperature range of 21° to 25°C. and gallons are U.S. measure.

[c]Sachets containing aluminium phosphide are permitted for use in some countries; manufacturers' recommendations are available from dealers.

may find refuge and multiply. Hall (1969) summarizes the different types of storage facilities in developing countries.

Forced distribution is an improved method of applying and distributing fumigants. An aeration system may be used to accomplish one exchange of air in an open system, or it may be used for more than one pass in a closed system. Some fumigators lift the heavy gases up to the surface grain one or more times during the exposure period by air-moving equipment to improve the insect kill at the grain surface. Forced distribution is discussed in detail in the section on aeration.

E. Frequency of Application and Exposure Period

The number and timing of fumigant applications depend chiefly on the need for fumigation as indicated by the presence of living insects. Effectiveness of previous treatments, opportunities for reinfestation, and rate and type of reinfestation should also influence the frequency of fumigations; certainly, grain stored in the warm southern areas usually requires more frequent fumigations than cool grain stored in the north.

The desired length of exposure and dosage depend on many variables, including the fumigant formulation. Exposure time and dosage are inversely related so that shorter exposures require higher dosages, and vice versa. Susceptibility of the insect is also important.

F. Insect Species and Stage

Harein and Krause (1964) noted that the fumigation efficiency of 80:20 (CCl_4:CS_2 by volume) to *S. oryzae* increased as the exposure periods were extended from 8 to 120 hr. Exposure recommendations vary from a few hours to several days. The more volatile fumigants such as methyl bromide usually require shorter exposure periods. Some fumigants may be left in the grain indefinitely without adverse effects and others need careful control.

The results of a fumigation are determined by several methods including use of gas analyzers, test insects, grain samples, and grain temperature observations. The use of gas analyzers and other simple methods to determine the gas concentrations in fumigated grain may be correlated with established dosage-mortality curves for specific insect species or stages (Sun, 1947, Whitney and Harein, 1959, Kenaga, 1961, and Harein and Krause, 1964). It may be convenient and desirable to confine test insects in cages and place them at strategic locations in the fumigation area. Representative grain samples may be collected, sifted, and examined to determine if the target insects are dead. Mortality observation of insects that develop within the confines of kernels would require incubation and subsequent examination for emerging adults.

Increased fumigant doses usually required are for massive insect populations. Such populations are often associated with relatively high-moisture grain. Large insect populations also create greater quantities of dust, frass, and chewed kernels. Insect colonies that have been established for extended periods are likely to be living in settled, well-compacted grain. Likewise, they will be found in pockets with considerable accumulations of their own by-products around them.

G. Advantages of Vacuum

The use of the vacuum chamber to improve the effectiveness of a fumigant in penetrating a commodity in relatively short periods is not new. The advances in vacuum fumigation including the behavior of the fumigant, sorption of fumigant by commodities and insects, and the subsequent response of the insects were reviewed by Bhambhein (1964). Vacuum fumigations can only be conducted in especially built chambers capable of withstanding external pressures up to one atmosphere with special facilities to evacuate the chamber within 15 min. and to introduce the fumigant. Earlier, hydrogen cyanide was the principal fumigant used in vacuum fumigations. In fact, the technique developed from the need to obtain greater penetration with hydrogen cyanide. Substitute fumigants now include methyl bromide and ethylene oxide-carbon dioxide mixtures. Phosphine is unstable at reduced pressures and must not be used in vacuum fumigations under any circumstances. Details on methods and dosages are explained by Monro (1969a).

H. Atmospheric Gases

As mentioned earlier, fumigants are represented by a number of chemicals that, as gases, penetrate the body of an insect via their respiratory system. The susceptibility of the insect is either directly associated with their rate of respiration (Bond, 1956) or, at least, with the uptake of fumigant. Hydrogen cyanide caused complete respiratory inhibition of *S. granarius,* a condition that increased their resistance to methyl bromide (Bond, 1961). Later Bond (1963) also reported that oxygen at and below 1 atmospheric pressure increased the toxicity of seven different fumigants to two species of insects.

Carlson (1966, 1967) found that preconditioning *T. confusum* with carbon dioxide or nitrogen before fumigation with methyl bromide produced a synergistic effect. However, he reported this response was correlated with insects at minimum respiration with no increase in susceptibility when fumigated during peak respiration. Ali Niazee and Lindgren (1969) suggested an explanation for the above contradictory information between Bond and Carlson. Carbon dioxide acts directly on the spiracular apparatus itself, causing it to open. This response diffuses the fumigant and, along with low detoxification caused by slow respiration, produces an increase in the susceptibility of the insects.

I. All Variables Considered

Sun (1947) pointed out a multiple of factors that influence the toxicity of fumigants to insects, including temperature, moisture, diet, stage and age of development, insect habits. These and many other variables were diagramatically expressed by Sun (1947) in Figure 2. Related fumigation and testing variables were researched by Whitney and Harein (1959) and Harein (1962).

V. INSECT RESISTANCE TO PESTICIDES AND FUMIGANTS

Different species of insects and different stages in the life history of a single species differ in susceptibility to fumigants. Thus the toxicity of each fumigant to each species, stage, and age should be understood to estimate dosages that will provide satisfactory control of the most hardy individuals.

Some apparent insect resistance to fumigants is not due to a resistance inherent in the insect's genetic make-up, but rather to a special environment that results from the insect's activities. For instance, insects that live within the protective walls of grain kernels usually require heavier fumigant doses than those living outside the kernels. This protection can be significant whether they are buried deep in the endosperm, as with weevil larvae, or just under the germ coat, as with *O. surinamensis* and *C. pusillus.*

Resistance or susceptibility of an insect may result from such physiological activities as its respiratory rate, its ability to close the openings to its respiratory system, and the quality and quantity of food consumed prior to fumigation.

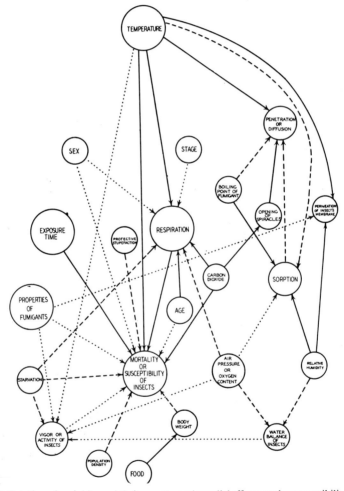

Figure 2. Relation of variables and their counter and parallel effects on the susceptibility of insects to fumigants. Source: modified from Sun (1947).

There are several definitions for resistance and tolerance. We often refer to resistance when an insect population demonstrates consistently greater survival following similar exposures to an insecticide. Tolerance is usually restricted to exposures where the insecticide has penetrated into the tissues of the insect but fails to produce death.

Only eight species of stored-grain insects were known to have developed resistance to insecticides by 1965 (Parkin, 1965a,b). The pesticides include malathion, lindane, pyrethrins, and methyl bromide, the most popular materials for chemical control of stored-grain insects. At least 13 species had developed pesticide resistance by 1970 (Dyte). Resistant strains have also been collected from several types of cereal products (Dyte and Blackman, 1970). The total number of all economically important insect- and mite-resistant populations was about 160 in 1964 and 224 in 1969 (Brown, 1969). It is apparent, therefore, that resistance has not developed as quickly among stored-grain insects as it has in insect pests in public health and agriculture. Innately tolerant stages of an insect may survive an exposure to an insecticide, reproduce and increase the selection of more tolerant progeny, thus providing the potential for the development of further resistant species.

Monro et al. (1961) reported an induced tolerance of the *S. granarius* to methyl bromide by using the survivors of an insect population following exposures as parents for the succeeding generation. This tolerance was retained for 23 generations after cessation of exposure. An increase of tolerance to other fumigants, not related to methyl bromide, was noted. Other laboratory population selections of stored-grain insects have also developed resistance to phosphine (Monro et al., 1972).

Resistance to specific fumigants and cross-resistance to other fumigants are definite possibilities under field conditions as well. If we understand the mechanisms of developing resistance and consider this information when establishing our control programs, we may escape procedures and conditions that could support the development of economically important resistant insect populations.

Lindgren and Vincent (1965) were only able to show small differences in the tolerance of *T. confusum* and *T. castaneum* to the fumigants ethylene dibromide, methyl bromide, and hydrogen cyanide. Two years later they reported the relative susceptibility of the same insect cultures to malathion and pyrethrins as determined by the topical-application method described by March and Metcalf (1949).

A pyrethrin-resistant strain of *S. granarius* increased from 18 times more resistant than a standard strain, as reported in 1960 (Parkin and Lloyd), to 52 times more resistant in 1963 (Lloyd and Parkin). They also noted positive cross-tolerance of *S. granarius* to dieldrin, carbaryl, lindane, malathion, dineseb, DDT, allethrin, synergized pyrethrins, and synergized allethrins. These tolerances were interpreted in relation to various environmental stresses. *S. granarius* also developed resistance to Bagon® and fenthion (Kumar and Morrison, 1967).

Although there are many possibilities of resistant insects in addition to those noted above, malathion-resistant stored-grain insects are our greatest concern because malathion is so widely used and because possible substitutes are difficult and costly to obtain, especially with increased legal restrictions in some countries.

Malathion-resistant *T. castaneum* are widely dispersed throughout international trade and both malathion- and lindane-resistant strains are being spread in ships to additional ports and new countries (Dyte and Blackman, 1970). Dyte and Blackman later (1972) reported a malathion cross-resistant strain of *T. castaneum* to be cross-resistant to malaoxen, diethyl malathion, phenthoate, and acethion. The cross-tolerance of *T. castaneum* to many insecticides is listed by Champ and Campbell-Brown (1970) and Bhatia et al. (1971). Significant cross-resistance was also apparent to arprocarle, carbaryl, diazinon, Gardona, and lindane. Even a cross-resistance from several conventional insecticides to synthetic juvenile hormones has been reported for *T. castaneum* (Dyte, 1972).

P. interpunctella has a resistance potential to malathion. One possible substitute would be dichlorvos, when supplied as vapor released from polyvinyl chloride strips (La Hue, 1969b).

FAO is currently beginning a worldwide survey of resistance in stored-grain insects in conjunction with the Commonwealth Scientific and Industrial Research Organization of Australia and the Pest Infestation Control Laboratory of the Ministry of Agriculture, Fisheries and Food in Slough, Bucks, England. Their objectives are to establish the insecticide and fumigant resistances and cross-resistance present throughout the world, to establish cultures of resistant strains for further laboratory investigations, and to redefine the importance of the major grain pests on a world basis. FAO has arranged to collect samples of pertinent insects via personal visits of an FAO officer to suspect populations or through established organizations. The USDA Stored-Product Insects Research and Development Laboratory in Savannah, Ga., is coordinating these resistant insect collections within the U.S.

VI. MILLS AND MILLING MACHINERY

Producing flour that will meet the required standards of purity and maintaining the flour in that condition until it reaches the consumer is one of the primary objectives of the milling industry. The other is making a profit. Both residual insecticides and fumigants have been useful in achieving this goal.

Pyrethrin is the safest insecticide to use in food premises. Bulk flour bins should not be sprayed or treated with any insecticide except pyrethrin, which is best applied as a mist or fog into the empty bins. Cotton (1963) recommended pyrethrin applied as an aerosol for flying insects. Premium-grade malathion is also widely used as a general mill spray.

Conventional fumigants including the residual fumigant dichlorvos have a significant value in managing insect populations in flour mills and adjacent storage, cleaning, and packing facilities. The kind of treatment, spot or general fumigation, depends on the type of infestation and the facilities involved.

The term *spot fumigation* refers to the fumigation of individual machines within a mill. Although a 7:3 mixture of ethylene dibromide and methyl bromide is commonly used, many other formulations and dosages have been recommended (Table IV). Hill and Simpson (1972) explain the disinfestation practices of a flour mill over an 8-year period by spot fumigation. Certain machines and their associated conveyors, elevators, etc., often showed the first signs of reinfestation. Fumigating such areas as needed will help a great deal in keeping the insect infestation at a low level.

Insect infestation within milling machinery can also be eliminated by fumigating the entire mill as required for a general fumigation. Except when using methyl bromide or phosphine, all residual flour should be removed before application. Cotton (1963) provides the details of a general fumigation procedure in flour mills. Dichlorvos has potential when applied as a vapor to control insects infesting packaged cereal products in warehouses (Harein et al., 1970).

VII. CHEMICAL-PACKAGE COMBINATIONS

The concern over insect infestation and the subsequent contamination of packaged food within marketing channels have led to the development of insect-resistant packages. Stored-product insects can penetrate, given sufficient time, all food-packaging materials except glass and metal. The most common species capable of establishing their own mode of entry are *R. dominica*, *T. mauritanicus*, and *L. serricorne* in the U.S. Most of the other species rely on finding holes or breaks in the package. A complete package closure can eliminate more than 75% of the potential insect infestation. Treating the packaging materials with specific insecticides provides a significant barrier for the remaining 25% as the approved insecticides are lethal, repellent, or both, to the insects. All of the research on the subject conducted from 1913 to 1969 is listed by Highland and Metts (1970).

Coating the exterior of multiwall Kraft paper bags with synergized pyrethrin, synergized allethrin, or methoxychlor provided effective barriers against insect penetration for 9 to 15 months (Davis and Laudani, 1956). A repellent treatment on multiwall bags with insect-tight closures protected the commodity from insects from 12 to 24 months (Highland et al., 1964). However, the synergized pyrethrins migrate through the multiwalled packages to contaminate the product inside. This migration problem will prevent the use of many compounds on packages unless additional barriers to prevent such migration are found (Highland et al., 1969).

In the U.S. it is legal to treat 50-lb. (22.7-kg.) or larger packages with synergized pyrethrin containing not more than 6 mg. of pyrethrins or 645 mg. of piperonyl butoxide per 930 cm.^{2} (1 ft.^{2}). A deposit of 0.47 mg. pyrethrins and 4.73 mg. piperonyl butoxide per m.^{2} on Kraft paper prevented insects from infesting packaged flour for 9 months (Highland, 1967). Carbaryl deposits of 6.04 mg. per m.^{2} prevented insect penetration for 18 months. Lindane (Majumder et al., 1961) and malathion (McFarlane, 1961) offer some use in improving the effectiveness of insect-resistant packages. Resmethrin, tetramethrin, *d*-transallethrin, or pyrethrins were also effective for 12 months (Highland and Merritt, 1973).

Loschiavo (1969) reported that the antifeeding chemical (4'- (3,3-dimethyl-1-trizeno) acetanilide) was useful in combating stored-product insects. More research may prove it to be effective as a laminate for package materials against infestation by insects.

VIII. INFESTATION IN TRANSIT

A major step in efforts to provide food to the world's growing human population is to have adequate facilities and management technology to protect it during distribution. This requirement applies to grain from the point of harvest, through multiple grain-handling and cereal product-processing channels, to wholesalers and retailers, and eventually to the consumer.

Types of conveyance differ widely depending on the developmental stage of the country and the area therein. In terms of volume within developed countries, virtually all grain moves through distribution channels in railway boxcars, trucks, and ships (Monro, 1969b). Although an increasing number of special-purpose railway boxcars, trucks, and ships are being used by industry, most of the grain is transported in vehicles built for multipurpose use. This includes grain destined for humans or animals plus an endless variety of nonfood commodities. Most of the vehicles used today were not designed to deter insect infestations.

TABLE IV

*Formulations and dosages of spot fumigants used to control
local infestations of insects and mites in mills using
exposures of 16 to 24 hr.[a]*

Mill Unit	Point of Application	Suggested Dosage		
		cm.^{3} (ml.)	British fl. oz.	U.S. fl. oz.
Elevator boots (each)	Nearest opening in spout to boot, or hole drilled in boot	150	5	6
Reel and purifier conveyors (each)	Pour along entire length	150	5	6
Reel inspouts	Into spout above	150	5	6
Conveyors	At convenient points along convenient length	150/m.	2/linear ft.	2/linear ft.
Sifter sections (each)	Hand-hole in spout above each section	150	5	6
Dusters (bran and shorts)	Hand-hole at top	300	10	12
Purifier inspouts	Into spout above purifier	150	5	6
Bins (when empty or almost empty)	Splash on walls near top	50/m.^{3}	5/100 ft.^{3}	6/100 ft.^{3}
Rolls, on each side	Into spouts above rolls	150	5	6

[a]Source: Modified from Monro (1969a).

The common railway boxcar is designed to carry anything. A wooden liner is usually provided to protect packaged materials from breakage and moisture. Even the roof may be lined with plywood to protect the product from condensation. End linings are generally installed vertically from floor to ceiling, providing four to six vertical compartments as the liners are bolted against the corrugated steel ends of the railway boxcars.

Commodities such as grain or cereal products soon accumulate behind the wall, end, or ceiling liners, especially if the product is blown into the railway boxcar. In addition, the doorpost and floors of these vehicles soon become cracked, broken, or gouged, providing areas for accumulation of products and a home for stored-grain insects.

A combination of air-blowing, followed by adequate vacuum-cleaning, appears to best remove residual commodity from railway boxcars. They should *not* be cleaned with water. The wet and moldy product that cannot be washed away provides an optimum environment for many species of insects, some not generally categorized as stored-grain insects, and microorganisms.

Fiberglas has been tested to fill the voids behind railway boxcar liners in an attempt to reduce the opportunity for product accumulation and insect infestation. Another effort to protect commodities in transit is to place them within a polyethylene liner which was sealed just prior to closing the railway boxcar. Neither method has been totally successful.

There is little chance of killing all insects residing behind the wall liners in railway boxcars, especially if they also have the protection provided by accumulations of grain and various cereal products. However, until railway boxcars are designed to eliminate such harborage sites, it would be advantageous to inhibit the migration of stored-grain insects to the commodities in transit. Dichlorvos dispensed as an aerosol may provide such protection; Schesser (1972) obtained 100% control of *T. confusum* exposed to dichlorvos in railway boxcars treated with 6 oz. of 6.5% dichlorvos per 141.5 m.^{3} of space.

It is not an uncommon practice to use barges to haul nonfood cargoes following a shipment of grain in bulk. A major concern, in addition to subsequent insect infestation, is improper cleaning before reloading with food or feed. Cleaning barges with raw untreated river water and not allowing adequate drying time also invite mold growth and mycotoxin development.

Pyrethrins synergized with piperonyl butoxide, malathion, methoxychlor, or dichlorvos, if applied correctly, are useful as protective sprays when applied to the walls and floor of empty railway boxcars, ships, and trucks. They have residual characteristics which help to reduce the migration and subsequent infestation of insects emerging from infestation sites in the structure of the vehicle.

Malathion is one of the most effective residual insecticides to combat insect infestations of stored grain or cereal products in railway boxcars. Schesser (1967a,b,c and 1972) tested different insecticide and fumigant formulations using various application techniques in an attempt to develop an improved method. One formulation consisted of a mixture of dichlorvos and malathion, the dichlorvos to produce lethal vapors and the malathion to serve as a contact toxicant. Schesser (1967b) found a formulation containing equal amounts of dichlorvos and malathion, to produce a total concentration of 2.5%, effective in disinfesting empty railway boxcars infested with *T. castaneum*. An emulsion containing 2.5% Gardona and 1.25% dichlorvos applied as a spray to the floor and walls of railway boxcars is also effective in controlling adult *T. confusum, S. granarius* and *R. dominica* and larval *T. inclusum* (Harein and Schesser, 1971). Pyrethrins plus piperonyl butoxide is effective when applied as a spray in ships and railway boxcars. Some countries rely on lindane dispensed from smoke generators for killing stored-grain insects in ships.

The type of surface receiving the insecticidal treatment influences the resulting protection provided for the grain against possible insect infestation. Concrete and other alkaline surfaces often reduce the toxicity of insecticides. This was noted first by Burkholder (1961) in the treatment of malathion on concrete and latex-painted surfaces to control dermestids. Later Burkholder and Dicke (1966a,b) conducted studies to investigate methods to prevent the detoxification of malathion and fenthion on several type surfaces. Painting or water-proofing various surfaces decreased the dosage required for adequate insecticidal activity. Incorporating 0.5% sodium carboxymethyl cellulose in malathion spray formulation also improved the persistence of its residues on an alkaline, cement substrate (Tyler and Rowlands, 1967). Talc or calcium carbonate also improved the efficiency of malathion on concrete (Slominski and Gojmerac, 1972). Lemon (1967a) confirmed that malathion breaks down rapidly on fresh concrete. Fenitrothion and bromophos lasted longer than malathion. On concrete surfaces Gardona was superior in effectiveness against *T. confusum* at dosages of 1,140 and 2,280 mg. per m.^{2} compared to malathion at 1,260 mg. per m.^{2}

Methyl bromide, hydrogen cyanide, and phosphine are the major fumigants used to disinfect empty vehicles before transporting grain or cereal products. Phosphine is especially effective for fumigating loaded boxcars in transit (Schesser, 1967c).

Fumigants are also useful for combating insects in empty or loaded carriers. Gray (1964) pointed out several items to consider in obtaining a safe and successful fumigation. These included the type of commodity and carrier, location, pest involved, time allowed, temperature, and means of aeration.

Undoubtedly methyl bromide has been the primary fumigant used for railway boxcars and ships. Phosphine is becoming a prime substitute for fumigating railway boxcars, particularly when the success of the fumigation must occur as the commodity is enroute (Schesser, 1967c).

Methyl bromide is distributed through bulk rice in railway boxcars by forced aeration, which gives good insect control. A similar system for recirculating fumigants in grain within railway boxcars was described by the USDA (1963). Monro's manual (1969a) is a detailed publication on the major insects and mites infesting ships and the approved methods of control.

IX. MICRO- AND MACRO-PESTS

In the U.S., the Federal Food, Drug, and Cosmetic Act requires that grain be clean, be stored under conditions that protect it from contamination, and be free of harmful residues of agricultural chemicals. In food grains this includes protection from insects, rodents, birds, and other filth-carrying agents. For example, under the U.S. Food and Drug Administration, wheat is subject to federal court seizure if it contains 7% or more insect-damaged kernels as determined by methods presented under the Official Grain Standards. Various grains can also be graded "weevily" under the U.S. Grain Standards Act if a 1-qt. (1.1-liter) sample contains more than one beetle or weevil.

The significance of stored-product insects and associated microorganisms, including their metabolic toxins, as contaminants of food and feed for man and animals is not well understood but needs immediate attention.

A. Bacteria

Van Wyk et al. (1959) isolated greater numbers of bacteria from *T. confusum* than from the food they were infesting. The bacteria also promoted the growth and reproduction of the beetles. The beetles were attracted more to the contaminated food than to bacteria-free sources. Bacteria from the interior of *S. granarius* ranged from 60,000 to 500,000 per 20 insects (Harein and De las Casas, 1968). These bacteria were *Escherichia intermedia, Proteus rettgeri, Bacillus subtilis, Serratia marcescens, P. vulgaris, Micrococcus* spp., *Streptococcus* spp., and various bacteria in the *Klebsiella-Aerobacter* group.

Increasing populations of *S. granarius* in stored grain are often accompanied by rapidly increasing numbers of storage fungi (Agrawal et al., 1957). These fungi contribute to the deterioration of the infested grain, as discussed in detail by Christensen and Kaufmann in Chapter 4.

Often the activity of these insects causes an increase in the moisture content of the grain and thereby expedites mold development (Agrawal et al., 1957, 1958; and Christensen and Hodson, 1960). *Aspergillus restrictus,* as well as other species in the *A. glaucus* group, was found in the proventriculus and intestines of the weevils, was recovered from their feces, and persisted in insects until they starved.

Salmonella spp. have also been isolated from cereal grains and subsequent milled products. In fact, *S. montevideo* has been one of the most frequently isolated serotypes from both human and nonhuman sources (Martin and Ewing, 1969). Salmonellae-contaminated barley was a source of a salmonellosis epidemic in Sweden (Silverstople et al., 1961). *S. montevideo* survived in wheat 28 weeks (Crumrine and Foltz, 1969). *S. oryzae, S. granarius, T. castaneum, O. surinamensis, R. dominica, T. mauritanicus* and *C. pusillus* successfully transmitted *S. montevideo* from contaminated to clean wheat (Crumrine et al., 1971). However, progeny from the offspring of these insect species had less ability than their parents to distribute *S. montevideo.*

The management of stored-grain insects by use of pathogenic microorganisms is not new but it has received increased attention with greater restrictions on insecticides. It also has become more attractive when the microorganism is harmless to nontarget organisms, plants, humans, and animals. The study of toxins produced by various bacterial and fungal pathogens is a particularly active field of research. Studies of such toxins may lead to the development of a new field of specific insecticidal compounds. *B. thuringiensis* is a commercially successful microbial insecticide, effective against at least 16 species of Lepidoptera.

B. Fungi

Many species of fungi that inhabit stored grain produce metabolites toxic to humans and animals (Brook and White, 1966, Christensen et al., 1968, Hesseltine, 1969, and Lillehoj et al., 1970). However, there have been relatively few studies on the toxicity of these metabolites to insects. Beard and Walton (1965) reported that water-soluble toxins from *A. flavus* were lethal to the larvae of the house fly, *Musca domestica.* Sinha (1966) observed mortality of larvae of *T. confusum* and *T. castaneum* when they were fed substrates containing *Streptomyces* spp., *Trichoderma* spp., *Penicillium funiculosum, P. terrestre,* and *A. fumigatus.* Matsumura and Knight (1967) found aflatoxins toxic to three species of insects, and the toxins reduced the viability of the insect eggs. Later Prasertphon and Tanada (1969) also studied the toxic effects of mycotoxins on insects. They obtained the mycotoxins from infected larvae.

C. Mycotoxins

Some mycotoxins alter the reproduction and survival of stored-grain insects. A similar investigation of mycotoxins that have already shown lethal properties to warm-blooded animals (Christensen et al., 1968) might reveal characteristics that have potential for combating insects. Only the exposure to *Chaetomium globosium* caused 100% mortality of the *T. confusum* (Rao et al., 1971). Exposure to a *Penicillium* isolate was second highest in toxicity, while all others were relatively ineffective. The isolates of *Aspergillus* spp. and *Alternaria* spp. had little effect on the production of *T. confusum* larvae, while *Fusarium* spp. enhanced larval production. Most of the *Penicillium* spp. and *Chaetomium* spp. reduced larval production. Little difference was noted in production of pupae.

F-2, an estrogenic metabolite produced by *Fusarium,* was ingested by *T. confusum* and *Alphitobius diaperinus,* retained through the insects' metamorphosis, and detected later in the adult insects even after their starvation and death (Eugenio et al., 1970). The amount of F-2 recovered from the insects was within the range (10 to 200 p.p.m.) of the F-2 contamination level in feed suspected to have produced illnesses in domestic animals.

T-2, a metabolite of *F. tricinctum,* will also lower the fertility and increase the fecundity of *T. confusum* (Wright, 1973).

Specific fungal isolates show promise as deterrents for growth or survival of *T. confusum* by killing the parents or affecting future generations. Pure fractions of certain fungal metabolites have clarified the association between these insects and mycotoxins. It appears, however, that only certain fractions of the metabolites affect insect growth and development, fertility, and fecundity.

The interrelationship between stored-product insects and mycotoxins produced by storage fungi should be investigated further, especially those mycotoxins known to have an adverse effect on higher animals including man. Studying the mode of action of specific mycotoxins may open the door to new or modified means of managing insect populations (Matsumura and Knight, 1967). In addition, the insects may serve as a tool to detect specific fungi or their mycotoxins within certain environments.

D. Control of Microbes and Their Metabolites

Propionic acid has been used in Britain and Canada for several years to protect grain stored at high moisture levels from deterioration by molds and bacteria. Recently mixtures of acetic and propionic acid became available in the U.S. for use as preservatives for high-moisture grain, especially corn. Mites, mainly *G. destructor* and *T. putrescentiae,* have been found active in barley 8 months after treatment with 0.8% propionic acid. Propionic acid or acetic acid at the recommended rates is not effective for the control of stored-product insects. Actually, insects are not a problem in stored grain that is above 15% moisture, since microorganisms inhibit their survival and proliferation. Insects thrive in grain at 9 to 12% moisture, and at that moisture level the acid mixtures are ineffective against the insects.

According to Dollear (1969), various methods that have been studied to detoxify aflatoxin-contaminated products involved physical separation, heat, solvent extraction, radiation, and microorganisms. None were entirely satisfactory. Other researchers have directed their efforts to prevent or inhibit aflatoxin production.

The fumigants ethylene oxide, methyl bromide, sulfur dioxide, and mixtures of ethylene dibromide with methyl bromide reportedly inhibit mold proliferation and the subsequent production of mycotoxin (Majumder et al., 1964, Narasimhan and Rangaswami, 1968, and Raghunathan et al., 1969). Davis and Diener (1967) conducted studies on the inhibition of aflatoxin production by *p*-aminobenzoic acid, potassium sulfite, and potassium fluoride. β-Aminobenzoic acid inhibited aflatoxin production at all concentrations used and, at the highest concentration, inhibited growth of the fungus as well. Potassium sulfite inhibited aflatoxin production without an apparent effect on the growth of the fungus. Potassium fluoride, at the highest concentration tested, inhibited both aflatoxin production and growth.

The organophosphate insecticide dichlorvos, at 20 p.p.m., prevented aflatoxin production on wheat (Rao and Harein, 1972). However, aflatoxin production was greater when the dosage of dichlorvos was reduced below 20 p.p.m., when the treatment followed rather than preceded inoculation, or when the substrate was either corn, rice, or peanuts instead of wheat. Dichlorvos at 20 p.p.m. also inhibited production of the estrogenic metabolite zearalenone from the fungus *F. roseum* var. *graminearum* growing on wheat and rice (Rao and Harein, 1973).

E. Mites

The importance of mite infestations on stored products has been the cause of some disagreements. Mites are usually detected on stored products when they are present in large numbers and appear as dust on the surface of bags, floors, walls, commodities, etc. In the worst cases the product reaches a condition easily recognized as deteriorated. Very often, however, mite infestations fail to reach such an extreme state and their damage is less evident (Oxley, 1948). Their presence is undesirable because of known medical significance for humans and animals (Terbush, 1972). This potential problem is also emphasized in Chapter 11.

The importance of physical factors such as temperature and moisture to the survival and development, as well as to the control of, mites on stored products is illustrated in Chapter 11 and more extensively discussed in Chapter 12.

Research on the chemical control of mites by specific acaricides has been slower and somewhat neglected compared to research on chemicals to protect stored products from insect attack. In fact, in the majority of the cases only chemicals with insecticidal properties have been examined as potential acaricides. Insecticide producing companies, facing the difficulties involved with the approval and registration of pesticides in the U.S., have concentrated on the development of insecticides, and development of acaricides has been a secondary effort.

The specific effect of some of the tested compounds emphasizes the need for accurate mite identification. A complex of morphologically similar species occurring in the same habitat, as in the *Acarus siro* group (Griffiths, 1964, 1970) requires precise testing to establish the response of the individual species commonly found in practical storage conditions. A few of the most common economically important species of mites that have been tested for their susceptibility to the candidate acaricides include members of the genera *Acarus, Tyrophagus, Glycyphagus, Caloglyphus, Typhlodromus,* and *Acaropsis.*

In general, stored-product mites are more difficult to control than are insects. The active stages are susceptible but the eggs are more tolerant, and the hypopus appears to be most difficult to kill. Often after the application of insecticides or fumigants, no mites seem to be active in the treated commodity, but a resurgence of the mite population may follow shortly thereafter, probably due to the hypopal stage that lived through the treatment. Predatory mites are also killed, allowing the survivors of the pest species to multiply unhindered (Norris, 1958).

Difficulties in the handling and confining of mites, and the lack of practical bioassay techniques, are two of the major obstacles in the development of acaricides.

Several methods have been used in the screening of possible acaricides. Treatment of a specific grain substrate and subsequent mortality evaluation of specific mites on that substrate introduce the possibility of many experimental variables. One major variable of the results is in the recovery of the treated mites (Krantz, 1956). However, the contact of the mites with the treated substrate or grain allows an evaluation of some of the slow-acting acaricides.

Glass containers were used to determine the extent of mite penetration through treated flour as an evaluation index (Krantz, 1956). The method suggests a useful tool for future work on protectant materials. Other devices like glass rings and polyethylene cake traps have also been used as confinement arenas for the tested mites. Researchers at Slough, Bucks, England, tested several surface treatments with the mites retained within a circle outlined with an electrically heated wire. Immersion tests, whereby groups of mites are dipped in an oil solution, have been used in the hope of getting a rapid indication of bioactivity as well as to determine the effects of several physical factors upon mite mortality.

As would be expected, a close comparison of the results obtained by different researchers on the effect of several chemicals on stored-grain mites is difficult owing to the widely different techniques, dosage rates, and mortality evaluations.

Among the several relatively nonvolatile insecticides used to control the mobile forms of grain mites, lindane has been reported to be effective for *A. siro* and *T. putrescentiae* (Krantz, 1956, and Marzke and Dicke, 1959). Wilkin and Hope (1973) reported lindane to be effective under practical conditions, and a widely accepted acaricide. Diazinon and synergized pyrethrins appear also to be effective against mites. Pyrethrins, by having lower mammalian toxicity, can be used more extensively.

The effectiveness of 21 compounds applied to grain as water-based formulations were tested against *A. siro, T. putrescentiae,* and *Glycyphagus destructor* (Wilkin and Hope, 1973). The mixture of lindane (2.5 p.p.m.) and malathion (7.5 p.p.m.) or single applications of chlorpyriifos at 2 p.p.m. and phoxim at 2 p.p.m. killed more than 75% of the mites of the above species within 1 day. The response of the three species of mites varied considerably. For instance, lindane was ineffective against *T. putrescentiae,* but the mixture of lindane and malathion was effective against all three test species.

The testing of several possible insecticide-acaricides on *A. siro* was initiated in 1958 by researchers at the Pest Control Laboratory in England. They started by screening select chemicals and determining the effects of various factors on their toxicity (Anon., 1958). They also tested dust applications on wheat germ in small cells under favorable conditions of temperature and relative humidity. Two years later Hope (1960) reported that only four of the chemicals, aldrin and diazinon at 1,000 p.p.m. and lindane and dieldrin at 250 p.p.m., were effective. Dichlorvos and the rodenticide (2-pivalyl-1,3-indano) at 1,000 p.p.m. protected the wheat germ from damage for over 2 months but failed to kill all the mites. Other substances including silica aerogels have been tested (Hope, 1962), but none approached lindane in effectiveness.

Aramite®, chlorobenzilate, Tedion®, Ovex®, and Kelthane® were tested (Strong et al., 1959) to evaluate their effectiveness against mites in rearing and testing areas and in weevil cultures. A mixture of 1:1 Kelthane and chlorobenzilate emulsifiable concentrate sprayed on testing areas plus Kelthane-treated cloths covering the shelves as a preventive measure eliminated the mites without apparently affecting the insects. A few organophosphorus compounds have also been tested as dusts on wheat germ. All have proven to be ineffective for the control of stored-grain mites.

Methyl bromide has been one of the most widely used fumigants against mites because of its high toxicity to the adult stages. Both the egg and hypopal stages are usually more tolerant. Barker (1967) showed that the eggs of *T. putrescentiae* are more tolerant to methyl bromide than are the immature and adult stages. He also showed that tolerance to methyl bromide varies with the age of the egg. Similar results were obtained by Amaro (1963) with the eggs of *A. siro.* Burkholder (1966), working with *A. siro* under laboratory conditions, determined several C×T products for methyl bromide.

Phosphine gives only partial control of mites (Heseltine and Thompson, 1957, and Sinha et al., 1967). As usual, the active stages of the mites seem to be susceptible but populations usually redevelop within a short time after treatment. Jalil et al. (1970) compared, under laboratory conditions, the toxicity of methyl bromide and phosphine to eggs and adults of *T. putrescentiae* and *Caloglyphus berlesei.* He also concluded that phosphine gave low mortalities even when used at high concentrations.

LITERATURE CITED

AGRAWAL, N. S., C. M. CHRISTENSEN and A. C. HODSON. 1957. Grain storage fungi associated with the granary weevil. J. Econ. Entomol. 50: 659-663.

AGRAWAL, N. S., A. C. HODSON, and C. M. CHRISTENSEN. 1958. Development of granary weevils and fungi in columns of wheat. J. Econ. Entomol. 51: 701-702.

ALI NIAZEE, M. T., and D. L. LINDGREN. 1969. Effect of carbon dioxide on toxicity of hydrocyanic acid and methyl bromide to adults of the confused flour beetle and granary weevil at two different temperatures. J. Econ. Entomol. 62: 904-906.

AMARO, J. P. P. 1963. Mortality and delayed development caused by methyl bromide applied to the eggs of the flour mite *Acarus siro* L. Unpub. Ph.D. thesis, Univ. Reading, England.

ANONYMOUS. 1958. Acaricides and stored-product mites. Pest Infest. Res. Rep., Slough, Bucks, England, p. 26.

ANONYMOUS. 1966. Phostoxin for the fumigation of grain. Deutsche Gesellschaft fur Schadlingsbekampfung. M. B. H. Frankfurt/Main. 31 p. (Revised).

ARMITAGE, H. M. 1955. Fumigation-eradication test on khapra beetle. Down Earth 10: 2-3.

ARMITAGE, H. M. 1956. The khapra beetle suppression program in the United States and Mexico. Proc. Int. Congr. Entomol. 10th 4: 89-98.

ASHMAN, F. 1966. An assessment of the value of dilute dust insecticide for the protection of stored maize in Kenya. J. Appl. Ecol. 3: 169-179.

ATTFIELD, J. G., and D. A. WEBSTER. 1966. Dichlorvos. Chem. Ind. (London) 1966: 272-278.

BAKER, J. E., and J. M. MABIE. 1973. *Tribolium confusum:* Food additives as ovicides. J. Econ. Entomol. 66: 765-767.

BANG, Y. H., and E. H. FLOYD. 1962. Effectiveness of malathion in protecting stored polished rice from damage by several species of stored grain insects. J. Econ. Entomol. 55: 188-190.

BANO, A., and S. K. MAJUMDER. 1968. Tricalcium phosphate as an insecticide. p. 177-185 in *Pesticides*. Acad. Pest Control Sci. Manipal Power Press, Mysore, India.

BARKER, P. S. 1967. Susceptibility of eggs of *Tyrophagus putrescentiae* (Schrank) (Acarina, Acaridae) to methyl bromide. J.

Stored Prod. Res. 2: 247-249.

BEARD, R. L., and G. S. WALTON. 1965. An *Aspergillus* toxin lethal to larvae of the house fly. J. Invertebr. Pathol. 7: 522-523.

BENNETT, R. G. 1969. The influence of age and concentration of fumigant on the susceptibility of pupae of *Tribolium castaneum* (Herbst) (Coleoptera, Tenebrionidae) to methyl bromide. J. Stored Prod. Res. 5: 119-126.

BERATLIEF, C., and S. ALEXANDRESCU. 1964. Effect of phosphine fumigation on the germination of wheat and maize seed. Probl. Agr. 16: 45-51.

BERCK, B. 1965a. Determination of fumigant gases by gas chromatography. J. Agr. Food Chem. 13: 373-377.

BERCK, B. 1965b. Sorption of ethylene dibromide, ethylene dichloride and carbon tetrachloride by cereal products. J. Agr. Food Chem. 13: 248-254.

BERCK, B., and F. A. GUNTHER. 1970. Rapid determination of sorption affinity of phosphine by fumigation within a gas chromatographic column. J. Agr. Food Chem. 18: 148-153.

BERCK, B., W. E. WESTLAKE, and F. A. GUNTHER. 1970. Microdetermination of phosphine by gas-liquid chromatography with microcoulemetric, thermoinic and flame photometric detection. J. Agr. Food Chem. 18: 143-147.

BHAMBHEIN, H. J. 1964. Recent advances in vacuum fumigation. World Rev. Pest Contr. 3: 53-56.

BHATIA, S. K., T. D. YADAV, and P. B. MOOKHARJEE. 1971. Malathion resistance in *Tribolium castaneum* (Herbst) in India. J. Stored Prod. Res. 7: 227-230.

BHATNAGAR-THOMAS, P. L. 1973. Control of insect pests of stored grains using a juvenile hormone analogue. J. Econ. Entomol. 66: 277-278.

BIELORAI, R., and E. ALUMOT. 1966. Determination of residues of a fumigant mixture in cereal grain by electron capture gas chromatography. J. Agr. Food Chem. 14: 622-625.

BINDRA, O. S., and T. S. SIDHU. 1972. Dissipation of malathion residues on maize grain in relation to dosage, storage conditions and baking. J. Food Sci. Technol. 9: 29-32.

BOND, E. J. 1956. The effect of methyl bromide on the respiration of the cadelle

Tenebroides mauritanicus (L.). Can. J. Zool. 34: 405-415.

BOND, E. J. 1961. The action of fumigants on insects. II. The effect of hydrogen cyanide on the activity and respiration of certain insects. Can. J. Zool. 39: 437-444.

BOND, E. J. 1963. The action of fumigants on insects. IV. The effects of oxygen on the toxicity of fumigants to insects. Can. J. Biochem. Physiol. 41: 993-1004.

BOND, E. J. 1973. Chemical control of stored grain insects. p. 137-179 in *Grain storage — Part of a system* (R. N. Sinha and W. E. Muir, eds.) 481 p. Avi Pub. Co., Westport, Conn.

BOND, E. J., and T. DUMAS. 1967. Loss of warning odour from phosphine. J. Stored Prod. Res. 3: 389-392.

BOND, E. J., and H. A. U. MONRO. 1961. The toxicity of various fumigants to the cadelle *Tenebroides mauritanicus*. J. Econ. Entomol. 54: 451-454.

BOND, E. J., H. A. U. MONRO, T. DUMAS, J. BENAZET, and E. E. TURTLE. 1972. Control of insects in empty cargo ships with dichlorvos. J. Stored Prod. Res. 8: 11-18.

BONDI, A., E. OLOMUCKI, and M. CALDERON. 1955. Problems connected with ethylene dibromide fumigation of cereals. II. Feeding experiments with laying hens. J. Sci. Food Agr. 6: 600-602.

BOWEN, M. F. 1961. Efficient utilization of paulins in fumigation and as covers for the protection of storage. J. Econ. Entomol. 54: 270-273.

BRIDGES, R. G. 1956. The fate of labelled insecticide residues in food products. V. The nature and significance of ethylene dibromide residues in fumigated wheat. J. Sci. Food Agr. 7: 305-313.

BRIEGER, H., F. RIEDERS, and W. A. HODES. 1952. Acrylonitrile: Spectrophotometric determination, acute toxicity and mechanism of action. Arch. Ind. Hyg. 6: 128-140.

BROOK, P. J., and E. P. WHITE. 1966. Fungus toxins affecting mammals. Annu. Rev. Phytopathol. 4: 171-194.

BROOKE, J. P. 1958. The effect of pyrethrins and piperonyl butoxide against the cacao moth *Ephestia elutella*. HB. Chem. Inc. p. 387.

BROOKE, J. P. 1961. Protection of grain in storage. World Crops 13: 27-30.

BROOKS, I. C., J. HAUS, R. R. BLUMENTHAL, and B. S. DAVIS, Jr. 1969. SBP-1382—A new synthetic pyrethroid. Soap Chem. Spec. (March-April).

BROWN, A. W. A. 1969. Nature and prevalence of resistance. Farm Chem. 132: 50-68.

BROWN, W. B. 1959. Fumigation with methyl bromide under gas-proof sheets. Pest Infest. Res. Bull. 1, 2nd ed. D.S.I.R., London. 44 p.

BROWN, W. B., and H. K. HESELTINE. 1949. Fumigation of grain in silo bins. Milling 112: 229-230, 233.

BROWN, W. B., and H. K. HESELTINE. 1962. The effect on flour of fumigation with methyl bromide. Pest Infest. Res. Rep., Slough, Bucks, England 1961: 37-38.

BROWN, W. B., H. K. HESELTINE, H. E. WAINMAN, R. W. TAYLOR, P. E. WHEATLEY, and A. H. HARRIS. 1968. Fumigation of stacks of bagged produce with phosphine. Pest Infest. Res. Rep., Slough, Bucks, England 1969: 50-52.

BRUCE, R. B., A. J. ROBBINS, and T. O. TUFT. 1962. Phosphine residues from phostoxin treated grain. J. Agr. Food Chem. 10: 18-21.

BURGES, H. D., and N. J. BURRELL. 1964. Cooling bulk grain in the British climate to control storage insects and to improve keeping quality. J. Sci. Food Agr. 15: 32-50.

BURKHOLDER, W. E. 1961. The toxicity of malathion to dermestids as influenced by various surfaces. Proc. North Centr. Branch Entomol. Soc. Amer. 16: 100-101.

BURKHOLDER, W. E. 1966. Toxicity of methyl bromide to *Acarus siro*, a cheese-infesting mite. J. Econ. Entomol. 59: 1110-1112.

BURKHOLDER, W. E., and R. J. DICKE. 1966a. The toxicity of malathion and fenthion to dermestid larvae as influenced by various surfaces. J. Econ. Entomol. 59: 253-254.

BURKHOLDER, W. E., and R. J. DICKE. 1966b. Evidence of sex pheromones in females of several species of dermestids. J. Econ. Entomol. 59: 540-543.

BUSHNELL, W. R. 1972. Elimination of microflora from barley kernels with ethylene oxide. Can. J. Plant Sci. 53: 47-52.

CALDERON, M., and Y. CARMI. 1973. Fumigation trials with a mixture of methyl bromide and carbon dioxide in vertical bins. J. Stored Prod. Res. 8: 315-321.

CARLSON, S. D. 1966. Fumigation of *Tribolium confusum* adults with 80:20 (CCl_4:CS_2) during carbon dioxide or nitrogen induced respiration or depression. J. Econ. Entomol. 59: 870-872.

CARLSON, S. D. 1967. Fumigation of the confused flour beetle with methyl bromide at high and low rates of respiration. J. Econ. Entomol. 60: 684-687.

CHAKRABARTI, B., and H. E. WAINMAN. 1972. Determination by gas chromatography of phosphine used in fumigation. Chem. Ing. Tech. 1972: 300-302.

CHAMP, B. R., and M. J. CAMPBELL-BROWN. 1970. Insecticide resistance in Australian *Tribolium castaneum* (Herbst) (Coleoptera, Tenebrionidae). II. Malathion resistance in Eastern Australia. J. Stored Prod. Res. 6: 111-131.

CHAMP, B. R., and J. N. CRIBB. 1965. Lindane resistance in *Sitophilus oryzae* (L.) and *Sitophilus zeamais* Motsch. (Coleoptera, Curculionidae) in Queensland. J. Stored Prod. Res. 1: 9-24.

CHAMP, B. R., R. W. STEELE, B. G. GENN, and K. D. ELMS. 1969. A comparison of malathion, diazinon, fenitrothion and dichlorvos for control of *Sitophilus oryzae* (L.) and *Rhyzopertha dominica* (F.) in wheat. J. Stored Prod. Res. 5: 21-48.

CHRISTENSEN, C. M., and A. C. HODSON. 1960. Development of granary weevils and storage fungi in columns of wheat. J. Econ. Entomol. 53: 375-380.

CHRISTENSEN, C. M., G. H. NELSON, C. J. MIROCHA, and F. BATES. 1968. Toxicity to experimental animals of 943 isolates of fungi. Cancer Res. 28: 2293-2295.

COGBURN, R. R. 1967. Fumigation of bucket elevators with phosphine gas to control rice weevil and red flour beetle adults. J. Econ. Entomol. 60: 1485-1486.

COGBURN, R. R., and E. W. TILTON. 1963. Studies of phosphine as a fumigant for stacked rice under gas-tight tarpaulins. J. Econ. Entomol. 56: 706-708.

CONWAY, J. 1966. The control of *Anagasta kuhniella* (Zeller) (Lepidoptera, Phycitidae) in metal bins using dichlorvos slow release PVC strips. J. Stored Prod. Res. 1: 381-383.

COOPER, C. V., and H. B. GILLENWATER. 1972. Preliminary evaluation of six candidate fumigants against stored-product insects. J. Georgia Entomol. Soc. 7: 250-253.

COTTON, R. T. 1963. *Pests of stored grain and grain products*. Burgess Pub. Co., Minneapolis. 318 p.

CRUMRINE, M. H., and V. D. FOLTZ. 1969. Survival of *Salmonella montevideo* on wheat stored at constant relative humidity. Appl. Microbiol. 18: 911-914.

CRUMRINE, M. H., V. D. FOLTZ, and J. O. HARRIS. 1971. Transmission of *Salmonella montevideo* in wheat by stored-product insects. Appl. Microbiol. 22: 578-580.

CUNNINGTON, A. M. 1965. Physical limits for complete development of the grain mite *Acarus siro* (L.) (Acarina, Acaridae), in relation to its world distribution. J. Appl. Ecol. 2: 295-306.

CUTLER, J. R., and G. HOSIE. 1966. Bird nests as sources of infestation of *Ptinus tectus* Boleldieu (Coleoptera, Ptinidae) and the distribution of this insect in stacks of bagged flour. J. Stored Prod. Res. 2: 27-34.

DAVIES, M. S., P. R. CHADWICK, J. M. HOLBORN, D. C. STEWART, and J. C. WICKHEM. 1970. Effectiveness of the (+)-trans-chrysanthemie acid ester of (±)-allenthrolone (bio-allethrin) against four insect species. Pestic. Sci. 1: 225-227.

DAVIS, D. F., and H. LAUDANI. 1956. Long-term insecticide tests. Mod. Packag. 29: 236-240, 332, 334, 337, 338.

DAVIS, N. D., and U. L. DIENER. 1967. Inhibition of aflatoxin synthesis by p-aminobenzoic acid, potassium sulfite and potassium fluoride. Appl. Microbiol. 15: 1517-1518.

DIETERICH, W. H., G. MAYR, K. HILDA, J. B. SULLIVAN, and J. MURPHY. 1967. Hydrogen phosphide as a fumigant for foods, feeds and processed food products. Residue Rev. 19: 135-149.

DOLLEAR, F. G. 1969. Detoxification of aflatoxins in foods and feeds. p. 359-391 in *Aflatoxin* (L. S. Goldblatt, ed.) 472 p. Academic Press, New York.

DOW CHEMICAL CO. 1957. Use of methyl bromide for the fumigation of grain by forced recirculation. Dow Chem. Co., Midland, Mich.

DUMAS, T. 1964. Determination of phosphine in air by gas chromatography. J. Agr. Food Chem. 12: 257-258.

DUMAS, T. 1969. Microdetermination of phosphine in air by gas chromatography. J. Agr. Food Chem. 17: 1164-1165.

DYTE, C. E. 1970. Insecticide resistance in stored-product insects with special reference to *Tribolium castaneum*. Trop. Stored Prod. Inf. 20: 13-18.

DYTE, C. E. 1972. Resistance to synthetic juvenile hormone in a strain of the flour beetle, *Tribolium castaneum*. Nature 238: 48-49.

DYTE, C. E., and D. G. BLACKMAN. 1970. The spread of insecticide resistance in *Tribolium castaneum* (Herbst) (Coleoptera, Tenebrionidae). J. Stored Prod. Res. 6: 255-261.

DYTE, C. E., and D. G. BLACKMAN. 1972. Laboratory evaluation of organophosphorus insecticides against susceptible and malathion-resistant strains of *Tribolium castaneum* (Herbst) (Coleoptera, Tenebrionidae). J. Stored Prod. Res. 8(2): 103-109.

EBELING, W. 1969. Use of mineral dusts for protection against insect pests with special reference to cereal grains. p. 103 in *Grain sanitation* (S. K. Majumder and J. S. Venugopal, eds.). Acad. Pest Control Sci. Manipal Power Press, Mysore, India.

ELMS, K. D., J. D. KERR, and B. R. CHAMP. 1972. Breakdown of malathion and dichlorvos mixtures applied to wheat. J. Stored Prod. Res. 8: 55-63.

ESTES, P. M. 1965. The effects of time and temperature on methyl bromide fumigation of adults of *Sitophilus granarius* and *Tribolium confusum*. J. Econ. Entomol. 58: 611-614.

EUGENIO, C., E. DE LAS CASAS, P. K. HAREIN, and C. J. MIROCHA. 1970. Detection of the mycotoxin F-2 in the confused flour beetle and the lesser mealworm. J. Econ. Entomol. 63: 412-415.

FISK, F. W., and H. H. SHEPARD. 1938. Laboratory studies of methyl bromide as an insect fumigant. J. Econ. Entomol. 31: 79-84.

FLOYD, E. H. 1971. Relationship between maize weevil infestation in corn at harvest and progressive infestation during storage. J. Econ. Entomol. 64: 408-411.

GIBICH, J., and J. R. PEDERSEN. 1963. Bromide levels in mill fractions of unfumigated and fumigated wheat. Cereal Sci. Today 8: 345-348, 354.

GILLENWATER, H. B. 1973. Personal communication.

GILLENWATER, H. B., G. EASON, and E. B. BAUMAN. 1972. Gas propelled aerosols and micronized dusts for control of insects in aircraft. 4. Potential for controlling stored-product insects. J. Econ. Entomol. 65: 1450-1453.

GILLENWATER, H. B., and P. K. HAREIN. 1964. A dispenser designed to provide large quantities of insecticide vapor. J. Econ. Entomol. 57: 762-763.

GILLENWATER, H. B., P. K. HAREIN, E. W. LOY, Jr., J. F. THOMPSON, H. LAUDANI, and G. EASON. 1970. Dichlorvos applied as a vapor in a warehouse containing packaged food. J. Stored Prod. Res. 7: 45-56.

GODAVARIBAI, S., K. KRISHNAMURTHY, and S. K. MAJUMDER. 1960. Studies on malathion for stored-product insect control. Pest control. Pest Technol., Suppl. Public Health Sanit. (London) 2: 12-15.

GODDEN, E., and HOWE, R. W. 1965. The susceptibility of the developmental stages of *Tribolium castaneum* to methyl bromide. Tribolium Inf. Bull. 8: 76.

GOSTICK, K. G. 1970. The effect of methyl bromide on seed germination. EPPO Public Ser. D. 15: 33-38.

GRAY, H. E. 1964. Fumigation of commodities in transit. Pest Contr. 32: 14-15.

GREEN, A. A., J. KANE, and J. M. G. GRADIDGE. 1966. Experiments on the control of *Ephestia elutella* (Hb.) (Lepidoptera, Phycitidae) using dichlorvos vapour. J. Stored Prod. Res. 2: 147-157.

GREEN, A. A., J. KANE, S. G. HEUSER, and K. A. SCUDAMORE. 1968. Control of *Ephestia elutella* (Hb.) (Lepidoptera, Phycitidae) using dichlorvos in oil. J. Stored Prod. Res. 4: 69-76.

GREEN, A. A., and P. S. TYLER. 1966. A field comparison of malathion, dichlorvos and fenitrothion for the control of *Oryzaephilus surinamensis* (L.) (Coleoptera, Silvanidae) infesting stored barley. J. Stored Prod. Res. 1: 273-285.

GREEN, A. A., P. S. TYLER, J. KANE, and D. G. ROWLANDS. 1970. An assessment of bromophos for the protection of wheat and barley. J. Stored Prod. Res. 6: 217-228.

GREEN, A. A., and D. R. WILKIN. 1969. The control of insects in bagged grain by the injection of dichlorvos. J. Stored Prod. Res. 5: 11-19.

GRIFFITHS, D. A. 1964. A revision of the genus *Acarus* L., 1758 (Acaridae, Acarina). Bull. Brit. Mus. Natur. Hist. Zool. 11: 415-464.

GRIFFITHS, D. A. 1970. A further systematic study of the genus *Acarus*, 1758 (Acaridae, Acarina). Bull. Brit. Mus. Natur. Hist. Zool. 19: 85-118.

GUNTHER, F. A., D. L. LINDGREN, and R. C. BLINN. 1958. Biological effectiveness and persistence of malathion and lindane used for protection of stored wheat. J. Econ. Entomol. 51: 843-844.

HALL, D. W. 1969. Food storage in developing countries. Trop. Sci. 11: 298-318.

HALL, D. W. 1970. Handling and storage of food grains in tropical and subtropical areas. FAO Agr. Development Paper 90. FAO, Rome.

HALL, R. C., D. L. BALLEE, G. W. BENNETT, and J. E. FAHAY. 1973. Persistence and distribution of gardona and dichlorvos in grain and grain products. J. Econ. Entomol. 66: 315-318.

HAMMER, O. H., and F. C. AMSTUTZ. 1955. Apparatus for more rapid vaporization of methyl bromide. Down Earth 11: 11-13.

HAREIN, P. K. 1960. Effect of ronnel upon the adult rice weevil, *Sitophilus oryzae*. J. Econ. Entomol. 53: 372-375.

HAREIN, P. K. 1961. Effect of dockage on the efficiency of 80:20 (carbon tetrachloride:carbon disulfide by volume) as a fumigant for adult rice weevil, *Sitophilus sasakii* (Tak.) in wheat. J. Kans. Entomol. Soc. 34: 195-197.

HAREIN, P. K. 1962. Fumigation efficiency as affected by exposures, formulations and by insect species and stages. J. Econ. Entomol. 55: 527-533.

HAREIN, P. K., and E. DE LAS CASAS. 1968. Bacteria from granary weevils collected from laboratory colonies and field infestations. J. Econ. Entomol. 61: 1719-1720.

HAREIN, P. K., and H. B. GILLENWATER. 1966. Exploratory tests with bromodan as a protectant for wheat against stored-product insects. J. Econ. Entomol. 59: 413-414.

HAREIN, P. K., H. B. GILLENWATER, and G. EASON. 1970. Dichlorvos space treatment for protection of packaged flour against insect infestation. J. Stored Prod. Res. 7: 57-62.

HAREIN, P. K., H. B. GILLENWATER, and E. G. JAY. 1970. Dichlorvos: Methods of dispensing, estimates of concentration in air and toxicity to stored-product insects. J. Econ. Entomol. 63: 1263-1268.

HAREIN, P. K., and G. F. KRAUSE. 1961. Differential sorption of fumigant formulations by wheat and relative toxicity to adult rice weevil, *Sitophilus sasakii*. J. Econ. Entomol. 54: 261-264.

HAREIN, P. K., and G. F. KRAUSE. 1964. Dosage-time relationships between 80:20

(CCl$_4$:CS$_2$) and the adult rice weevil, *Sitophilus oryzae*. J. Econ. Entomol. 54: 521-522.

HAREIN, P. K., and H. R. G. RAO. 1972. Dichlorvos and gardona as protectants for stored wheat against granary weevil infestations in laboratory studies. J. Econ. Entomol: 1402-1405.

HAREIN, P. K., and J. H. SCHESSER. 1971. Unpublished research.

HAREIN, P. K., and R. L. SOLES. 1964. Fumigant toxicity of 1,2,3-tribromopropene, ethylenimine, crotyl bromide and carbon tetrachloride to stored-product insects. J. Econ. Entomol. 57: 369-370.

HAYWARD, L. A. W. 1962. Ground nuts. Rep. W. Africa Stored Prod. Res. Unit 1961: 12-15.

HAZLETON, L. W. 1968. The arrival of phostoxin. Pest Contr. 36: 26, 30, 32, 34.

HESELTINE, H. K. 1961. The use of thermal conductivity meters in fumigation research and control. Pest Infest. Res. Bull. 2, Agr. Res. Council, London. 12 p.

HESELTINE, H. K., and A. ROYCE. 1960. A concentration-time product indicator for fumigations. Pest Technol. 2: 88-92.

HESELTINE, H. K., and R. H. THOMPSON. 1957. The use of aluminum phosphide tablets for the fumigation of grain. Milling 129: 676-677, 730-732, 774-775, 778, 783.

HESSELTINE, C. W. 1969. Mycotoxins. Mycopathol. Mycol. Appl. 39: 371-383.

HEUSER, S. G. 1969. Determination of fumigant residues in cereals and other food-stuffs: a multidetection scheme for gas chromatography of solvent extracts. J. Sci. Food Agr. 20: 566.

HEUSER, S. G., and K. A. SCUDAMORE. 1966. A rapid method for sampling dichlorvos vapour in air. Chem. Ind. (London) 1966: 2093-2094.

HEUSER, S. G., and K. A. SCUDAMORE. 1969. Determination of fumigant residues in cereals and other foodstuffs: A multi-detection scheme for gas chromatography of solvent extracts. J. Sci. Food Agr. 20: 566-572.

HEUSER, S. G., and K. A. SCUDAMORE. 1970. Selective determination of ionized bromine and organic bromides in food stuffs by gas-liquid chromatography with special reference to fumigant residues. Pestic. Sci. 1: 244-249.

HIGHLAND, H. A. 1967. Resistance to insect penetration of carbaryl-coated Kraft bags. J. Econ. Entomol. 60: 451-452.

HIGHLAND, H. A., D. F. DAVIS, and F. O. MARZKE. 1964. Insect-proofing multiwall bags. Mod. Packag. 37: 133-134, 136-138, 195.

HIGHLAND, H. A., and P. H. MERRITT. 1973. Synthetic pyrethroids as package treatments to prevent insect penetration. J. Econ. Entomol. 66: 540-541.

HIGHLAND, H. A., and C. E. METTS. 1970. A bibliography of insect-resistant packaging, 1913-69. U.S. Dep. Agr.-Agr. Res. Serv. 51-36. 16 p.

HIGHLAND, H. A., M. SECREAST, and P. H. MERRITT. 1969. Packaging materials as barriers to piperonyl butoxide migration. J. Econ. Entomol. 63: 7-10.

HILL, E. G., and W. J. SIMPSON. 1972. Disinfestation of a flour mill by spot fumigation. Milling 154: 26-28.

HILL, E. G., and R. H. THOMPSON. 1968. Pesticide residues in foodstuffs in Great Britain. V. Malathion in imported cereals. J. Sci. Food Agr. 19: 119.

HOPE, J. A. 1960. Acaricides and stored-product mites. Pest Infest. Res. Rep., Slough, Bucks, England, p. 33-34.

HOPE, J. A. 1962. Acaricides. Pest Infest. Res. Rep., Slough, Bucks, England, p. 35.

HOUSE, H. L., and A. R. GRAHM. 1967. Capric acid blended into foodstuff for control of an insect pest, *Tribolium confusum* (Coleoptera:Tenebrionidae). Can. Entomol. 99: 994-999.

HOWE, R. W., and B. D. HOLE. 1966. The susceptibility of the developmental stages of *Sitophilus granarius* (L.) (Coleoptera, Curculionidae) to methyl bromide. J. Stored Prod. Res. 2: 13-26.

HOWE, R. W., and B. D. HOLE. 1967. Predicting the dosage of fumigant needed to eradicate insect pests from stored products. J. Appl. Ecol. 4: 337-351.

JACOBSON, M. 1958. Insecticides from plants. A review of the literature 1941-1953. U.S. Dep. Agr. Agr. Handbook 154. 299 p.

JALIL, M., I. J. ROSS, and J. G. RODRIGUEZ. 1970. Methyl bromide and phosphine as fumigants for some acarid mites. J. Stored Prod. Res. 6: 33-37.

JAY, E. G., H. B. GILLENWATER, and P. K. HAREIN. 1964. The toxicity of several dichlorvos (DDVP) and naled formulations to the adult confused flour beetle. J. Econ. Entomol. 57: 415-416.

KADOUM, A. M., and D. W. LA HUE. 1969. Effect of hybrid, moisture content, foreign material and storage temperature on the degradation of malathion residue in grain sorghum. J. Econ. Entomol. 62: 1161-1164.

KADOUM, A. M., and D. W. LA HUE. 1972. Degradation of malathion on viable and sterilized sorghum grain. J. Econ. Entomol. 65: 477-500.

KANAZAWA, J. 1963. Determination of chloropicrin in fumigants by gas-liquid chromatography. Agr. Biol. Chem. (Tokyo) 27: 159-161.

KANE, J., and A. A. GREEN. 1968. The protection of bagged grain from insect infestation using fenitrothion. J. Stored Prod. Res. 4: 59-68.

KAZMAIER, H. E., and R. G. FULLER. 1959. Ethylene dibromide: Methyl bromide mixtures as fumigants against the confused flour beetle. J. Econ. Entomol. 52: 1081-1085.

KENAGA, E. E. 1958. Calibration of thermal conductivity units for use with commodity fumigants. Down Earth 14: 6-7, 16.

KENAGA, E. E. 1961. Time, temperature, and dosage relationships of several insecticidal fumigants. J. Econ. Entomol. 54: 537-542.

KING, D. R., E. O. MORRISON, and J. A. SUNDMAN. 1962. Bioassay of chemical protectants and surface treatments for the control of insects in stored sorghum grain. J. Econ. Entomol. 55: 506-510.

KIRKPATRICK, R. L. 1966. Toxicity of seven candidate fumigants to stored-product insects. J. Econ. Entomol. 59: 558-560.

KIRKPATRICK, R. L., P. K. HAREIN, and C. V. COOPER. 1968. Laboratory tests with dichlorvos as a wheat protectant against rice weevils. J. Econ. Entomol. 61: 356-358.

KLINE, G. L., and H. H. CONVERSE. 1961. Operating grain aeration systems in the hard winter wheat area. U.S. Dep. Agr. Marketing Res. Rep. 480. Washington, D.C. 22 p.

KOUCHEROVA, S. G., and F. T. LISITSYN. 1962. The gas analyzer and its use in quarantine fumigation. Zashch. Rast. Moscow 7: 52.

KRANTZ, G. W. 1956. A laboratory method for testing grain protectants against the grain mite. J. Econ. Entomol. 49: 813-814.

KROHNE, H. E., and D. L. LINDGREN. 1958. Susceptibility of life stages of *Sitophilus oryzae* to various fumigants. J. Econ. Entomol. 51: 157-158.

KUMAR, V., and F. E. MORRISON. 1967. Carbamate and phosphate resistance in adult granary weevils. J. Econ. Entomol. 60: 1430-1434.

KUNZ, S. E., E. O. MORRISON, and D. R.

KING. 1964. The effects of grain moisture content, grain temperature, and dockage on the penetration of hydrogen cyanide. J. Econ. Entomol. 57: 453-455.

LA HUE, D. W. 1966. Evaluation of malathion, synergized pyrethrum and diatomaceous earth on shelled corn as protectants against insects in small bins. U.S. Dep. Agr. Marketing Res. Rep. 768. Washington, D.C. 10 p.

LA HUE, D. W. 1967. Evaluation of malathion, synergized pyrethrum and a diatomaceous earth as protectants against insects in sorghum grain in small bins. U.S. Dep. Agr. Marketing Res. Rep. 781. Washington, D.C. 11 p.

LA HUE, D. W. 1969a. Evaluation of several formulations of malathion as a protectant of grain sorghum against insects in small bins. U.S. Dep. Agr. Marketing Res. Rep. 828. Washington, D.C. 19 p.

LA HUE, D. W. 1969b. Control of malathion-resistant Indian-meal moths *Plodia interpunctella* with dichlorvos resin strips. Proc. North Centr. Branch Entomol. Soc. Amer. 24: 117-119.

LA HUE, D. W. 1970a. Evaluation of malathion, diazinon, a silica aerogel and a diatomaceous earth as protectants on wheat against lesser grain borer attack in small bins. U.S. Dep. Agr. Marketing Res. Rep. 860. Washington, D.C. 12 p.

LA HUE, D. W. 1970b. Laboratory evaluation of dichlorvos as a short-term protectant for wheat, shelled corn, and grain sorghum against stored grain insects. U.S. Dep. Agr.-Agr. Res. Serv. 51-37. Washington, D.C. 25 p.

LA HUE, D. W. 1971. Controlling the Indian-meal moth in shelled corn with dichlorvos PVC resin strips. U.S. Dep. Agr.-Agr. Res. Serv. 51-42. Washington, D.C. 9 p.

LA HUE, D. W. 1973. Gardona as a protectant against insects in stored wheat. J. Econ. Entomol. 66: 485-489.

LA HUE, D. W., and E. B. DICKE. 1971. Phoxim as an insect protectant for stored grains. J. Econ. Entomol. 64: 1530-1533.

LA HUE, D. W., and C. C. FIFIELD. 1967. Evaluation of four insect dusts on wheat as protectants against insects in small bins. U.S. Dep. Agr. Marketing Res. Rep. 780. Washington, D.C. 24 p.

LE GOUPIL. 1932. Les properties insecticides du bromure de methyl. Rev. Pathol. Reg. 19: 167-172.

LEMON, R. W. 1966. Laboratory evaluation of some organophosphorus insecticides against *Tribolium confusum* Duv. and *Tribolium castaneum* (Hbst.) (Coleoptera, Tenebrionidae). J. Stored Prod. Res. 1: 247-253.

LEMON, R. W. 1967a. Laboratory evaluation of malathion, bromophos and fenitrothion for use against beetles infesting stored products. J. Stored Prod. Res. 2: 197-210.

LEMON, R. W. 1967b. The effect of fenchlorphos on *Sitophilus* spp. (Coleoptera, Curculionidae). J. Stored Prod. Res. 3: 397-400.

LICHTENSTEIN, E. P. 1966. Insecticides occurring naturally in crops. Advan. Chem. Ser. 53: 34-38.

LILLEHOJ, E. B., A. CIEGLER, and R. W. DETROY. 1970. Fungal toxins. p. 2-106 in *Essays in toxicology* (F. R. Blood, ed.), vol. 2, 219 p. Academic Press, New York.

LINDGREN, D. L., F. A. GUNTHER, and L. E. VINCENT. 1962. Bromide residues in wheat and milled wheat fractions fumigated with methyl bromide. J. Econ. Entomol. 55: 773-776.

LINDGREN, D. L., H. E. KROHNE, and L. E. VINCENT. 1954. Malathion and chlorthion for control of insects infesting stored grain. J. Econ. Entomol. 47: 705-706.

LINDGREN, D. L., and L. E. VINCENT. 1960. The relation of moisture content and temperature of stored grain to the effectiveness of grain fumigants under forced circulation. J. Econ. Entomol. 53: 1071-1077.

LINDGREN, D. L., and L. E. VINCENT. 1965. The susceptibility of laboratory reared and field collected cultures of *Tribolium confusum* and *T. castaneum* to ethylene dibromide, hydrocyanic acid and methyl bromide. J. Econ. Entomol. 58: 551-555.

LINDGREN, D. L., and L. E. VINCENT. 1966. Relative toxicity of hydrogen phosphide to various stored-product insects. J. Stored Prod. Res. 2: 141-146.

LINDGREN, D. L., L. E. VINCENT, and H. E. KROHNE. 1954. Relative effectiveness of ten fumigants to adults of eight species of stored-product insects. J. Econ. Entomol. 47: 923-926.

LINDGREN, D. L., L. E. VINCENT, and R. G. STRONG. 1958. Studies on hydrogen phosphide as a fumigant. J. Econ. Entomol. 51: 900-903.

LINSLEY, E. G. 1944. Natural sources, habits and reservoirs of insects associated with stored food products. Hilgardia 16: 187-224.

LISCOMBE, E. A. R. 1963. Hydrogen

phosphide in tablet form as a grain fumigant. Res. Farmers 8: 6-7.

LLOYD, C. J., and P. S. HEWLETT. 1958. Relative susceptibility to pyrethrum in oil of Coleoptera and Lepidoptera infesting stored products. Bull. Entomol. Res. 49: 177-185.

LLOYD, C. J., and E. A. PARKIN. 1963. Further studies on a pyrethrum-resistant strain of the granary weevil, *Sitophilus granarius* (L.). J. Sci. Food Agr. 9: 655-663.

LOSCHIAVO, S. R. 1969. Effects of the antifeeding compound Ac-24055 (4-(3,3)-dimethyl-1-triazene acetanilide) on the survival, development, and reproduction of some stored-product insects. J. Econ. Entomol. 62: 102-107.

MAJUMDER, S. K., J. K. KRISHNA RAO, and H. G. SETHUMADHAVAN. 1961. Insect-proofing of gunny bags for grain storage. Res. Ind. 6: 391-393.

MAJUMDER, S. K., K. S. MARASIMHAN, and H. A. B. PARPIA. 1964. Microecological factors of microbial spoilage and the occurrence of mycotoxins on stored grains. p. 27-47 in *Mycotoxins in foodstuffs* (G. N. Wogan, ed.). M.I.T. Press, Cambridge, Mass.

MAJUMDER, S. K., and J. S. VENUGOPAL. 1968. Pesticidal minerals. p. 190-199 in *Pesticides*. Acad. Pest Control Sci. Manipal Power Press, Mysore, India.

MALLING, H. V. 1969. Ethylene dibromide: A potent pesticide with high mutagenic activity. Abstr. 38th Ann. Meeting Genetics Soc. Amer., Madison, Wisconsin. Genetics 61: 539.

MALLIS, A. 1969. *Handbook of pest control,* 1148 p. McNair-Dorland Co., New York.

MALONE, B. 1969. Analysis of grains for multiple residues of organic fumigants. J. Ass. Offic. Anal. Chem. 52: 800-805.

MARCH, R. B., and R. L. METCALF. 1949. Laboratory and field studies of DDT resistant house flies in southern California. Calif. Dep. Agr. Bull. 38: 93-101.

MARTIN, W. J., and W. H. EWING. 1969. Prevalence of serotypes of Salmonella. Appl. Microbiol. 17: 111-117.

MARZKE, F. O., and R. J. DICKE. 1959. Laboratory evaluations of various residual sprays for the control of cheese mites. J. Econ. Entomol. 52: 237-240.

MATSUMURA, F., and S. G. KNIGHT. 1967. Toxicity and chemosterilizing activity of aflatoxins against insects. J. Econ. Entomol. 60: 871-872.

MATTSON, A. M., J. T. SPILLANE, and G. W. PEARCE. 1955. Dimethyl 2,2-dichlorovinyl phosphate (DDVP), an organic phosphorous compound highly toxic to insects. J. Agr. Food Chem. 3: 319-321.

McDONALD, L. L., and H. B. GILLENWATER. 1967. Relative toxicity of Bay 77488 and Dursban against stored-product insects. J. Econ. Entomol. 60: 1195-1196.

McDONALD, L. L., and R. D. SPEIRS. 1972. Toxicity of five new insecticides to stored-product insects. J. Econ. Entomol. 65: 529-530.

McFARLANE, J. A. 1961. Malathion water-dispersible powder for the protection of bagged foodstuffs from insect infestations. Trop. Sci. 3: 114-126.

McFARLANE, J. A. 1970. Treatment of large grain stores in Kenya with dichlorvos slow-release strips for control of *Cadra cautella*. J. Econ. Entomol. 63: 288-292.

McGAUGHEY, W. H. 1969. Malathion residues on rice. Rice J. 72: 3, 5.

McGAUGHEY, W. H. 1970. Evaluation of dichlorvos for insect control in stored rough rice. J. Econ. Entomol. 63: 1867-1870.

McGAUGHEY, W. H. 1971a. Malathion on milling fractions of three varieties of rough rice: Duration of protection and residue degradation. J. Econ. Entomol. 64: 1200-1205.

McGAUGHEY, W. H. 1971b. Diatomaceous earth for confused flour beetle and rice weevil control in rough, brown and milled rice. J. Econ. Entomol. 65: 1427-1428.

McGREGOR, H. E. 1961. Evaluation of phosphine gas as a fumigant for shelled yellow corn stored in concrete silo-type storage. Northwest. Miller 265: 38-39.

McGREGOR, H. E., and L. I. DAVIDSON. 1966. Phosphine fumigation of processed commodities. Northwest. Miller 273: 11-12.

MILES, J. W., G. O. GUERRANT, M. B. GOETTE, and F. C. CHURCHILL. 1971. Studies on the chemistry, methods of analysis and storage stability of malathion formulations. Tech. Rep. Series 475, Expert Committee on Insecticides, Geneva. 72 p.

MINETT, W., and P. WILLIAMS. 1971. Influence of malathion distribution on the protection of wheat grain against insect infestation. J. Stored Prod. Res. 7: 233-242.

MONRO, H. A. U. 1969a. Manual of

fumigation for insect control. Food Agr. Org. United Nations, Rome. Manual 79. 381 p.

MONRO, H. A. U. 1969b. Insect pests in cargo ships. Can. Dep. Agr. Publ. 855. 39 p.

MONRO, H. A. U., C. R. CUNNINGHAM, and J. E. KING. 1952. Hydrogen cyanide and methyl bromide as fumigants for insect control in empty cargo ships. Sci. Agr. 32: 241-265.

MONRO, H. A. U., A. J. MUSGRAVE, and E. UPITIS. 1961. Induced tolerance of stored-product beetles to methyl bromide. Ann. Appl. Biol. 49: 373-377.

MONRO, H. A. U., E. UPITIS, and E. J. BOND. 1972. Resistance of a laboratory strain of *Sitophilus granarius* to phosphine. J. Stored Prod. Res. 8: 199-207.

MOORE, S., and G. C. DECKER. 1961. Control of the Angoumois grain moth *(Sitotroga cerealella)* in stored earcorn with malathion in Illinois, 1959-1960. J. Econ. Entomol. 54: 479-482.

MOSTAFA, S. A. S., A. H. KAMEL, A. K. M. EL-NA HAL, and F. M. EL-BOROLLOSY. 1972. Toxicity of carbon bisulfide and methyl bromide to the eggs of four stored-product insects. J. Stored Prod. Res. 8: 193-198.

NARASIMHAN, K. S., and G. RANGASWAMI. 1968. Effect of some fumigants on the microflora of sorghum seeds. Indian Phytopathol. Soc. Bull. 4: 57-64.

NORRIS, J. D. 1958. Observations on the control of mite infestations in stored wheat by *Cheletus* spp. (Acarina, Cheyletidae). Ann. Appl. Biol. 46: 411-422.

OLOMUCKI, E., and A. BONDI. 1955. Problems connected with ethylene dibromide fumigation of cereals. I. Sorption of ethylene dibromide by grain. J. Sci. Food Agr. 6: 593-600.

OXLEY, A. T. 1948. The scientific principles of grain storage. Chap. 13, p. 90-96 in *Mites as pests of stored grain.* Northern Pub. Co., Liverpool.

OZER, M. 1961. Phostoxin in degisik doz, muddet ve isida *Calandra granaria* L. Ve *Calandra oryzae* L. nin biyolojik safhalarina karsi toksik etkisi. Koruma 2: 19-35.

PARKIN, E. A. 1963. The protection of stored seeds from insects and rodents. Proc. Int. Seed Test Ass. 28: 893-909.

PARKIN, E. A. 1965a. The onset of insecticide resistance among field strains of stored-product insects. XII. Int. Congr. Entomol. 657-658.

PARKIN, E. A. 1965b. The onset of insecticide resistance among field populations of stored product insects. J. Stored Prod. Res. 1: 1-38.

PARKIN, E. A., and C. J. LLOYD. 1960. Selection of a Pyrethrum-resistant strain of the grain weevil, *Calandra granaria* L. J. Sci. Food Agr. 11: 471.

PARKIN, E. A., E. I. C. SCOTT, A. N. BATES, and D. G. ROWLANDS. 1962a. The malathion treatment of malting barley. Pest Infest. Res. Rep., Slough, Bucks, England 1961: 32-33.

PARKIN, E. A., E. I. C. SCOTT, and R. FORESTER. 1962b. The resistance of field strains of beetles. Pest Infest. Res. Rep., Slough, Bucks, England 1961: 34-35.

PEDERSEN, J. R. 1960. Susceptibility of certain stages of the rice weevil to a methallyl chloride fumigant formulation in wheat of various moistures. J. Econ. Entomol. 53: 288-291.

PHILLIPS, G. L. 1957. Experiments on distributing methyl bromide in bulk grains with aeration systems. U.S. Dep. Agr., Marketing Res. Rep. 150. Washington, D.C. 60 p.

PHILLIPS, G. L., and J. W. BULGER. 1953. Analysis of methyl bromide by measurements of thermal conductivity. U.S. Dep. Agr., Bur. Entomol. Plant Quarantine, E851. Washington, D.C. 8 p.

PHILLIPS, G. L., and H. D. NELSON. 1957. Permeability of methyl bromide of plastic films and plastic and rubber-coated fabrics. J. Econ. Entomol. 50: 452-454.

PRASERTPHON, S., and Y. TANADA. 1969. Mycotoxins of entomophthoraceous fungi. Hilgardia 39: 581-600.

QUINLAN, J. K. 1972. Malathion aerosols applied in conjunction with aeration to corn stored in a flat storage structure. Proc. North Centr. Branch Entomol. Soc. Amer. 27: 63-65.

QURESHI, A. H., E. J. BOND, and H. A. U. MONRO. 1965. Toxicity of hydrogen phosphide to the granary weevil, *Sitophilus granarius,* and other insects. J. Econ. Entomol. 58: 324-330.

RAGHUNATHAN, A. N., M. MUTHU, and S. K. MAJUMDER. 1969. Control of internal fungi or sorghum by fumigation. J. Stored Prod. Res. 5: 389-392.

RAO, G. H. R., E. CESARIA, C. M. CHRISTENSEN, E. DE LAS CASAS, and P. K. HAREIN. 1971. Survival and reproduction of confused flour beetles exposed to fungus metabolites. J. Econ. Entomol. 64: 1563-1565.

RAO, G. H. R., and P. K. HAREIN. 1972. Dichlorvos as an inhibitor of aflatoxin production on wheat, corn, rice and peanuts. J. Econ. Entomol. 65: 988-989.

RAO, G. H. R., and P. K. HAREIN. 1973. Inhibition of aflatoxin and zearalenone biosynthesis with dichlorvos. Bull. Environ. Contam. Toxicol. 10: 112-114.

REYNOLDS, E. M., J. M. ROBINSON, and C. HOWELLS. 1967. The effect on *Sitophilus granarius* (L.) (Coleoptera, Curculionidae) of exposure to low concentration of phosphine. J. Stored Prod. Res. 2: 177-186.

ROAN, C. C., and B. P. SRIVASTAVA. 1965. Dissipation of diazinon residues in wheat. J. Econ. Entomol. 58: 996-998.

ROBINSON, J. R., and E. J. BOND. 1970. The toxic action of phosphine—Studies with PH₃: Terminal residues in biological materials. J. Stored Prod. Res. 6: 133-146.

ROUT, G., and R. N. MOHANTY. 1967. Studies on hydrogen phosphide against the rice weevil. J. Econ. Entomol. 60: 276-277.

ROWLANDS, D. G. 1964. The degradation of malathion on stored maize and wheat grains. J. Sci. Food Agr. 15: 824-829.

ROWLANDS, D. G. 1967. The metabolism of contact insecticides on stored cereal grains. Res. Rev. 17: 105-177.

ROWLANDS, D. G. 1970. The metabolic fate of dichlorvos on stored wheat grains. J. Stored Prod. Res. 6: 19-32.

ROWLANDS, D. G. 1971. The metabolism of contact insecticides in stored grains. II. 1966-1969. Res. Rev. 34: 91-161.

SCHESSER, J. H. 1967a. A comparison of two fumigant mixtures for disinfesting empty railway freight cars. Northwest. Miller 274: 10.

SCHESSER, J. H. 1967b. A dichlorvos-malathion mixture for insect control in empty railcars. Amer. Miller Process. 95: 7-10.

SCHESSER, J. H. 1967c. Phosphine fumigation of processed cereal products in rail cars. Amer. Miller Process. Jan: 8-13.

SCHESSER, J. H. 1972. Boxcar research with dichlorvos aerosol. Proc. North Centr. Branch Entomol. Soc. Amer. 27: 56-57.

SECREAST, M. F., and R. S. CAIL. 1970. Improved procedure for determining malathion residues in stored agricultural products. U.S. Dep. Agr.-Agr. Res. Serv. 51-53. Washington, D.C. 8 p.

SHEDD, C. K. 1953. Resistance of grains and seeds to air flow. Agr. Eng. 34: 616-619.

SHUEY, W. C., V. L. YOUNGS, and M. E. GETZENDANER. 1971. Bromide residues in flour streams milled from fumigated wheats. Cereal Chem. 48: 34-39.

SILVERSTOPLE, L., U. PLAZIKOWSKI, J. KJELLANDER, and G. VAHLNE. 1961. An epidemic among infants caused by *Salmonella muenchew*. J. Appl. Bacteriol. 24: 142-143.

SIMMONS, P. 1960. Escape of methyl bromide through wallboards. J. Econ. Entomol. 53: 968-969.

SINCLAIR, W. B., D. L. LINDGREN, and R. FORBES. 1962. Recovery of ethylene dibromide residues from fumigated whole kernel and milled wheat fractions. J. Econ. Entomol. 55: 836-842.

SINCLAIR, W. B., D. L. LINDGREN, and R. FORBES. 1964. Effects of temperature, reduced pressure, and moisture content on sorption of ethylene dibromide by wheat and corn. J. Econ. Entomol. 57: 470-475.

SINHA, R. N. 1966. Development and mortality of *Tribolium castaneum* and *T. confusum* (Coleoptera: Tenebrionidae) on seed-borne fungi. Ann. Entomol. Soc. Amer. 59: 192-201.

SINHA, R. N., B. BERCK, and H. A. H. WALLACE. 1967. Effect of phosphine on mites, insects and microorganisms. J. Econ. Entomol. 60: 125-132.

SLOMINSKI, J. W., and W. L. GOJMERAC. 1972. The effect of surfaces on the activity of insecticides. Wis. Univ. Res. Rep. 2376. 8 p.

SOLES, R. L., and P. K. HAREIN. 1962. The fumigant toxicity of two new chemicals to stored-product insects. J. Econ. Entomol. 55: 1014-1015.

SPEIRS, R. D. 1962. Contact, residue and vapor toxicity of new insecticides to stored-product insects. U.S. Dep. Agr. Marketing Res. Rep. 546. Washington, D.C. 31 p.

SPEIRS, R. D., and J. H. LANG. 1970. Contact, residue and vapor toxicity of new insecticides to stored-product insects. II. U.S. Dep. Agr. Marketing Res. Rep. 546. Washington, D.C. 35 p.

STEVENSON, J. H. 1958. The effect of pyrethrins and piperonyl butoxide against the moths *Plodia interpunctella* and *Ephestia cautella*. Chem. Ind. (London) 1958: 827.

STOREY, C. L. 1967. Comparative study of methods of distributing methyl bromide in flat storages of wheat: gravity-penetration, single pass and closed recirculation. U.S. Dep. Agr. Marketing Res. Rep. 794. Washington, D.C. 16 p.

STOREY, C. L. 1971. Distribution of grain fumigants in silo-type elevator tanks by aeration systems. U.S. Dep. Agr. Marketing Res. Rep. 915. Washington, D.C. 17 p.

STOREY, C. L., L. D. KIRK, and G. C. MISTAKOS. 1972. Fate of EDC-CCl₄ (75:25) residues during milling and oil extraction of soybeans. J. Econ. Entomol. 65: 1126-1129.

STRONG, R. G. 1969. Relative susceptibility of five stored-product moths to some organophosphorous insecticides. J. Econ. Entomol. 62: 1036-1039.

STRONG, R. G. 1970a. Distribution and relative abundance of stored-product insects in California: A method of obtaining sample populations. J. Econ. Entomol. 63: 591-596.

STRONG, R. G. 1970b. Relative susceptibility of *Attagenus alfierii* and *A. megatoma* larvae to several organophosphorus insecticides. J. Econ. Entomol. 63: 286-287.

STRONG, R. G. 1970c. Relative susceptibility of confused and red flour beetles to twelve organophosphorous insecticides with notes on adequacy of the test method. J. Econ. Entomol. 63: 258-263.

STRONG, R. G., and D. L. LINDGREN. 1959a. Effect of methyl bromide and hydrocyanic acid fumigation on the germination of rice. J. Econ. Entomol. 52: 706-710.

STRONG, R. G., and D. L. LINDGREN. 1959b. Effect of methyl bromide and hydrocyanic acid fumigation on the germination of oats. J. Econ. Entomol. 52: 415-418.

STRONG, R. G., and D. L. LINDGREN. 1959c. Effect of methyl bromide and hydrocyanic acid fumigation on the germination of barley. J. Econ. Entomol. 52: 319-322.

STRONG, R. G., and D. L. LINDGREN. 1960. Germination of cereal, sorghum, and small legume seeds after fumigation with hydrogen phosphide. J. Econ. Entomol. 53: 1-4.

STRONG, R. G., and D. L. LINDGREN. 1961. Effect of methyl bromide and hydrocyanic acid fumigation on the germination of corn seed. J. Econ. Entomol. 54: 764-770.

STRONG, R. G., G. R. PIEPER, and D. E. SBUR. 1959. Control and prevention of mites in granary and rice weevil cultures. J. Econ. Entomol. 52: 443-446.

STRONG, R. G., and D. E. SBUR. 1961. Evaluation of insecticides as protectants against pests of stored grain seeds. J. Econ. Entomol. 54: 235-238.

STRONG, R. G., and D. E. SBUR. 1964a. Influence of grain moisture and storage temperature on the effectiveness of five insecticides as grain protectants. J. Econ. Entomol. 57: 44-47.

STRONG, R. G., and D. E. SBUR. 1964b. Protective sprays against internal infestations of grain beetles in wheat. J. Econ. Entomol. 57: 544-548.

STRONG, R. G., and D. E. SBUR. 1968. Evaluation of insecticides for control of stored-product insects. J. Econ. Entomol. 61: 1034-1041.

STRONG, R. G., D. E. SBUR, and R. G. ARNDT. 1961. Influence of formulation on the effectiveness of malathion, methoxychlor and synergized pyrethrum protective sprays for stored wheat. J. Econ. Entomol. 54: 489-501.

STRONG, R. G., D. E. SBUR, and G. J. PARTIDA. 1967. The toxicity and residual effectiveness of malathion and diazinon used for protection of stored wheat. J. Econ. Entomol. 60: 500-505.

SU, H. C. F., R. D. SPEIRS, and P. G. MAHANY. 1972a. Citrus oils as protectants of black-eyed peas against cowpea weevil: Laboratory evaluation. J. Econ. Entomol. 65: 1433-1436.

SU, H. C. F., R. D. SPEIRS, and P. G. MAHANY. 1972b. Toxicity of citrus oils to several stored-product insects: Laboratory evaluation. J. Econ. Entomol. 65: 1438-1441.

SUN, U. P. 1947. An analysis of some important factors affecting the results of fumigation tests on insects. Univ.Minn. Agr. Exp. Sta. Tech. Bull. 177. 104 p.

TELFORD, H. S., R. W. ZWICK, P. SIKOROWSKI, and M. WELLER. 1964. Laboratory evaluation of diazinon as a wheat protectant. J. Econ. Entomol. 57: 272-275.

TERBUSH, L. E. 1972. The medical significance of mites of stored food. FDA By-Line No. 2. FDA Bureau of Foods 57-70. Washington, D.C.

THOMPSON, R. H. 1966. A review of the properties and usage of methyl bromide as a fumigant. J. Stored Prod. Res. 1: 353-376.

THOMPSON, R. H. 1970. Specifications recommended by the United Kingdom Ministry of Agriculture, Fisheries and Food for the fumigation of cereals and other foodstuffs against pests of stored products. EPPO Public Ser. D. 15: 9-25.

THOMPSON, R. H., and E. G. HILL. 1969. Pesticide residues in foodstuffs in Great Britain. XI. Further studies on malathion in imported cereals. J. Sci. Food Agr. 20: 293.

TKACHUK, R. 1972. Phosphorus residues in wheat due to phosphine fumigation. Cereal Chem. 49: 258-267.

TYLER, P. S., and A. A. GREEN. 1968. The effectiveness of fenitrothion and malathion as grain protectants under severe practical conditions. J. Stored Prod. Res. 4: 119-126.

TYLER, P. S., and D. G. ROWLANDS. 1967. Sodium carboxymethyl cellulose as a stabilizer for malathion formulations. J. Stored Prod. Res. 3: 109-115.

U.S. DEPARTMENT OF AGRICULTURE. 1962. Method and equipment for bulk treatment of grain against insects. U.S. Dep. Agr. Marketing Res. Bull. 20. Washington, D.C. 7 p.

U.S. DEPARTMENT OF AGRICULTURE. 1963. A portable recirculation system for fumigating bulk products in freight cars. U.S. Dep. Agr. Marketing Res. Bull. 24. Washington, D.C. 4 p.

VAN WYK, J. H., A. C. HODSON, and C. M. CHRISTENSEN. 1959. Microflora associated with the confused flour beetle, *Tribolium confusum*. Ann. Entomol. Soc. Amer. 52: 452-463.

VARDELL, H. H., H. B. GILLENWATER, M. E. WHITTEN, A. COGLE, G. EASON, and R. S. CAIL. 1973. Dichlorvos degradation on stored wheat and resulting milling fractions. J. Econ. Entomol. 66: 761-763.

VENUGOPAL, J. S., and S. K. MAJUMDER. 1964. Active mineral in insecticidal clays. Abstracts, Symposium on Pesticides. Mysore, India. 30 p.

VINCENT, L. E., and D. L. LINDGREN. 1972. Toxicity of phosphine to the life stages of four species of dermestids. J. Econ. Entomol. 65: 1429-1431.

WATTERS, F. L. 1956. Pyrethrins-piperonyl butoxide as a residual treatment against insects in elevator boots. Cereal Chem. 33: 145-150.

WATTERS, F. L. 1959. Effects of grain moisture content on residual toxicity and repellency of malathion. J. Econ. Entomol. 52: 131-134.

WEBLEY, D. J., and C. E. McKONE. 1963. The estimation of dichlorvos vapour.

Arusha Tanganyika, Trop. Pest Inst., Misc. Rep. 424.

WHITE, G. D., W. L. BERNDT, J. H. SCHESSER, and C. C. FIFIELD. 1966. Evaluation of four inert dusts for the protection of stored wheat in Kansas from insect attack. U.S. Dep. Agr.-Agr. Res. Serv. 51-8. Washington, D.C. 21 p.

WHITNEY, W. K. 1961. Fumigation hazards as related to the physical, chemical and biological properties of fumigants. Pest Contr. 7: 16, 18-21.

WHITNEY, W. K. 1963. Minimizing residues from methyl bromide fumigation of wheat. Down Earth 19: 4-6.

WHITNEY, W. K., and P. K. HAREIN. 1959. Effects of number of test insects, exposure period and post treatment interval on reliability of fumigant bioassay. J. Econ. Entomol. 52: 942-949.

WHITNEY, W. K., O. K. JANTZ, and C. S. BULGER. 1958. Effects of methyl bromide fumigation on the viability of barley, corn, grain sorghum, oats and wheat seeds. J. Econ. Entomol. 51: 847-861.

WHITNEY, W. K., and H. H. WALKDEN. 1961. Concentrations of methyl bromide lethal to insects in grain. U.S. Dep. Agr. Marketing Res. Rep. 511. Washington, D.C. 25 p.

WILKIN, D. R., and J. A. HOPE. 1973. Evaluation of pesticides against stored product mites. J. Stored Prod. Res. 8: 323-327.

WINTERINGHAM, F. P. W. 1955. The fate of labelled insecticide residues in food products. IV. The possible toxicological and nutritional significance of fumigating wheat with methyl bromide. J. Sci. Food Agr. 6: 269-274.

WITT, P. R., Jr., L. CASE, and E. ADAMIC. 1960. Malathion treatment of barley as related to malt quality. Amer. Soc. Brew. Chem. Proc. p. 51.

WOODROFFE, G. E. 1961. Natural sources of domestic insects: A fundamental approach for the stored products entomologist. Sanitarian. 4 p.

WORSLEY, R. R., and G. LE. 1934. The insecticidal properties of some East African plants. Ann. Appl. Biol. 21: 649-669.

WRIGHT, V. F. 1973. A model to study the effects of mycotoxins on insects utilizing *Tribolium confusum* DuVal and metabolites of *Fusarium* spp. M. S. Thesis. Univ. Minn. 93 p.

CHAPTER 7

RODENTS

KENTON L. HARRIS

O'D. Kurtz, Inc.
Baltimore, Maryland

I. SIGNIFICANCE

A. General

From pre-biblical times, sporadic efforts have been made to eliminate rats and mice; and yet it is a general rule of thumb that, in any given area, the rat population equals that of the human. Specific charges in the indictment of the rat as a destroyer and polluter of food are manifold: the rat stands guilty as charged and warrants our special attention.

Next to man, commensal rats and mice are the most destructive vertebrate animals on earth. The genus *Rattus* alone has 570 named forms — more than any other genus of mammals. The Norway rat (*Rattus norvegicus*), the black rat (*Rattus rattus rattus*), the grey-bellied rat (*Rattus rattus alexandrinus*), the Polynesian rat (*Rattus exulans*),and the house mouse (*Mus musculus*) cause the most extensive damage. Two or more of these species are found in all countries of the world and in many lands they are joined by other destructive native rodents, such as the bandicoot rat of India and Ceylon. Together, they destroy many million tons of food each year. Economic losses due to rodents are so large and so widespread that they defy precise estimation.

Control techniques are not equally effective against all species. For example, the Hawaiian sugar industry annually spends about $300,000 for rat control but continues to suffer losses estimated to total $4,500,000 each year (Dykstra, 1966). Robinson (1965) reports that with the decline of the Norway and black rat in Hawaii — possibly, in part, through control, but more likely because they are less successful competitors — the Polynesian rat has taken over. Control procedures which give some relief from damage by Norway and black rats have not been successful against the Polynesian rat. In the U.S., it has been noted that infestations of house mice also tend to become more severe following the elimination of rats from buildings (Dykstra, 1966).

Rodents will gnaw through almost any object in their path to obtain food and shelter, and to wear their incisors, which grow continuously — about 4 in. a year in the Norway rat. This gnawing often results in extensive damage to buildings. It has been estimated that 25% of fires of unknown origin are started by rodent damage to electrical wiring.

Rat populations in the U.S. were probably at their highest levels relative to man during the later 1800's and early 1900's. In 1941, Silver reported that, in 1915, almost all large cities had a ratio of one rat to every person, and that this ratio was reduced by one-half during the next 25 years. However, the ratio on farms remained the same, at about two rats to one person. Total annual economic losses were estimated at $189,000,000.

In 1953, Mills estimated that there were 100,000,000 rats in the U.S. and that each of these rodents caused an average of $10 in damage per year. Thirteen years later, he estimated that there were about 10% fewer rats. This reduction was attributed to the wide-scale use of anticoagulant rodenticides, better sanitation, and improved building construction.

On a worldwide basis, it has been reported that 33,000,000 tons (3.55%) of bread grains and rice in storage are lost to rodents each year and that more than one-fifth of the foodstuffs planted by mankind every year never reach human consumption because of pests and disease (Ling, 1961). One of the most dramatic yet accurate summaries of the rat vs. man is that in *Meet the Rat* (World Health Organization, 1967).

Damage varies from place to place and year to year, and fluctuates with changes in rodent populations. An eruption of rats occurred in the Philippines during 1952–54 and is reported to have involved from 200 to 2,000 rats per hectare. Losses totaled upwards of 90% of the rice, 20 to 80% of the corn, and 50% of the sugarcane (Townes and Morales, 1953). A similar eruption was reported during 1956 in Madagascar where the destruction of rice was so extensive that a national emergency was declared. By the spring of 1966 the rodent population had declined sharply (Madsen, 1966).

Peak infestations of house mice have also occurred at periodic intervals. Laurie (1946) noted that their numbers in stacks of stored grain in England totaled as many as 0.43 per cubic foot. They reached tremendous numbers during an Australian mouse plague in 1916 when populations were estimated at 80,000 per acre or 17 per square yard in stacks of grain stored in the open. An outbreak among house and field mice occurred on California farms in 1926, at which time Hall (1927) calculated the weight of mice in the area at 2,468 lb. per acre, the ratio being about 85% house mice and 15% field mice (*Microtus*).

Damage by rodents occurs during all phases of food production, processing, and utilization. Losses in fields of rice, sugarcane, corn, cocoa, and coconut are particularly serious in tropical regions. H. A. B. Parpia, Director of the Central Food Technological Research Institute, Mysore, India (undated) estimated overall losses of grain from rodents in India at 25% in the field before harvest and 25 to 30% in storage. Other Indian sources refer to a figure of 1,000,000 tons of stored food and seed grains destroyed by rodents annually, exclusive of losses before harvest (Garg and Agrawal, 1963; Sinha and Ram, 1963. See also Parrack, 1967).

Dykstra (1966) stated that rats eat about 10% of their weight in food each day, and contaminate a great deal more with their droppings and urine, thereby rendering it unfit for human consumption. During a "Clean Grain Program" carried out over a period of 4 years in the late 1950's, the U.S. Food and Drug Administration seized 208 carloads of wheat because of excessive contamination by rodents. During the period of April 1965 to April 1966, the Food and Drug

Administration destroyed 417,000 lb. of rodent-contaminated food products and required that another 4,308,000 be converted to livestock feed. Fines totaling $23,140 were imposed. Additional seizures are also made each year by U.S. State and local health departments.

Until recent times it was the general practice for the Food and Drug Administration to permit rodent- or bird-contaminated foods to be denatured and diverted to animal feed. Cars of grain, especially wheat, have been diverted to feed use when found to contain rodent excreta in excess of the specified tolerance. The FDA no longer authorizes denaturing for animal feed except where the feed product will be treated by sufficient heat to kill *Salmonella* organisms. This action was taken because of the steady increase in the incidence of human Salmonellosis reported in the U.S. (Dykstra, 1966).

Dykstra (1966) reports that the manner by which contamination occurs is illustrated by what happens if one rat were left free in a warehouse for 1 year. During that time it would eat approximately 27 lb. of food and deposit about 25,000 droppings, weighing between 2 and 4 lb. During the same period a single house mouse would eat approximately 4 lb. of food and deposit about 17,500 droppings. Barnett's findings (Barnett, 1951) from a 1951 study of rat damage to wheat in England were summarized as follows: "Small enclosed populations of the common brown rat (ten to twenty-six rats), each with access to one ton of sacked wheat for 12-28 weeks, cause a loss in weight of 4.4 per cent of the wheat. *70.4 per cent of the wheat was fouled* and had to be cleaned before use. The main monetary loss was due to damage to sacks. Total monetary loss was 18.23 per cent of the original value of the wheat and sacks."

Dykstra (1966) reported and summarized the comments of an industry representative who followed food shipments from U.S. processing plants to the foreign consumers. In recent years the U.S. food-processing industries have spent large sums of money for cleaning equipment, improved storage facilities, and preventive sanitation programs. Food products leaving these industries are clean. Unfortunately, much of that which is exported becomes contaminated by rodents before it reaches the consumer. Representatives from U.S. food-processing industries have toured many countries of the world studying the problems of shipment and storage of their products. Reports indicate that severe losses are caused by rats and mice. Damage to packaged goods has been estimated to run from 60 to 80% in some instances. Damage to packages affords easy entry to other spoilage organisms. In many instances, there was no attempt to control the rodents or to store the food products properly. Much of the damage and loss could have been avoided by simple and inexpensive storage and warehousing practices. Rotation of food such as "first-in, first-out"; storage off the floor and away from walls; protection from water; and removal of refuse from the food-storage area are simple but effective aids to the reduction of losses. Dykstra (1968) further summarized the economic losses.

I estimate that it would take a train 2,800 miles long to carry the grain India's rats eat each year.

It is impossible and undesirable to make a distinction between "storage" rodents and their occurrence in the total environment. They move in and out of man's immediate ecology. Indeed, it is just this resiliency that makes them such formidable enemies, in constant guerilla-warfare, with food as the stake.

A review of the economic importance of rats and mice would be incomplete without reference to the cost and efficiency of existing control measures. The four main control methods are rodent-proofing, trapping, fumigation, and poison baiting, and each method has its disadvantages. It is difficult and expensive to completely mouse-proof a building and, in any case, mice may be carried into buildings within commodities. Traps are probably the most economical and efficient way of clearing out very small and contained infestations, but they are of little value in dealing with populations dispersed over wide areas. Fumigation is an effective means of destroying rodents living in large stacks of foodstuffs, but it is a costly operation, usually involving a team of skilled operators. Poison baiting is the most commonly used control method. In the West, quick-acting or acute rodenticides have now been largely abandoned in favor of the less hazardous anticoagulants, but zinc phosphide and other violent poisons remain in use where a quick, cheap kill is essential. Treatments, however, are often protracted or not completely successful, and may be demanding in terms of time and labor (Rowe, 1966).

The importance of the economics of rodent control cannot be over-estimated. Current comments on the seriousness of the problem and assessments on current trends in research and control are given in several reports of meetings and general bulletins: WHO, 1966; Asian-Pacific Interchange, 1968; Rockefeller Foundation, 1970; Perti et al., 1971; and Pingale et al., 1967.

B. Local Storage Aspects

Any discussion of rodent depredations to stored cereals and cereal grains needs to be considered in the light of the many types of storage structures used over the world. For many reasons it is not always practical to store grain in tight metal or concrete structures.

As Spencer (1954) stated, the storage of cereal grains and their products is not confined to modern elevators and rodent-proof warehouses where protection against loss and contamination by rats and mice would be relatively simple. Even in recent years, in the U.S., Canada, and Australia, some threshed wheat from bumper crops has been piled on the ground with little or no protection from rodents, birds, insects, and weather. Throughout the world, grains of all types are stored on farms and in small communal centers where the greater portion is without benefit of even partially rodent-proof structures. Aside from the miscellany of sheds and bins of all types, we find grain held in ricks (field stacks of unthreshed grain) for periods of 3 to 9 months in England and parts of eastern Europe (Southern and Laurie, 1946); in underground pits in France (Vayssiere, 1948); in sand ditches covered by sand and in "shounas", which are little more than fenced yards under the open sky, in Egypt (Attia, 1948); in open-ended bamboo-mat cylinders in China (Mao, 1948); and in many other ways. It is true that the grower absorbs a great deal of the loss inflicted by rodents on farm-stored grain; nevertheless, the impaired quality and the increased cost of the portion that reaches the market are passed on to the cereal processor and thence to the public.

In 1967-69 I found much local grain storage areas in India to be simply piles on the open ground, in open stalls in local markets, in portions of the living quarters, in burlap sacks, etc.; and my co-workers reported similar conditions to be widespread over the world.

On the other hand, I have seen Southeast Asian grain-storage structures that may not have met Western industrial specifications but which admirably suited local needs and cost requirements. Huge clay and dung jars in the Rajasthan Desert of India have stood the test of thousands of years, and so long as they are attended and watch kept for signs of burrowing by rats—which is the case, since they are as much a part of the household as any precious family item—they allow the grain to dry, keep it from rats, and allow the heat from the sun to kill insects.

Similarly, bamboo mat huts and cylinders in Bihar permit the grain to swell and shrink with the severe moisture changes of the area. True, they present almost insurmountable problems in preventing losses to rats, but metal bins present local cultural as well as engineering problems and cannot be introduced willy-nilly simply because the rats are destroying the grain.

Corncribs and similar structures still have a useful function and will be with us for a long time where grain must be air-dried. The losses to rodents and insects in these structures can easily reach 25%—and I have seen it higher.

C. Grain Contamination

Of serious concern in addition to the quantity consumed or lost is that the remainder is contaminated with rodent urine, excreta, hair, and extraneous debris. Southern and Laurie (1946) remarked after watching the threshing of grain held in field ricks, "It is an impressive sight to watch a sack (intended for chaff and dust from the thresher) filling up almost entirely with mouse droppings." An undue proportion of the expense of flour milling must be devoted to screening, washing, scouring, aspirating, and otherwise cleaning grain before it enters the break rolls. Grain-cleaning machinery in use today, even though designed specifically to remove rodent filth, does not do a complete job (Harris et al., 1952; Harris et al., 1953; Nicholson and Harris, 1964). Mouse pellets, being approximately the size of a grain of wheat, are very troublesome. Even at the present writing there is no completely effective process for removing rat pellets from corn or mouse pellets from wheat, but a detailed discussion of this subject is beyond the scope of this chapter. However, the following is a partial summary of the situation: Dry cleaning of corn with rat pellets allows some of the pellets to remain in the cleaned corn (Harris et al., 1953). The same is true for mouse pellets in wheat (Harris et al., 1952). Water flotation with or without wet scouring removes additional pellets, but also smears some pellet debris over the grain so that hairs may be found in milled products. Dry cleaning also may release hairs into the air-discharge system so that the air intake requires effective filtering.

Milling of degerminated corn meal and grits largely removes even traces of pellet fragments and hairs (Harris et al., 1953), and the highly purified flour streams contain less rodent pellet hair fragments than the high-ash streams (Harris et al., 1952).

Rodent urine may penetrate into corn to the extent that it is not entirely removed even by the steeping process of wet milling (Nicholson and Harris, 1964), and readily enters kernels of both wheat and corn at the attachment point.

In other words, commensal rats and mice are responsible for a great amount of the rodent droppings, hairs, and urine found in foodstuffs. In the case of grain, contamination can occur prior to storing if the grain is cut and left lying in fields before threshing; and additional filth can accrue through the use of already contaminated machinery (Dykstra, 1959). Threshed grain taken from corn ricks which were infested by 50 or more house mice had an average number of 11 droppings per pound (Rowe et al., 1961). One mouse can produce 50 or more droppings in a day, and those fairly close in size and shape to small cereal grains are extremely difficult to remove at an economical cost. Contamination of processed foods frequently occurs in mouse-infested food stores and although financial losses cannot be assessed, this contamination can lead either to the outright rejection of food or to its relegation to use as animal feed and, in some situations, to prosecution by public health authorities. The droppings themselves contain hairs, and imported manufactured foods such as biscuits have been condemned in the past by countries with high sanitation standards because they contained fragments of mouse hairs derived from droppings milled with flour (Rowe, 1966).

Besides destroying the fouling stored foodstuffs and crops, rodents are also sometimes responsible for damage to nonedible manufactured goods and buildings. On occasion they enter and nest in electrical conduits and telephone wiring encasements, gnaw at the insulating materials, and put electrical installations out of action. Their presence in such places constitutes a permanent fire hazard (Rowe, 1966).

In spite of the better storage conditions ordinarily available for finished cereal products, rodent contamination, torn sacks, and broken retail packages result in staggering waste from the standpoint of human consumption. Indifference or negligence sometimes contributes to the rodent losses, even in modern mills and warehouses where reasonably effective means of rat and mouse control are available (after Spencer, 1954).

D. Farm and Environmental Considerations

Although this discussion is limited to the problems of grain storage, we can hardly disregard the general rodent problem of the farm (Linduska, 1942) and community (Mayne, 1948), or of the town and city in which the cereal is held. The cost of maintaining rodent-free storage will be in direct ratio to the degree of reinvasion of the premises from the surrounding rodent population reservoir, against which no rodent-proofing is entirely effective.

There are many examples of rat control attempted at a cost well beyond the projected savings on a purely economic basis. That is, health and aesthetics aside, there are many situations where it does not pay to control rats. Moreover, it would certainly be unduly costly to chase down the last breeder and eliminate it. Local villagers in developing countries recognize this and cooperate with the authorities only as long as the authorities furnish the work and materials.

Such may also be the case in urban areas when, since the advent of DDT and other chemical insect controls, rats may be a minor health hazard and do perform a useful function in starting the biodegradation of garbage that otherwise would result in foul-smelling, fly-producing litter. In some Asian cities, rats are a major factor in garbage removal, and the same may be the case in European and American slums and slum-industrial areas. The 1970 Rockefeller Conference

(Rockefeller Foundation, 1970) at long last opened up the possibility that there may be undesirable, or at least unknown, consequences in total elimination of rats.

II. TYPES OF RODENTS

In most of the industrially advanced parts of the world, the major rodent pests of stored grains and cereal products are the two rats and one mouse discussed in the subsequent parts of this section on commensal rodents — that is, rodents living with or literally "eating at the same table" as man. However, wild rats do invade man's food stores, and some discussion of them follows.

A. Wild

Many investigators have reported on the depredations of wild rats on grains and cereals. Parrack (1967) has 641 entries in his bibliography for India, and the Asian-Pacific Interchange (1968) deals with this and related problems. Pingale et al. (1967) report their own work and that of others, describing *Bandicota bengalensis, B. indica, B. gigantea, Leggada nagarum, L. booduga, Golunda ellioti, G. gujarate, Tatera indica, Mus booduga,* and many other wild species associated with rural and urban food storage.

The work of Spillett (1968) is a recent classic on the lesser bandicoot rat in an urban ecology and delineates the shifting population changes from the pressures of aggressive rats adapting to a new environment.

Many "field" rats will invade stored cereal foods, and their prevalence and significance usually are related to warm and underdeveloped cultures where they can readily shift from field to storage conditions. For example, *B. bengalensis* exists wild in Indian fields and the same species is a commensal rat in many cities and villages. Moreover, when living with or near man, the human-related ecology is close to that of *Rattus norvegicus* insofar as types of damage and control are concerned.

Under rural conditions in developing countries or when there is a glut of grain stored on the ground, in open stalls and living quarters, in woven mats or unprotected sacks, the local field rats may become temporary or permanent invaders.

Many species of small rodents cause damage to stored cereal grains on farms. In North America these include deer mice (*Peromyscus*), meadow mice (*Microtus*), wood rats (*Neotoma*), various ground squirrels (including *Citellus, Eutamias,* and *Tamias*), and tree squirrels (*Sciuridae*, in part). Their control is so varied as to require treatment elsewhere than in this chapter. As previously stated, much of the grain held on farms is in very loosely constructed buildings or shelters. It is not unusual for domestic poultry and pigeons, as well as sparrows and other seed-eating small birds, to have access to this grain. While that eaten by poultry cannot be said to constitute a waste of grain, certainly the sanitary condition of the grain over which these birds have fed creates a milling problem. In a similar fashion, the domestic cat, so often used to cope with the rodent problem, is no less objectionable, as it hunts rodents, and also beds and defecates in this same grain (after Spencer, 1954).

B. Commensal

Commensal rodents occur with man almost all over the world. It would be impractical here to identify the hundreds of forms of rats and mice that constitute this group. For example, more than 50 subspecies of roof rats (*Rattus rattus* Linnaeus) have been described in the Central and Southern Pacific area alone. For practical control considerations the commensal rodents can be grouped into three types: burrowing rats, climbing rats, and mice. For purposes of this discussion, commensal rodents are *Rattus norvegicus,* the Norway rat; *R. rattus,* the black rat, roof rat, etc., and *Mus musculus,* the house mouse. The major readily discernible characteristics are shown in Figure 1.

RATS

The Norway rat has grizzled reddish to grayish brown fur on the back and sides. The underparts are tinged gray to yellow-white. Black individuals also occur. In some areas one-quarter of the Norway rats are black. White and white-spotted individuals occasionally occur. The white laboratory rat is the albino form of the Norway rat (Brown, 1960).

Three color phases of the roof rat occur in the U.S., but every degree of intergradation occurs between them. *Rattus rattus rattus,* the black rat, is black to slate-colored on both the back and the belly. *Rattus rattus alexandrinus,* the alexandrine rat, has a tawny back, and a grayish white, but never clear white or lemon-colored, underside. The hairs on the underside are slaty at the base, except occasionally on the throat and chest, where the hairs continue the same color to

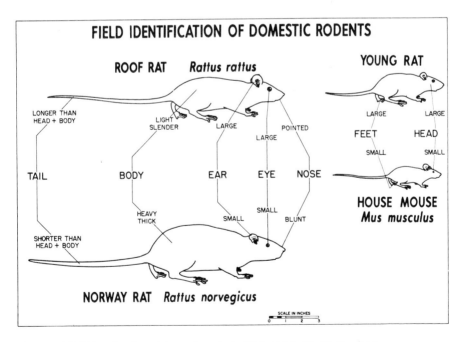

Figure 1. Field identification of domestic rodents. (U.S. Public Health Service.)

the base. *Rattus rattus frugivorus*, the fruit rat or tree rat (sometimes called the white-bellied or yellow-bellied rat), also has a tawny back, but its underside is white or lemon-colored. The hairs on the underside are white or buff-colored to the base. In populations of roof rats, one of these color phases may be more common than the others, depending somewhat on the degree of geographic isolation. However, all three color phases and intergradations among them often occur in single populations (Brown, 1960).

The general color of the house mouse is grayish to brown. Occasionally, black or pale gray individuals occur. The underside may vary from white to dark gray (Brown, 1960).

Rodents of the murine group are most abundant in eastern and southeastern Asia. All evidence indicates that the Norway rat, the roof rat, and the house mouse are native to Asia and have spread from there throughout the world (Brown, 1960).

When one tries to trace the story of the spread of the roof rat through history, the thread is lost along about the 11th century. At that time, however, it was busy over most of Europe. A guess is that it entered Europe via the Mediterranean area during the Crusades. In Europe the roof rat has two distinct color phases: the black rat of Western Europe, and the brown alexandrine rat common around the Mediterranean. When this species was carried to the Americas, however, this situation changed. These introductions into North America began well before 1750, and roof rats were well known throughout French, English, and Spanish colonies. Here the color phases from all parts of Europe were dumped together in the same ports, where they interbred freely. As a result, today in North America all the color phases can crop up in one population. Often a single litter of young roof rats will contain both black and brown animals (Brown, 1960).

Information on the local distribution of roof rats within their geographic range is not too satisfactory. They are less dependent on man than is the Norway rat, except in the most adverse portions of their geographic range. In tropical regions, roof rats frequently live in the forests away from human habitation. They are a common pest of coconut palms where they may live for generations completely out of contact with the ground. In the U.S. they have been trapped in the Everglades National Park at a distance of 7 miles from any human structure. The majority of rural rats in many parts of southeastern U.S. are roof rats. With the propensity of these rats to move into rural or sophisticated storage structures, these population reservoirs are highly significant factors in control.

There is evidence that the Norway rat is a later species which evolved in or near the center of origin of the *Rattus* group. As the more highly developed, more aggressive Norway rat spread outward from Asia, the more primitive roof rat disappeared over much of its original range (after Brown, 1960).

The Norway rat first appeared in Europe in the 1700's. It spread so rapidly that the Europeans called it the "Wanderatte" or migratory rat. Soon after the Norway rat reached Western Europe, it was carried to the New World. Here it quickly began spreading outward from the seaports, especially along the east coast of North America (Brown, 1960).

Throughout much of its range, the Norway rat is closely associated with man and his buildings. This applies even in rural areas where the bulk of the Norway rats live in fields and depend on man's crops. There are persistent reports that, when crops are harvested, these rats shift their activities to farm buildings. This is especially noticeable in the fall of the year, when, with the crop harvest, they will usually leave the fields or become very localized around especially good food sources such as shocked corn. At the time of the new crop year the fields are repopulated by rats and mice from farm buildings, dumps, and other spots with year-round infestations.

With man providing their food, they have been found living and breeding in a 0° F. cold-storage vault.

There are areas within the range of the Norway rat where their numbers are very low. This is especially true in the mountainous and arid regions. In Montana, Norway rats are reportedly found only in the eastern part of the state and in a few central counties; the lack of human habitation and the relatively arid countryside make it difficult for them to spread. Where spreading does occur, it is slow and follows highways or railroads (Tryon, 1947). I have observed comparable situations in India with similar but specifically unidentified rats.

Norway rats can survive quite independently of man, however, as in wet areas and shorelines where the rats depend on those foods that are washed up on the shores or that can be secured from the marine plants and animals.

The present distribution of the Norway and roof rats appears related to two factors: competition between the two species, and the reaction of both to different climates. When the aggressive Norway rat and the roof rat compete for the same areas, the Norway rat becomes dominant, and the roof rat disappears. Only under special conditions do both species live in the same area. In one eastern seaport, roof rats live in the top of a grain elevator and Norway rats live in the bottom. This is probably because roof rats are better climbers than Norways. It is generally only in situations such as these that roof rats are found living in Norway rat territory (Brown, 1960).

As the Norway rat approaches tropical regions, the picture is altered by its reaction to the warmer climate; it appears definitely to be an animal of the temperate climates. In its original range in Asia it is restricted to temperate regions. In the tropics it is found only in seaport areas. On the other hand, the roof rat is common today throughout the tropics. This is true both in its native area and in areas where it has been introduced. In these areas roof rats commonly inhabit regions far removed from man's activities (Brown, 1960).

Warmer climate has slowed, but by no means has stopped, the advance of the Norway rat. In southwestern Georgia from 1946 to 1952 Norway rats overran 1,000 square miles of country where the roof rat previously had been dominant. This was a gradual advance of 20 miles overland in 6 years, in a relatively warm climate. Today, in this area the roof rat has largely disappeared and the Norway rat is dominant (Brown, 1960).

This pattern is complicated by rodent population shifts in warmer areas of the world where aggressive native rats are encountering man and his stored food grains under conditions where the local rats can move, for example, into territory previously held by *R. norvegicus, R. rattus,* or other local rats.

Spillett (1968) has summarized the upswing of *B. bengalensis* at the expense of *R. rattus* and *R. norvegicus* in Bombay and Calcutta. The shifting of populations with changes from rural to urban conditions, in urban human living and food-handling conditions, with the sudden introduction of new species into various

Pacific Islands, has been reported in some detail (for example Wilson, 1968 and Wodzicki, 1968).

The burrowing Norway rat has extended itself via migration and commerce over the globe. It easily adapts itself to all manner of human installations—residences, buildings, livestock and poultry sheds, sewers, and garbage dumps. In the more temperate zones or seasons it has its burrows in the fields and along banks of streams and ditches. It nests in shallow burrows (Pisano and Storer, 1948) or beneath low platforms and floors, in double walls, in long-unmoved stores such as machinery, merchandise, and foodstuffs, but principally at ground-floor levels. In feeding it is omnivorous, accepting meats, fish, cereals, fruits, and vegetables.

Roof rats are typically climbing rats. They are nimble, and can negotiate the rough outer walls of a building, small-diameter perpendicular pipes or pipes of any diameter that are within an inch of a wall, electric wires and telephone cables, vines, and trees. By such means they gain access to buildings in innumerable places (unscreened windows, roof ventilators, unused chimneys, vent pipes, etc.) and, if not crowded to the upper floors by an accompanying infestation of Norway rats, will nest throughout the building (Spencer, 1954).

MICE

House mice (*Mus musculus* Linnaeus) represent the third group of commensal rodents.

It appears that the house mouse first moved from Asia into the Mediterranean area and then into Western Europe. From there man carried it to the New World. Because the house mouse is so small and requires so little food, it has spread much farther than the Norway or roof rats. Today it is found from the tropics to the arctic regions all over the world. In North America it is found throughout the U.S., southern and western Canada, and the Alaskan coastal regions and Aleutian Islands.

The house mouse has the widest distribution of the three murine rodents, and appears to be the least dependent on man over most of this range. In Nova Scotia it has been taken from runways of meadow mice in midwinter. There are reports that in Michigan some house mice leave the fields in late fall, but others remain away from habitations all winter in cultivated and recently abandoned fields. In some areas in the southeastern U.S., house mice are more abundant than any other species of rodents. They have been captured in open tundra in Alaska miles from any human settlement. In and around buildings, of course, house mice occupy a great variety of places (Brown, 1960).

Mice are very small; adults weigh but .5 to .75 oz (15 to 25 g.) and measure 6 to 8 in. in total length, with the tail about equaling the head and body. They are brown in color with pale underparts, and the tail is sparsely haired.

Because of their small size, secretive nature, and ability to live without water for considerable periods, the distribution of house mice throughout the world has been speeded by transport in bales of goods and packages of foodstuffs. Since they climb readily, they infest a building at all levels. Their nests are hollow balls of shredded paper, cloth, or fibrous waste located in dark recesses of the building and in food stocks that are moved infrequently (Spencer, 1954).

Dykstra (1966) reports that from earliest times the house mouse has been regarded as a serious pest. Although in some countries it is considered to be primarily a pest of growing agricultural and garden crops, in the majority it is regarded chiefly as a pest of stored food products and as a potential danger to public health. In regions where field-living house mice thrive, they appear to fluctuate considerably in numbers from year to year, and occasionally populations reach plague proportions. In a heavy outbreak in Australia in 1916-17, large stocks of grain stacked in the open were almost totally destroyed, and poisoned mouse carcasses were estimated by the ton. Localized outbreaks have occurred in several parts of South Australia. House-mouse densities as high as 80,000 per acre were estimated in an eruption in California in 1926, which occurred when conditions (mild winter, abundant food and cover, and few predators) were particularly favorable for population increase. Similar mass outbreaks have been reported in Russia.

Such plagues can cause spectacular losses to growing and stored field crops, but the accumulated losses to foodstuffs, and the incidental destruction and disease attributable to smaller, more widespread commensal house-mouse populations are of far greater importance. Although circumstantial evidence indicates that house mice cause severe economic losses, precise information on actual losses, as with most rodents, is difficult to obtain and is so scanty that accurate assessments cannot be made (Rowe, 1966; see also for detailed summary).

House mice are basically seed and grain feeders, but they will attack an astonishing variety of other foodstuffs, and they thrive in places where there is a diversity of foods. In domestic premises, the losses of foodstuffs can be heavy if house mice are allowed to increase unchecked, but they are mainly more irritating than expensive, and serious depredations are usually the result of poor hygiene and neglect. Unfortunately, in contrast to the rat, many people tolerate the house mouse or are unaware of its existence until it has become well established and has spread to neighboring areas (Rowe, 1966).

The most serious losses to foodstuffs caused by house mice occur in premises storing food in bulk, such as shop stores, bakeries, mills and warehouses in urban areas, animal feed stores, granaries, and corn and hay ricks on farmland. In some of these types of environment, mice are responsible for more damage than are rats. An adult mouse eats only about 3 g. of food per day, equivalent to 70 to 100 whole wheat grains; but direct losses based on this figure, even if the numbers of mice were known, would be minimal and unrealistic. This is because the house mouse is an exceptionally wasteful feeder, and through its habit of discarding partially eaten foods it usually destroys more food than it consumes. Southern and Laurie (1946) found, for example, that over 10% of the grain threshed from heavily infested corn ricks in Britain consisted of nibbled particles which were useless for milling purposes, and that this loss exceeded the calculated amount of grain eaten. Fortunately, changes in agricultural practice have largely eliminated this hitherto important reservoir for house mice on farmland. Other problems have arisen, however, and house mice are, for example, a troublesome pest in present-day broiler and deep-litter poultry houses (Rowe, 1966).

Apart from the food they eat or destroy, house mice are responsible for "invisible" losses. Stacks of bagged grain and flour under long-term storage have been known to collapse as the result of mouse damage, and rebagging costs may exceed the cost of the foodstuffs actually eaten. Much food spillage arises as a result of the search by house mice for nesting material. Well-built mouse nests are substantial affairs from 4 to 6 in. in diameter, and containers made from coarse sacking, cardboard, paper, and cloth are both susceptible to penetration and are frequently used for nesting material. In stocks of bagged flour, mice frequently burrow into the middle of a sack and carry in sacking for a nest (Rowe, 1966).

III. RODENT BIOLOGY IN RODENT CONTROL

A. Life History and Habits

Preventing losses to or contamination of stored food grains depends upon three factors: environmental distribution; the pressures of the population, and migration and transportation into controlled areas; and to the population dynamics and biology. Poisoning and trapping alone are of no avail, and even "rodent-proofing" needs to be designed and maintained within a biological perspective.

The life of the average rat or mouse is fairly short, and the young mature rapidly. The gestation period of the Norway and roof rats is 22 days, and that of the house mouse is 19 days on the average. Female rats and mice can mate within 48 hr. after they have borne young. It is possible, then, for females to be producing young almost continuously. Fortunately for control efforts, several things act to slow this reproduction. Mating is not always successful, or is not even attempted immediately after young are born. Then, too, if a female is nursing young and is also pregnant, birth of the new litter may be delayed as much as a week. The length of this delay depends on the number of nursing young and the size of the unborn litter (Brown, 1960).

Young rats and mice enter this world none too gently, and birth is precarious at best. Large litters are the rule, and some of the newborn may be killed and eaten. Although the female remains quiet, she is very nervous and may be disturbed by intrusions. Disturbance of the nest by other individuals may cause litter destruction either by the mother or by other mice. Often when a rat or mouse nest containing young is disturbed, the mother will move the young to another place. Many litters thus moved probably do not survive. And yet, communal nesting or the use of a single nest by two or more female mice with litters is a frequent occurrence. In any event, although large numbers of young rats and mice may be born, many of them die or are killed before they are weaned (after Brown, 1960).

Those young rats and mice which survive the accidents at birth grow rapidly, although they are virtually helpless. For about 3 weeks the young depend on the mother for food, but begin to take solid food in the middle of the third week. At the end of this period they can live away from the mother if forced to. Mice can actually survive on solid food as soon as the eyes are open at 2 weeks, although they normally do not begin to take such food until a few days later (Enzmann, 1933). In the wild, the mother rat or mouse may feed her litters until they are 4 to 5 weeks old. By this time their activity is essentially adult except for sexual behavior and fighting. These latter activities appear later and at the same time, in rats at 2 to 3 months of age, and in mice when they are about 2 months old (after Brown, 1960).

There are several aspects of rodent biology that relate so closely to control, to their pressures on stored cereals, and to rodent exclusion that they must be emphasized here. In doing so I have followed the excellent U.S. Public Health Service Training Guide by Brown (1960), which itself is a condensation of the voluminous rodent literature.

There are daily patterns of activity among rats and mice. When food is abundant, the rat shows the greatest activity during the first half of the night, becoming most active at or shortly after dusk. This activity continues until about midnight. The house mouse has a similar pattern of nocturnal activity, and in addition has a second lesser activity peak starting well after midnight and lasting until dawn. This may also be true with many rats. Superimposed on this nocturnal activity are short periods of restlessness and activity occurring every few hours throughout the day and night.

The major pattern of nocturnal activity breaks down, however, when the individual is hungry. In Bombay I have seen rats, conditioned to the sound of falling garbage, foraging out into the area between buildings immediately after the "splat" of refuse hitting the pavement from an upper-floor window in full sunlight. What appeared to be *R. norvegicus* or *B. bengalensis* entered food godowns and foraged in small mills in Calcutta in midmorning on a sunny day.

Rats and mice prefer to use regular paths and runways, especially along walls, stacks of material, or other objects that present a vertical plane. They will remain under or behind things as much as they can. If food is in the open they will dart out and back as quickly as possible. The farther away from safe and familiar runways that traps and baits are placed, the less is the likelihood that they will be visited. However, in Bombay food godowns are owned by Jains who, because of religious beliefs, welcome rats. I have seen *R. rattus* moving actively at any time of the day with little fear of being seen or of being close to man. While they were undoubtedly more active at night, the rats had become conditioned to a freer association with man.

Rats and mice often carefully avoid strange objects, even strange food. This "strange-object" reaction is the basis for many beliefs about the "wily" and "intelligent" rat. A trap or a new poison bait is probably first avoided as a new object, not as a lethal device.

Rats may avoid new foods for several days, and when they do begin to take a new food they may take only "token" amounts. If these amounts contain a sublethal dose of a poison that makes a rat sick, the avoidance reaction is strengthened. This is the biologic basis for prebaiting with unpoisoned bait before poison is added.

In environments such as warehouses and garbage dumps where "strange objects" and a variety of foods appear regularly, there may be little or no avoidance reaction, and rats and mice may accept anything edible.

Roof rats and house mice are notoriously good climbers, and the Norway rat can climb very well if it has to — even crossing city streets on telephone wires. Both rats and mice travel via wires, and can climb any vertical surface where they can get toenail holds, including brick and stucco. Vines, and drainpipes where the rat can brace its back, are perfect runways. However, in controlling rats it is important to distinguish between the possible and probable. It is unlikely that rats will scale high concrete walls unless driven by hunger or danger.

Rats can reach 13 in. up a wall. Allowing for a safety factor, the clear distance for rat guards should be 18 in. They can do a standing high jump of almost 2 ft., and with a running start and a bounce, can clear a bit over 3 ft. The house mouse can do a running jump of 2 ft. Out and down, from 25 ft. it can cover 8 ft. horizontally.

All three are good swimmers. They will search for exits (drains) under water and will negotiate toilet traps. Sewer systems may be regular highways.

Rats and mice will nest in any safe spot close to food and water: between double walls, in false ceilings, and in rubbish accumulations. The Norway rat is a good burrower; the roof rat prefers upper reaches of structures. Mice will burrow or not, depending upon the nesting requirements. There are reports of extensive rat tunnels, at times down to 5 or 6 ft., in soft earth or fill. Rats digging down along a wall will keep close to the wall, not moving back to go around an obstruction. If they reach a horizontal lip extending out from the wall they will give up and stop their digging.

Rodents' front or incisor teeth grow throughout life—about 4 to 5 in. per year. They will gnaw almost anything and, as a matter of fact, must do so to prevent being killed by their own teeth.

Rodents will eat almost anything but do have decided preferences. They like meat, grain, grain products, eggs, potatoes; but have less preference for raw beets, peaches, onion, celery, cauliflower, green peppers, and most highly spiced foods. In citrus groves they eat citrus; in open fields, beetles and caterpillars; in households, cockroaches and other insects; in hatcheries, young birds. While there are reports of rats eating manure, repeated checks in India showed no rodent damage to dung cakes stored for fuel. Apparently the poorly fed cattle of this area left little food value in their dung.

Reports on water requirements are conflicting. However, rats need .5 to 1 oz. water per day when eating dry cereals, but mice require very small amounts (3/100 oz. per day), if any.

Rodents have an excellent sense of touch through their face whiskers and longer guard hairs over the body. Vision is not as well developed as is that of humans, and they are color blind. They have a keen sense of smell, recognizing other rats, rats of the opposite sex, part of the "colony", and strange rats. Much needs to be known about repellents and bait attractants. However, fear that they will be warned by odors of man around traps and baits is unwarranted. The odor of man is a close, everyday experience.

Hearing and direction orienting by hearing are excellent.

B. Recognition of Rodent Infestations[1]

Inspections for the presence of rats and mice are an essential part of protecting stored cereals from loss and contamination. Obvious evidence of their presence are sightings of the animals themselves, rodent noises, droppings, runways, tracks, and chewed or gnawed materials. In addition, rat and mouse feces are one of the best indications of infestation. Rat, mouse, and larger cockroach droppings are shown in Figure 2. Norway rat droppings are the largest, ranging up to .75 in. long. Cockroach droppings are roughly hexagonal in cross section.

Fresh droppings are soft enough to be pressed out of shape without crumbling

---

[1]After Brown, 1960.

and often have a glistening, moist appearance. The color varies according to the kind of food eaten, but is usually black or nearly black. Depending on climatic conditions, droppings soon become dry and hard. Later the surface becomes dull; and eventually they assume a grayish, dusty appearance, and may crumble easily when pressed.

The quantity and sizes of fresh droppings found in an area may give an indication of the number of animals present. Fresh droppings mean that at least one rat or mouse is present. Since only rarely are Norway and roof rats found occupying the same area, presence of several sizes of fresh droppings means that several ages of rats are present and that they probably are reproducing. Droppings are most numerous along runways, near harborage, in secluded corners, and near food supplies.

The number of rodent droppings found in any area depends not only on the amount of rodent activity but also on how often floors are swept, how rapidly stored goods are moved, and on the presence of dung-eating insects. The absence of droppings may not always mean absence of rodents, for droppings are present irregularly in infestations. Sometimes they are abundant; sometimes scarce. On the other hand, the presence of old droppings, even in quantity, does not mean that the area currently is infested.

Since rats and mice generally occupy only a limited area, they may use the same pathway many times. Out of doors or on earthen floors these runways may appear as clean-swept, well-packed earth paths 2 to 3 in. wide. In dusty areas, runways may consist of tracks made in dust by passing rats or mice (Figure 3). Occasionally even the line of a dragged tail may be seen. In many areas rats and

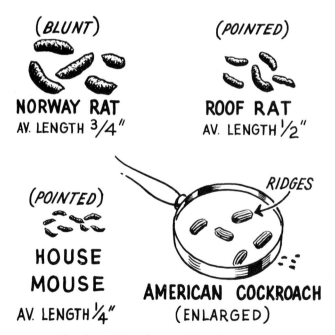

Figure 2. Rat, mouse, and cockroach droppings. (U.S. Public Health Service.)

Figure 3. Rat tracks. (U.S. Public Health Service.)

mice leave dark smears or rub marks when rubbing against objects, from natural oils and dirt on their bodies.

Outdoors, runways can be found in dense vegetation such as lawn grass, and even on bare earth. However, the location of runways usually reflects the rodent's generally secretive habits. Most often they are found along walls, under boards, behind stored objects and accumulated litter, and in similar places.

Rat and mouse runs in or on buildings are often marked by more or less extensive rub marks. These may be found around gnawed holes (Figure 4), along pipes and beams, on the edges of stairs, along walls, or anywhere else that the rodent is likely to travel. Swing marks made by rats passing under floor joists along a beam generally indicate the presence of roof rats. Norway rat runs are more often near the floor. House-mouse runs may be anywhere, and are difficult to locate because they are small and often very faint. It is especially important to search behind vertical pipes near walls for evidence of rub marks. Small vertical pipes and columns are a favorite means by which rats and mice travel from one floor to another.

Tracks may be found anywhere along rat and mouse runs, both out- and indoors. Tracks are more clearly seen by side illumination from a flashlight than by direct light from above. Especially good places to find tracks are in dust in little-used rooms and in mud around outdoor puddles. Rat tracks are fairly large. The hind foot of a walking Norway rat may leave a print 1.5 in. long. Roof rat prints are about the same size. Mouse footprints are rarely even .5 in. long, and are much closer together than those of rats.

A helpful procedure for tracking is the use of a fine dust. Any fine powder like pyrophyllite or flour may be dusted on a suspected runway and inspected later for footprints. The powder should be spread smoothly to a depth of no more than 1/8 in.

By tracing rat and mouse runs, the harborage, the food and water supply, and the means of entry into buildings may be revealed. This information will greatly facilitate control measures.

Figure 4. Gnawed and greasy rat hole (arrow). (U.S. Public Health Service.)

Recent gnawings through wood, cardboard containers, etc., can be distinguished by the fresh, light-colored appearance of the gnawed surface and the presence of small chewed pieces or cuttings in the vicinity. The edges of the gnawed area become darkened in a few days, and small cuttings are soon scattered or swept away. Another method of determining the age of gnawed openings is by noticing the sharpness of the bitten edges. A freshly gnawed opening has sharp edges which scratch the animals as they pass through. They will stop and nibble at the offending edge, so that, as the openings become older, they acquire well-rounded edges.

Norway rats prefer to live in the ground. Their burrows are easy to recognize and relatively easy to find. They occur along the outside walls of buildings, around outbuildings, and in dirt basements. Away from buildings, burrows can be found in embankments, hedgerows, and under heavy growths of brush and bushes. When burrows are found in the absence of Norway rats, they may have been made by roof rats, although this is not a common habit of the latter. House mice living in and around buildings seldom burrow; however, those living in fields or near farm buildings very commonly do. Their holes are much smaller than those of rats, averaging about a 1 in. diameter (rat holes average around 3 in. in diameter).

Often the age of rat and mouse burrows may be determined by how worn they appear. Holes in current use are free of dust and cobwebs and may have a slick, beaten-down appearance. Fresh earth pushed out of the entrance in a fan-shaped pattern also indicates recent use.

Burrow systems generally are shallow and often complex. Several holes may lead to the same system, some of them partially hidden by debris. It is necessary, therefore, that a careful search for all holes be made before such measures as burrow gassing are attempted.

Urine stains and hairs may occasionally be encountered during infestation surveys. Urine stains are often used by government inspectors and professional food plant hygienists as evidence of the presence of rodents, and, used with care, they are reliable indices. On some materials such as cardboard, paper, and some sacking they show clearly; but in other cases they are revealed only by their fluorescence under ultraviolet light. However, materials other than rodent urine which are often found around stored cereals will fluoresce. Certain floor treatments fluoresce, as do oils used to lubricate bag stitching.

The microscopic identification of rodent hairs is beyond the scope of this discussion (Harris et al., 1960).

The mousy or ratty odor sometimes associated with mice or rats requires experience and a careful judgment to identify with certainty.

C. Summary of Rodent Habits and Introduction to Control[2]

Rats and mice are secretive and wary. Although they may be seen feeding at almost any hour of the day, the high point of their activity is at night, especially during the first few hours after dusk. In addition to using darkness as a cover, both rats and mice avoid open spaces and have their runways along walls and behind and under obstacles; they also keep as close to some place of refuge as possible. Food occupying an exposed position is removed piecemeal to a protected site before being eaten. Even within their accustomed haunts, any disturbance such as an unusual sound, change of lighting, or presence nearby of man or animals will cause temporary cessation of rodent activity. The passing of a train, or the wind rattling the sheet-iron roof of the shed, will cause rats to stop their feeding visits to a pile of grain.

Within a grain elevator or mill where little change is made from day to day in the structure, arrangement of machinery and stores, and the conduct of operations, Norway rats tend to form regular habits of travel, of feeding, and of food selected, in marked contrast to rats occupying a city waste dump. Habit, combined with natural wariness, causes a temporary avoidance of anything new, whether it be a trap, permanent bait station, or harmless obstacle placed in the rats' regular runway.

Even the introduction of food may be a change to be avoided, and changes in the food—such as from wheat to bread—will immediately reduce consumption temporarily.

Rats and mice require three conditions to maintain their populations in connection with storage of grain: secluded shelter, adequate food, and a minimum of competition. Rat-free premises can be attained by attacking the problem from any one of the three approaches; but a combination is usually more practical.

From a long-range viewpoint, construction of rodent-proof storages and buildings is the most inexpensive type of rodent control. In fact, rodent-proofing is a very necessary feature of any new grain-storage structure designed to deliver

---

[2] After Spencer, 1954.

products to producers or consumers with a minimum loss in quantity and quality. Obviously, rodent-proofing is an essential part of the general sanitation program. The process of cleaning grains that have become contaminated with filth (hair, urine, and feces of domestic pets, rodents, and birds) is so costly, and so exacting are U.S. government regulations with respect to the marketing of contaminated consumer products, that the industry is seriously engaged in basic food sanitation, including rodent control.

Low-cost construction with local building materials, such as is characteristic of many farm grain storages, need not sacrifice rodent-proofing. As vulnerable a storage as a corncrib can be made rodent-proof with proper attention to such features as wire mesh hardware cloth, eave design, off-ground clearance, and rat shields.

D. Ecology of Rodent Control

There is no simple, foolproof panacea for rodent control in grain storage. It has been demonstrated time and again that the intelligent use of simple techniques plus painstaking attention to detail is more successful than blindly following dicta or massive wars against rats.

Whatever is attempted needs to be attempted within the parameters established by the biology of the rodents involved, their general and specific habits, the dynamics of rodent population changes, and from the standpoint of their three basic needs: Shelter, food and water, and a minimum of competition.

Of first importance is a knowledge of the kinds of rodents on given premises. Information as to size will give an index of the mesh that must be employed in rodent-proof screens; familiarity with the climbing or burrowing habits will indicate the thoroughness with which the building will have to be made rodent-proof; and data on food habits will point to the baits that will be most acceptable in control operations. Consideration of the feeding range of an individual species is of primary importance in the placement of baits and traps.

RODENT MOVEMENTS

A colony of house mice may exist in the cluttered corner of a room or in the interior of a pile of sacked grain or flour without leaving a sign of activity a yard away. Southern and Laurie (1946) report that house mice living under "domestic" conditions occupy an area averaging only 50 sq. ft. In stacks of unthreshed grain they found mice occupying a similar area within the stack, but with little vertical movement within the stack. When poisoned baits were placed shoulder high completely about the perimeter of the stack, dead mice were confined largely to this level when the stack was examined at threshing. The Norway rat has a much wider range but again is no great traveler. Davis et al. (1948) live-trapped, marked, and released 1,112 Norway rats in the city of Baltimore and on an adjacent farm (Davis, 1948). Of the marked rats recovered, approximately 80% were caught within 40 ft. of the original sites. Their movements, however, depend a great deal on the character of their habitat. Long trails may connect suitable harborage with a source of food supply. Petri and Todd (1923), in studying the home range of *Rattus rattus* in Egypt, reported a restricted range, but H. J. Spencer (1954) suggests that roof rats in southeastern U.S. may range throughout a city block if harborage and food are thus separated.

The reluctance of commensal rodents to cross open spaces is another trait that limits and modifies their feeding range. Even in artificially supersaturated populations, Norway rats seldom left the city block in which they were released (Calhoun, 1948). Depending upon population pressures, city streets may be reasonably effective deterrents to movements of the Norway rat. The roof rats, making use of electric overhead cables and similar travel lanes, are not so limited by open spaces (Spencer, 1954). Thus, reinfestation of an elevator or mill located in a city is most likely to result from rats harboring in the immediate vicinity, in the company yards, or in neighboring premises; and attention should be directed toward maintaining this buffer area (Spencer, 1954).

POPULATION DYNAMICS[3]

Background. All over the world the existence of rats and mice living on man's stored foods attests to the success that rodents have had in mankind's war on rats. Nowhere has the battle been won by either side. Wherever rats are competing with man for his stored cereals, man is killing them; but a distinction needs to be made between killing rats and controlling them.

A single pair of Norway rats and their progeny can produce more than 1,500 rats in a year. This is a theoretical possibility, given outside support and assistance. It is quite obvious that this does not happen in nature. To accomplish this feat, man would have to provide food and water, disperse the offspring to new habitats at an optimum rate, provide harborages, control the temperature and humidity, keep competition down, and prevent predation and disease. The rats alone cannot do all this for themselves and the natural environment will not do this for them.

To put the situation in another light, rodent populations stop growing because of factors controlling their growth. Chief among these are food and water. Rats living in an alley and dependent upon garbage dropped there by humans will increase in numbers up to the limit that the garbage will support; surplus animals above this number will starve, be eaten by stronger competitors, or be forced to move away.

Factors other than food may limit the population. Predators may keep skimming off the rats. In this case there would be some more food for the survivors, and breeding would accelerate and the basic number would be maintained. Humans may act as predators by poisoning or trapping rats, but this would not change the number in the area unless drastic steps were taken through a massive campaign, but even then migration from adjacent areas into the alley would keep the supply somewhat constant.

Even a grain storage area with plentiful food has limiting factors. These may be water, disease, the number that man will tolerate, and overcrowding. Perhaps the human activity and constantly shifting environment will control the number of rats by denying safe harborages and subjecting the rats to more stress than they can accommodate to.

In his now classic work, Davis (1948, 1949) showed that each area has an ability to support a certain number of rodents. This capacity is related to food, harborage, living space, and other necessities of life. The number of rats will

---

[3]After Brown, 1960.

increase until this capacity is reached, and then the increase will slow down and level off (also Brown, 1953; Young et al. 1950). Poisoning will reduce the numbers of rats only temporarily, because the ability of the environment to support the population remains unchanged.

With this quick look at population dynamics, what are the responsible factors? Davis (1950) points out that these are reproduction, mortality, and movements. Reproduction is a plus. Mortality and movements are minuses.

Reproduction is highly variable. Depending on the human cropping and other patterns there may be two rat breeding peaks; one peak; or no peaks, with uniform breeding all year. In general, breeding is at a minimum during the coldest and during the hottest parts of the year. Knowledge of rodent breeding thus focuses attention on control via breaking into the reproductive cycle at its weakest part, when reproduction is naturally low. Poisoning at the high points will harvest more rats but poisoning at the low points will reduce the population more.

The actual reproduction rate usually is lower than the reproduction potential. The oestrus cycle, the number of embryos that actually mature and are born, and survival of the weanlings are influenced by many environmental factors including, for example, food availability.

Mortality rates are also highly variable and, like reproduction, respond to outside forces to limit population size in response to the ability of the environment to support the population. Although healthy, well-fed, and relatively unpressured Norway rats can live for 2 years, few do so, and most succumb much sooner. Davis (1948) found that only about 5% of the rats on a Maryland (U.S.A.) farm lived 1 year. In another study Davis (1953) showed that, from birth on, for every rat alive at the end of a year over 16 had died. He estimated the average life of a wild Norway rat after weaning to be about 6 months. I saw, and had reported to me verbally, catastrophic fluctuations in obvious rat signs (burrows and field-crop damage) in India that probably indicated fluctuations in population sizes that reduced the rats to small residual carry-over numbers between periods of food availability.

Movements appear to be less a factor in determining population densities than reproduction and mortality. Rats and mice, like many other wild animals, usually spend their lives in a very limited area, and only when pushed by necessity will they move any great distance. The size of the home range depends on the nearness of necessities of life. A rat living under an open garbage can near a leaky faucet has all it needs right there.

A rat is safest in its home range, where it knows the location of food, water, and safe harborages. Pushed out by local pressures, it is at the mercy of predators and, of course, it immediately encounters other rats who are in their own home territory. A nightly municipal rat-killing program in Bombay, India, that returned about 4,000 rats per 24 hr. was probably simply skimming off the outcasts and strays that would have ordinarily died anyhow without the intervention of man. The following are some observations on the sizes of home ranges.

The range of Norway rats in Baltimore (U.S.A.) seldom exceeded 100 to 150 ft., and that of roof rats living in open areas in Hawaii seldom exceeded 200 ft. (Spencer and Davis, 1950).

Brown (1953) found that over 97% of house mice in and around a barn moved less than 50 ft.; over 79% moved no more than 30 ft.

Young et al. (1950) found that in buildings in Wisconsin (U.S.A.) 90% moved no more than 30 ft., and 70% moved no more than 10 ft.

This does not mean that some individuals will not go great distances. Some rats regularly move hundreds of feet between food and harborage. Brown (1960) and King (1950) recorded a house mouse with a home range of 113 ft.

Rats will migrate from flooded fields, and their movement between buildings and fields in the spring and fall is well known. Marked rats have been captured miles from the point of release. Rats and mice regularly relocate as passengers with man and his goods via land, sea, and air, and rat and mouse populations continually push on their peripheries like molecules of gasses distributing themselves in the available space.

This is a basic problem in controlling rodents by killing them. A trapping or poisoning program in one block of a city, in one food storage warehouse, in one farm barn will keep killing rats that spread into the "vacuum" created by the control program. Poisoning rats in local village stores will give only temporary relief if the rats are allowed to move in from the surrounding areas. The humans eventually lose interest in the killing program and within a month or so after it stops the rat menace is right back where it was before "control" began. Therefore: RODENT CONTROL NEEDS TO BE BASED ON SOUND ECOLOGICAL PRINCIPLES THAT WILL, IN EFFECT, LIMIT POPULATIONS BY LIMITING THE AVAILABILITY OF THE NECESSITIES OF LIFE *and* BY EXCLUDING THEM FROM STORED FOODS BY BUILDING THEM OUT AND BY POISONING AND TRAPPING THOSE WITHIN.

Brown (1960) divided the limiting factors in population size as follows:

PHYSICAL ENVIRONMENT

Food and water. The chief sources of rodent food in urban areas are stored products and garbage. In rural areas crops are important and there may be movement between crops in the field to farm, village, and town food stores.

Flat storage warehouses are particularly vulnerable, as are retail stores, and especially small local outlets in developing countries. Food in small stores and homes is particularly subject to house mice.

Garbage is a chief reservoir of rodent populations that spread to storage areas.

Harborage presents no problem to the rats and mice if they are tolerated in buildings used by man. An important item is alternate harborages that can serve as reservoirs for reinfestation.

Climate is a factor for commensal rats living wild. In food-storage areas there is a year-round situation often unrelated to seasonal changes. As noted earlier, rodents will survive subfreezing temperatures if suitable food and harborage are available.

BIOLOGICAL ENVIRONMENT

Predation. Many animals prey on rats and mice. The most conspicuous of these is man, using traps, poisons, gas, and other tools. Other predators include cats, dogs, foxes, mongooses, ferrets, hawks, owls, and snakes.

Much of the information on predation suggests that the intensity of predation depends on the density of the rodent population, not the rodent population on the predators. For example, the higher the rat population, the more will be killed by cats. When the population is low the predators turn to other foods — or themselves are reduced in number — and the rat population increases again.

Jackson (1951) concluded that in residential areas cats had no effect on the number of Norway rats and that the cats killed rats that would die anyway to maintain a stationary population. However, Davis (1957) found that farm cats killed enough rats to prevent the expected upsurge of rats in the spring.

Cats and dogs often do more apparent than real service in controlling rats and mice, since they keep the rodents out of sight, where pets cannot reach them. Cats and dogs do assist in limiting the spread of rodents into the pets' home ranges. This is related to the dangers inherent in occupying a strange area known to the pet but where the rodent has not yet established safe runways, hiding places, etc. Thus, a cat would be useful in slowing reinfestation in rural grain stores freed from rats by other means.

Predation by hawks and owls is highly variable, as is any control by predation. The predator and prey are locked in a food relationship, with the predator as dependent on the prey as the prey is on escaping the predator. Suffice to say here that although predators may make serious inroads on rodents in the field, they cannot be relied on to control rodents in stored cereal grains and their products — *and this includes cats.*

Parasites and disease will not be discussed here except to say that in spite of sporadic and recurring optimistic reports, rodent diseases have never been successfully used to control rats or mice. Moreover, the diseases thus far used to control rats are closely related to diseases of man, and their use — even for field trials — requires very careful consideration.

COMPETITION

This is a complicated bio-social problem intimately affecting animal populations including rodents and will be only briefly mentioned here (Barnett, 1955; Brown, 1953; Calhoun, 1950; Christian and Davis, 1956; Davis, 1949; Southwick, 1955; Southwick, 1955a; Ulrich, 1938; Venables and Leslie, 1942).

Norway rats will replace roof rats. The lesser bandicoot rat is enlarging its range at the expense of the Norway rat in Bombay, Calcutta, etc. (Spillett, 1968). Norway rats separate by layers in grain stacks, with rats above and mice below.

Intraspecific social ranks are established by fighting, and social rank affects reproduction, longevity, and range, including access to nearby food. Much research is currently underway on this general subject.

THE BASIC ECOLOGICAL PRINCIPLE IN RODENT CONTROL, THEN, IS TO DENY RODENTS ACCESS TO FOOD — either refuse or stored food grains. This, and control by killing with poison baits and trapping, fumigants, repellants, etc., will be discussed in the final section.

IV. CONTROL MEASURES AGAINST RATS AND MICE

A. Sanitation

Cleaning away food and trash refuse, to deny rodents food and harborages, is the essence of rodent control. Without it control is virtually impossible unless a massive effort is maintained in the most skilled hands. Even in modern concrete and metal grain-storage facilities outside rats will seek entrance. From time to time rodents will slip in through unnoticed openings, through untended or badly fitting doors, or with grain or food shipments. A clean warehouse or plant is the best guarantee that the rodents or their signs will be noticed before they have multiplied and spread and have contaminated too much food. In a clean, orderly storage area it is relatively simple to maintain a continuous control program or to undertake complete eradication.

No matter what techniques are used in grain-storage rodent control, it is essential that good housekeeping be practiced within a building to limit places where rodents can nest, and as far as possible to keep food from their reach. New rodent-proof structures must be carefully maintained. This phase receives too little attention, with the result that the substantial expenditures on original construction are often wasted. In a busy mill, alterations, machinery placements and repairs, plumbing, and electric wiring changes are being made, and often involve breaking the outside protective "armor." Loading doors and windows are often broken, screens and metal ventilators become rusted and weakened, storm and other weather damage occurs, all of which should receive prompt attention and repair.

In the larger commercial establishments it is suggested that regular monthly itemized inspections be made by designated employees for the purpose of locating and repairing rodent and insect entries. Likewise, old structures benefit by inexpensive and partial rodent-proofing. For farm corncribs to the large terminal elevator and warehouse, instructions are available governing patch-repair. Weights of sheet metal that will withstand rodent gnawing, gage and mesh size of wire screen that prevents rats or mouse entry, formulas for cement, directions for construction of "curtain walls," designs for constructing guards on pipes, electric wiring, flues, and ventilators, and plans for flanging doors and windows are all readily available. These simple measures will more than pay for the cost of their installation in preventing rodent damage and contamination (Anon., 1947; Silver et al., 1942; Spencer, 1954; Storer and Mann, 1948).

Good housekeeping is equally essential whether the structure is rodent-proof or not. Orderliness is a boon to storage operations and at the same time contributes materially to rodent infestation control. Dead storage areas that contain broken or old machinery and parts that "might sometimes be useful" are excellent nesting refuges for rodents, as are jumbled accumulations of discontinued stock items, cartons, and other containers. All rooms within the building should be policed to reveal storage of any items that are rarely moved and which thus form rodent harborage. The program should include the elimination or correction of sealed-off areas such as double walls, enclosed platforms and stairways, and other boxed-in shaftways and machinery to which rodents have access for nesting. Attics should be free of litter and easily accessible to regular inspection and control. Basements and substructure areas that have dirt floors in which rats burrow should either be sealed off by concrete curtain walls or covered with concrete. By these means the building becomes less habitable for rodents that *require* seclusion (Spencer, 1954).

The sanitation program needs to be carried out on a scheduled basis. The cleaning in cereal grain storage will involve dusting and sweeping, and should thoroughly cover the facility to encounter any rodent pellets, trails, tracks, small openings with or without "grease stains", and chewings. Thus, regular sanitation policing should include sanitation inspections. If any signs are encountered they should be brought to the attention of responsible management.

Trash and refuse should never be allowed to accumulate inside or in the immediate periphery of the plant. Refuse gathering and storage facilities should have sufficient capacity to contain all accumulations between collections.

Rats and mice will even establish themselves in large concrete terminal elevators, and they too need to have a rodent inspection program. However, as a general rule rodent infestations of cereal grains and products are usually confined to farm, village, country storage, and flat-type warehouse storage. The essence of rodent control in this and any food storage is to build the rats and mice out.

B. Rodent-Proofing

GENERAL PRINCIPLES OF RAT-PROOFING

Each separate structure presents its individual problem, but there are two general principles that apply in all cases and that should be kept in mind when the rat-proofing of any building is being considered. First, the exterior of those parts of the structure accessible to rats, including porches or other appurtenances, must be constructed of materials resistant to the gnawing of rats, and all openings must be either permanently closed or protected with doors, gratings, or screens; second, the interior of the building must provide no dead spaces, such as double walls, spaces between ceilings and floors, staircases, and boxed-in piping, or any other places where a rat might find safe harborage (Silver et al., 1942).

RAT-PROOFING IN RURAL AREAS

The cost of rat-proofing many American farms would amount to less than the loss occasioned by rats on the same farms during a single year. In no other place is rat-proofing more badly needed or less often accomplished than on farms and in rural storage. This is especially true in less developed countries.

A rodent-proof farm is not necessarily one in which the entire farmstead is absolutely proofed, but rather one where conditions are so unfavorable for any invading rodents that they either will desert the premises of their own accord or may be easily routed. The source of the trouble on almost any heavily rodent-infested farm can be traced directly to conditions that furnish safe refuges near abundant food. The commoner of these breeding places are beneath wooden floors set a few inches off the ground in poultry houses, barns, stables, granaries, corncribs, and even residences; in piles of fuel wood, lumber, and refuse; in straw, hay, and manure piles that remain undisturbed; beneath concrete floors; and inside double walls. In rat-proofing a farm or village, attention should be paid to premises outside of the actual grain-storage areas (Silver et al., 1942).

Rural storage needs to be constructed of rodent-impervious materials such as concrete or sheet metal.

In general purpose areas where grain is stored, halfway measures dealing with harborage control, concrete floors, metal sheathing, etc., are seldom successful, and grain should be kept in rodent-proof bins. However, corncribs and similar structures used to store damp grain need special attention, and rat-proofing can be accomplished in several ways.

Probably the simplest way to accomplish rat-proofing and aeration is to cover all ventilation walls with woven wire mesh, with two or three strands per in. Mouse-proofing can be accomplished by the use of sheet metal barriers around the legs or part way up the sides to prevent mice from climbing in.

Except for unusual local conditions, rodent-proofing farm or household granaries requires concrete or metal. There are primitive mud and mat structures in lesser developed areas that are maintained rodent-free, or nearly so, but they require more time-consuming attention than most people in industrial countries are willing to devote to the task.

Even concrete, steel, or aluminum in rural areas require soundly designed plans and solid construction to prevent cracks from inadequate footings, sagging or bulging walls, or similar defects. The failure of many such structures to keep out rodents has been caused more by poor construction than by inadequate design or materials.

RODENT-PROOFING URBAN STRUCTURES[4]

Rodent-proofing in cities, as well as towns and farms, requires detailed attention to the exterior and surroundings. If the locality is heavily infested with rats, some are almost certain sooner or later to find their way into the building, however well protected against them it may be. Accumulations of trash usually contain waste food and are certain to attract rodents and furnish an ideal breeding place for them. Rat harbors, such as wooden floors and sidewalks very near the ground, should be removed or replaced with concrete, and piles of lumber and various materials stored out of doors should be removed or elevated 18 or more inches. Particular care should be taken to see that sheds and other outbuildings, porches, steps, loading platforms, and similar structures on the premises are made rat-proof, either by the use of concrete, by elevation, or by keeping them open to the light and easily accessible.

In old buildings, a thorough inspection should be made of the building itself and note taken of alterations and repairs necessary for a thorough job of rat-proofing. Inspection should begin in the basement. Doors and windows should fit snugly, particularly doors leading to outside stairs or elevators, and these should also be provided with automatic closing devices. Windows and ventilators should be screened or covered with gratings, the openings not more than half an inch square for rats, one-fourth inch for mice. Defects in basement floors should be repaired with concrete, and floor drains should be fitted with tight covers.

Sidewalls should be carefully inspected; and all openings made for plumbing, electric-wire conduits, areas around windows and doors, and unpointed joints in masonry walls (frequently left when the exterior of the wall is hidden from public view by porches or platforms) should be carefully closed with cement mortar.

All openings between floors and in partitions made for the passage of pipes and wires, and any defects in the wall, should be closed with metal flashing. All dead spaces throughout the building, such as boxed-in plumbing, spaces behind

[4]From Silver et al., 1942.

or beneath built-in cabinets, counters, shelving, bins, and many similar places, should be removed, opened up, or effectively and permanently proofed against rats.

The roof rat is an expert climber and frequently enters buildings by way of the roof. Where this occurs, similar care must be taken with the upper floors and roofs of buildings. Doors at the top of stairs and elevators should fit snugly, and all ventilators, exhaust fans, unused chimney flues, and other openings should be screened. Broken skylights and openings under eaves and places where electric wires enter the building should be repaired or closed.

Old warehouses are particularly difficult to rodent-proof because of their location, construction, the high traffic into the building, and the stored foods. It is essential that the building itself have a concrete or masonry foundation, concrete floors, and especially constructed, tight-fitting metal doors. The doors are particularly vulnerable. They are frequently jammed or bent and should be carefully watched for defects and immediately repaired.

Because of their high traffic flow, warehouses will become rodent-infested and require permanent bait stations, traps, and regular inspections for rodent signs.

Most modern reinforced-concrete grain-storage facilities are about as rodent-proof as practical construction will allow, and the following is simply a listing of salient points to be used as a check list (Scott and Borom, 1965).

1. Sloppy construction cannot be tolerated. Sheet metal must be smooth, even, and neatly finished, as should be the surfaces of concrete or other building materials.

2. Concrete foundations and lower building walls need to be of a good mixture, solidly poured, and without cracks.

3. Curtain walls may be used to protect otherwise vulnerable foundations (Figure 5). Curtain walls are not needed if the foundation rests on rock or hard pan.

4. A concrete floor is more effective than deep foundations or a curtain wall.

5. Metal structures require adequate solid concrete foundations.

6. Openings for pipes, wires, etc., require permanent seals — usually metal, treated plastic shields, or concrete.

7. Ventilator screens should have no holes over .25 in. in diameter for mouse and rat stoppage. Such screens or expanded metal require inspection at regular intervals.

8. Remember that windows and doors used by man are subject to damage and require frequent inspections. Some damage is unavoidable, and employees need to be encouraged to report damage to doors, door jambs, windows, screens, and other entry ways. (See Anon., 1947; Holsedorf, 1937; Scott and Borom, 1965; Silver et al., 1942.)

9. Low ground-level vents require particular attention.

10. All drains should be covered with heavy metal covers with slits or holes not over .5 in.

11. The roof should be examined if there is any possibility that rats can gain access to it. Especial attention should be given to screening in ventilators and vent pipes and to flashings along parapet walls.

12. Many types of pipe and wire guards are figured in Denny (1937); Holsedorf (1937); Mallis (1964); and Scott and Borom (1965).

In spite of all precautions, some few rats and mice will get into grain-storage areas and it will be necessary to control them. While rodent control by means of poison baits, traps, and fumigants is a never-ending, uphill battle in the total environment, in a well-constructed grain elevator, warehouse, or individual metal bin, the rodents inside the structure are walled off from escaping and from rapid replenishment from outside sources, and killing is an effective way to control them.

C. Rodent Control Through Poisoning

Although the entire chapter is a summary of volumes on the subject, as a practical matter control through poisoning especially needs to be taken into account in these two final sections on rodent-stoppage, when the reader seeks specific and immediate practical methodology. Attention is directed to the references at the end of this chapter, and especially to Bjornson and Wright (undated); Brown (1960); Chitty and Southern (1954); and Mallis (1964).

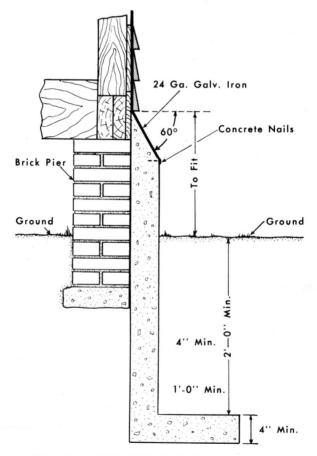

Figure 5. Curtain-wall installation. (U.S. Public Health Service.)

Rodent-poisoning campaigns to control rats and mice in grain stores cannot be relied on alone except in the most expert and persistent hands. This discussion assumes that we are dealing with infestation in a well-constructed and well-maintained facility.

POISON BAITS

There is a decided lack of unanimity in recommendations on poisons or bait formulations. Opinions vary widely even on such basic questions as whether the bait material should be different from or similar to the foods generally available in the storage area. Spencer (1954) states that it is wise to select for baits foods not available among the stocks to which the rodent has access. Johnson and Bjornson (1964) state that frequently the foods rats eat most often are best accepted in poison baits, but then exceptions are noted.

Opinions also vary on the poison itself, whether to use a single-feeding dosage or the multiple-feeding anticoagulants, and which of several kinds of each. Indeed, different situations and different factors are often involved. In a well-controlled private warehouse a more active or "dangerous" poison could be called for that might not be acceptable in a village market where some poisoned grain could find its way into food. Moreover, there is no question but that the priceless ingredient of a poison bait is the expertness of the user.

Liquid baits have proven effective in controlling rat infestations because in grain storage the normal sources of water for rodents are either limited or wholly absent. Aqueous solutions or suspensions of certain poisons are well accepted. The addition of not more than 10% of sugar to the water sometimes improves acceptance. Milk and tomato puree are two other liquids successfully employed (Spencer, 1954).

Bait is selected on considerations other than palatability. With solid foods, moist baits are generally better accepted than dry. But moist baits and liquids such as milk and tomato puree spoil rapidly in warm weather. If a more permanent type of food bait is required for use in protected stations, a cereal-base bait with sugar and an animal or vegetable fat is suggested (Barnett and Spencer, 1953). Another consideration is the possible contamination of stored grains and cereal products by poisoned baits exposed for rodent control. To prevent a rat from removing poisoned bait from an otherwise safe placement, the bait should be finely pulverized so that no large pieces can be dragged off to other parts of the building. In this regard, liquid baits are especially safe, as they must be ingested where placed. Finally, there is the technical problem of choosing the bait to fit the poison, as the two must be chemically compatible for purposes of toxicity and absorption (Spencer, 1954).

RODENTICIDE SELECTION

The species of rodent to be controlled will often dictate the poison that must be used. This is an extremely important consideration, for stored grain is often beset not with one but with several species of rodents. Arsenic, phosphorus, thallium, and sodium fluoroacetate and the anticoagulants are the only ones that will control a mixed rodent infestation of Norway rats, roof rats, and house mice with any degree of success. Red squill, ANTU, and barium carbonate are poor mouse poisons, and strychnine is a very poor rat poison. ANTU is roughly 50 times more toxic to Norway rats than to roof rats, and thus has limited usefulness (Spencer, 1954).

In the early modern era of rodent control, red squill was commonly used. Thallium sulfate, arsenic, and phosphorus — all violent poisons — were used for special problems. Strychnine was used for the nibbling house mouse. And fumigation was common in the U.S.

Prior to World War II zinc phosphide came into general use when red squill, strychnine, and thallium sulfate supplies were limited.

Sodium monofluoroacetate (compound 1080) was developed during the war and, aside from a bad reputation gained through inexpert use, this extremely toxic, non-antidote poison is still an excellent rodent poison. Its use is now restricted to qualified trained personnel (Spencer, 1944; Ward and Spencer, 1947).

Warfarin, the first of the anticoagulant poisons, began its triumphant march into rodent-control history in 1950. Among other anticoagulants are Pival, Fumarin, PMP, diphacinone, Rodafarin (India). The anticoagulants require 5 or more days of repetitive feeding to bring about death by internal hemorrhages in rats. This makes it costly in time, in poison, and, in underdeveloped countries, in the bait base. When competing with other foods it has severe disadvantages in a solid bait; but like 1080, it may be used in water.

I have found zinc phosphide the poison of choice in many parts of India. It produces a quick and dramatic early kill, but leaves a significant proportion of the rodents unpoisoned.

For general information on rodent poisons, note especially Bjornson and Wright, undated, and Johnson and Bjornson, 1964.

A limited number of specific references to rodent poisons are given below:

Anticoagulants:	Crabtree, 1950; Hayes and Gaines, 1950; Heal, 1954; Link et al., 1956; Mollaret, 1957; Overman et al., 1944.
ANTU (Norway rats only):	Richter, 1945.
1080:	Dykstra, 1950; Kalmbach, 1945; Pollitzer, 1954.
Fluoroacetamide:	Bentley et al., 1961; Brooks, 1963.
Zinc phosphide:	Pollitzer, 1954; Pingale, Pingale et al., 1967.

Two methods are used to expose poison bait for rodent control. One involves the thorough coverage of the premises with small pieces, or teaspoonfuls, of baits containing a poison that will kill in a single feeding. The residual bait, following 24 hr. of rodent feeding, is usually collected and destroyed. The second method is the long-term exposure of large quantities of bait in some type of covered container. Such placements are semipermanent and are serviced and refilled at regular intervals. Very few poisons can be used both ways. For example, rodents may develop a tolerance to certain rodenticides following nibbling or cautious feeding. Mice that survive their first contact with strychnine and have it available for repeated slow feeding may consume large quantities without harmful effect. A tolerance is also acquired toward ANTU, but more often avoidance is the chief factor in continued survival. Such tolerances are temporary and once the feeding on those poisons ceases it is usually lost within a month. These poisons are therefore unsuited for permanent bait stations. The same is true of red squill and zinc phosphide, which have such a distinct taste or odor that they are shunned after a first feeding. Even sodium fluoroacetate, which has relatively little taste and is extremely toxic in small quantities, is often avoided following a sub-lethal feeding. Thallium sulfate has possibilities both in single exposures and in permanent stations, but even it is far better in the former category (after Spencer, 1954).

It is practical to expose very toxic poisons in permanent bait stations constructed to prevent accidental access by man or domestic animals. However, there is the additional problem of access of the poisoned animal — still containing an excess of the lethal agent — to cats, dogs, pigs, and other animals. Sodium fluoroacetate (1080) is almost 50 times as toxic to dogs as to rats, so that a dog eating one 1080-poisoned rat could receive a fatal dose of the poison (Spencer, 1944; Ward and Spencer, 1947). Thallium and arsenic also possess the possibility of secondary poisoning.

Zinc phosphide largely decomposes in the rodent and has little secondary hazard, as phosphorus compounds are unstable and tend to lose their poisonous properties. Red squill and the anticoagulants also have virtually no secondary hazard.

Coloring the bait is sometimes used as a warning to humans but is of varying effectiveness in discouraging birds and other animals.

Liquid baits have been used in the U.S. to control rats, and reached a high popularity with the introduction of sodium fluoroacetate. Water may be had without cost, the solutions are simple to prepare, and the efficiency of rat control thereby compares favorably with that of any food bait prepared with a similar rodenticide. Sodium arsenite, thallium sulfate, and sodium fluoroacetate (listed in order of increasing effectiveness), and the new anticoagulants Warfarin and Pival are the poisons so used. Sodium fluoroacetate at 12 g. to 1 gal. of water is the most toxic, and, largely because so little of the poison solution need be taken, is a very effective control agent. Liquid Warfarin baits have proven effective but solutions of the sodium salt tend to mold, with subsequent loss in acceptance (after Spencer, 1954).

With water, no cautious "new food" reaction is evoked; thus water-based poisons may be very effectively used in grain elevators and warehouses. However, the use of any poison, even the anticoagulants, in a food establishment needs to be carefully controlled.

Poisonous tracking dusts have been successfully used. They eliminate the need for the rodent to eat a poisoned carrier. When well placed along runways, in double walls, etc., the rodents pick up the poison on their feet, fur, and tails and inadvertently swallow the poison during normal grooming. Finely powdered DDT and ANTU in talc have been used. However, many workers now feel that the wholesale dusting with rodenticides is to be discouraged.

The carrier is as important as the poison itself. I have seen moldy, out-of-condition, and low grade mill offal used for rat control in Bombay, India, that was not competing well as a bait with the naturally available foods. Preferred baits in the U.S. are generally formulated around whole coarse-ground yellow corn meal (Johnson and Bjornson, 1964; Communicable Disease Center, 1964). Rolled oats is often used in England, and in the U.S. it is mixed into the corn meal.

There are many formulas involving sugar, edible oils, and other taste adjuncts. Typical formulas are: 1) 1 part Warfarin, Pival, Fumarin, etc., to 19 parts corn meal; 2) 1 part Warfarin, etc., to 12 parts corn meal, 5 parts rolled oats, 1 part sugar, 1 part vegetable oil.

A good rule of thumb regarding the taste of bait is that if man will accept the material rats and mice will also. The experience of some workers is that rats prefer clean, sound baits to moldy or otherwise decomposed materials.

Thorough mixing of the bait and poison is necessary. When large quantities are to be repeatedly prepared, a mechanical mixer is essential and mixing by electric or other power is usually required. A warning color, or charcoal, should be added during mixing.

The use of oil can induce rancidity; sugars can ferment; many baits readily mold; and for some wet, hot areas, especially prepared and mixed baits are called for.

For maximum kill, an adequate number of bait stations must be well placed in runways, near burrows and gnawed holes, where there are rat droppings, and other signs of infestation. Place baits as close as possible to runs and harborage. Remember that rats and mice stay close to home.

PLACEMENT OF SINGLE DOSE POISON BAITS[5]

Wrap "one-shot" poison food baits in 4 in. × 4 in. paper squares to form "torpedoes" about the size of a candy kiss. One pound of bait will make about 80 to 90 such "torpedoes." These may be tossed readily into otherwise inaccessible places. Rats prefer to carry their food to their harborage to eat it.

Use poisoned water only where other animals cannot get to it. Use containers that will not spill, such as glass casters or low metal cups. Chicken founts are satisfactory for permanent stations. Water baits are most effective where other sources of water are limited or can be eliminated, as in the case of feed mills or granaries. Normal sources of water *must* be eliminated to assure successful results.

Be generous with baits. Rodents have a limited "home range", usually less than 150 ft. for rats and 30 ft. for mice. Too few baits, poorly placed, may miss many rats. Bait liberally where signs of rat activity are numerous and recent. In light or moderate infestations "torpedoes" containing a single dose of poison have given good control when applied at a minimum rate of 40 per small business establishment. As many as 100 to 200 such baits may be required for premises with heavy rodent infestations. Place baits in hidden places out of the reach of children and pets. Inspect and rebait as needed, using another poison and bait material when the rats become shy of the original baits.

Pre-baiting for several nights with unpoisoned bait is useful, particularly for "bait-shy" rats. However, it is costly for large-scale use and meets resistance in food-short developing countries. Pre-baiting increases acceptance, indicates preferred baits, and shows how many baits are needed and where.

---

[5]After Bjornson and Wright, undated.

PLACEMENT OF ANTICOAGULANT BAITS[6]

Anticoagulants are not "one-shot" poisons. They require a different method of use from other rodenticides. Bait mixtures are frequently placed in paper plates or permanent bait stations, the number of plates or bait stations varying with the infestation. Small plates will hold one-quarter to one-half lb., whereas many permanent bait stations hold over a pound of bait mixture. Be liberal in baiting. Anticoagulant bait mixtures are usually exposed for a minimum of 2 weeks, but where reinfestation is likely, a few may be maintained permanently. *Repeated doses must be consumed by the rodent for a period of 5 or more consecutive days to kill.* Therefore:

1. Protect other animals, and shield baits from the weather by bait boxes, boards, pipes, cans, or other devices.

2. Note locations of all bait containers so that inspections can be made rapidly and the consumed bait replaced. A numbered sequence of stations is desirable. Bait consumption is generally heavy right after initial placement, making daily inspection and replacement advisable for the first 3 days after regular feeding begins.

3. Smooth baits at each inspection so that new signs of feeding will show readily.

4. Replace moldy, wet, caked, or insect-infested baits with fresh ones.

5. If successive inspections show the bait undisturbed, move it to an area showing fresh rodent signs.

Use shallow bait containers fastened to floor surfaces, or of sufficient weight to prevent the rodents from overturning or dragging them to their burrows. A nail through the container into the floor reduces spillage. (See Figure 6.)

D. Fumigation

Fumigation is an excellent means of eliminating rodents and insects quickly in a sealed building, a hold of a ship, a boxcar, grain elevator, or sealed bin, but the use of some fumigants is extremely dangerous and even the less hazardous ones should be used only by trained workers. The fumigants most commonly used are hydrogen cyanide (Amer. Cyanamid Co., 1951), methyl bromide (Dow Chem. Co., 1957; Mallis, 1964), and during the last 6 years aluminum phosphide preparations that generate phosphine gas. Aluminum phosphide in stabilized pellets is known as Phostoxin in the western countries. A similar product in India is called Celphos (Excell Industries, Bombay, India).

All of these fumigants are probably better known for their insect-control uses. However, the advent of aluminum phosphide in a stabilized form has made available a fumigant that is easily transported, useful in large or small areas, relatively safe to use, and easily applied. It has direct application in treating burrows along foundations, etc. (Pingale et al., 1967; and personal observations). In some parts of the world aluminum phosphide preparations are rapidly replacing calcium cyanide dust for burrow fumigation (see references above, and personal observations). Tarpaulin fumigation using Phostoxin for insects (Cogburn and Telton, 1963) will also kill all contained rodents.

---

[6]After Bjornson and Wright, undated.

Figure 6. Permanent bait stations. (U.S. Public Health Service.)

E. Trapping[7]

Traps have a definite place in rodent-control activities. Their use is indicated: 1) to kill rats where the use of poisoned baits would be too dangerous, 2) to avoid dead-rat odor, 3) to eliminate bait-shy rats, and 4) when live rats are needed for research or survey needs. However, traps are costly in time and money to purchase and use, and their use requires expert knowledge and experience.

The most commonly used traps are the snap trap and the steel (animal) trap. Snap traps, sometimes called wood traps or breakback traps, have a flat wooden or metal base, and they kill by means of a heavy wire, actuated by a coil spring released by a trigger. These are the most common traps in use by the general public. The size is approximately 3.5×7 in. for rats and 2×4 in. for mice. No bait is needed when the trigger is expanded and the trap placed directly in a rat runway.

Steel traps, with a platform trigger and two steel jaws which are snapped together by means of a single flat spring, are used unbaited. Steel traps with approximately 3.5-in. jaws are effective for rats, but usually most of the rats caught will be taken alive when traps are collected the morning following the night of their capture.

Cage or box-type traps are sometimes used for trapping rats or mice, but have not been efficient in control programs.

---

[7]After Johnson and Bjornson, 1964.

Usually the catch in any type of trap will be best the first night, provided the traps are carefully placed. Therefore, it is important to set out a sufficient number. A second reason for setting many traps is that with average settings and infestations, usually no more than 10 to 20% of the traps may be expected to catch rats in a single night. If a trapper catches a rat in each trap the first night, it is an indication that he did not put out enough traps. When traps remain empty at the same location for a week or more, it may be erroneously concluded that no more rats are present. Because rats quickly become "trap-shy" or "trap-wise", trap location should be changed frequently. In using baited traps, the bait also may be changed. Traps require servicing at least daily. It is best to set them late in the afternoon so they will not be disturbed accidentally by workers.

Trapping requires considerable time in the setting and daily servicing of traps if good catches are expected. Rats, and especially mice, often trigger traps without being caught. Therefore, traps need attention every working day. One worker cannot adequately attend more than 200 traps. Morgan and co-workers (1943) found it possible, by setting numerous traps, to reduce even large rat infestations to proportions manageable by subsequent poisoning operations.

Traps should be cleaned as necessary to ensure efficient operation. If the base becomes split, the trigger bent, the spring weakened, or the trigger release rusted, the traps should be repaired or replaced. A trap that rocks in its setting will generally not catch rodents, and warped traps are unserviceable. Many persons believe that the eradicator must wear gloves when handling traps to avoid leaving human odors, but these odors do not deter rats that live in close association with and are accustomed to the odor of man. It is also unnecessary to wash, boil, sterilize, or smoke the traps to remove the odor of previously caught rats (Storer, 1952).

SNAP TRAPS

Snap traps usually kill rats caught in them. Occasionally a trap will be sprung and a dead rat will be found nearby, having been hit in the head by the wire jaw. All traps should be set on hair-trigger, so they will be activated by a slight touch. The trigger at set position should be nearly parallel to the base of the trap. Snap traps may be used baited or unbaited.

Baited snap traps. A solid bait about the size of the end of the index finger is fastened securely to the trigger. Baits may be of any food attractive to rats. The baited traps should be placed in or very near rat runs. Traps near a wall or other vertical surface should be placed at right angles to the wall, with the trigger end toward the wall. Thus, a rat running along the wall from either direction will discover the bait on the trigger readily. Camouflaging traps by sprinkling dust, straw, or other suitable material over all except the bait is desirable, but care should be taken to prevent interference with trigger or spring action. On earth floors, the base of the trap may be worked down into the soil until the top is flush with the ground level, for increased effectiveness. Sufficient clearance for the trap to spring should always be provided. Baited traps may be fastened so that a rat caught by the tail or foot cannot drag them away; however, this rarely happens.

Perishable baits should be replaced at least every third day. Permanent-type bait or a bait containing a preservative may be exposed longer. Rancid or moldy material usually will not tempt a rat. It is desirable to change bait materials every

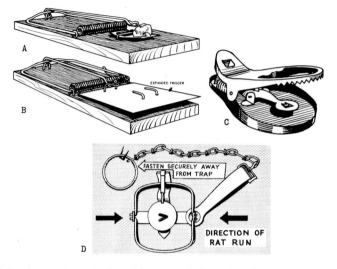

Figure 7. Rat and mouse traps. A, Baited snap trap. B, Expanded platform snap trap. C, Steel jaw trap. D, Steel animal trap.

few days, switching to an entirely different type (for example, from meat to fish or grain). If a bait is eaten from the trigger without springing the trap, usually the setting is improper or the trap defective. Rat baits sometimes are eaten by mice or insects without triggering the trap.

Mice can be readily controlled with small baited wooden snap traps (see Figure 7). The wire jaw of a rat trap frequently passes over a mouse, leaving it uninjured. Mice do not seem to become trap-wise as readily as rats. They are also more inquisitive, nibbling small bits of food here and there, and feeding frequently. Use many traps if mice are abundant. Place them along walls, with trigger end against the baseboard, at 2- to 3-ft. intervals, near all their harborage holds, or around stacks of food materials. Good baits for mice are bacon, peanut butter, candy (chocolate and gum drops), fresh bread, cake, doughnuts, apples, rolled oats, cheese, or sweet potatoes. Singe cheese or bacon to increase appetizing odor. The trigger setting should be delicate for maximum results (Bjornson, 1961).

Unbaited snap traps. Snap traps may be used unbaited if the bait pan is enlarged to provide a platform on which rats may step to release the trigger (Figure 7B). It can be enlarged by fastening a 1.5 in. square of fly screen or cardboard securely to the trap trigger or bait retainer. Fly screen may be soldered to the trigger or cardboard may be wired in place. Traps so modified are termed expanded trigger traps, and the *expanded portion must be placed directly in rat runs since there is no bait to lure rats.* Boards, boxes, or other obstructions should be placed beside or immediately behind such traps to guide rats into them. To place unbaited traps effectively requires a good knowledge of rat habits; the trapper must know exactly where the rats are traveling in order to catch them. Camouflaging may help to catch any experienced rats after the first few days of trapping.

Expanded trigger traps are placed in rat runs, corners, at burrows and hole openings, and in other locations where rats are traveling. For roof rats and mice, particularly, they may be placed on shelves, tops of fixtures, beams, pipes, and other overhead runways. Wood traps can be suspended either horizontally or vertically on the beam, with the trigger in the rodent's normal path.

OTHER TRAPS AND DEVICES

Other techniques have been employed in rodent control. Electric traps; barrel traps, for enticing rodents into situations where they will drown; filling burrows with water; flame throwers for burrow control; glue boards; shooting; and clubbing have all been tried with greater or less degrees of success—mostly less.

The ferret and mongoose have turned into pests as serious as the rodents they were to eliminate (Spencer, 1950; Pollitzer, 1954). Cats and dogs have been mentioned in the discussion of rodent biology.

So-called "rat-virus" reports have invariably turned out to be a reworking of tests using food-borne bacteria which are as dangerous to man as to rodents and are to be avoided. As yet no disease specific to rats and mice has been discovered.

Several repellents have been suggested and used, again with greater or less degrees of success. The U.S. Department of the Interior Predator and Rodent Control Group, Denver, Colo., has a repellent evaluation program underway. Odor repellents need to be both volatile and persistent — a difficult requirement to satisfy.

Ultrasonic devices are of limited usefulness, although successful in making rats wary or causing them to avoid an area for a few days. The animals become used to the presence of the new sound and soon ignore it.

In essence, rodent control in grain storage areas requires sound construction, to build rodents out; maintenance of the premises in a sanitary manner; and such poisoning or trapping as may be required to keep the inevitable invaders from establishing themselves and multiplying.

LITERATURE CITED

AMERICAN CYANAMID Co. 1951. *Fumigation Manual*. 30 Rockefeller Plaza, New York.

ANONYMOUS. 1947. Detailed diagrams illustrating rodent proof repairs. U.S. Pub. Health Serv.: Atlanta, Ga.

ASIAN-PACIFIC INTERCHANGE. 1968. Rodents as factors in disease and economic loss. Proc., East-West Center, Honolulu, Hawaii.

ATTIA, R. 1948. p.105-109. Typical methods of handling and storing grain in Egypt. In: *Preservation of Grain in Storage*. FAO/UN Agr. Studies No. 2.

BARNETT, S. A. 1951. Damage to wheat by enclosed population of *R. norvegicus*. J. Hyg. 49(1): 22-25.

BARNETT, S. A. 1955. Competition among wild rats. Nature 175: 126-127.

BARNETT, S. A., and SPENCER, M. M. 1953. Experiments on the food preferences of wild rats. J. Hyg. 51: 16-35.

BENTLEY, E. W., et al. 1961. Sodium fluoroacetate and fluoroacetamide as direct poisons for control of rats in sewers. J. Hyg. 59: 135-149.

BJORNSON, B. F. 1961. House mouse, public health importance, biology and control. U.S. Pub. Health Serv., Communicable Disease Center, Atlanta, Ga.

BJORNSON, B. F., and WRIGHT, C. V. (undated). Control of domestic rats and mice. U.S. Dept. H.E.W., Pub. Health Serv. Training Guide.

BROOKS, J. E. 1963. Fluoroacetamide. Calif. Vector Views. 10(1): 1-3.

BROWN, R. Z. 1953. Social behavior, reproduction, and population changes in the house mouse. Ecol. Monog. 23: 217-240.

BROWN, R. Z. 1960. Biological factors in rodent control. U.S. Dept. H.E.W., Pub. Health Serv. Training Guide.

CALHOUN, J. B. 1948. Mortality and movements of brown rats (*R. norvegicus*) in artifically supersaturated populations. J. Wildl. Manage. 12: 167-172.

CALHOUN, J. B. 1950. The study of wild animals under controlled conditions. Ann. N.Y. Acad. Sci. 51: 1113-1122.

CHITTY, D., and SOUTHERN, H. N. 1954. *Control of Rats and Mice.* Oxford Univ. Press: London. 3 vol.

CHRISTIAN, J. J., and DAVIS, D. E. 1956. The relationship between adrenal weight and population status in urban Norway rats. J. Mammal. 37: 475-486.

COGBURN, R. R., and TILTON, E. W. 1963. Studies of phosphine as a fumigant for sacked rice under gas-tight tarpaulins. J. Econ. Entomol. 56: 706-708.

COMMUNICABLE DISEASE CENTER. 1964. Report on public health pesticides. Pest Contr. 32: 11-32.

CRABTREE, D. G. 1950. Raticidal potentialities of WARF-42. Soap Sanit. Chem. 26: 131-137.

DAVIS, D. E. 1948. The survival of wild brown rats on a Maryland farm. Ecology 29: 437-448.

DAVIS, D. E. 1949. The role of intraspecific competition in game management. Trans. N. Amer. Wildlife Conf. 15: 225-231.

DAVIS, D. E. 1950. The mechanics of rat populations. Trans. N. Amer. Wildlife Conf. 15: 461-466.

DAVIS, D. E. 1953. The characteristics of rat populations. Quart. Rev. Biol. 28: 373-401.

DAVIS, D. E. 1957. The use of food as a buffer in predator-prey systems. J. Mammal. 38: 466-472.

DAVIS, D. E., et al. 1948. Studies on home range in the brown rat. J. Mammal. 29: 207-225.

DENNY, O. E. 1937. Some experiments with rats and rat guards. Pub. Health Rep. 52: 723-726.

DOW CHEMICAL CO. 1957. Fumigating buildings with methyl bromide. Midland, Mich.

DYKSTRA, W. W. 1950. As reported in Pest Control 18(3): 14.

DYKSTRA, W. W. 1959. Food contamination by rodents and birds. Cereal Sci. Today 4(10): 303-304.

DYKSTRA, W. W. 1966. The economic importance of commensal rodents. In: *WHO Vector Control Seminar on Rodents and Rodent Ectoparasites.*

DYKSTRA, W. W. 1968. The economic importance of rodents. In: *Rodents as Factors in Disease and Economic Loss.* Asian-Pacific Interchange, East-West Center, Honolulu, Hawaii.

ENZMANN, E. V. 1933. Milk production curve of albino mice. Anat. Rec. 56: 345-358.

EXCELL INDUSTRIES (undated). Celphos. Excell Industries, Jogeshwari, Bombay, India.

GARG, D. N., and AGRAWAL, H. S. 1963. Rats and mice in U.P. and their control. Kanpur Agr. Coll. J. 23(1): 9-15.

HALL, E. R. 1927. An outbreak of house mice in California. Univ. of Calif. Pub. Zool. 30: 189-203.

HARRIS, K. L., et al. 1952. An investigation of insect and rodent contamination of wheat and wheat flour. J. Ass. Offic. Agr. Chem. 35(1): 115-158.

HARRIS, K. L., et al. 1953. An investigation of rodent and insect contamination of corn and corn meal. J. Ass. Offic. Agr. Chem. 36(4): 1011-1037.

HARRIS, K. L., et al. 1960. Microscopic analytical methods in food and drug control. U.S. Food and Drug Adm. Tech. Bull. No. 1.

HAYES, W. J., Jr., and GAINES, T. B. 1950. Control of Norway rats with residual rodenticide Warfarin. Pub. Health Rep. 65: 1537-1555.

HEAL, R. E. 1954. Which rodenticide is best? Pest Contr. 22(7): 26-54.

HOLSEDORF, B. E. 1937. The rat and ratproof construction of new buildings. Pub. Health Rep. Supp. No. 131.

JACKSON, W. B. 1951. Food habits of Baltimore, Maryland cats in relation to rat populations. J. Mammal. 32: 458-461.

JOHNSON, W. H., and BJORNSON, B. F. 1964. Rodent eradication and poisoning programs. U.S. Dept. H.E.W., Pub. Health Serv. Training Guide.

KALMBACH, E. R. 1945. Ten-eighty, a war-produced rodenticide. Science 102: 232-233.

KING, O. M. 1950. An ecological study of the Norway rat and the house mouse in a city block in Lawrence, Kansas. Trans. Kans. Acad. Sci. 53: 500-528.

LAURIE, E. M. O. 1946. The reproduction of

house mice. Proc. Roy. Soc. Biol. No. 872.

LINDUSKA, J. P. 1942. Winter rodent population in field-shocked corn. J. Wildl. Manage. 6: 353-362.

LING, L. 1961. Man loses a fifth of the crops he grows. Atlantis 1-68, special issue for FAO, Freedom from Hunger.

LINK, K. P., et al. 1956. Anticoagulants—are recommended dosages for Norway rats too high? Pest Contr. 24(8): 22-24.

MADSEN, C. R. 1966. Of rice and rats. U.S. Bur. Sport Fish. Rept.

MALLIS, A. 1964. *Handbook of Pest Control.* McNair-Dorland: New York.

MAO, Y. T. 1948. Methods of grain storage in China. p. 123-125. In: *Preservation of Grain in Storage.* FAO/UN Agr. Studies No. 2.

MAYNE, R. 1948. The specific conditions found in farm storage of grain in Belgium and means used in reducing storage losses from insects and rodents. In: *Preservation of Grain in Storage.* FAO/UN Agr. Studies.

MILLS, E. M. 1953. Rats — let's rid of them. U.S. Bur. Sport Fish. Circ. No. 22.

MOLLARET, L. 1957. The use of anticoagulants in the deratization of war ships. Rev. Hyg. Med. Soc. (Paris) 5: 396-403 (in French).

MORGAN, M. T., et al. 1943. Med. Officer 70: 37, 45.

NICHOLSON, J. F., and HARRIS, K. L. 1964. Removal of urea from corn by the steeping process of wet corn milling. J. Ass. Offic. Agr. Chem. 47(4): 734-737.

OVERMAN, R. S., et al. 1944. Studies on the hemmorhagic sweet corn disease. XIII. J. Biol. Chem. 153: 5-24.

PARPIA, H. A. B. (undated). Food losses in India. Mimeograph. Personally received in 1967.

PARRACK, D. W. 1967. A bibliography of rodent literature with emphasis on India. Johns Hopkins Center for Medical Res. and Training, Calcutta.

PERTI, S. L., et al. 1971. Proceedings and Recommendations of International Symposium on Bionomics and Control of Rodents. Sci. and Tech. Soc., Kanpur-4, India.

PETRI, G. F., and TODD, R. E. 1923. Observations in Upper Egypt on the range of house rodents, *Rattus rattus* and *Acomys cahirinus*. Cairo Pub. Health Labs., Rep. and Notes 5: 14-18.

PINGALE, S. V., et al. 1967. *Rats*. Foodgrain Technol. Res. Ass. of India. Hapur, India.

PISANO, R. G., and STORER, T. I. 1948. Burrows and feeding of the Norway rat. J. Mammal. 29: 374-378.

POLLITZER, R. 1954. *Plague.* WHO Monograph Series No. 22. WHO, Geneva, Switzerland. 698 pp.

RICHTER, C. P. 1945. The development and use of alphanaphthylthiourea as a rat poison. J. Amer. Med. Ass. 129: 927-931.

ROBINSON, W. B. 1965. The Hawaiian rat problem. U.S. Bur. Sport Fish. Rept.

ROCKEFELLER FOUNDATION. March 1970. Bellagio, Italy, Conference on the control of rodents. Rockefeller Foundation, New York.

ROWE, F. P. 1966. Economic importance of the house mouse. In: WHO Vector Control Seminar on Rodents and Rodent Ectoparasites.

ROWE, F. P., et al. 1961. The poison-baiting of corn ricks with particular reference to the control of house mice. Ann. Appl. Biol. 49: 571-577.

SCOTT, H. G., and BOROM, M. 1965. Rodent-borne disease control through rodent stoppage. U.S. Dep. H.E.W., Pub. Health Serv.

SILVER, J. 1941. The house rat. U.S. Wildlife Circ. No. 6.

SILVER, J., et al. 1942. Rat-proofing buildings and premises. U.S. Fish and Wildl. Serv. Conserv. Bull. 19.

SINHA, S. S. P., and RAM, S. K. 1963. Rats and their control. Bihar Agr. Coll. Mag. 13(1): 44-49.

SOUTHERN, H. N., and LAURIE, E. M. O. 1946. The house mouse in corn ricks. J. Anim. Ecol. 15: 134-149.

SOUTHWICK, C. H. 1955. The population dynamics of confined house mice. Ecology 36: 212-225.

SOUTHWICK, C. H. 1955a. Regulatory mechanisms of house-mouse populations. Ecology 36: 627-634.

SPENCER, D. A. 1954. Chapter VI in *Storage of Cereal Grains and Their Products.* Amer. Ass. Cereal Chem.: St. Paul, Minn.

SPENCER, H. J. 1944. Compound 1080, sodium fluoroacetate, its efficiency as a raticide. Nat. Res. Council, Insect Control Rep. 162. mimeo.

SPENCER, H. J. 1950. Mongoose control research report. U.S. Fish and Wildl. Serv.

SPENCER, H. J. 1954. Personal correspondence reported in Spencer, 1954

SPENCER, H. J., and DAVIS, D. E. 1950. Movements and survivals of rats in Hawaii. J. Mammal. 31: 154-157.

SPILLETT, J. J. 1968. The ecology of the lesser bandicoot rat in Calcutta. Johns Hopkins Univ. Thesis. Baltimore, Md.

STORER, T. I. 1952. Controlling rats and mice. Calif. Agr. Exp. Sta. Circ. 410. University of California, Berkeley.

STORER, T. I., and MANN, M. P. 1948. Bibliography of Rodent Control and Bibliography of ANTU. U.S. Pub. Health Serv. Rep. No. 1.

TOWNES, H., and MORALES, J. 1953. Control of field rats in the Philippines. Plant Ind. Dig. 16(12): 3-12.

TRYON, C. A. 1947. Entrance and migration of the Norway rat into Montana. J. Mammal. 18: 188-189.

ULRICH, J. 1938. The social hierarchy in albino mice. J. Comp. Psychol. 25: 373-413.

VAYSSIERE, P. 1948. p. 79-83. Specific conditions in France. In: *Preservation of Grain in Storage*. FAO/UN Agr. Studies No. 2.

VENABLES, L. S. V., and LESLIE, P. H. 1942. The rat and mouse populations of corn ricks. J. Anim. Ecol. 11: 44-68.

WARD, J. C., and SPENCER, D. A. 1947. Notes on the pharmacology of sodium fluoroacetate. J. Amer. Pharm. Ass. 36: 59-62.

WILSON, E. J. 1968. In: *Rodents as Factors in Disease and Economic Loss*. Asian-Pacific Interchange, East-West Center, Honolulu, Hawaii.

WODZICKI, K. 1968. In: *Rodents as Factors in Disease and Economic Loss*. Asian-Pacific Interchange, East-West Center, Honolulu, Hawaii.

WORLD HEALTH ORGANIZATION. 1966. Seminar on rodents and rodent ectoparasites. WHO Vector Control, 66-217, Geneva, Switzerland.

WORLD HEALTH ORGANIZATION. 1967. Meet the rat. WHO, Geneva, Switzerland.

YOUNG, H., et al. 1950. Localization of activity in two indoor populations of house mice. J. Mammal. 31: 403-410.

CHAPTER 8

WHOLE GRAIN STORAGE

J. E. B A I L E Y

Cargill, Inc.
Cargill Building, Minneapolis, Minnesota

I. GENERAL CONSIDERATIONS

A. Functions and Definitions

A safe storage place must be provided for the greater part of the grain produced until it is needed for consumption, since grain production is seasonal, and consumption is continuous.

A whole kernel of grain is a fruit containing a seed able to withstand remarkably well the ravages of weather through a complete cycle of seasons, and to finally sprout and grow when conditions are right. It is not especially well suited for, bulk storage, however, and the food it carries for the new plant is attractive to such predators as molds, insects, and rodents from which man must protect it if he is to save it for his own use.

Storage facilities take many forms, ranging from piles of unprotected grain on the ground, underground pits or containers, piles of bagged grain, to storage bins of many sizes, shapes, and types of construction. Major classifications are farm storage, bin sites, country elevators, and terminal elevators.

Nearly all storage of grain off the farm that produced it is in specially constructed facilities called grain elevators. They are so called because grain is elevated, usually in buckets attached to a belt, and poured into storage bins. Also, grain is removed from storage by again elevating it and pouring it by gravity into transport equipment, such as trucks, railroad cars, barges, or other vessels.

In addition to storage, elevators provide facilities for sorting, cleaning, sizing, drying, and fumigation of grain. They serve the marketing system by equating supply with demand, by providing convenient means for transferring title by endorsement of warehouse receipts, and by transferring grain from one transportation facility to another such as from trucks to cars, cars to barges, and barges to ocean vessels.

B. Conditions of Safe Storage

Safe storage must maintain grain quality and quantity. This means protecting

333

it from weather, molds and other microorganisms, from addition of moisture, destructively high temperatures, insects, rodents and birds, from objectionable odors and contamination, and unauthorized distribution.

C. Quality Measurement

Quality measurements are necessary for marketing so that buyer and seller may agree on value without samples of each lot of grain in hand, and for the processor to obtain the desired quality. They are also necessary to determine possible quality losses during storage.

Quality measurements need to be fast and simple, because of large grain volumes handled at elevators and the large number of units to be tested. They need to measure useful characteristics, but should not require expensive equipment or highly skilled personnel.

The governments of the U.S. and Canada have standardized these measurements to systems of numerical grades and grading factors considered most useful to marketing and processing. Professional inspectors, employed or licensed by government, are trained in taking these measurements and certifying grades. (See U.S. Grain Standards, Publication of USDA).

II. KINDS OF STORAGE FACILITIES

A. On the Ground

Grain is piled on the ground unprotected only between harvest and the availability of transport equipment with which it can be moved to a safer place. Losses are small for short periods because a smooth-surface pile of grain sheds rain down its slopes quite well, permitting it to penetrate only an inch or two. But with time, depressions develop in the surface allowing rain to soak downward and destroy columns of grain. The floor of the pile absorbs moisture from the ground, and surface water creeps under the edges of the pile. The grain is exposed to rodents, birds, insects, and wind so that losses become severe within a few weeks.

B. Underground

Underground storage was probably the principal method used to accumulate surpluses in primitive societies, and it can still be found in our time. (See Chapter 10.) Its advantages are the grain's protection from seasonal and daily temperature fluctuations, inhibition of insects and molds by a tendency toward low oxygen and high carbon dioxide contents in the interseed air, and simple construction methods. Its principal drawback is the high cost of grain handling.

C. Bagged

Bags of grain may be piled under any convenient shelter away from weather and predators. Bags can be transported and handled without special equipment. But both bags and bag storage space become expensive, particularly where manpower costs are high.

D. Farm Bins

Farm storage space is needed for three reasons: to hold the crop immediately after harvest, until it can be moved to better storage space, or to market; the producer can decide to delay marketing his grain; he can hold it for later consumption on his own farm.

Farm storage may consist of any available space that will hold grain and keep out rain or snow, ranging from small wooden enclosures in the barn, through small round steel bins with capacities of from 1,000 to 3,000 bushels (25 to 80 metric tons), to silo-type or quonset hut bins of larger capacities.

The predominant type of farm storage in the past has been the corn (maize) crib. Formerly, all maize was harvested unshelled as ear corn. Maize ripens while moisture content is still above 30%, and in the northern half of the U.S., moisture does not fall to safe storage levels before winter. If shelled and stored at those high moisture levels, maize would soon spoil. However, picked unshelled, stored on the cob, and exposed to continuous circulation of outside air, moisture content falls slowly to safe levels, and little or no quality loss occurs. The crib can be constructed of wood strips, woven wire, snow-fencing, or any type of masonry, as long as air can move freely.

Grain stored in bulk maintains quality better in small than in large lots. Farm storage tends to maintain the original condition of grain better than elevator storage, provided grain is not exposed to any moisture increase or to rodents, birds, or insects.

Farm storage space has increased rapidly in recent years because of increasing amounts of shelled corn and for other reasons. It now far exceeds grain storage space off the farm.

E. Bin Sites

In recent years, much of the surplus grain owned by the U.S. government has been stored in farm-type bins in large numbers, called bin sites. Bin capacities usually range from 2,000 to 3,300 bushels (50 to 83 metric tons). Bins are constructed mostly of steel or aluminum, but also of wood or plywood, insulation board, or even of cement-asbestos board. Capacity of many storage sites has been increased by adding quonset or shed-type bins each of which holds from 25,000 to 40,000 bushels (625 to 1,000 metric tons).

Quality maintenance in these small bin-site bins is much the same as in grain elevator bins and will be discussed later.

F. Country Elevators

Country elevators receive grain directly from producers. Their principal function is to accumulate grain from nearby farms, to reload it into transportation facilities such as trucks, railroad cars, or barges, and to send it to market. In addition, they offer storage space and other services. They were originally intended to serve an area limited by horse and wagon delivery of grain, and their storage capacity was therefore very small. Truck transport from farms has broadened access areas, and elevator sizes have increased accordingly, with the smaller country elevators tending to disappear.

The largest elevators approach the size of terminal elevators and are often

§ 26.327 Grades and grade requirements

Wheat

(a) Grade and grade requirements for all classes of Wheat except Mixed Wheat. (See also § 26.328.)

Grade	Minimum test weight per bushel		Maximum limits of—						
			Defects					Wheat of other classes[1]	
	Hard Red Spring Wheat or White Club Wheat	All other classes and sub-classes	Heat-damaged kernels	Damaged kernels (total)	Foreign material	Shrunken and broken kernels	Defects (total)	Contrasting classes	Wheat of other classes (total)
	Pounds	*Pounds*	*Percent*	*Percent*	*Percent*	*Percent*	*Percent*	*Percent*	*Percent*
U.S. No. 1	58.0	60.0	0.1	2.0	0.5	3.0	3.0	1.0	3.0
U.S. No. 2	57.0	58.0	.2	4.0	1.0	5.0	5.0	2.0	5.0
U.S. No. 3	55.0	56.0	.5	7.0	2.0	8.0	8.0	3.0	10.0
U.S. No. 4	53.0	54.0	1.0	10.0	3.0	12.0	12.0	10.0	10.0
U.S. No. 5	50.0	51.0	3.0	15.0	5.0	20.0	20.0	10.0	10.0
U.S. Sample grade.									

U.S. Sample grade shall be wheat which does not meet the requirements for any of the grades from U.S. No. 1 to U.S. No. 5, inclusive; or which contains more than two crotalaria seeds (*Crotalaria spp.*) in 1,000 grams of grain, or contains castor beans (*Ricinus communis*), stones, broken glass, animal filth, an unknown foreign substance(s), or a commonly recognized harmful or toxic substance(s); or which is musty, sour, or heating; or which has any commercially objectionable foreign odor except of smut or garlic; or which contains a quantity of smut so great that any one or more of the grade requirements cannot be applied accurately; or which is otherwise of distinctly low quality.

[1] Red Durum Wheat of any grade may contain not more than 10.0 percent of wheat of other classes.

Figure 1. U. S. Department of Agriculture. Wheat grading standards.

referred to as sub-terminals. They offer large storage space, fast handling facilities, and often specialize in relieving a group of country elevators by moving grain into transport equipment such as barges or hopper car trains.

G. Terminal Elevators

Usually located in transportation terminals and larger markets, terminal elevators range in total storage space from 200,000 to 20 million or more bushels (5,000 to 500,000 metric tons). They receive grain from country elevators by truck or railroad and transfer it to storage or into other transportation equipment such as barges or other vessels. They usually include high-capacity equipment for cleaning, drying, and conditioning of grain.

1.8   U.S. DEPT. OF AGRICULTURE
WHEAT

(b) Grades and grade requirements for Mixed Wheat. (See also § 26.328.) Mixed Wheat shall be graded according to the U.S. numerical and U.S. Sample grade requirements of the class of wheat which predominates in the mixture, except that the factor "wheat of other classes" shall be disregarded.

§ 26.328 Special grades, special grade requirements, and special grade designations

(a) Tough wheat—(1) Requirements. Tough wheat shall be wheat which contains more than 13.5 percent of moisture.

(2) Grade designation. Tough wheat shall be graded and designated according to the grade requirements of the standards applicable to such wheat if it were not tough, and there shall be added to and made a part of the grade designation the word "Tough."

(b) Smutty wheat—(1) Requirements. Smutty wheat shall be wheat which has an unmistakable odor of smut or which contains balls, portions of balls, or spores, of smut in a quantity equivalent to more than 14 balls of average size in 250 grams of wheat.

(2) Grade designation. Smutty wheat shall be graded and designated according to the grade requirements of the standards applicable to such wheat if it were not smutty; and

(i) In the case of smutty wheat which has an unmistakable odor of smut, or which contains balls, portions of balls, or spores, of smut, in excess of a quantity equal to 14 balls but not in excess of a quantity equal to 30 balls of average size in 250 grams of wheat, there shall be added to and made a part of the grade designation the words "Light Smutty"; and

(ii) In the case of smutty wheat which contains balls, portions of balls, or spores, of smut, in excess of a quantity equal to 30 balls of average size in 250 grams of wheat, there shall be added to and made a part of the grade designation the word "Smutty."

Figure 2. Farm bin.

III. STRUCTURAL REQUIREMENTS OF STORAGE BINS

A. Upright or Silo-Type Bins

Early elevators were built of wood which was plentiful and cheap. Storage bins were built up by laying planks flat in piles so that walls were solid wood 8 in. (20 cm.) thick at the bottom and 4 in. (10 cm.) near the top. Foundations, beams, spouts, roofs, and scales were also made of wood. Since this type of construction constituted a serious fire hazard, other materials soon came into use. A metal jacketing over the wood came first, and bins built completely of steel followed. The slip-form for construction of round concrete bins was developed about 1900 and is now in general use.

The slip-form consists of a concentric double-ring form into which concrete is poured. As the concrete in the lower part sets, the forms are jacked upward and more concrete is poured in. The process must go on without interruption until the desired height is reached. It produces a bin in one solid and continuous piece of concrete. As these round bins are usually constructed in rows so that one straight-line conveyor can serve a group of them, a whole series of bins, each with its own slip-rings, may be built simultaneously. Often two or more rows of round bins are built side-by-side to form a block of bins. The areas between the circles also become bins, and are called interstitial or star bins. Sometimes indentations between circles of outside rows of the block are walled off to form additional small bins called pockets. Other bin shapes have also sometimes been used.

Figure 3. Corn crib.

There is no formula for the best height for storage tanks. Concrete tanks have been built at heights of from 80 to 140 ft. (24 to 43 m.). Factors affecting height include available ground area, desired storage volume, weight the earth will bear, cost of elevating compared with cost of conveying, and the type of workhouse to be built. Steel bins are always round. Though some other shapes such as oval or hexagonal have been tried with concrete, the round form gives the greatest strength with the least material.

The designer can choose between hoppered or flat bin bottoms. Hoppers with sloping floors are convenient, since all grain flows out by gravity, and they are self-cleaning and do not require shoveling. Flat bottoms are cheaper to construct and give slightly more storage space, but cause some delay in loading out, as shoveling is slow. In general, hoppered bottoms are best if bins are likely to be completely emptied more than three times a year.

Figure 4. Bin site.

Figure 5. Country elevators (wood).

Bin size affects management and economies. Since the cost per bushel (or metric ton) of storage space rises sharply as bins become smaller, the tendency is to build larger bins. Small bins, however, also have advantages. Grains of varying qualities can be separated better in small-bin storage. If large bins cannot be kept fairly well filled, much of the storage space is wasted. It is usual, therefore, to build bins in graduated sizes, such as in ratios of 5-10-20-50. Using one or more bins, lots of almost any size can be made to fit capacity without wasting space. Similarly, if a large bin is partly emptied, there will be a smaller bin to which the balance can be transferred, thus making the entire capacity of the larger bin again available.

B. Flat Bins

The pressure of grain surpluses requiring safe storage for long periods has led to the construction of auxiliary bins of large capacity in connection with terminal elevators in the U.S., Canada, and Argentina. They provide ample storage space at the lowest possible cost. To attain that objective, the bins are built wider and lower than conventional silo storage, to reduce costs and side-pressures. Floors are directly on the ground, handling equipment is kept at a minimum, and the roof tends to follow the slope of the pile of grain. Sometimes flat storage consists of nothing more than a shed-type, sloping roof just sufficient to cover a pile of grain near the elevator. Large bins may be directly attached to the elevator or may be constructed only adjacent to it. Round steel bins with capacities of 400,000 to 2 million bushels (10,000 to 21,000 metric tons) are coming into general use.

Most flat storage bins are equipped for filling them, usually by gravity, sometimes with the assistance of power shovels. Most require power shovels to move the greater portion of the grain to handling equipment, which conveys it into the elevator where it is transferred to other storage bins or loaded out with the elevator's handling equipment.

IV. GRAIN HANDLING EQUIPMENT

A. Receiving and Shipping

Capacities. Handling capacity must be related to storage capacity, among

Figure 6. Country elevators (concrete).

other things. Where most of the grain is received and shipped via railroad, the typical terminal has receiving capacity sufficient to fill its storage space in about 40 two-shift working days. Elevators in one-crop areas often have greater receiving capacity to fill storages while the crop is moving. Elevators farther from

Figure 7. Country elevators (steel).

Figure 8. Terminal elevator.

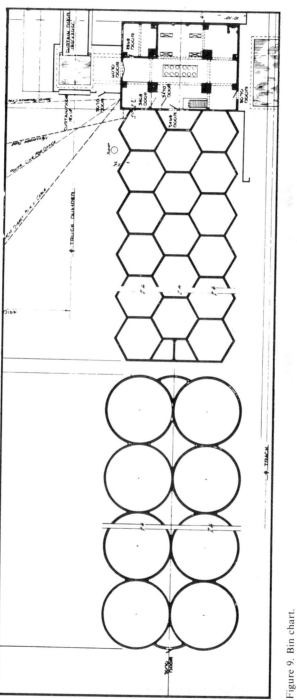

Figure 9. Bin chart.

Figure 10. Flat storage bins.

producing areas or in the path of continuous grain movements may have much less receiving capacity.

Truck unloading capacity of elevators is increasing, but may not yet be related to storage capacity, except in country elevators.

Handling capacity must also be related to transportation facilities. Where, for example, Great Lakes steamers or export vessels are loaded or unloaded, it is desirable to be able to completely load or unload a vessel in one day. At transfer elevators, where grain is moved from steamer to cars or barges, it should be possible to load grain out of the elevator as fast as it can be received.

Modern truck dumpers are able to unload more than 15 large trailer trucks per hr., or at least 12,000 bushels (330 metric tons). Two men with power shovels can unload two boxcars or about 4,000 bushels (110 metric tons) per hr., while a car dumper can unload up to 10 cars per hr., or about 20,000 bushels (550 metric tons). Hoppered cars carrying 3,600 bushels (100 metric tons) can often be dumped at 10 per hr. Car loading capacities range from one per hr. at country elevators to 10 or more per hr. at terminals. Many export elevators are able to load grain into vessels at 100,000 bushels (2,750 metric tons) per hr.

Methods. When grain is received at an elevator, it is elevated to the top of the storage structure by a leg, consisting of an endless vertical belt to which buckets are attached. The lower end of the leg casing, called the boot, contains a tail pulley under which the belt runs. As buckets are swept under it and again start upward, they scoop up their loads of grain. When they reach the top of the leg they pass over a head pulley and turn downward, thus dumping their loads of grain into a receiver, or garner. From the garner grain flows either by gravity into

Figure 11. Car dumper.

a bin, or onto a conveyor belt which carries it over the bin tops until a tripper pours it into the selected bin.

When grain is to be removed from storage, it flows from the bin bottom onto a belt or other horizontal conveyor, is carried to a leg, elevated into a garner and scale, and poured into the carrier.

Because handling capacity must be provided for peak loads for short periods, the handling equipment of grain elevators is seldom efficiently used. Storage tends to be filled only at the beginning of surplus years, and at best can average only half full for the crop year. While receiving equipment must be ready for a high volume when the crop is moving in, it is used only intermittently at other seasons. Loading out of storage tends to be spread over the balance of the year as needed for consumption. Thus the amount of handling equipment to be available for a given storage space requires careful study.

B. Cleaning and Drying

Cleaning Equipment. The term cleaning includes a variety of operations. It may refer to the separation of weed seeds or other impurities from grain, to classification of kernels by length or width, to separation of different kinds of grain from each other, or to washing. Each kind of grain and each impurity is a separate problem. Only three cleaning methods are commonly used in elevators employing air, perforated screens, or indents.

A lighter material may be separated from a heavier material by means of air streams. A precise separation is seldom achieved with air alone. Air is used mostly to supplement the other methods, but nearly all types of cleaners employ some type of aeration.

Perforated screens are the main feature of most cleaners. Screens may be formed of perforated metal sheets or of wire woven into screens with the desired

Figure 12. Truck dumper.

openings. Grain is passed over the screen in thin streams, while the screens usually are vibrated. Sometimes slotted screens are used to separate thin from plump kernels of the same kind of grain, or different grains from a mixture, or weed seeds and broken kernels from whole kernels, or other foreign matter from grain. Another machine has wires precisely spaced to form slots in a rotating drum to sort kernels by width.

To separate kernels of different lengths, pockets or indents are formed in the faces of discs or in the inside of cylinders. Only grain of the desired length will fit into the indents, to be lifted out of the grain mass and spilled into prepared receivers.

Dryers. Nearly all terminal elevators have some artificial grain drying equipment. Drying is accomplished by heating air to reduce its relative humidity. For example, air at 80% relative humidity heated to 200° F. (93.33° C.) will be reduced to below 3% relative humidity. Passing it through or over the grain carries away moisture. (See Chapter 1.)

Increasing use of field shelling in maize harvesting encourages the earliest possible harvest time, which means maize with moisture contents of up to 30%. Since maize will spoil quickly at any moisture content above 23%, nearly all of it must be dried immediately. This has led to a sharp increase in the drying capacities of most country elevators, and also to the increasing use of farm dryers.

C. Scales and Weights

While a bushel is a unit of volume, the bushels by which grain is measured are units of weight, and all grain entering or leaving storage must be weighed.

Figure 13. Export elevator.

Figure 14. Hopper scale.

Boxcar loads of grain may be weighed on platform scales incorporated into the tracks at the elevator or elsewhere in the railway system. But the most common method is to convey the grain into a hopper scale, usually of around 2,500 bushel capacity. In spite of this weight of almost 70 tons or more, these scales are remarkably precise, and often maintain accuracy within + or –0.01% for long periods.

Truck shipments are weighed in various ways. Sometimes there is a platform scale in the roadway approaching the unloading pit on which trucks are weighed before and after unloading. In other elevators, the dumper platform itself is the scale platform. Sometimes the pit into which the grain is dumped is the hopper scale or grain is elevated into a hopper scale. Small automated scales are also used.

D. Automation

High labor costs inevitably lead to labor-saving devices, and modern elevators employ both remote control and automation to save man-hours. For example,

Figure 15. Control panel.

switch engines may be radio-controlled with one man dumping the contents of a car or truck and directing the grain all the way into storage by simply pushing a button for the selected bin. On the way it may be automatically sampled and the sample conveyed into the inspection room, where part of the inspection takes place automatically. Also on the way, grain will be automatically weighed, either electronically off the old-style beam scale or by translation of electric impulses from a strain gauge into weight. These weights will be recorded in the office or accumulated by a computer recording the contents of each bin.

Similarly, when loading out of storage, an electric signal opens particular gates to desired rates of flow. Grain is directed to the proper shipping bin or loading spout and automatically weighed and inspected on the way, while a record is kept of the quantities shipped. Bin measuring devices show in the office how much grain remains in the bins after job completion.

E. Behavior of Grain in Bulk Handling

Clean, dry grain poured into a pile usually forms a slope with an angle from the horizontal of about 27°, sometimes referred to as the angle of repose (Airy, 1898; Caughey et al., 1951; Ketchum, 1919; Stahl, 1948). Damp grain, or grain containing many impurities or smaller particles, forms a slightly steeper slope. Some of the heavier grains of uniform size flow out to a slightly flatter slope. The slope is a little steeper when the bin is first filled but will flatten with time.

This angle of repose forms a conical pile, with its base limited by the bin walls and with its apex at the center of the filling stream. Therefore, if the stream entering the bin is in the center, grain may be poured in until the cone reaches the point of entry. Since grain slopes at about 27° to the bin walls, the space around the cone will be wasted unless it is filled by other means.

Similarly, the hopper at the bottom of a round bin must be cone-shaped, with a slope greater than the angle of repose. The smaller the bin, the steeper must be the angle, because of the wedging action of the funnel-shaped hopper. Any hopper wastes space, but a hopper with its lowest point in the center of the bin wastes the least.

All grain settles or packs in storage. Clean, heavy wheat may pack only 0.6% of its volume, while lightweight oats may pack as much as 28%. Some of this packing occurs during the first filling because of the grain's own weight. Settling continues during the entire storage period. Reasons for settling are in part the collapse of such materials as hulls, stems, beards, germ points, or even whole kernels, with a slight increase in the weight of a measured bushel (test weight) ensuing during storage.

The pressure on the bin floor, or on any of the grain anywhere in the bin, is not proportional to the height of the grain above, because much of the grain's weight is supported by the bin walls. Each kernel rests on several kernels below it, so that some of its weight is distributed laterally, until this outward pressure reaches the bin walls and by friction rests on them. This is responsible for the tendency of grain in a bin to arch or bridge from wall to wall (where height exceeds diameter), at least until the draw-off gate is opened, when the bridging effect is broken, shifting weight from walls to floor.

Ketchum (1919) summarized certain conclusions about grain pressures:

1. The pressure of the grain on bin walls and floors follows the law of semifluids, which is entirely different from the law governing the pressure of fluids.

2. The lateral pressure of the grain on bin walls is less than the vertical pressure, being 0.3 to 0.6 of the vertical pressure, and increases very little after a depth of 2.5 to 3 times the bin width or diameter.

3. The ratio k of the lateral to the vertical pressure (which can be determined only by experiment) is not a constant but varies with different grains and bins.

4. The pressure of moving grain on the walls of the bins is slightly greater than that of stationary grain.

Grain tends to separate into heavier and lighter components when poured into or drawn from a bin. When entering a bin, the heavier grain falls faster and straighter, while lighter particles float outward because of air resistance, so that chaff and dust accumulate toward the bin walls.

When the stream of heavy grain reaches the pile's apex, smaller particles such as weed seeds, broken kernels, or heavy dust particles are trapped between larger kernels. They remain at the pile's center, while whole grain kernels flow away down the slope producing a core of high-dockage grain in the center of the pile. This core of fines is called a spoutline. Since the interstices between kernels amount to more than 30% of the space occupied by the grain, fines in this spoutline may reach and exceed 30% also.

When the draw-off gate of a bin is opened, the column of grain directly above the opening flows out first. This column widens toward the top and grain in the center flows faster so that a cone-shaped depression soon appears on the column's surface. Grain from the surface flows into this depression and down to the draw-off. Therefore, grain in the center of a bin leaves it first.

V. MAINTAINING QUALITY IN STORAGE

A. Basic Threats

Christensen and Kaufmann (1969) reported that "Grains and seeds are both exceedingly durable and highly perishable....Good storage practices aim to maintain conditions in the grain that will preserve the marketing and processing qualities of the grain at as high a level as possible, and basically this means elimination of damage caused by insects, mites, and fungi, plus protection from rodents and birds."

It can be maintained that destruction begins when storage begins, with the rate of quality loss depending on storage conditions. If all outside contamination of grain in storage can be prevented, that rate is slowest when the grain is the driest and coolest, since growth rate of fungi depends on moisture and temperature, and that of insects mainly on temperature.

B. Insects

Insects and mites are a hazard to stored grain in several ways. Some devour whole kernels, others consume broken kernels and dust. All cause rises in grain temperature and moisture. All contaminate the grain, and particles of insects may get into grain products where, though harmless, they are aesthetically objectionable.

Grain-infesting insects are very sensitive to temperatures. They multiply slowly or not at all below 60°F. (15.56°C.), and they cannot survive in temperatures of 107°F. (41.67°C.) or above. They appear to thrive best at about 85°F. (29°C.), and at that level their life cycles may be as short as 30 days. These insects may get into the grain in the field, harvesting machinery, farm bins or trucks, country elevators, or during bin-site storage, so that after 80 days of storage at temperatures above 70°F. (21.11°C.) any lot of stored grain is likely to show evidence of insects. Insects infesting stored grains and grain products can be controlled effectively by fumigation. (See Chapter 5.)

C. Fungi

"Only recently have fungi been recognized as a major cause of spoilage in stored grains and seeds....The major types of losses caused by fungi growing in stored grains are these: 1) decrease in germinability; 2) discoloration of part (usually the germ or embryo) or all of the seed or kernel; 3) heating and mustiness; 4) various biochemical changes; 5) production of toxins that if consumed may be injurious to man and to domestic animals; 6) loss in weight" (Christensen and Kaufmann, 1969). They divide fungi invading grains and seeds into two groups, primarily on the basis of their behavior: field fungi and storage fungi.

Damage by field fungi is usually caused before harvest. While it may affect appearance and quality at that time, there is no further damage during storage. In fact, damage may disappear in storage, particularly if storage fungi are active, so that a high count of kernels carrying field fungi indicates that the lot of grain from which the sample was taken was stored under good conditions and did not lose quality during storage.

"As the grains proceed from the farm to terminal, the number of kernels with relatively deep invasion by storage fungi increases, and unless the temperature or the moisture content, or both, of the stored grain is lowered enough to stop the growth of storage fungi, they will continue to grow, and eventually cause germ damage, mustiness, heating, caking, and bin-burned grain" (Christensen and Kaufmann, 1969). (See Chapter 4.)

D. Moisture

Among the several kinds of storage fungi each has its own moisture preference, beginning at about 13.5%. However, each grows faster as moisture content rises.

Mold growth increases at an accelerating rate during storage because molds improve their growing conditions by their own growth, raising both temperature and moisture content. So in any lot of stored grain, these events can be observed: Mold spore count increases slowly and temperatures rise very slowly. At about 90°F. (32°C.) odors, some germ discoloration, and small increases in fatty acids become evident. At about 110°F. (43°C.), strong odors, usually sour, browning of kernels, sharp increases in fatty acids, and some moisture increases are measurable. At about 135°F. (57°C.) there is a pause in the temperature rise, but kernels are likely to be black, highly rancid, and collapsing. With oilseeds, other organisms and chemical reactions now take over and increase temperatures still further.

The relative humidity of interseed air is directly related to the moisture content of grain, and they move toward equilibrium with one another with surprising rapidity. These equilibrium levels are known and predictable. (See Chapters 1 and 12.) For instance, if air were drawn downward during foggy weather, through a bin of low-moisture winter wheat, grain within inches of the surface would rise to more than 20% moisture content within a day, but grain moisture content 3 ft. (1 m.) below would remain unchanged. Conversely, whenever grain is exposed to air of lower than its equilibrium relative humidity, it gives up moisture to the air. This is the process by which grain dries both naturally and artificially. It is also the method by which a mixture of grain of different moisture contents moves toward uniformity.

Unfortunately, this is also the cause of many grain condition problems, usually by translocation of moisture or moisture transfer. Whenever the temperature in any quantity within a mass of grain differs from another part, moisture is carried from warmer to cooler areas by convection and deposited. Most grain storage starts in late summer or fall when grain is warm. As the weather cools, convection currents begin to move upward in the warmer grain. When they reach the cooler surface, the air temperature is reduced, and its relative humidity approaches or passes saturation.

For example, wheat stored at 12% moisture content is in equilibrium with interseed air at about 60% relative humidity, if the temperature is about 80°F.

(27°C.). But when this air rises to the surface and cools to 60° F. (15.56° C.), its relative humidity approaches saturation, and the wheat near the surface begins to absorb moisture from the air. If the air cools further, it passes the saturation point, and free water will begin to be deposited. In cold weather water often drips from roof supports back into the grain or runs down the inside of bin walls. Conversely, care must be taken not to pass warm, humid air through cold grain, because the air cools, its relative humidity increases, and moisture is absorbed by the grain.

It is difficult to measure grain moisture content accurately, partly because the moisture content of any lot is really an approximate average of the moisture content of its individual kernels, and there are variations in any sample. Moisture content of grain in the field can vary 4% within a few feet, and even more between different parts of the field in addition to variations during a harvesting day. Many truckloads from many fields enter one country elevator or one boxcar during harvest. Since no elevator has bins enough to precisely segregate according to moisture content the grain it receives, loads of varying moisture levels go into any one bin. Differences in temperatures cause moisture movements as described above.

Further, moisture meters are not precise. (See Chapter 1.) Repeated tests of the same sample (ignoring sampling errors) with the same or different testing equipment gives different results. Samples were tested on the four most generally used makes of moisture meters and oven-dried, with the results shown in Table I.

TABLE I
Moisture testing results

| Sample | Meter | | | | Oven Drying |
	1 %	2 %	3 %	4 %	%
1	14.20	14.20	13.31	13.51	14.2
2	13.70	13.40	13.85	12.70	14.3
3	14.30	14.00	13.44	12.76	14.5
4	13.30	14.60	16.35	13.97	14.5
5	14.77	14.50	15.00	13.52	15.1

Any calculations of safe storage life based on reported moisture content are not very dependable, are subject to wide errors, and necessitate constant vigilance.

E. Temperature

As stated previously, temperature is as important as moisture content in determining the storage life of grain. Molds grow slowly, and some not at all, below 50° F. (10° C.), but do serious damage at 85° F. (29.44° C.), if moisture conditions are favorable. Temperatures of grain at harvest and entry into storage range from 103° F. (39.44° C.) for wheat, rice, and sorghums in the South of the U.S., to 60° F. (15.56° C.) for all grains in the North.

Grain is an excellent insulator and changes its own temperature very slowly. Grain in concrete bins without air circulation will change only a few degrees through months of cold weather. Cold grain put into storage in winter remains cold through the summer. A range of 20° may be found in 5 ft. (1.5 m.) in a grain mass, so that differences persist for a long time if loads of grain of different temperatures are put in storage. Grain next to the steel wall of a bin exposed to the sun may reach 130° F. (54.44° C.) during the day, but the temperature of grain 4 ft. (1.22 m.) away remains unchanged. Small lots, such as farm bins, follow outside temperatures to some extent, with a time lag, but large lots may retain essentially the same temperature they had when loaded into the bin for months or even years.

For the same reasons, overheating in a grain mass may proceed undetected for dangerously long periods and completely destroy small amounts of grain. Bins thought to be in good condition are often found to contain clusters of badly damaged grain. In fact, temperatures are seldom uniform throughout any bin or lot. When loads of grain of different temperatures are put into storage, grain near walls and surfaces soon acquires a higher or lower temperature, and condition problems raise temperatures in some areas. Wherever temperatures differ, convection currents begin to move moisture from warmer to cooler portions. Moisture is absorbed by surface grain in cold weather, condenses on roof supports, drips back into the grain, or condenses on walls and runs into the grain. When that happens, molds grow profusely, surface grain rots to depths of 8 to 10 in. (20 to 24 cm.), some sprouting occurs, grain becomes caked with mold growth to depths of several feet, and heating resulting from rapid growth of molds may work downward into the grain mass.

When cold grain is added to a bin of warm grain, moisture moves up into the cold grain. A bin of cold grain next to a bin of warm grain causes condensation on the wall of the warm bin. Cold grain exposed to warm outside air increases in moisture content. During artificial cooling its altering of moisture contents must be considered.

Temperature and moisture together largely determine the length of safe storage life in addition to many other conditions, such as proportion of kernels infected by fungi and the degree to which they are infected, previous storage conditions, cleanliness and soundness of the grain, insect and mite infestation, and age. Approximate predictions of safe storage life are possible, however, as shown in Table II.

TABLE II
Safe storage life

Grain Temperature		Moisture Content, %						
°F.	°C.	14	15.5	17	18.5	20	21.5	23
					Days			
50	10.00	256	128	64	32	16	8	4
60	15.56	128	64	32	16	8	4	2
70	21.11	64	32	16	8	4	2	1
80	26.67	32	16	8	4	2	1	0
90	32.22	16	8	4	2	1	0	
100	37.78	8	4	2	1	0		

F. Spoutlines

Spoutlines in large masses of grain often shorten storage life abruptly. Whenever grain is poured into a pile, the fines accumulate at the pile's peak, filling interstices between kernels, while whole kernels slide or flow down the slope. The resulting vertical core begins a few feet off the floor and extends to the peak of the pile. Its width is proportional to the width of the bin and to the percentage of fines in the original grain. But the center of the core is a solid mass, almost completely stopping any air circulation, accumulating heat and preventing the escape of any heat that may be produced by the activity of fungi, insects, mites, or other causes.

Most spoutlines larger than 8 ft. in diameter eventually begin to heat, usually in about 50 days. This heating will move upward and outward. As temperatures increase, heating rate and mold growth increase. Temperatures in the core soar toward 135° F. (57° C.), bad odors, at first musty, then sour, appear. Grain in the core turns from brown to black, moisture condensation appears on the surface, and eventually heating spreads throughout the entire bin. In oilseeds, such as flax and soybeans, temperatures above 200° F. (93° C.) have been reported.

G. Remedial Actions

The threat of grain quality loss in storage is always present. All possible measures must be taken to prevent it. First, storage must be provided that protects the grain from hazards such as weather, insects, and rodents. Next, grain with characteristics enhancing storage life, such as low moisture content, low temperatures, low mold count, and freedom from insects must be selected. If moisture content is dangerously high, the grain may be dried. If temperatures are too high, they can be reduced by aeration. If insects are present, fumigation will control them. Mold growth, the principal danger, is inhibited by lowering both moisture and temperature.

Once the grain is in storage, its condition must be constantly known. The surest way is to examine actual samples at frequent intervals, but it is difficult to obtain dependable samples from a large grain mass. Fortunately, nearly all threats to grain quality cause temperature rises, so a constant record of grain temperature can warn of impending loss. For this reason, adequate temperature reading equipment is absolutely essential in all grain storage.

To obtain temperature readings, thermocouples are placed in the stored grain mass, either by hanging wires in the empty bins and pouring grain around them, or by pushing them into the grain after the bin is filled. A potentiometer translates electrical forces into temperature readings. When read and compared at weekly intervals, any rises may be identified. Any persistent increase or any rise of more than 2 or 3 degrees indicates impending quality loss, and prompt action must be taken.

Many elevators are equipped for reading of all thermocouples at a single location, the elevator office. Each thermocouple is connected in succession to the reading device, while an operator records the temperatures registered. Or, the same equipment may be automated, moving from one reading to the next at fixed time intervals to allow easy recording. Automatic recording equipment is also available.

Sometimes it may be already too late to save the grain entirely depending on the cause of the heating. If insects are the culprits, fumigation may stop further damage but temperatures somewhere in the grain mass may have already risen higher than those read by the thermocouples. Because of the low conductivity of grain readings lag behind. In any case, any rise in temperature resulting from insect activity encourages growth of fungi which may aggravate the heating process. Nothing will stop this but cooling or drying, or both.

Aeration. When the outside air is cooler than the stored grain it can be used quite efficiently to cool the grain by forced ventilation or aeration. This method has been used in rough rice storage for many years, but has been applied only recently in storage of other grains. The USDA introduced it in bin-site storage and in grain stored in idle ships in the early 1950's. Industry had experimented with aeration earlier, but at first too high a rate of airflow and too large temperature differences caused more damage than could be prevented. By circulating natural outside air through the grain for fairly long periods, however, the grain temperature could be reduced to outside temperatures. In some cases of small-bin storage, this could be accomplished with windpower using cowl ventilators. Powered fans were necessary in larger bins. (See Chapter 12.)

Usually perforated air ducts are placed on the bin floor or walls before filling it. After the bin is filled, as air is drawn out of the ducts, it is also drawn downward through the grain. Customary flows range from 1/30 c.f.m. per bushel to 1/2 c.f.m. per bushel. Each accomplishes the objective, the only variables being time and horsepower.

Airflow rate for drying or cooling is an expression of the volume of air per unit of time in relation to a quantity of grain. Common expressions for grain are cubic feet per minute (c.f.m.) per bushel (or cwt.), and cubic meters per minute per metric ton (t.).

$$1 \text{ c.f.m.}/\text{cwt.} = 0.624 \text{ m.}^3/\text{min.}/\text{t.}$$

Horsepower requirements vary with airflow rate, kind of grain, and the distance the air must travel through the grain. For instance, 1/20 c.f.m. per bushel in a shallow bin of maize meets low resistance, raising static pressure in the grain to only 1 in. (2.54 cm.) of water or less and thus requiring little horsepower. But an airflow of 1/10 c.f.m. per bushel through 100 ft. (30 m.) of wheat would result in a static pressure of around 25 in. (63.5 cm.) of water, far beyond any practical range because horsepower requirements would be out of reach.

Example: Approximate static pressures
(in. of water)

	Maize	Wheat
At 1/20 c.f.m./bu. through 50 ft.	1.0	3.3
At 1/10 c.f.m./bu. through 50 ft.	1.8	6.9
At 1/20 c.f.m./bu. through 100 ft.	3.0	13.0
At 1/10 c.f.m./bu. through 100 ft.	7.3	25.0

The purpose of aeration is to cool grain to a temperature low enough to reduce or inhibit the activity of fungi and insects, and to establish a uniform temperature

Figure 16. Aeration duct.

throughout the grain mass and thus prevent moisture translocation. The time required to cool grain varies with the airflow rate and with the amount of evaporative cooling. At 1/10 c.f.m. per bushel in the bin, the cooling front moves through the bin in about 100 hr. If outside temperatures are below 50° F. (10° C.), aeration will put the grain in fairly safe condition for long-term storage in 4 or 5 days. The airflow rate must be adequate to cool the entire contents of the bin before deterioration begins. Even in warmer weather, aeration may help to keep grain in good condition by removing heat and moisture resulting from mold and insect activity, by equalizing temperatures, and by removing odors.

H. Costs

Aeration is the least costly of all preservation measures. One cooling often costs less than 1/10 cent per bushel. But transferring from bin to bin often costs 1/2 cent per bushel per turn, and several turns may be required to maintain grain quality. Drying artificially is costly, in addition to the weight loss that it causes. Fumigation usually costs from 1/2 cent to 1 cent per bushel. Mold inhibitors are uneconomical and also of questionable effectiveness.

Costs of storing grain are those of storage space and the cost of maintaining quality. When sound, dry, cool grain enters storage, the condition-keeping costs are likely to be low. When unsound, high-moisture, warm grain is stored, grain conditioning costs are high and continuous, and the cost of losses may be immediate and disastrous. Only long experience and a thorough knowledge of the behavior of grain in storage will lead to dependable assessments of storage risks.

Cost of storage space is almost entirely fixed, as operating costs in the absence of condition problems will rarely reach 1/2 cent per bushel per year. Fixed costs

Figure 17 Dust explosion

consist of depreciation, interest, taxes, and insurance. These annual costs depend in turn on initial construction costs, which may range from 30 cents per bushel for one large flat-storage bin without any handling equipment, to 4 dollars per bushel where small bins, high-capacity equipment, and related facilities are added. However, the biggest factor in determining cost per bushel is the degree to which storage space is used. For instance, in a small elevator whose initial construction cost was 1 dollar per bushel of storage space, the cost per bushel per year is roughly 10 cents per bushel, provided the space is fully used throughout the year. But if the available space is used only half the time, the cost per bushel stored is 20 cents. If the space is half filled half the time, the cost may reach 40 cents per bushel.

VI. OPERATING HAZARDS AND SAFETY MEASURES

The most troublesome operating hazard in grain storage is dust brought about mostly by bruising or abrasion of grain. It includes bran flakes from the skin, finely broken hairs from the brush, particles of endosperm from broken kernels, pieces of chaff and straw, and soil particles. It is so fine that it easily becomes airborne to constitute a pollutant and also at times a fire and explosion hazard.

Wherever grain is moved in the open, these fine particles escape and float in the air. While grain dust is relatively harmless even when inhaled (many elevator workers appear unharmed after working in it for 30 or 40 yrs.), many people object to having it settle on residential areas near the elevator, and dust collection becomes necessary. Filtering all, or as much as possible, of the air within or escaping from the elevator can remove these fine particles. Activities outside the elevator, such as shoveling or pouring grain from trucks or cars, grain drying or cleaning, or pouring grain from the elevator into cars or vessels, will inevitably stir up dust which needs to be collected. This can become an expensive part of moving grain into or out of storage.

The second hazard from dust is the possibility of explosions. A dust explosion can shatter a concrete bin wall, scatter a concrete headhouse over several blocks, and even lift bins of grain weighing hundreds of tons. While modern technology has somewhat reduced this hazard they still occur. In the past, dust explosions have caused immense damage and even loss of life.

One of the most severe occurred in 1878 wrecking the Washburn-Crosby flour milling complex in Minneapolis. Another happened in Chicago in 1921 in the Armour grain elevator, then the largest and most modern structure of its kind. Portions of the elevator were entirely destroyed, and blocks of concrete weighing tons were thrown 200 yd. away.

These explosions are caused by the combustion of grain dust suspended in air. They have been reproduced on a miniature scale in the laboratory, the conditions under which they occur have been studied, and three ingredients have been isolated: a suitable mixture of dust and air, a spark or any temperature of 400° F. (204° C.), and a confined area. Modern elevators are built with few confined areas, sparks or high temperatures in an elevator are carefully avoided, and as far as possible, dust is kept out of the air.

The spark or flame that initiates an explosion may be produced in many ways. It may be caused by a nail in the shoe of a worker, the edge of a shovel striking concrete hard enough to produce a spark, a defective motor or switch, defective wiring, static electricity, a hot bearing, a contraband cigarette, or a broken light bulb.

There are often two stages in a dust explosion. Upon ignition, there is a flash of flame accompanied by a gust of air which lifts fine dust lodged on walls, floor, and other surfaces. The dust cloud thus created immediately ignites to cause a second and much more powerful explosion. In an unrestricted area, the air pressure caused by the sudden rise in temperature and the products of combustion are dissipated as a rapidly moving pressure wave. But in enclosed areas, such as basements under bins, bins themselves, or the headhouse, the pressures build up in a fraction of a second to shatter the strongest barriers.

VII. STORAGE CAPACITIES

Only approximate figures are at hand comparing grain produced with available storage space.

The USDA Crop Reporting Service disclosed in December 1970 that the crop harvested in the U.S. in 1970, consisting of maize for grain, all wheat, oats, barley, rye, flax, grain sorghum, and soybeans, totaled 8,709 million bushels and that 6,264 million bushels had been sold off the farm. The same source reported that on January 1, 1971, stocks of these grains in the U.S. were:

on farms,	4,849 million bushels;
in CC bin sites,	126 million bushels;
in mills and elevators,	3,213 million bushels;
Total	8,188 million bushels.

These figures indicate a carry-over of 2,404 million bushels, probably mostly in farm storage. At about the same time, it was reported that off-farm storage capacity totaled 5,703 million bushels. These figures show that there is farm storage available for more than half of each crop, that commercial storage capacity is available for at least 90% of the portion of the crop that leaves the farm where it was produced, and that on January 1, 1971, commercial storage capacity was 56% occupied.

LITERATURE CITED

AIRY, W. 1898. The pressure of grain. Proc. Inst. Civil Eng. (London) 131: 347-358.

CAUGHEY, R. A., C. W. TOOLES, and A. C. SCHEER. 1951. Lateral and vertical pressure of granular materials in deep bins. Iowa State Univ., Eng. Exp. Sta. Bull. 172.

CHRISTENSEN, C. M., and H. K. KAUFMANN. 1969. Grain storage: The role of fungi in quality loss. Univ. Minn. Press: Minneapolis, Minn.

KETCHUM, M. S. 1919. The design of walls, bins and grain elevators (3rd ed.). McGraw: New York.

STAHL, R. M. 1949. Engineering data on grain storage. Agr. Eng. Data 1. Amer. Soc. Agr. Eng. (St. Joseph, Mich.).

U. S. DEPARTMENT OF AGRICULTURE. 1970. Official grain standards of the U.S. C&MS, Grain Division.

CHAPTER 9

BULK STORAGE OF FLOUR

DONALD E. SCHAETZEL

General Mills, Inc.
Minneapolis, Minnesota

I. INTRODUCTION

Concentration of milling capacity in large modern units and accompanying changes in merchandising methods have made the storage of grain and mill products challenges of major importance.

Wheat presents the most acute problem because it is produced in a short season and must be stored in convenient locations to keep mills operating throughout the year. The development of large concrete grain silos provided a satisfactory solution.

Until recently, flour and other mill products were stored almost entirely in sacks or barrels in multifloor warehouses. The only accumulation in bulk was a small amount held in packer bins, and this was never more than the mill's production of a few hours.

The trend today is toward installation of large-capacity bins that may hold the mill production of many hours or days. Flour is drawn from such bins for blending, direct packing, or bulk loading. While under some circumstances these bins may be used to store flour for relatively long periods, the storage time is usually short as compared with that for wheat. In the following discussion, "bulk storage" is applied to those systems in which mill products are accumulated in large bins other than those normally used to feed the packers.

II. GENERAL OBSERVATIONS

A. General Description

Bulk storage plants for flour consist essentially of bulk bins constructed of concrete, steel, or glass-lined steel; a system to transport mill products and by-products to the bins; and a system of feeders and conveyors to move flour and millfeed to packaging lines, bulk railroad cars, and bulk trucks, and to transfer from one bin to another.

Figure 1 shows a diagram of a modern bulk storage system that includes storage of all mill products. The intake system is designed to mill capacity while

361

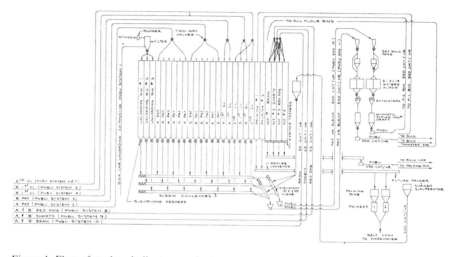

Figure 1. Flow of modern bulk storage plant.

the discharge system is sized to the requirements of packing and/or bulk loading. Rates between these two systems vary greatly.

Care must be taken that millfeed, bran, shorts, red dog, and screenings are so stored as to not permit them, or their dust, to ever contaminate flour products. Many millers do not tolerate millfeed to be stored in bulk flour buildings, others physically separate millfeed from flour product bins by a wall in the bulk house, while still others agree to have adjoining bins but intake and discharge systems must be completely separate down to and including the dust collecting system.

Although packers are common to all milling plants, the introduction of bulk storage imposes certain modifications on the packing system. These are so closely connected with planning and operation of the whole bulk storage layout as to warrant special consideration. Therefore, a section of this chapter is devoted to the specific problems of packing from the bulk storage system.

As a general rule, the bulk storage section starts after flour is transported to bulk bins. This assigns to the miller the responsibility for all aspects of production, including rebolting of the finished product and moving it away from the mill. Some mills operate with the responsibility of the miller ending before the rebolt sifters. Thus the bulk storage operator is responsible for rebolt, weighing, and transport to the bulk bins.

Series of automatic scales or belt-type scales are necessary for accounting purposes since some low-volume streams may accumulate for days or even weeks before being packed. With the older methods of continuous packing, packing rate about equaled production rate, and mill yields and inventory could be readily computed from warehouse tallies. With bulk storage systems, the amount of stock in bins can be determined by calculating from in-and-out tallies or by direct measurement with: 1) the old, reliable method of dropping a tape measure down the bin; 2) sonar level measure units in the bin with a console read-out; or 3) pressure tapes hanging in the bin with a console read-out.

The most costly and least desirable method is removing the product from bins, weighing, and rebinning it.

A highly desirable, although not strictly essential, feature of a good bulk storage plant is a transfer system by which material can be shifted from one bin to another. This can be done in a number of ways to be discussed later in some detail.

B. General Considerations

Published literature suggests that early bulk storage plants were built for the purpose of blending flours to increase the uniformity of the product and to make it possible to meet specifications more accurately. In the last few years, however, bulk storage has been considered more a means of reducing the cost of warehousing, packing, and shipping. The reasons for this additional emphasis are simple. First, the tremendous increase in labor cost has made reduction of handling an economic necessity. Second, a plant designed for blending is often very large, and greatly increased construction costs made it necessary to use large plants to the best possible advantage to justify the investment.

C. Economic Considerations

The economic justification of a capital expenditure for bulk storage is twofold: labor savings and operational improvements. Labor savings are more readily evaluated with the capital outlays which make them possible, and therefore easier to justify. Nevertheless, there is sometimes greater profit in increasing the total value of products by operational improvements than in decreasing the labor cost of producing them.

Labor can be saved in packing operations through bulk storage and, through elimination of warehouse handling, in shipping. Packing cost can be reduced in two ways. First, doing all packing in one shift eliminates extra supervision, laboratory control, and shift premiums required for night work. Second, the introduction of modern high-speed packers reduces the amount of labor required in the packing operation itself.

With bulk shipment by rail and trucks, sufficient flour of a specific grade must be binned before loading of the bulk vehicles. The ideal bulk loading rate is a maximum of several hours to load a railroad car and minutes to load a truck.

Consideration must also be given to what is often referred to as "semi-bulk" loading or tote bins. These are approximately 3,000-lb. containers for service to smaller bakeries that cannot afford either the space for or cost of bulk bins.

The most expensive operation in the mill outside of the cost of wheat is probably the packing in 2-, 5-, 10-, 25-, and 100-lb. bags. If all packaging could be eliminated and only bulk shipments made, the economics of a mill would be unbelievable.

Where mill products are packaged or bagged, shipping cost can be reduced in two ways.

Chutes and/or movable conveyor can transport bags directly to rail car or truck. This is practical only when the packing is so organized that each product is packed at a rate just sufficient to keep a loading crew fully occupied. In the traditional packing department, where all products are packed continuously, the rate of production of all grades, except those produced in largest volume, is too slow for efficient loading.

Secondly, palletizing with lift trucks moving pallets to rail car or truck has often resulted in a warehouse of working aisle size.

With bulk storage it is no longer necessary to pack all products simultaneously, since it is possible to set up high-speed or conventional auger packing lines with a capacity equal to the efficient shipping rate and to pack various products one after another. If total packing capacity requires more than one shipping crew, the desirability of packing two or more products simultaneously rather than in succession must be considered. This permits each line to pack the same product for a longer period and facilitates prompt completion of mixed loads.

Whether savings in packing and shipping by use of bulk storage are possible depends largely on the operation's efficiency without bulk storage. Most small mills ship on day shift only, even though they pack continuously. For these mills, daylight packing eliminates most of the warehouse handling of the products packed on two night shifts. Some large mills, on the other hand, ship on all three shifts. To convert to daylight packing would require a tremendous increase in trackage to permit shipping at the greatly increased rate required. It is doubtful whether the cost of such extra trackage, in addition to extra bins, conveyors, and packing facilities necessary for day-shift packing, could be justified by any potential labor savings. At the same time, these mills may save packing and shipping labor by installing bulk storage and using high-speed packers on three shifts, because they could then pack fewer products at a time and handle the grades produced in smaller volume more efficiently.

D. Operational Advantages

Bulk storage offers the following benefits.

1. Reduction of labor for packing and rehandling of off-grade flour.
2. More controlled feed-in of off-grade flour to the finished flour stream.
3. Longer running time of the mill on each flour grade, thus more uniformity of the product and less set-back flour owing to grade changes on the mill.
4. Ability to accumulate saleable lots of flours produced at very slow rates, such as second clears, with less risk of their becoming infested than when they are accumulated in a warehouse.
5. Improved uniformity of each grade obtained by blending from several bins of the same grade when packing.
6. Production of special grades by blending from bins of previously analyzed standard flours.
7. Ability to obtain analytical data on finished flours or their components before the flours are packed.

Many of these operational improvements are virtually impossible to evaluate. It is therefore common to design a bulk storage plant to permit certain definite labor savings, and then to make changes after start-up to realize more benefits in the form of operational improvements and flexibility. This is not entirely satisfactory, as modifications desirable from an operating standpoint, which would have been inexpensive if made during original construction, are too costly once the plant is built. A more careful consideration during the design stage of operational improvements is well worthwhile.

<h3 style="text-align:center">III. THE BULK STORAGE PLANT</h3>

A. Relation of Plant Size to Desired Functions

A company contemplating bulk storage for the first time must decide how much storage to build. Some plants hold as little as 2 or 3 days' production while others hold more than a month's production. All of these may be considered by their owners to be good investments. In general, operators of any plant complain that it is too small, that a few more bins would be advantageous. In the absence of some unusually favorable factor, such as an idle and well-placed building of the right size and type for bulk storage, the cost of construction is so large that it is essential to know as many facts as possible in advance about functions to be performed, savings to be expected from the performance of these functions, and the cost of providing required facilities.

B. Preliminary Planning

Preliminary planning should consist of the scope of the functions to be performed by the bulk storage, such as: 1) Is flour to be treated in the mill or after bulk storage; 2) is blending to be accomplished in the draw-off system; if so, list all blends and their composition of other flours; 3) to what degree is the blending going to be limited; 4) list of flour or grades to be stored; 5) past grades and blends produced and cwt. of each; 6) allocation of storage volume to each grade; 7) packing capacity for packages and bags of various sizes; 8) bulk loading capacity; 9) the likelihood and combination of blending, treating, and packing different grades of flour; 10) number of packing shifts scheduled per day; 11) handling systems in warehouse for bagged products; 12) desirable flexibility of the system; 13) future expansion of present mill and bulk storage; and 14) elimination of redundancy.

Estimated storage costs should be compared with estimated savings to analyze the project's worth and acted upon accordingly. If maximum investment cannot be justified, the project may be reduced in steps, eliminating the least promising functions first and making cost-versus-savings comparisons at each step.

At some point, a minimum amount of function and operations will be reached where no further reductions can be made without jeopardizing the complete purpose of the bulk plant. Likewise, a maximum investment is set by the savings accomplished. These two critical conditions must meet before a bulk plant can become a reality.

C. Storage Capacity

The optimum plant allows all packing to be done in 8 hr. per day. This requires a storage section with capacity for 16 hr. production (plus working room) and a section capable of packing all products of 24 hr. in 8 hr., or at three times the production rate. A comparatively small additional investment to increase storage capacity to 40 hr. of production and packing rate to 3.6 times the production rate permits the mill to operate 6 days per week with packing still confined to five 8-hr. shifts. With a plant of this size, certain operational improvements, such as longer mill runs, can also be obtained. When the mill is operating only 5 days per week, it permits the accumulation of carload lots of small-volume grades in the bins.

To enable a plant to pack and ship continuously without overtime, storage capacity must be increased to 64 hr. production and packing capacity to 4.25 times the production rate. With a plant of this size, it should also be possible to reduce warehousing and to ship a large portion of the production directly from the packers or to bulk cars or trucks.

Bulk flour storage will probably not allow accumulation of flours so as to take advantage of market fluctuations. The rate of production and cost of bulk storage do not allow any extra profit on long storage of flour from a few cents variation of the price of flour.

In addition to flour storage, successful installations have been made which also include storage of millfeeds in bulk. In deciding the size of the bulk storage plant, consideration should be given to the possibility of providing for feeds storage. A detailed discussion of this subject is beyond the scope of the present chapter. For more information, see page 334.

D. The Bin Block

There are two basic construction materials for large flour bins, i.e., reinforced concrete and sheet steel, with several variations in the fabrication method of each of them.

The optimum cross-section size of a concrete bin is 7×7 ft. (2.13×2.13 m.). These dimensions can vary depending on space available. Slip-form is the most economical method of construction for concrete bins. Bin interiors should be troweled as the form is raised during construction. Surfaces need to be only relatively smooth. A glass-smooth surface encourages bridging of stored material. Many plants installed epoxy-coated walls in the belief that slipperiness would aid in the discharge, but in almost every case the smooth coating had to be removed before the bin discharged properly. Slight roughness of walls allows a percentage of the product weight to transfer to vertical walls, thus reducing product compaction in the lower section of the bin, and in turn reducing the bridging of the product at or near the hopper line. Experience shows that a concrete bulk bin used immediately after being poured caused hang-ups for 18 months, then hang-ups ceased, whereas no hang-up occurred in a bulk house of the same design when the concrete could cure and dry for 4 months. In the latter case, bin covers and feeders were not installed, and natural air movement through the bins aided in the drying process.

The use of concrete presents two major problems.

1. Moisture may migrate through bin walls from a high-moisture product to one of low moisture content, as for example when sugar with a moisture content of 2% is stored in one bin next to one containing flour with a moisture content of 13.5%. Moisture migrates to the sugar causing it to cake and become impossible to withdraw from the bin. Although this example is a little afield from a flour mill bulk storage, it does occur at other food and cereal plants.

2. Flour conveyed directly from the mill is warm and moist. Condensation occurs if and when it is placed in a cold bin. Since concrete has a very poor

insulation value, the temperature of the bin wall approaches the ambient outdoor temperature. To prevent condensation, the concrete must be above the dew point of the entrained air.

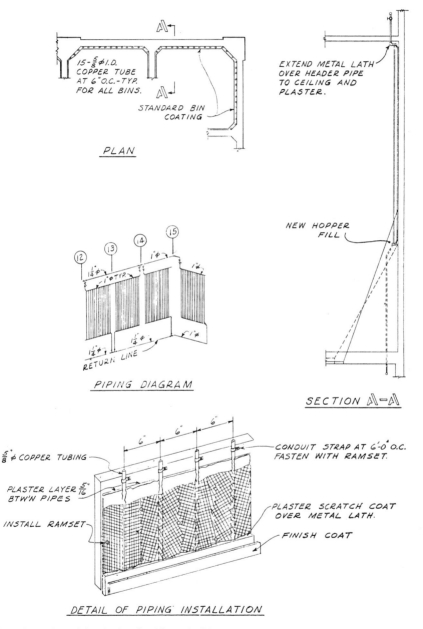

Figure 2. Typical piping for heating bin wall with warm water.

Two methods are employed to combat this problem:

a) The outside wall of the bulk house is of double construction, with an air space between outside and bin walls. With the first floor heated, natural circulation occurs in the air space and maintains a bin wall temperature which prevents condensation.

b) Installation of a hot-water heating system in the bin walls with a continuous flow of hot water to offset the heat loss of the wall to the outside air. This method is generally used when concrete bins are converted to use for flour storage. Figure 2 shows a typical piping diagram and installation of water-heated walls.

Steel bins do not allow moisture migration but still present a condensation problem. Normally the steel bins are housed in a sheet metal, transite, or block-skinned building. This building shell is heated, thus reducing condensation and caking on bin walls. It is considered good practice to sandblast the top one-third of the bin interior and coat it with an FDA (Food and Drug Administration)-approved lacquer varnish or penetrating wax to prevent rusting and corrosion of the steel.

Housekeeping with steel bins presents particular problems. FDA and the plant sanitation staff expect the outside of all bins, braces, girds, and beams on the building to be kept free of flour dust. Tall bins require a system of catwalks to allow proper cleaning. A partial solution would be a floor at the hopper break point or lower and also a floor at the bin's top level, preventing dust from lodging on the steel above, between the floors. Thus housekeeping will be restricted to the bin top and discharge floors, with only occasional cleaning of the bin barrel sections and building walls being required.

Those who use steel bins claim that they are less likely to give trouble with arching and flushing, while those who use concrete bins point to the space savings. Steel bins are easier to fabricate and can be more readily installed in existing structures. Use of concrete demands a very high quality of workmanship coupled with good design. Not every contractor who may be willing to undertake construction of concrete bins can offer this combination of skills. If competent designers and fabricators for both types of structure are available, the decision can be made on the basis of cost, with complete confidence that the chosen system will work satisfactorily.

Reinforced concrete is likely to be less expensive for a very large installation where a new building is required. Steel is likely to be cheaper for very small installations, especially if an existing building can be used. For many installations, the two materials will be competitive in price. If ground area is severely limited, there is a slight advantage in concrete bins because they are made in rectangular shape and give better space utilization. This advantage may not be great, however, because the thicker walls of concrete bins and the air space necessary around bin sections to prevent condensation in all but the warmest climates largely offset the waste space between round bins.

E. Ventilation of Bins

As a bin is being filled, air must find its way out of the bin at the same rate that flour enters. A simple method to achieve this without blowing out flour is to have an outlet at the top of the bin connected to a dust collecting system. The dust collecting system may have either centralized or individual bin vent filters. The hood and its location should be such that excessive selected material is not drawn into the dust system. With the use of individual bin vent filters, the location of the suction point on the bin top loses its importance. Condensation is another problem, especially if the area above the bins is not kept very warm. Flour enters bins at a relatively high temperature and moisture content, and thus the air above the flour in the bin becomes very humid and, if allowed to cool appreciably, will deposit water which drips back into the bin and forms dough. Ventilation by drawing off air continually from each bin reduces this difficulty. Fresh air introduced from the area above the bins lowers the average humidity of the air in the spaces above the flour to safer levels.

With present air pollution laws, FDA regulations, and OSHA regulations, it is almost mandatory that a suction system be utilized while filling a bin. Larger air volumes are necessary if the bin is filled pneumatically than if it is filled from a collector, elevator head, or screw conveyor system. Since a dust collection system with filters is expensive to install and has no processing value, a knowledgeable professional should design it.

F. Size and Number of Bins

Bin sizes and number to be built are among the first decisions to be made in planning a bulk storage plant. In the basic planning of the system, storage capacity is considered in terms of the mill's hourly productive capacity. However, a certain storage capacity can be achieved in a number of ways, depending on the size of individual bins chosen. This choice has considerable bearing on the cost of the project. A few operating factors must be balanced against cost factors in deciding on bin sizes.

Bins of the same size offer advantages and disadvantages. Bin sizes are often arbitrarily selected, especially in the case of small bins whose cost per cwt. rises very rapidly. Cost increases result not only from increased building costs, but also from additional equipment for the intake and discharge of each bin. Generally, the capacity of each bin should have some simple relationship to either the rate of manufacture or to a shipping unit size.

Each bin must have a discharge feeder and drive requiring at least 20 sq. ft. (1.86 m.^{2}) of area, which sets a minimum on the cross-sectional area of bins. Some designers agree that a cross-sectional area of about 60 sq. ft. (5.57 m.^{2}) is as large as is practical, although some of the reasons for setting this limit are not clearly understood or agreed upon. One of the best reasons for limiting the cross-sectional area of a bin is that the bin height increases rapidly as the cross-section of the bin increases because of the steep slope required in hoppers and space wasted in hoppering. Other reasons are based on operating difficulties with large bins.

Height of bins is likely to be influenced by the height of adjacent buildings or by some other extraneous factor. In the absence of such restrictions, bins have been built as tall as 100 ft. (30 m.) without operating difficulty. This appears to be considered the upper limit with usual ranges between 75 ft. (23 m.) and 100 ft. (30 m.). Local building codes may specify the maximum height of a new building.

The weight of flour is reported as 35 to 40 lb. per cu. ft., but the method of transporting flour to bins and the time flour has been stored in bins dictate its specific weight. In tests conducted by the Fuller Co. and General Mills, Inc., flour on an "airslide" had specific weights as low as 10 lb. per cu. ft. Naturally, as the flour falls in the bin and comes to rest, the air will leave the entrainment of the flour, and the weight per cubic foot will increase to a normal of 35 lb. per cu. ft. after a period of time. It is theoretically conceivable that a bin with the capacity calculated from its volume and 35 lb. per cu. ft. of 100,000 lb. would hold approximately 43,000 lb. for a period of time if filled at a high rate and with an airslide conveyor.

Possibly the soundest approach is to decide first the number of bins required to take care of all products plus extras for working room. The number of hours of production these bins would hold if they were all of the maximum practical size should then be determined. If this capacity is more than is considered desirable, the bin size is reduced until the grade most rapidly produced will just fill a bin in the required time. If it is not enough, a sufficient number of bins is added. This will probably give the most economical storage that will operate satisfactorily. Starting the design with a limit on total storage volume is likely to result in smaller (and more) bins giving less total storage but not necessarily lower cost.

An example may serve to clarify this point. A mill wishes to provide bulk storage for seven grades of flour produced at the following average rates in sacks per hour: A, 13; B, 50; C, 75; D, 163; E, 200; F, 237; G, 250. Flour D must go to the storage bins with two different treatments; the change-off flour must also be accommodated; and as the most complicated run produces three grades of flour, three extra bins should be allowed for working room. At least 12 bins are thus required. With bins having a capacity of 2,000 sacks, the flour could be accumulated for the following periods: A, 154 hr.; B, 40 hr.; C, 26.7 hr.; D, 12.3 hr.; D_1, 12.3 hr.; E, 10 hr.; F, 8.4 hr.; G, 8 hr.

For minimum daylight packing, storage must be provided for the production of each grade being produced within 16 hr. plus extra bins for working room and change-off. Grades D, D_1, E, F, and G would each require two bins; but as not more than two of them are made at one time, only two extra bins need be considered. Total requirement is therefore 14 bins.

If a smaller bin size is chosen to reduce excess capacity provided for low-volume flours, some savings in bin construction will be effected. This will, however, be more or less completely offset by the cost of extra feeders required for the additional bins for the more rapidly produced grades. Accordingly, the total capital expenditure will probably equal that for a plant having a larger total storage capacity. In some plants, a bin is allocated for change-off flour, but it may be better to provide a bin or bins for that purpose adjacent to the mill rather than in the bulk storage plant.

IV. THE FLOW OF FLOUR

A. The Intake System

The system conveying products from mill to bins must be capable of delivering each of the various products made simultaneously to a separate storage bin. It must be possible to switch any product stream from one bin to another without interrupting the flow. During binning, there will be three mill streams whose amounts may be 65, 30, and 5% of the mill production, requiring three conveying

TABLE I
Conveying equipment: advantages and disadvantages

	Advantages	Disadvantages
Screw conveyors	Low horsepower per unit weight conveyed Simple and common design Easily opened for cleaning Slow r.p.m. Low maintenance Unlimited number of discharge and inlet points	Must be cleaned periodically Drop-bottom design recommended True alignment increases installation cost Layer of flour remains in trough, thus possible infestation harbor Can be only in straight line; additional conveyors needed to turn corners
Bucket elevators	Extremely efficient machine Low horsepower per unit weight elevated Large volume of material conveyed per sq. ft. floor area used Low to medium maintenance	Very dusty operation; needs suction to eliminate dust Motor location always in inconvenient place Major cause of mill and elevator fires or explosions Elevator bucket replacement often difficult
Air slides	Extremely high volume transported for area of conveyor Swift movement of product Relatively low horsepower needed on low-pressure fan Can be cheaply diverted to any number of bins Can be curved to change direction	Must slope conveyor down hill to flow properly Dusty discharge; need suction at discharge System must be very tight-fitting Up to 1/4 in. residue of flow on fabric bottom when turned off
Pneumatic systems	Most sanitary conveyance available Does not reduce moisture content of flour Conveying lines can bend and weave around obstacles or to other bins with ease Simple operation and installation	System chokes more readily when overloaded than elevators or screw conveyors High horsepower per unit of weight conveyed Motor-blower package relatively large Produces high decibel level of noise at blower location

systems with these capacities. If finished grades are being binned, mill flour may consist of one, two, or three grades, and provision must be made for handling the various combinations. This is most simply done with three conveying systems with capacities of 100, 50, and 10% of the mill production. For most mills the same conveyors, with some alteration in speed, would serve for either condition.

As previously noted, scales or weighing devices are either part of the responsibility of the mill or of the bulk house. After the flour is weighed, it is conveyed mechanically or pneumatically to the bins. By means of slides, mechanical conveyors, or switch valves in pneumatic bins, the flow can be directed to any pre-specified bin. Entoleters (infestation destroyers) can be used on flours before they enter the bins. Use of the entoleter before binning does not assure infestation-free flour when it is withdrawn from the bin. For a discussion of the "sterile zone" on the bin discharge, see page 375.

Because a dump scale used to weigh flours creates a pulsating flow, each scale must be fitted with a discharge hopper designed to absorb the surge and enable the conveyor to spread the load over the interval between dumps. Since it is impractical to adjust the system so precisely that the hopper is just empty when the next dump arrives, the conveyor must be slightly over capacity and will sometimes run empty. It must therefore be a type which can run empty without suffering damage or excessive wear. The hopper should be large enough to prevent flour from interfering with the scale's action.

Since the scale causes high variation of flow rates, blending after a dump scale is impossible without further holding bins and metering devices. With dump scales, flour should be blended prior to weighing or after discharge from bulk bins.

The various types of equipment used on both the intake and discharge of bulk bins are the same, each with advantages and drawbacks. The major ones are listed in Table I.

Drop-through entoleters are available for mechanical systems and blow-through entoleters fit into pneumatic lines and operate in conjunction with pneumatic systems.

B. The Discharge System

Conveying systems from bins to packers, bulk truck, or railroad can be designed to meet specific requirements of the bulk storage system. The simplest and easiest procedure, as far as the bulk operator is concerned, is to draw a mill-prepared blend from a bin and transport it to the packer, car, or truck. It may, however, be desirable to draw approximately equal amounts from two or more bins to increase product uniformity or to blend the contents of several bins in precise proportions to produce the desired grade from mill streams in the bins. In other installations, two or more packers may be fed from one conveying or blending system, or two or more complete systems may be required, each capable of feeding one or more packers. Where two complete systems are required, each may be able to draw from all bins, each may serve a separate group of bins, or some bins may be served by both discharge systems and others by only one.

When blending capabilities are added to the bulk house, motors or drives of variable speeds are a necessity on the bin feeders.

C. Hoppers

In the past, it was standard practice to put a steel hopper on concrete bins. In recent years satisfactory hoppers have been built with approximately the upper half made of concrete and the lower half of metal.

Hopper shape is determined by the shape of the bin, the inlet, and the feeder into which it discharges. Feeder size is determined to some extent by the capacity required. For small flows, such as in blending systems, wing-type feeders with square inlets are satisfactory if the diameter of the bin is not too large. A discharge opening of only 1 sq. ft. from a bin of 7 sq. ft. will constantly plug or choke. For larger capacities, double-screw conveyors, with positive, infinitely variable speed reducer drives, are commonly used. These have rectangular inlets whose width is determined by the sizes of screws, and whose length can be varied to fit the bin. One rule of thumb is that the feeder inlet area should be about 20% of the bin area.

The area of an ideal hopper outlet is larger than the barrel of the bin. Although this is possible with certain ingredients in feed mills, it is impractical in a flour bulk house. The next best solution would be to have hopper outlet area equal that of the bin. This is impractical because of lack of room for drives and because the live bottom discharge would feed at such a high rate that no conveying or packing system could handle the flow.

Generally, no hopper surface should be inclined less than 70° from horizontal. When possible, three straight sides are desirable. On round bins, this allows two areas for expansion in the bin when drawing off, thus reducing some of the bin pressure that could cause bridging. It is also common to construct hoppers in such a way that the side opposite the slope is vertical, or with two straight sides. Both round and square bin hoppers can be constructed with straight sides, but the round bin hopper will be a little more costly, because sheet metal work is more complex. These rules of thumb tend to reduce bridging of the product.

However, hoppers from round steel bins constructed without vertical sides operate satisfactorily, leaving the necessity for vertical sides open to question. It is much more important that there be neither ledges nor sharp corners. One serious defect in some early designs was the bolting of hoppers to insides of walls. Today, hoppers on concrete bins are attached to the bottom of the bin wall without ledges at the point of attachment. This joint is sometimes subjected to tremendous pressure and must be carefully sealed to prevent leaks.

It is obvious from the above that there is no absolute formula for design of flour bins that will completely prevent bridging or hang-ups. All bin designers stay therefore well within the limits of the rules of thumb provided by experience.

Flat-bottom bins have also been used in bulk houses to save the space otherwise needed for the hopper. These bins can range up to 20 ft. (6 m.) in diameter and have a discharge opening in the floor center. Because flour naturally bridges over this relatively small opening, a rotating screw conveyor is installed on the bin bottom to deliver the product into the bin opening. Changing the discharge rate of this arrangement is more difficult than that of more conventional bin dischargers.

D. Feeders

Of the several types of feeders, those most widely used are:

1. Wing-type feeders, also referred to as rotary-type, range in size from 12×12 in. to 16×47 in. Since they are volumetric by design, feed rates through rotary feeders are very accurate, with a free flow to them and a constant specific weight of the flour.

2. Screw feeders normally have two screws side by side, driven in opposite rotation. Screw flights are tapered from the full diameter at the discharge end to about 30% of the flight height at the far end. Many engineers prefer a variable pitch on the screw flight to facilitate an even draw-down across the full width of the bin outlet.

3. Air slide feeders give nearly all flour in bin hoppers the flow characteristics of water. Any crack, hole, or other opening causes a flow of product. While this quality eliminates bridging in the area of aeration, it also makes the flood of flour out of the bin difficult to control. Slides have proved ineffective, as slight openings only act as weirs in the existing hydrostatic condition. At a bulk storage plant in Louisville, Kentucky, with air slide bin dischargers, a small bin and a level sensor above a wing-type feeder had to be installed on each bin in the bulk house to control and meter the flour from the bin.

Movable hoppers flexibly connected to bin walls have proved satisfactory. However, increased cost of the hopper itself and special structural supports tend to rule this out in favor of more conventional feeders.

All feeders should be calibrated through their operating range. Wing-type feeders are the most reliable for a direct ratio of feed to r.p.m., but the few minutes spent calibrating the feeder is well worthwhile.

E. Control of Flour to Packers

Flour travels from feeders through the conveying system to rebolt sifters and entoleters into the feed hopper of the packer. If the hopper becomes full, a bindicator switch stops the motor driving the feeders; if it becomes empty, another bindicator starts the feeders. The operator adjusts the flow rate with the variable speed drive on the feeders to keep the packer hopper partly full, without having feeders continually going on and off.

If two packers are to be supplied from one conveying system, care must be taken to prevent trouble when one packer does not operate continuously. If each packer has its own sifter, neither sifter will take the full stream. The full stream will overload the other sifter if one packer hopper fills up. This problem can be solved by having all sifters discharge into a common hopper or distributing conveyor from which the packers draw. Such a system will permit one product to be packed into two different containers simultaneously.

If two different products are to be packed at the same time, a second complete conveying system must be set up to feed the second packing unit. As each bin usually has only one feeder under it, provision must be made to shift each feeder to either conveyor system. It may not be necessary for both conveying systems to serve all bins, but there should be at least some bins served by both systems.

F. The Transfer System

The principal need for a transfer system with intake and discharge conveyor systems designed for highest flexibility is to permit the transfer of flour from one bin to another. For example, two partly filled bins of the same product may need to be combined into one, or a blend of flour from several bins may be drawn and put into a special bin.

A transfer elevator leg may be needed in a mechanical house, while in a pneumatically operated house only a switch valve in the pneumatic line to the packers with pneumatic line to the distribution system on the bin top may be necessary.

Scheduling of the transfer operation is necessary if the transfer system uses a portion of the intake system to reach the bin and/or a portion of the discharge system to draw from bins. The normal loading, packaging, and intake systems can operate if the transfer system is completely independent. The bulk loading system is quite often used for transfer, since truck and rail car loading are done in less than a complete shift.

G. Sterile Zone

The sterile zone consists of a rebolt sifter to dress the flour just before leaving the bulk house and an entoleter to destroy any infestation that may have developed since the previous entoleter treatment. This zone is located just before the packaging area and just before the bulk scale in the system leading to bulk trucks and rail cars.

V. THE PACKING DEPARTMENT

The packing department must be capable of packing the mill's total production during its working hours. In mills without bulk storage, this requires a sufficient number of packers to pack each grade at the maximum average rate at which it is produced. The standard auger packer can be operated by one man at an average rate of 60 cwt. sacks per hr. Any grade produced at a slower rate is not fully efficient. Packing on day shift only is possible with bulk storage requiring an average rate of at least three times the mill production rate. To obtain maximum efficiency in day-shift packing, the shipping rate must at least equal the packing rate so that a major portion of the production can be conveyed directly from packers to shipping docks.

A. Packing Rates

If the production schedule calls for grinding 6 days per week but for only 5 days' packing and shipping, the packing and shipping rates must be increased, as noted earlier, to 3.6 times the production rate. To grind continuously for 7 days per week, while still packing and shipping in five shifts, requires an average packing rate of 4.25 times the production rate. These figures refer to average rates sustained for a full 8 hr. If the actual operating time of the packers is only 7 hr. per shift, the packing rate during the operating period must be correspondingly greater. If packers have to change frequently from one product to another, effective packing time may be much less than 7 hr. per shift. Similarly, if trackage is so limited that cars have to be switched into and out of shipping docks several times per shift, the actual time spent in loading cars may be considerably less than 7 hr. per shift, and the actual shipping rate must be correspondingly greater.

Before the development of high-speed packers, packing rates could only be increased by installing more packers, and the mill converting to day-shift packing was faced with either building a new packing facility or greatly enlarging its existing one. New packers, however, capable of handling up to four times as much flour per machine, with very little more floor space, make it possible to convert to day-shift packing the same space previously used for continuous packing.

B. Size of Packages

Not many years ago, 100-lb. cotton or jute sacks were used for most of the flour produced in America. More recently paper has become increasingly important, and now its use about equals that of cotton. Jute sacks are seldom used in domestic trade but are still fairly popular for export markets. Another important development is the increasing use of smaller packages which are almost exclusively made of paper. Packages of 25 lb. and smaller are not filled on regular packers, but are handled with entirely different machinery. One such unit can pack and seal approximately 600 10-lb. packages per hr., handling the same amount of flour as an auger packer, but requiring three operators, two of whom may be persons of slight physical strength. The total amount of flour sold in small packages is relatively small. Although many mills do not pack any small packages, some pack most of their production for grocery stores. These mills have much greater difficulty in adjusting their packing operations to fluctuations in the ratio of large to small packages, because labor requirements are so much greater for small packages.

A mill with a packing capacity of 4.25 times its production rate should be able to pack without overtime even when the mill runs continuously. Unless, however, the capacity is properly distributed between large and small packages and between large paper and cotton sacks, it may be necessary to run part of the packing department overtime to meet a heavy demand for a particular size or type of package, while the rest of the packers are idle. For this reason, a mill with a diverse trade and subject to wide demand fluctuations should install packing equipment as versatile as possible. In this case, the total packing capacity which ensures that no overtime be incurred is considerably more than 4.25 times the production rate, but it is seldom all used at once. If bins are to maintain a varying inventory, the packing capacity is determined by the maximum rate at which the sales department wishes to ship. This may be much greater than 4.25 times the production rate.

C. High-Speed Packers

The first high-speed packer to be developed was the valve bag packer. This is an excellent machine proved through many years of service. Its main limitation is that it can be used only for filling paper bags, and the special patented valve bag must be used. If a mill has sufficient demand for flour in paper bags to keep one of these machines busy continuously it is probably still the most economical way to pack.

More recently, two other types of high-speed packers have been developed which can handle both cotton and open-mouth paper bags. These more versatile machines are still being improved, but at present neither operates equally well with cotton and paper. However, a mill with a fluctuating demand for both types of bag should consider one of the machines.

Machines imported from Europe have made high-speed packaging of 2-, 5-, 10-, and 25-lb. family packages possible. These machines are a vast improvement over old machines made in the U.S.

D. Other Packing Problems

Although some mills with bulk storage may not have high-speed packers, they nevertheless want to reduce the number of grades being packed simultaneously and thus simplify the conveying system from bins to packers and increase packing and shipping efficiencies. The simplest way is to pack one product at a time, requiring only one conveyor system from bins to packers. With separate packers for paper and cotton sacks, it may sometimes be desirable to pack the same product in the two different containers at the same time, necessitating two product streams from packers to warehouse and loading docks. If these two streams are wanted at different destinations, there must be either two separate conveying systems from the packers or a merging device to put bags from different sources on one conveyor and a sorting station somewhere along the route to separate cotton from paper bags. If some packers can pack either paper or cotton sacks, and there are separate conveyors from the packers, these packers must have a means of delivering to either conveyor.

Since mills usually pack only one or two grades in this manner, they must be able to supply the small-package line with the proper grade when the main packing department is packing other grades. This can be accomplished with a special conveying system from the bulk bins for this unit, or with auxiliary storage bins which are filled when the grade is being produced or when it is being packed, and from which the small package line draws.

One high-speed packer should be adequate for a 2,000-cwt. mill, but a second machine should be available, since it is unwise to tie the operation of the mill to a single packer. Only larger mills need consider packing more than one product at a time when high-speed packers are used. The deciding factor is shipping facilities. One high-speed packer keeps a shipping crew reasonably busy, but the stream from two such packers working on the same product can be handled by a crew less than twice as large. If most of the mill's production is shipped in straight carload lots, it is most economical to pack one product at a time. If, on the other hand, most shipments consist of two or more products, the large mill should be able to pack at least two products simultaneously, unless it has sufficient trackage to spot all cars for a day's shipping at one time. Under the latter conditions, different products can be loaded into all cars in sequence and dispatched at the end of the shift.

E. Sanitation

With increased emphasis on sanitation, requirements have risen from the "I-suppose-we-have-to-do-it" to a primary demand. Rebolting of flour through 9xx silk has long been the accepted method for removing all insect life, and the method is theoretically sound. Recently entoleters have come into common use to destroy insects and insect eggs that may be in the flour. However, it is nigh impossible to maintain all sieves in perfect condition and to prevent an occasional leak in the rebolt sifter, hence constant checking must be maintained on the rebolt sifter.

Present marketing conditions and emphasis on customer satisfaction make it equally important that flour packed is free of infestation. The sterile zone assures the packing of such flour. If flour is held in a bin for any appreciable time, the insects may establish breeding spots, and a minor leak on the rebolts may cause infestation of a large quantity of flour. The only sure way of decontaminating an infested bin is to empty it completely and treat the contents with a penetrating fumigant such as methyl bromide. The flour removed can be fumigated in sacks. Fumigants must be FDA-approved.

Infestation can best be prevented with an entoleter impact machine. This machine does not require careful maintenance to keep it at top efficiency. It does not replace rebolting for removal of other foreign material, but it ensures that occasional leaks through the rebolts do not cause infestation in the bins. The cost of an entoleter on the inlet of each bin is prohibitive in most cases. It is therefore usually placed just ahead of each conveyor serving the bins or on each stream from the mill, as discussed previously.

Flour has always been rebolted immediately before packaging, and this is probably desirable. However, it does not seem necessary to rebolt through very fine cloth more than once. If flour is rebolted through 9xx as it leaves the mill, any contamination other than insect eggs it may receive subsequently can be removed on a coarse screen, such as 38-wire.

Effective sanitation can be obtained with entoleters at the mill and rebolt sifters clothed with 9xx silk followed by entoleters over each packer. A somewhat less expensive method for as good or better protection would include: rebolt sifters clothed with 9xx at the mill, entoleters on each stream, rebolt sifters clothed with 38-wire, followed by entoleters over each packer. The entoleters over the packers are probably the least essential in this system, although they are most often installed in this location. If bins are kept free of insects and reasonable housekeeping is maintained in the packing department, there should be no need for entoleters at the packers. However, by the same reasoning, if the mill is kept free of insects, there is no need for entoleters at the bin inlets. Each added precaution is merely insurance against serious consequences resulting from conditions which are not normally expected to occur.

VI. BULK STORAGE OF MILLFEEDS

Although the discussion of bulk storage has been confined to flour, and rightly so, because it is the principal product of wheat milling, it is recognized that the millfeeds—bran, shorts, and middlings—can also be stored in bulk. Indeed, in a milling system designed for packing a 24-hr. production in 8 hr., bulk storage must be provided for all products of the mill.

There are some special considerations in the bulk storage of millfeeds that almost warrant a separate treatise. However, as many of the considerations are common to both flour and feeds, it may suffice to point out here only a few of the specific differences to emphasize that additional factors must be assessed when extension of bulk storage is being planned to accommodate all other products of the mill.

Bulk storage of feeds is both simpler and more complex than that of flour. There are fewer products, they are not usually blended, and they are almost universally packed in 100-lb. bags or in bulk. Furthermore, as feeds represent only about 25% by weight (about 33% by volume) of total mill products, the production rate is relatively low and fairly constant. These factors tend to simplify planning for space.

However, disposal methods for feeds are more varied in one sense than those for flour, and the kind and amount of storage to be provided must be planned in detail. Furthermore, owing to the nature of these products, difficulties with compacting in the bins, with discharge, and with conveying create problems for which completely satisfactory solutions are not obtainable. Feeds flow less readily from bins than do flours, but with live-bottom bin dischargers and cable-supported discs in the bin, flow of millfeed is no longer a problem in bulk storage. It is even more important with millfeeds than with flour that bin walls not be glass-smooth.

Millfeeds may be disposed of in one or more of three different ways: in 100-lb. bags; in bulk cars; and by direct, continuous transfer to an adjacent formula feed mixing plant where they are received into appropriate bins. Frequently all three means of egress from the mill are used.

Bagging feeds is not any more complex than bagging flour, except for the behavior of these soft-textured products in large bins. Feeds may be packed throughout 24-hr. days, since the packing crew needed is small. A 6,000-cwt. mill produces feeds at about 85 cwt. per hr., an amount that can be handled easily by a small crew. If, however, part of the feed output is being loaded in bulk cars or diverted to a formula feed plant, the small amount to be packed in bags scarcely warrants the cost of keeping the packing crew on during two night shifts, and it becomes relatively expensive to do so. Under these circumstances, bulk storage with only daylight packing would be justified economically.

Another consideration is that of loading cars "off the line," either in bulk or in bags. When drawn from bulk storage, feeds can be loaded into cars at 1 to 2 hr. per car, but the full output of bran or shorts from a 6,000-cwt. mill would require 20 to 24 hr. to make up a carload. Loading straight cars of feeds from bulk storage is more economical and avoids long tie-up of carloading spots. For these reasons, some mills may justify bulk storage for millfeeds, even though they may not be able to justify it for flour.

High-speed packers for feeds, designed to handle 60 to 80 bags per hr., are available. However, there is scarcely a plant on this continent that could keep one of these packers running steadily off the line of production. Only with adequate bulk storage could the installation of such packers for feeds be justified.

VII. PROBLEMS ARISING FROM BULK STORAGE

Thus far considerations pertinent to planning, installing, and operating a bulk storage system for flour have been discussed. The treatment of the subject has of necessity been generalized and would perhaps fit best into the planning of completely new units. It is fully realized that most bulk storage plants erected in the next few years will be adjuncts to existing flour mills or to plants consuming a large amount of bulk material, each of which will be unique in its layout, capacity, and operation. The introduction of bulk storage of flour into an existing mill brings in its train a number of technical and operating problems not normally encountered in conventional mills, particularly in the smaller ones. These problems cannot be dealt with in any detailed manner because they vary with each mill. However, this chapter would not be complete without a survey of difficulties to which to be alert in related operations once the bulk storage has been installed.

As these problems arise from the introduction of new operations and from acceleration or grouping of otherwise familiar operations, they must each be studied individually. Partial or complete solutions have been found for some of them, but no attempt will be made here to describe these solutions or to judge the merits of various methods of solution. Usually, recognition of the problem will provide a lead to its solution.

Bulk storage itself is a new operation that presents problems not encountered before. While there may be a tendency to consider bulk storage bins merely as extensions of packer hoppers, this view is incorrect for various reasons. Arching in a hopper can be remedied with a mallet, but arching in a large bin may require elaborate means of correction. The collapse of arched flour does not destroy a packing hopper, but it can cause serious damage to an incorrectly designed bin. Flushing in a packing hopper occurs right in front of the operator, and he can stop it immediately, but flushing through a feeder in a large bin chokes equipment following the feeder.

Carry-over of stock in a distributing screw conveyor can be serious where this method is used to deliver flour to a group of storage bins.

Condensation causes little trouble in a conventional mill where warm flour is handled in warm surroundings until it is in the sack. However, with bulk storage which may or may not be adequately protected, the flour can misbehave in many ways due to condensation, and the nature of the trouble may not always be apparent. For example, arching may occur in a bin which has never arched before, if the temperature has dropped just enough to cause condensation at critical points.

Aside from storage itself, other operations may be introduced for the first time with bulk storage. Automatic scales and/or belt scales are normally provided to weigh the streams to storage. Besides weighing the streams, scales interrupt and bunch them, causing irregular flow which must be allowed for in the design of the conveying system beyond the scales.

Blending and treatment of flour streams, if added to the system, is a new operation. More pitfalls in the blending of flours are likely to be encountered than in the blending of other materials. The accuracy of conventional blending equipment depends on a number of variable conditions which need to be understood and allowed for:

1) Accuracy of calibration;

2) inherent differences in different flours;

3) linearity of feeder response;

4) effect of pressure variations on feeder response, and frequency and magnitude of pressure variations;

5) variations in flour density;

6) existence and effectiveness of alarms, interlocks, and other protective devices;

7) the human element.

Blending difficulties may occur even if blending is not a normal operation. For example, in the absence of proper interlocks, the discharge system may accidentally draw from more than one bin at a time, thus mixing flours inadvertently.

In some plants, proper use of bulk storage may make it necessary to use more than one high-speed packer on one stream of flour. There is nothing unusual in the use of more than one conventional packer on one stream, and balancing the loads is not difficult. The hopper over the packer is large in relation to the packing rate. If one packer stops, there is ample time to adjust the stream rate, speed up the other packers, or switch in a spare packer. But with high-speed packers, the hopper may contain only a few minutes' supply, and if one packer does not function properly, there will be a choke unless it is prevented automatically.

A bin level indicator on each hopper ordinarily shows when it is too full, or better, stops the feed when this occurs. However, the feed is stopped to all packers and before production can be resumed, the feed rate must be adjusted to suit the remaining packers, and the slide controlling the supply to the defective packer must be closed. All of this must be done manually and takes time. It has to be done again in reverse as soon as the defective packer is ready to restart. Moreover, as most delays are of unknown duration when they begin, operators will, if left to themselves, let the whole system remain idle during the delay with consequent unnecessary production loss.

A sterile zone is commonly installed above the hopper of each high-speed packer, and sifters are supplied from a common conveyor. If instead all rebolt sifters form a common conveyor from which each packer hopper is fed, the problem is greatly simplified. The system stops and starts more often since the feed rate exceeds the packing rate by some small margin, but no harm is done. With rebolt sifters designed to carry only normal operating loads, however, stopping one of them will automatically overload the remainder and a choke inevitably results.

The most serious problem arising from acceleration and grouping of operations may well be a failure to grasp just how much acceleration is involved. As equipment becomes larger, it becomes expensive to "overdesign." Large equipment is therefore usually devised close to expected requirements, and it may be impossible as well as undesirable to overload it. Thus, a 2-hr. interruption of packing in 24 hr. requires a 10% acceleration to catch up, but a 2-hr. interruption in an 8-hr. day requires a 33% speed-up to catch up in 1 day. The extra capacity needed to meet emergencies of this kind must be planned into the design of all equipment in the discharge system—feeders, conveyors, elevators, sifters, and packers. Conventional auger packers have a reserve capacity which can be exploited by a skillful operator. High-speed packers, however, have a maximum speed which is in effect the normal operating speed, and there is no inherent extra capacity.

The delivery of sacks from packing room to warehouse or to cars at three or four times the previous rate may disrupt the normal handling method at the receiving end, since only a limited number of men can be usefully employed at a conventional receiving table. Any irregularity in the stream rate or any interruptions cause further troubles which tend to be cumulative.

If the stream is too large or if it is required at more than one destination at one time, some form of splitting or sorting must be used. In conventional mills, sorting occurs either at the sewing machine, usually by the sewing machine operator, or at a sorting table. A sorting table may be practical in mills with individual sewing machines, with or without high-speed packers and with a large stream, since there is no longer a sewing position where sacks can be sorted. The introduction of bulk storage may therefore bring with it the need for entirely new methods of sorting, splitting streams of bags, or palletizing.

In some cases the problem is reversed. Rather than splitting, streams need to be merged or both processes may occur in the same plant. Merging is needed when the production from more than one packer is required at one destination or must travel a common route. In the conventional mill with auger packers and a common sewing machine, the merging is taken care of by individual operators who select a suitable place on the sewing belt to deposit each bag. With individual sewing machines, operators no longer need to handle bags to get them away. To have men lift bags onto a common belt just to merge their production becomes a waste of labor. Mechanical merging devices are then required.

Packing and handling of short runs and small packages may become unexpectedly complicated when bulk storage is introduced. At higher packing speeds, a short run becomes a shorter run, and the time of changing runs and the amount of mixed flour which must be set aside become much more significant. Small packages are handled on special machinery operating at a speed far below the normal packing rate in terms of pounds of flour per hour. Allowance must therefore be made for the time the discharge system is to be operated at this reduced rate, unless a separate discharge system is used for small packages.

Of operating problems brought about by bulk storage, the only one new in kind rather than in degree is probably that of production records. As soon as some production is binned and not packed, mill production and packing room production are no longer the same. Automatic scales on each stream measure mill production, and packer tallies give packing room production. Inevitably over a time there are gains or losses which must be known. This can only be done by either emptying the bins or taking inventory. Accountants tend to be skeptical of bin soundings and even of weigh-ups. They prefer to have bins run out, which of course defeats the object of having bins. Weigh-ups are expensive, both in equipment and time. Even sounding takes time better used otherwise. Much distress can be avoided if methods for obtaining required records are decided upon before construction, and equipment, such as the automatic systems previously mentioned, can be arranged accordingly.

VIII. CONCLUSION

Most of the considerations necessary for careful and intelligent planning of bulk storage for flour have been enumerated. Recognizing that each milling plant is unique in its physical aspects and in its operation, specific details which can best be worked out on the actual job have been deliberately avoided. For management, engineering, and operating departments, this chapter should serve to point out the many factors that must be thoroughly considered in planning the installation of bulk storage facilities for flour. Going beyond the actual bulk storage unit itself, this chapter also deals with some problems that may arise as consequences of such installation.

The many advantages of bulk storage of flour can be fully realized only if all factors involved are thoroughly known and studied before the final plan is accepted. Most difficulties usually attendant to the start-up of a new bulk storage system can be avoided, or at least reduced in severity, if the project is carefully planned with full recognition of all effects the system may have on the entire milling plant.

CHAPTER 10

AIRTIGHT STORAGE

M A R Y B. H Y D E

Ministry of Agriculture, Fisheries, and Food
Pest Infestation Control Laboratory, Slough, Bucks, England

I. INTRODUCTION

Although in recent years there has been a marked increase in the use of airtight storage, it is by no means a new method of preserving grain. From ancient times people in countries in southern Europe, the Middle East, and the drier parts of America and Asia have stored grain in simple underground pits, as described by Doyère (1862), Attia (1948), Cotton (1961), and Janjua and Nasir (1948). These pits were not always airtight, but were usually lined with straw or chaff which absorbed moisture entering from the soil or through leaks in the cover. This dampened straw became moldy, and in so doing used up the oxygen in the air in the pit, which usually contained very dry grain. An early writer on the pit stores in Malta (Jones, 1842) claimed that a certain amount of dampness was essential for successful storage, but recent work (Hyde and Daubney, 1960) has shown that neither damp grain nor straw is necessary if the pit is completely waterproof and airtight.

In recent years airtight storage has been developed both to control insects in dry grain, and to prevent mold growth in high-moisture grain.

II. THE PRINCIPLE OF AIRTIGHT STORAGE

Whether the grain is dry or damp, the principle of airtight storage is the same — depletion of the oxygen in the airtight structure to a level which kills or inactivates the harmful organisms, either insects or molds, before they have become numerous enough to cause serious damage to the grain. Although this removal of oxygen usually results from respiration of the pests themselves, oxygen-free atmospheres can also be produced artificially.

All living organisms require energy, which is normally produced by the activity known as respiration. The respiratory processes associated with the storage of grain have already been described in Chapter 2 (p. 56), but they will be summarized briefly here to explain the principle on which airtight storage is based. Normally, in air, respiration involves the breakdown of carbohydrates (either those of the grain itself or of the food consumed by insects or molds) according to a general equation, which for a hexose sugar such as glucose may be represented as

$$C_6H_{12}O_6 + 6O_2 \rightarrow 6CO_2 + 6H_2O + 677 \text{ kcal.}$$

in which the oxygen required is absorbed from the air. As well as carbon dioxide and water, a considerable amount of energy, in the form of heat, is produced in the process.

The respiration of dry, uninfested grain is relatively low, but in the presence of insects the rate of respiration, as measured by production of carbon dioxide, is much higher, as shown in Table I (compiled from Lindgren, 1935), which also reveals that the rate is greater at a higher temperature. Lindgren's results showed that although the rate of respiration of infested grain was less at low moisture contents, owing to high mortality of the insects, there was little increase in output of carbon dioxide by the insects as the grain moisture content was increased from 14.0 to 17.4%, indicating that the insects were little affected by increase in moisture content over 14%. In contrast to insects, most fungi are unable to develop at relative humidities below 70%, which, in cereal grains, corresponds to a moisture content of about 14%; and such grain, if uninfested by insects, has the low rate of respiration expected of a dormant seed.

Bailey and Gurjar (1918) were among the first to show that the respiration of grain increased with increase in moisture content, but they did not distinguish the respiration of the grain itself from that of the fungi that developed at moisture contents above about 15%. Later work (Milner et al., 1947a) showed that the rapid increase in production of carbon dioxide in grain above 15% moisture content was accompanied by an increase in the number of molds on the grain (Table II). If growth of molds was inhibited by treatment with fungicidal or fungistatic substances such as thiourea or 8-hydroxyquinoline sulfate, the same authors showed (1947b) that the rate of respiration remained low, even at a moisture

TABLE I

Influence of moisture content and temperature on the respiration of rice and granary weevils in wheat[a]

	Carbon Dioxide Production in 24 hr., mg.					
	Wheat respiration per 100 g.		Respiration per g. of weevils			
Wheat Moisture			*Sitophilus oryzae*[b]		*Sitophilus granarius*[c]	
%	25°C.	35°C.	25°C.	35°C.	25°C.	35°C.
8.7	trace	trace	75.8	64.5	119.3	114.5
10.7	trace	0.2	150.0	107.7	117.4	212.9
14.0	0.7	1.4	206.4	261.3	169.7	244.9
15.2	1.0	2.2	201.9	289.4	170.8	248.2
17.4	13.2	21.2	204.8	232.0	190.8	225.1

[a]Compiled from Lindgren (1935).

[b]At 8.7% moisture, 35.2 and 100% of the rice weevils were dead at 25° and 35°C., respectively; at 10.7% moisture, the corresponding figures were 3.6 and 77.6%.

[c]At 8.7% moisture, 0.5 and 48.8% of the granary weevils were dead at 25° and 35°C., respectively; there was little mortality at 10.7% moisture.

TABLE II

Relationship of moisture content to respiratory rate and mold growth[a]
(Regent wheat after respiratory trials at 30°C.)

Moisture Content, Initial %	Respiratory Rate, Final Day mg. CO_2	Mold Colonies per mg.
12.3	0.07	0.5
13.6	0.11	0.1
13.8	0.23	0.1
14.5	0.57	0.4
15.4	2.53	4.8
16.3	23.35	396
16.8	20.3	209
18.5	111.0	2,275
20.8	604.9	11,300
25.2	1,724.8	37,500
30.5	1,282.0	63,500
38.6	4,666.5	67,000

[a]After Milner et al. (1947a).

content of 20% (24 to 26 mg. of carbon dioxide per 100 g. wheat in 24 hr., compared to 273 mg. in the untreated control, after 10 days).

Most animals and plants, including many fungi, need oxygen for their respiration, and die, or at least cease to grow, in conditions of low oxygen. Some organisms, however, including certain yeasts and many kinds of bacteria, are able to respire in the absence of oxygen (so-called anaerobic respiration), breaking down the carbohydrate less completely than in the presence of air, and producing substances such as lactic or acetic acids, or alcohol. The last reaction, occurring particularly with yeasts, may be shown as

$$C_6H_{12}O_6 \rightarrow 2C_2H_5OH + 2CO_2 + 22 \text{ kcal.}$$
(hexose)   (ethyl alcohol)

Such a fermentation results in considerably less production of energy (heat) than in the aerobic process (22 kcal. per gram-molecule of hexose sugar, compared to 677 kcal. in the presence of oxygen).

These factors are important when considering the airtight storage of grain. If dry grain in an airtight container is infested by insects, the insects will soon use up the available oxygen and will become asphyxiated. Most species of stored-products insects will be killed when the oxygen concentration has fallen to about 2% by volume of the intergranular air (Bailey, 1965). Fungi can still grow at a very low oxygen concentration, down to about 0.2% (Peterson et al., 1956). At an oxygen tension between 0.5 and 1% certain microorganisms, including a number of yeasts, can proliferate rapidly, if the temperature is suitable, and cause deterioration of the grain (Burmeister et al., 1966). Thus it is very important with damp grain that the storage structure is completely airtight: whereas for insect control a very slight leak can be tolerated, this would be disastrous with high-moisture grain.

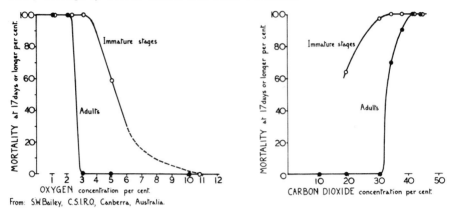

Figure 1. Mortality of adults of *Sitophilus granarius* in relation to concentration of oxygen (left) and of carbon dioxide (right).

III. MODERN DEVELOPMENTS

Vayssiere (1940, 1948) was one of the first modern advocates of airtight storage, especially as a means of controlling insect infestations in dry grain. It is rather surprising that it has been so slow to develop, in view of its advantages over other forms of storage, including pest control without the use of toxic chemicals. However, in recent years airtight storage is being increasingly used to store both dry and high-moisture grain. Because they present different problems, it is convenient to consider the two types of grain separately.

A. Dry Grain

The value of airtight storage to control insects was appreciated many years ago by Cotes (1888), who stated that "the only method to prevent destruction of grain by weevils is to make the granary air-tight"; but it was some time before scientific investigations provided evidence to support this view.

During the first World War, Dendy (1918) and Dendy and Elkington (1918, 1920) carried out a classic series of tests in sealed containers which confirmed that insects are killed when the respiration of the insects has used up most of the oxygen and has produced a relatively high concentration of carbon dioxide. With the easing of pressures after the war, little attention was paid to their findings.

Many workers since then have shown that the removal of oxygen, rather than accumulation of carbon dioxide, is the lethal factor. Bailey's (1955) results for *Sitophilus granarius* are given in Figure 1, which shows (right frame) that in high-oxygen atmospheres (15 to 21%), the carbon dioxide must be as high as 36% to attain significant insect mortality. Bailey (1956, 1957, 1965) later extended his studies to other stored-product insects with similar results, which were later confirmed by other workers (e.g. Harein and Press, 1968).

The rate at which oxygen decreases and carbon dioxide increases depends on the density of the insect population, the temperature, and whether the container is completely sealed. Figure 2, adapted from Oxley and Wickenden (1963), shows

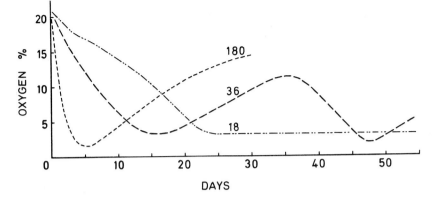

Figure 2. Concentration of oxygen in containers with a slight leak, with different populations of insects (18, 36, and 180 adults of *Sitophilus granarius* per standard 3-lb. container of wheat).

that in a container with a slight leak, a heavy infestation is eliminated, whereupon the oxygen concentration rises again. With a lighter population the oxygen is reduced more slowly, and not all the insects are killed, but they maintain themselves at a low level in a sublethal concentration of oxygen. It is very difficult to make a large container completely airtight, and a slight leak must be expected in most commercial structures. Tests have shown (Figure 3, based on results from

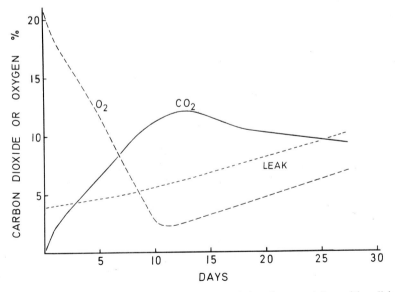

Figure 3. Concentration of oxygen and carbon dioxide in a 7-ton container with a slight leak, filled with wheat infested artificially with *Sitophilus granarius* adults at a rate of about 37 insects per lb. of wheat.

Storage-pit (*Banda*) of Jabbalpur.

Figure 4. Section of a storage pit *(banda)* as used at Jabalpur, India, about 10 ft. in diameter and 15 ft. deep. [Fletcher and Ghosh, 1920.]

Hyde et al., 1961) that a slightly leaky container can be satisfactory in practice; if the rate of entry of oxygen is less than about 0.5% of the free air space per day, a moderate infestation will be destroyed and the oxygen concentration will then increase at a rate equivalent to the "leakiness" of the container. Moreover, and especially in tropical countries, even if an infestation is not completely eliminated, partial control is a valuable achievement, as it prevents the development of a heavy infestation, and reduces the amount of damage to the grain.

The structures used for the airtight storage of dry grain range from the relatively small pits of Asia and the Middle East to large 1,000-ton units made of vapor-proofed concrete or, more recently, of butyl rubber or other flexible material.

PIT STORES

The simple pits in India, Egypt, and nearby countries are still lined with straw or chaff, and covered with a layer of straw and soil or mud, which, because of the depth of soil used, makes a reasonably airtight structure. They have been described by Attia (1948), Janjua and Nasir (1948), and Pruthi and Singh (1950). Most are simple cylindrical or rectangular pits (Figure 4) constructed in very dry areas in a very stable soil, or, as in Cyprus and Malta (Hyde and Daubney, 1960) they are flask-shaped structures with a narrow neck, hollowed out of solid limestone rock, and known as *"fossae"*. According to de Boisgelin (1804), the Malta pits, which were constructed about 1660, were originally lined with *"pozzolana"*, a glazed cement-like substance which would have made them both waterproof and airtight. Over the years this rendering became defective, and a straw lining was used to absorb moisture, as already described. The Maltese pits are gradually being superseded by large concrete nonairtight silos, as port facilities increase, but a number are still in use.

Spafford (1939) was one of the earliest of modern investigators to study pit

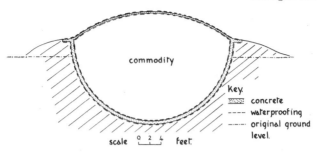

Figure 5 Vertical section of a pit with a permanent roof, in Argentina. [Hall et al.,1956.]

storage, in Australia. His pits were simple hollows or trenches in the soil, filled with "weevily wheat" and covered with a waterproof sheet and a layer of earth. He seemed to have accepted as inevitable a certain amount of damage to the peripheral grain through entry of soil- and rain-water, but concluded that on the whole storage was satisfactory, as the main mass of grain remained sound and sweet, and most of the insects were killed.

Kelly et al. (1942) reported tests in an underground concrete bin in Kansas, filled with wheat of 13% moisture content. After storage for more than a year, the grain developed a musty or sour odor, apparently due to the accumulation of moisture in certain areas. There was some fall in germination and increase in free fatty acids, although bread made from the milled wheat had no abnormal smell or taste. Shellenberger and Fenton (1952), in reviewing the Kansas and other

Figure 6. Experimental concrete pit at Morogoro, Tanzania. The grain is being sampled for insects through a temporary hole in the roof. [Hall et al., 1956.]

experiments, concluded that an effective water-vapor barrier would overcome the problem of increase in moisture and could lead to the widespread adoption of pit storage by farmers in the U.S. But their ideas were not developed in practice at the time.

It was not until the stringencies of World War II forced the Argentine government to devise means of storing the large amounts of grain that could not be exported that pit storage was developed on a large scale. The construction of these pits is described by López (1942, 1946). Initially they were made simply, of "soil-cement" with a temporary cover of bitumenized felt covered with soil. Later, more robust concrete pits, with bitumen waterproofing and permanent roofs, were constructed, each holding about 500 tons of grain (Figure 5). The Argentine Ministry of National Economy published in 1951 a report on their subsequent development, and on the condition of the stored grain. Wheat of 12 to 13% moisture content showed no significant change after 18-months' storage. The protein, gluten, and maltose values were maintained, and there was only a slight fall in germination. Flour milling and baking tests were satisfactory. Subsequently, the use of underground silos in a number of South American countries (Argentina, Venezuela, and Paraguay) has developed further, and several million tons of grain are now so stored annually.

Meanwhile, smaller-scale tests were being carried out in Africa and elsewhere. Swaine (1954) describes tests in three 120-ton pits in East Africa, carefully constructed of concrete, waterproofed with bitumastic and white oil paints, and with bitumenized felt covers (Figure 6). At that time the importance of reduction in oxygen to kill insects was not fully appreciated, and only the concentration of carbon dioxide was measured. This never exceeded 10%, which suggests that the pits were not completely airtight. Nevertheless, after storage periods of 12 to 18 months, most of the maize was considered to be satisfactory, although not all the insects were killed, and there was some local damage to the grain where water had got in.

In a test in England in a 60-ton concrete pit proofed with bitumen and containing maize of 13% moisture content artificially infested with *Sitophilus oryzae*, Oxley et al. (1957) showed that all the insects were killed in the first few weeks. This must have been owing to depletion of oxygen, as the carbon dioxide concentration remained at a low level, probably due to its absorption by the new cement of the pit walls. On emptying the pit after 5 years' storage, it was found (Hyde et al., 1961) that most of the maize was in good condition, except for a small quantity at the top, which had increased in moisture content due to migration of moisture to the cooler surface, and to entry of rain water through leaks at the sides of the single-layered bitumen felt cover. Such moisture migration is always a problem where there is a temperature gradient in a bulk of grain, whether in airtight conditions or not.

Hyde and Daubney (1960) showed that wheat of 13% moisture content could be stored satisfactorily in a "*fossa*" in Malta that had been proofed with bitumen and rendered with cement, without using the traditional straw lining. There was some loss in grain viability towards the base of the 50-ft. (15 m.) deep structure, hollowed out of the rock, presumably due to lack of oxygen. The protein content of the grain remained unaffected, but there were some changes in sugars and in free fatty acid content, although not enough to affect the commercial quality of the wheat. The mold count of the grain was low, except at the top, and at the base of the neck there was a high count of yeasts, characteristic of a nearly oxygen-free atmosphere in moist grain (see p. 407).

Other workers have investigated the traditional earth pits (Calderon and Donahaye, 1963) and have attempted to improve their airtightness (Donahaye et al., 1967) by lining the pit with a bag made of polyvinyl chloride (PVC), which gave satisfactory results until it was damaged by rodents.

Conclusions on Pit Stores. From what has been said above, some general conclusions can be drawn on the use of pits for storing dry grain. They provide a simple form of storage, and so are particularly suitable for long-term use, both for famine and strategic reserves and for storage of seasonal surpluses to ease marketing problems. They can, of course, also be used for short-term storage, especially for grain which is heavily infested.

Being underground, with much of their periphery in contact with the soil, these pits ensure a more even, and often lower, temperature than prevails in an above-ground structure (Hyde, 1958) (Figure 7). This is particularly important in hot climates, and in countries subjected to seasonal extremes of heat and cold, as it reduces the risk of migration of moisture.

It is important that certain precautions are taken to make the pits as airtight as possible, and a proofed concrete structure is to be recommended. Careful siting of the pits is essential, to prevent entry of soil water. They should preferably be

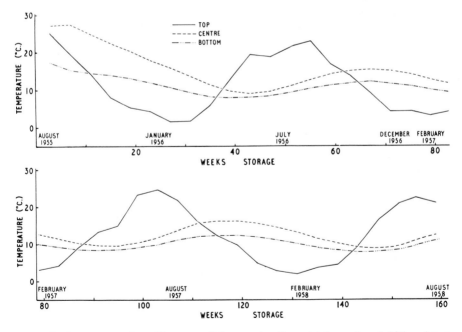

Figure 7. Temperatures in a 60-ton proofed concrete pit containing maize at 13% moisture content, artificially infested on filling with *Sitophilus oryzae*.

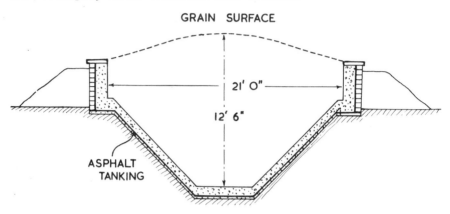

Figure 8. Section of grain storage pit in an area with a high water table in the soil. [Oxley et al., 1956.]

constructed in a dry area, with the soil water table well below the bottom of the pit at all times of the year. In such situations, the waterproofing layer can be applied as a paint to the inner surface of the concrete. If there is any danger of the water table rising, the pit should be of "tanked" construction, with the proofing layer sandwiched between two layers of concrete, to prevent its being lifted off by water seeping from the soil. In such situations there should be as little excavation as possible, an above-ground element being supported by back-fill from the excavation

Figure 9. Applying cement to the hessian lining of a 10-ton storage bin. The cement is later waterproofed and the hessian lining removed. [British Crown copyright. Reproduced by permission of the Controller of Her Britannic Majesty's Stationery Office.]

(Figure 8). The site should preferably be on a slight slope, to avoid flooding during heavy rain, although Doyère (1862) reported successful storage in metal-lined pits at Cherbourg, France, that were sometimes submerged by the sea at high tide!

The roof should be waterproof and strong, and particular care should be paid to its junction with the walls, to ensure continuity of the vapor barrier and to prevent rain water from getting in. Covering the roof with soil insulates it from solar heat. Otherwise, even in temperate climates, it should be painted with white or aluminum paint, to reflect heat. Simple roofs of bituminized felt can be satisfactory, particularly if made of two layers, with wire-netting between to give support (see Figure 6). It is, however, sometimes preferable, especially in permanent installations, to have rigid covers, often made of waterproofed concrete, suitably supported, and provided with manholes for filling and emptying. The covers of such apertures must be provided with airtight gaskets. If a pit is long and narrow, it is sometimes desirable to divide it into compartments, by vertical partitions, to make more manageable units. It is important, initially, that the pit is filled to capacity, to reduce the amount of free air space and thus the amount of oxygen available to the insects in infested grain.

If practicable, especially in pits intended for long-term storage, simple means of measuring temperature, and the oxygen and carbon dioxide content of the air, can be provided. Means for periodical sampling of the grain may also be useful. Experience has shown (Hyde et al., 1961) that the entry of air when sampling through a small aperture is insignificant over the short period required for sampling.

ABOVE-GROUND STORES

Because of the high cost of metal, and the difficulty of making above-ground structures airtight, less expensive forms of construction have been investigated in recent years, for the airtight storage of dry grain.

Rigid Structures. Pradhan et al. (1965) developed a simple form of above-ground silo, the so-called *"Pusa"* bin, in which a lining of polyethylene sheeting is sandwiched in the mud wall of a rectangular earthern structure. Wheat of 7 to 10% moisture content was stored successfully in these bins for more than 3 years without loss of viability.

Giles (1965) showed that although not all the insects were killed in bitumen-treated mud granaries in northern Nigeria, the numbers were appreciably reduced. McFarlane (1970) treated with oil or varnish the gourds traditionally used in Africa to store grain, and achieved a degree of airtightness sufficient for reasonable insect control.

A simple form of silo consisting of a hessian lining cement-rendered to a metal-mesh cage has been studied experimentally (Oxley et al., 1957). After the hessian was filled with grain, a thin layer of cement was applied to the outside (Figure 9). The cement was later treated with bitumen to make the structure airtight. This form of construction, in the 10-ton size investigated, seems to have possibilities for village storage in developing countries, and warrants further trials under practical conditions.

On a much larger scale, eight 1,000-ton proofed concrete silos were constructed in Cyprus in 1955 (Hall et al., 1956). These so-called "Waller" bins consist of a conical pit element, 30 ft. (9 m.) deep and 60 ft. (18 m.) in diameter, above which there is an above-ground dome-like component, the design of which is based on a

Figure 10. A 1,000-ton "Ctesiphon" silo under construction in Cyprus.

catenary arch. This construction was used in the world's largest single-span brick arch, built at Ctesiphon, near Baghdad, about 570 A.D., and the silos are sometimes known as "Ctesiphon" bins. The construction of the dome consists in applying a very thin shell of concrete over hessian draped on temporary supports (Figure 10), and then proofing it externally with bitumen, followed by a coat of white reflective paint. Although initially intended for long-term reserves, the silos in Cyprus have been successfully used for seasonal storage continuously since their erection. As a result of this experience, 70 similar silos were erected in Kenya in 1967, and are being used with reasonable success for both wheat and maize. Basically they are an extension of a pit, with a domed roof, but the above-ground part is larger than the pit component.

Flexible Silos. Tests on other forms of above-ground structure have included silos in which a flexible bag made, for example, of butyl-rubber sheeting, is supported in a metal-mesh cylinder (Figure 11). In Israel, Navarro et al. (1968) found that in heavily infested wheat the oxygen concentration fell to 2.2% within 5 days, arresting the initial infestation and preventing further development of insects. The germination of the wheat was affected, presumably by lack of oxygen, but the free fatty acids and baking properties remained unchanged during the 6-month storage period.

Other tests in butyl-rubber silos recently carried out in Nigeria and Kenya indicate (personal communication) that these structures can be satisfactory in tropical conditions if there is no degradation of the sheeting.

These small flexible silos, with bags of butyl rubber or PVC, are easily transported and erected and so can be used as "treatment" bins for already-infested grain. In a recent experiment in Britain (results not yet published), N. J. Burrell obtained a 99.9% kill of a heavy mixed infestation in "heating" wheat on a farm where for various reasons it was not possible to fumigate the grain or to treat it with a contact insecticide, by placing it in a butyl-rubber silo.

Another development in the use of butyl rubber is silos of up to 1,000-ton capacity, the so-called "Cherwell" silos (Figure 12), which are being used in a number of countries for storing dry grain. These are usually filled and emptied pneumatically, the bag being inflated during these processes. After filling, the bag is allowed to collapse on the grain. The high cost of the pneumatic conveying equipment detracts from the relatively low-cost construction of these silos, but other, cheaper methods of filling and emptying have been investigated, particularly in Canada. As with the smaller, flexible silos, the bags provide a very economical means of storage and have the same advantage of mobility, as they can be transported easily and erected on any piece of smooth ground. They are therefore particularly suitable for emergency stores, especially in countries where the size of harvest and duration of storage vary from year to year. Several of these silos are in use in Europe, North and South America, Asia, and Australasia, but thus far few details are available of their efficiency under tropical conditions. Bags composed of a light-colored laminate which would reduce the absorption of heat by the normally black butyl-rubber sheeting have also been produced. Rodent-proofing measures are discussed later (p. 411).

Figure 11. Silos of butyl-rubber bags supported by metal mesh. These silos are being used to store damp grain, but are also suitable for dry grain. [Hyde, 1968.]

CONCLUSIONS

Airtight storage provides a useful method of preserving dry grain in good condition; preventing infestation by insects; and killing any insects present when the grain is put into store, without the use of toxic chemicals. The basic properties of the grain are unaffected and it can be used successfully for milling and baking. Airtight storage is not usually recommended for grain intended for malting, or for seed grain, but there are indications that if the grain is very dry, i.e., with a moisture content 1 to 2% lower than that normally recommended for safe storage in air under particular conditions, the germination remains at a satisfactory level, and the grain can be used for seed.

B. High-Moisture Grain

In recent years various factors have contributed to the need to store grain at a higher moisture content than is considered safe for open storage, i.e., above 14 to 16%. Increased yields, and the almost universal use in many temperate countries of combine harvesters, have resulted in the production, at harvest, of large quantities of high-moisture grain which are too much for the capacity of the drying installations available. Moreover, recent developments in increasing the cereal component of the ration for stockfeed have required that the grain is rolled, and not ground, before feeding. For such processing the grain must be damp. Farmers were asking "why dry the grain at harvest, to have to wet it again later?" The answer was found in airtight storage, by which high-moisture grain can be safely stored for feeding to livestock on the farm of origin without the development of molds.

Aniskin (1968) gives a comprehensive review of the literature on the airtight storage of damp grain, and Culpin (1969) has summarized its advantages and disadvantages, compared with other methods of storage.

Figure 12. A 1,000-ton butyl-rubber silo, suitable for dry grain. [Crown copyright.]

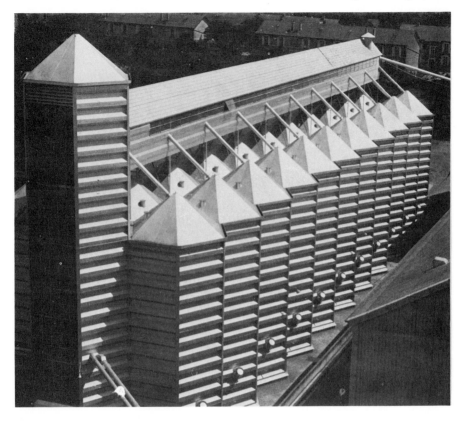

Figure 13. Hexagonal welded metal silos at Pithiviers, France. Each bin holds 200 tons of wheat. [Hyde, 1968.]

The modern use of airtight storage for high-moisture grain stems from 19th Century experiments in France. Doyère (1862), in tests on wheat for naval stores and stored provisions for the army (to hold stocks from times of plenty for less fruitful years), showed that the changes occurring in the grain, i.e.,development of odor and changes in chemical properties, were less at the lower temperatures provided by semi-underground silos. Wheat of up to 17% moisture content was successfully preserved in such hermetic silos without, as Doyère says, "it being necessary to create a vacuum, nor to introduce any gas, nor any other foreign substance".

Müntz (1881), commissioned by the General Omnibus Company of Paris to provide storage for the oats and maize needed for its 2,000 horses, devised silos with a wall of masonry lined with bolted metal plates. He showed that as long as the silos remained airtight, storage was satisfactory, but that at moisture contents above 17% a certain amount of fermentation occurred, in proportion to the moisture content of the grain, resulting in production of considerable carbon dioxide. In spite of the taint that developed, the grain was acceptable to the horses.

No further developments took place until the classic experiments of Blanc (1938, 1939). His investigations, in above-ground welded metal silos or drums containing wheat of 16.2% moisture content, showed that the grain remained in good condition, with no loss of baking quality, during two seasons of storage. Diurnal changes in temperature were transmitted only to the outer few centimeters of grain, and there was no increase in moisture content, except through a faulty manhole cover.

World War II prevented further experimentation, but by the early 1950's hermetic silos were being used in France on farms and in agricultural co-operatives to store moderately damp grain, sometimes up to 19% moisture, but generally at about 17% (Manessier, 1950). The silos, usually of welded construction, are of either round or hexagonal cross-section (Pasfield, 1953). Each bin is of up to 200-ton capacity and these are often erected in blocks of 40 or more (Figure 13). The wheat from these silos, although sometimes showing a slight taint, is accepted for milling, being blended with open-stored dry wheat and used for breadmaking in the usual way.

In Britain and America, airtight storage is not generally used for millable wheat, but mainly to store high-moisture barley, maize, or oats intended for animal feed. Recent changes in stock-feeding practice, to a high-cereal ration of rolled grain, provided an impetus for storing undried grain in sealed silos. In Britain bolted metal bins of galvanized or vitreous-enamelled steel (the so-called "glass-lined" silos) have since the early 1960's been used mainly to store barley of 18 to 22% moisture content, but sometimes up to 25%. Flexible bag silos, of butyl rubber or PVC, are also used, especially for smaller quantities of grain (20 to 40 tons). In the U.S. the grain, generally maize, has often over 30% moisture content, especially if it is stored in "conventional" concrete tower silos or in horizontal "bunker" silos (see p. 412).

CHANGES DURING STORAGE

Although there is little change in the properties of dry grain during airtight storage, in damp grain (over 16% moisture content) certain changes occur which affect the commercial use of the grain.

Composition of the Intergranular Air. Above a relative humidity of 70%, which in cereal grains corresponds to a moisture content of about 14%, the microorganisms present on the grain at harvest can use up the oxygen in the intergranular air, with corresponding production of carbon dioxide. Some of the aerobic organisms are not killed by the removal of oxygen, but remain in a "dormant" condition. After the oxygen has been eliminated, if the moisture content is more than 16%, there is a further, anaerobic production of carbon dioxide, to as much as 95% of the intergranular air, depending on the moisture content of the grain (Kleev, 1948; Shvetsova and Sosedov, 1958; Hyde and Oxley, 1960; Meiering et al., 1966; Dexter et al., 1969). A typical result is shown in Figure 14.

In completely sealed containers the high concentration of carbon dioxide and low oxygen is maintained as long as the containers remain sealed. In practice, however, some compensating device is needed to allow for changes in pressure in metal silos, and there is usually some entry of oxygen and escape of carbon dioxide, the concentration of which falls to a value which many workers (Harvey, 1965; Burmeister et al., 1966; Hyde and Burrell, 1969) have found to stabilize at between

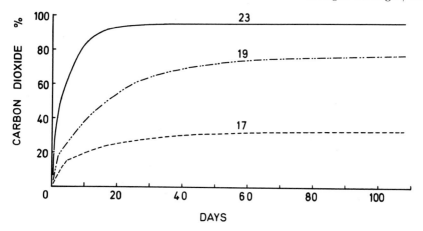

Figure 14. Production of carbon dioxide in wheat at moisture contents of 17, 19, and 23%, in 10-ton welded metal silos. [Hyde, unpublished.]

15 and 25%, even during emptying of the silo (Figure 15), as the oxygen entering when grain is removed is soon replaced by carbon dioxide due to the respiration of the aerobic microorganisms still present. The decrease in carbon dioxide is less in flexible bag silos (Hyde, 1970) (Figure 16), which respond to pressure changes without loss of gas to the air.

Temperature. Several observers (Foster et al., 1955; Hyde and Burrell, 1969) have found that there is usually a slight rise in temperature shortly after a silo is sealed, during the period of intense production of carbon dioxide, followed by a progressive fall as the grain mass cools during autumn and winter (Figure 17). The slight initial rise in temperature is not enough to produce the "damp grain heating"

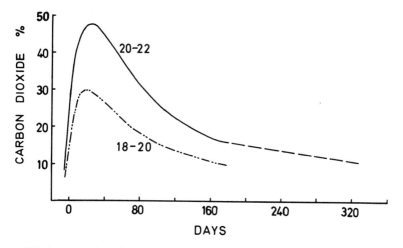

Figure 15. Concentration of carbon dioxide in commercial bolted metal silos containing barley at moisture contents of 18 to 20% or 20 to 22%. [Hyde and Burrell, 1969.]

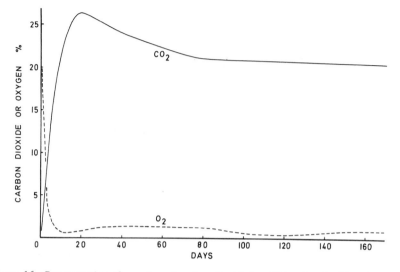

Figure 16. Concentration of oxygen and carbon dioxide in a 20-ton butyl-rubber silo of barley at 20% moisture content. [Hyde, unpublished.]

normally associated with extensive mold growth. It has already been shown (p. 385) that the anaerobic phase produces only a relatively small amount of heat. Most investigators have confirmed Blanc's (1938) findings that diurnal changes in temperature are only transmitted to the outer few centimeters of grain. The temperature of the grain near the walls of a silo falls more quickly than that in the main mass of grain (Figure 18, from Hyde, 1970), producing a temperature gradient which affects the moisture content of the grain (see p. 401). In commercial silos there is often a rise in temperature in the spring, in grain remaining in a partially emptied silo, to a value above the mean ambient temperature (see Figure 17). This rise is generally attributed to "damp grain heating" due to mold growth in the higher concentrations of oxygen than present (see p. 407).

Appearance, Smell, and Taste of the Grain. In properly conducted airtight storage there is little change in the appearance of the grain, which remains bright and free-flowing, with no visible growth of mold. The anaerobic fermentation that occurs at moisture contents above 16% produces a sour-sweet smell and bitter taste, which increase with increasing temperature and moisture contents (Foster et al., 1955; Hyde and Oxley, 1960). Guilbot and Poisson (1963) have shown (Table III) that there is a sharp threshold for the development of odor in the grain, at about 16% moisture content. At higher moistures, and if the storage period is prolonged (i.e., more than a few months) the taint is not removed by subsequent airing or drying, and in milling wheat it is transmitted to the flour, thus rendering the grain unfit for breadmaking.

At high moisture contents (above 25%) the grain, especially maize, tends to become very dark and soft, and the smell is less sweet and more like that of green silage (Meiering et al., 1966). It is thought that this very damp grain may have a large proportion of immature kernels, with a high sugar content, and that the

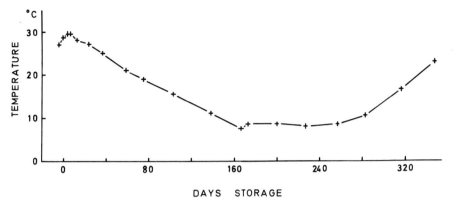

Figure 17. Temperature at center of bolted vitreous-enamelled metal 60-ton silo containing barley at 18 to 22% moisture content. [Hyde, unpublished.]

browning may be due to a nonenzymatic reaction of the Maillard type, as described by Cole and Milner (1953) and Linko (1960), or that it may be microbiological in origin (Desikachar et al., 1959).

Moisture Content. In containers airtight enough to prevent entry of oxygen and loss of carbon dioxide, one would not expect there to be any appreciable change in the moisture content of the grain. In general, there is no overall change, but many workers have found an increase in moisture content of grain at the top and sides of a silo, presumably resulting from increase in intergranular humidity, as the outer layer of grain cools more rapidly than the main bulk, as shown in Figure 18 (Hyde,

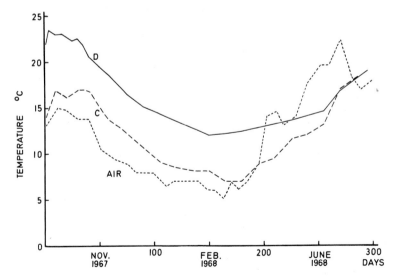

Figure 18. Temperature at the center of a butyl-rubber silo (C) and a PVC silo (D), both containing barley at 19% moisture content, compared with the outside (i.e., wall) temperature.

TABLE III

Development of odor in wheat during airtight storage[a]

Moisture Content of the Grain %	Days Required for Development of Odor at Storage Temperatures of	
	15°C.	22°C.
23	10	8
21	23	11
19	40	20
17	60	3–40
15	≥600	≥150

[a]Guilbot and Poisson (1963).

1970). Le Du (1968) reports an increase to 22.4% moisture content in wheat initially at 16% when in metal silos. Similar results have been obtained in flexible bag silos (Table IV), where the tests also showed that if the moisture content was uneven on filling of the silo, it remained so throughout the storage period. In some silos the dampest grain is often lightly "caked", and does not flow freely to the auger when the silo is emptied. In more extreme cases (and especially in tall metal silos, where there is compaction of the rather soft grain), at moisture contents over 22% there may be some "bridging", a more severe form of caking, often associated with the growth of yeasts (see p. 409).

TABLE IV

Moisture content of barley in a butyl-rubber silo[a]

Horizontal Layer	Vertical Row				
	I	II	III	IV	V
6 (top)	19.6[b]	18.4	18.1	19.1	19.4
	(20.5)	(23.1)	(17.1)[c]	(24.1)	(20.9)
5	20.8	19.4	19.1	20.3	20.2
	(20.8)	(20.0)	(19.7)	(20.1)	(21.1)
4	19.4	19.1	18.9	18.7	18.8
	(19.7)	(18.0)	(18.1)	(18.8)	(18.9)
3	18.0	18.0	17.8	18.0	17.6
	(18.0)	(17.8)	(17.7)	(17.5)	(18.0)
2	17.5	17.0	16.7	17.1	17.1
	(17.8)	(17.1)	(17.4)	(17.1)	(17.4)
1 (bottom)	17.3	20.5	17.7	17.4	17.2
	(17.0)	(17.3)	(17.3)	(17.4)	(17.5)

[a]Hyde (1970).

[b]The upper figures in each pair are the moisture contents (%) on filling; the lower figures (in parentheses), those on emptying.

[c]At the top, the center had been insulated by the bunched-up fabric of the bag, and the grain therefore had changed less in temperature than elsewhere at the surface.

Viability. Loss of viability is one of the criteria most widely used for assessing grain damage, as germination can be determined fairly simply, and is readily impaired by unsatisfactory storage conditions. It is not surprising that, in the oxygen-free conditions that develop during airtight storage, the germination of the grain is affected. The extent of the damage depends on the temperature and moisture content of the grain. Many workers (Kleev, 1948; Hyde, 1965; Meiering et al., 1966) have shown that the germination falls to zero in a few weeks at moisture contents of 22% or more, although at 14% moisture content or less the viability is maintained at a reasonably high level for a considerable period (Figure 19, from Hyde, 1965). This loss in viability precludes the use of airtight storage for damp grain intended for seed or malting.

Chemical Composition. Various workers have investigated the chemical changes occurring during the airtight storage of damp grain (Nikitinskiĭ, 1955; Oxley and Hyde, 1955; Shvetsova and Sosedov, 1958). Some typical results are given in Table V, which shows that below a moisture content of 16% the properties remain almost unaltered. At higher moistures other workers found that there is virtually no change in protein or total nitrogen. The main changes are an increase in reducing sugars and a decrease in nonreducing sugars. At moisture contents up to 25%, there is little increase in acidity, in contrast to the changes that take place in green silage, where there is appreciable production of lactic acid. In grain at moisture contents above 25% there seems to be a form of fermentation different from that occurring in drier grain, more akin to that in green silage, and there may then be an increase in acidity. Foster et al. (1955) found an increase in fat acidity after a few weeks in maize of 27% moisture content, but none in grain at 18% until after 70 weeks' storage. Meiering et al. (1966) reported an increase in pH at a moisture content of 28.5%, although at 22.5% there was little change. Tests by Burrell (personal

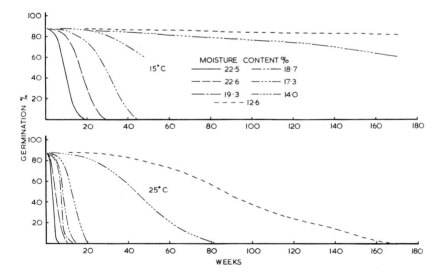

Figure 19. Fall in germination during airtight storage at various moisture contents, at temperatures of 15° and 25°C.

TABLE V

Some biochemical changes in wheat after 7 months' hermetic storage[a]

Moisture Content %	Ash Content %	Acidity (on Alc. Extract)	Total Nitrogen %	Fat %	Reducing Sugar %	Nonreducing Sugar %	Starch %	Catalase (ml. 0.1N KMnO$_4$)
12.1[b]	1.70	3.6	2.74	2.05	0.16	1.96	65.0	34.8
12.1	1.68	4.2	2.73	1.87	0.10	2.05	64.0	26.0
14.0	1.69	4.0	2.81	1.86	0.15	2.04	64.3	25.0
16.4	1.72	4.2	2.64	1.91	0.28	1.62	65.0	24.4
17.7	1.78	4.2	2.66	1.91	0.36	1.44	64.5	22.2
19.9	1.73	5.6	2.68	1.90	0.82	0.81	64.1	17.0

[a]Taken from Shvetsova and Sosedov (1958).
[b]Original wheat.

communication) have, however, shown that change in pH is a function of temperature as much as of moisture content, even in high-moisture grain (up to 29% moisture). The biochemical changes occurring during airtight storage are complicated, and need further investigation.

Baking Quality. As with other chemical changes, there is little deterioration in the breadmaking qualities of wheat if the moisture content is less than 16 to 17% (Blanc, 1938). Nikitinskii (1955) and Meiering et al. (1966) found that the baking qualities were still satisfactory after 2 months' storage at 21 to 22% moisture content. Shvetsova and Sosedov (1958) reported that the loaf volume actually increased after hermetic storage in wheat at 12 to 16% moisture content, presumably due to the usual improvement associated with aging, found also in open-stored grain. With damper grain (18 to 20% moisture content) the quality of

TABLE VI

Baking quality of wheat from sealed containers[a]

Variety	Moisture %	Storage Periods weeks	Dough Properties[b]		Bread Properties	
			Extensibility	Spring	Loaf volume ml.	Texture and color
Yeoman	12.7	0	16.0	420	605	Normal
Yeoman	19.2	7	14.0	507	595	Normal
Yeoman	19.2	13	11.4	710	650	Normal
Yeoman	19.2	52	9.8	765	510	Close and dark
Atle	14.6	0	22.5	400	582	Normal
Atle	24.7	15	...	...	605	Close, slightly dark, slight taint
Atle	24.7	33	9	570	587	Dark, slight taint

[a]From Oxley and Hyde (1955).
[b]On Simon Extensometer.

Figure 20. Loaves baked from wheat stored hermetically for 33 weeks at 19 (lower row) and 23% (upper row) moisture contents.

the flour is affected by airtight storage, and the loaves have a taint, but are otherwise similar to those made from drier grain. At still higher moistures or with prolonged storage the gluten is severely affected, and both the volume and texture of the bread are damaged (Oxley and Hyde, 1955), as shown in Table VI and Figure 20.

These results show conclusively that airtight storage at a moisture content above which it can be safely stored in open storage, especially if the grain is cooled by ventilation (see Chapter 11), is unsuitable for wheat for breadmaking.

Dry-Matter Losses. With the adoption of airtight storage for damp grain used for animal food, the amount of dry-matter loss became of paramount importance, as viability, baking quality, and such factors need not be considered in feed grain.

Results from a number of laboratory-scale tests and practical trials showed relatively little loss in dry matter at moisture contents below 18% (Ekström et al., 1965; Burmeister et al., 1966; Meiering et al., 1966; Dexter et al., 1969). At 22 to 25% moisture the loss was still generally less than 1%, but in damper grain the dry-matter loss increased appreciably, so that at 33 to 35% moisture it was 3 to 4% after 6-months' storage. Forbes (1965), reporting dry-matter losses of 2 and 4% for barley at 22 and 35% moisture, respectively, found that losses in dry matter were less in grain to which water had been added than in grain of corresponding moisture contents without added water. This supports the view (Isaacs, 1961) that water

TABLE VII

Feeding trials with pigs[a],[b]

	Lot 1[c]	Lot 2[d]
Pigs per lot	15	15
Average initial weight, lb.	85.9	86.7
Final initial weight, lb.	191.1	188.4
Average daily gain, lb.	1.50	1.45
Average daily feed, lb.		
Maize	5.06	4.52
Supplement, 40% protein	0.47	0.73
Feed per 100-lb. gain, lb.	368	362

[a]From Foster et al. (1955).

[b]Over a 10-week test period.

[c]Fed 27% moisture content maize stored in sealed bins (for 2 seasons).

[d]Fed 13% moisture content maize stored in conventional bins.

added to maize to raise its moisture content to 30% or more reduces dry-matter loss (see p. 412).

Feeding Value. In the 1950's, the so-called "glass-lined" bolted metal bins and the conventional concrete silos originally intended for ensiling green fodder began to be considered for the airtight storage of high-moisture grain for feeding to livestock. Determination of the feed value of the grain therefore became of primary importance, and numerous feeding trials were undertaken (Foster et al., 1955; Oxley and Hyde, 1957; Isaacs et al., 1958; Isaacs, 1959). Foster et al. (1955) report results on trials with pigs. Their conclusions, from results summarized in Table VII, that high-moisture grain is as good an animal feed as normal dried grain, were confirmed by other workers (Forbes, 1965; Ekström et al., 1965; Riggs, 1969). The early claims of increased palatability and higher conversion ratios were not always supported by later tests (Harvey, 1965; Hurst, 1965). Morris and Isaacs (1965) concluded that there was probably a loss of feed efficiency in pigs, but not in cattle. Krall (1969), in trials with barley of 35% moisture, found no significant difference from normal, mature, dry grain. This seems to be the general conclusion, as long as the grain remains free from molds.

Microflora. Successful airtight storage of high-moisture grain depends on the creation and maintenance of low-oxygen conditions in which most molds are unable to grow, for the equilibrium relative humidity of the damp grain is well above the minimum, about 70%, required for mold growth in open storage. It has already been noted (p. 173) that under laboratory conditions many fungi are micro-aerophilic, and can grow at very low oxygen tensions. But there is no doubt that the growth of many of the usual storage fungi is much reduced in conditions of low oxygen (Brown, 1922; Golding, 1940a; Peterson et al., 1956), such as exist in many of the commercial "sealed" silos, where a concentration of oxygen as low as 0.2% can sometimes be obtained, although it is usually higher than this, being about 0.5 to 1%. Increase in carbon dioxide can also contribute to inhibiting the growth of molds (Golding, 1940b), but, as with insects (p. 386) it is the decrease in oxygen that is the decisive factor.

In well-managed airtight silos, where entry of oxygen is reduced to a minimum, the grain remains bright and free from visible molding. The "field fungi" present at harvest are either eliminated at high moistures (over 20%) or may survive in reduced numbers at moisture contents lower than this (Clarke et al., 1967, 1969). After the oxygen concentration has fallen to a low level there is usually an increase in the number of bacteria and yeasts (Nichols and Leaver, 1966). Teunisson (1954a and b) was one of the first to report growth of yeasts in "sealed" silos. Other investigators (Hyde and Oxley, 1960) suggested that these organisms can only develop in containers in which there is a slight leak. This suggestion was substantiated by later work, such as that by Nichols and Leaver (1966), which indicated that most commercial "sealed" silos are not completely airtight. Nichols and Leaver also showed that there was an increase in lactobacilli, as well as yeasts, but a decrease in molds, in well-managed commercial silos. In the presence of air—in nearly empty silos—they found that various thermophilic organisms, including actinomycetes, developed, causing bridging and spoilage of the grain. Burmeister and Hartman (1966) and Burmeister et al. (1966) also found that the number of molds initially present decreased during storage, and thought that increase in the growth of yeasts inhibited the growth of filamentous fungi.

Clarke et al. (1967, 1969) distinguished a number of phases in the succession of microorganisms found in "sealed" silos on British farms: a) the colonization of the grain before harvest by so-called "field fungi" (*sensu* Christensen and Kaufmann, 1965); b) a fall in the numbers of these fungi, correlated with depletion of oxygen and accumulation of carbon dioxide; c) the most characteristic phase, comprising abundant growth of yeasts of the genera *Candida* and *Hansenula*, usually when the oxygen was between 1 and 2% and the carbon dioxide between 15 and 40%; d) at the higher oxygen levels found in partially emptied silos, an ordinarily mesophilic fungal flora, mainly species of *Penicillium* and *Aspergillus*; and e) finally, mesophilic fungi with fairly high temperature optima, e.g., *Absidia corymbifera*, and true thermophils, such as *Mucor pusillus*, growing in association with "hot spots" in silos where temperature measurements were available, and doubtless also in others where they were not.

Gonen and Calderon (1968) reported a similar sequence of fungi in sorghum of 16 to 19% moisture content stored in experimental metal containers.

Several of the microorganisms in all these phases are potentially capable of causing certain infections, allergies, and poisoning in the animals consuming the grain. It is therefore very bad practice to feed moldy grain from sealed silos to livestock. There is also the danger of illness in people handling the moldy grain, either from respiratory irritation or allergies. More investigations are needed on the toxicity to man and beast of moldy grain, whether from sealed silos or from open storage.

PRACTICAL CONSIDERATIONS

The requirements for airtightness are more stringent for damp grain than they are for insect control in dry grain. Consequently, many of the structures described as being suitable for dry grain are unsatisfactory for damp grain. For instance, ordinarily vapor-proofed concrete does not seem to be adequate, and damp grain is seldom stored in concrete pits or above-ground concrete silos, except in the special circumstances mentioned below (p. 412). Specially constructed metal silos of up to

200-tons' capacity are commonly used. Flexible bag silos, of butyl rubber or PVC supported in metal-mesh cages, are widely used, usually in sizes of 20 to 40 tons. On a smaller scale, storage in 1-cwt. (50 kg.) heavy-gauge polyethylene sacks can be satisfactory.

Storage in Metal Silos. Ideally, metal silos should be of welded construction; but this is expensive and seldom is practical for on-site erection, except for large installations, as in some agricultural co-operatives in France (Figure 13). It is more usual to have a bolted metal construction (Figure 21), the silo being erected on the site, top first, and jacked upwards as construction proceeds. Special care is required with the mastic applied to the bolted seams, to ensure that the silo is as airtight as possible; a pressure-test is usually applied on completion, and should be repeated at intervals during the life of the silo. The steel plates used for the silos are sometimes galvanized or treated with epoxy-resins, but more commonly they are given a strong

Figure 21. Sixty-ton bolted vitreous-enamelled ("glass-lined") steel silos used for storing high-moisture barley. [Hyde, 1968.]

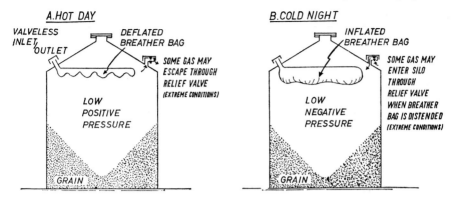

Figure 22. Method of action of a "breather-bag" in a silo used for the storage of high-moisture grain. [British Crown copyright. Reproduced by permission of the Controller of Her Brittanic Majesty's Stationery Office.]

vitreous-enamel finish, either dark blue or green. This treatment does not improve the airtightness, but protects the steel from corrosion by silage acids. The vitreous-enamelled or "glass-lined" silos were developed originally in the U.S. for green silage, although they are now being widely used for damp grain. Morris and Isaacs (1965) and Culpin (1969) give general accounts of their management.

For successful storage it is necessary to remember a number of important points. The silo should be filled as quickly as possible, so that oxygen-free conditions can soon become established. If filling is protracted, it is essential that the manhole and auger covers are replaced when filling is not actually in progress. Equal care should be taken on emptying. The silo should be filled as completely as possible, to ensure a minimum of free air space.

To overcome changes in pressure during storage, due to atmospheric conditions or resulting from the high production of carbon dioxide, a pressure-release valve is fitted at the top of the silo, operating at a positive or negative pressure of only a few centimeters of water. The original American silos were, and still are, provided with a breather bag, placed in the air space above the grain (Figure 22). This bag opens only to the outside air, and by expanding or collapsing can respond to appreciable changes in pressure (Newman and Brook, 1971), without allowing any air to enter the silo. Most of the silos developed later in Britain do not have this breather-bag device, and rely only on a pressure-release valve. They also have a simpler form of bottom unloader than the American silos, which originally used a sweep-arm unloader to deal with the green silage, which could not flow freely to a fixed auger at the base.

The metal silos are filled from the top and emptied from the bottom, sometimes by a special sweep-arm auger which overcomes problems of "bridging" in very damp grain (see p. 402). Simpler unloading systems include the so-called "trident" device, the auger being placed in one of three positions in tubes on the base, and moved to another as unloading proceeds and grain ceases to flow to the original position. Bridging problems can be reduced by filling the silo first with some grain drier than that added later, if available. Unloading a small amount of grain as the silo is being filled will help, as will also removing a little grain every few weeks during any long period when the grain is not being drawn upon for feed (Isaacs, 1961). Once withdrawal begins, regular opening, e.g. twice-weekly, with removal of a smaller quantity of grain, is more satisfactory than removing a larger amount of grain less frequently. In this way the amount of oxygen entering at any one time is kept to a minimum, and is soon absorbed by the microorganisms on the grain. In all rigid structures it is difficult to avoid entry of air as grain is removed, and various methods have been studied to prevent this. Venting through a series of gas-storage cells has been investigated by Fredericks (1960) and Isaacs (1961). Purging with an inert gas has also been considered (see below).

Once grain has been withdrawn from the silo, it will soon become moldy in the open air. This spoilage is least in cold weather and greatest in very damp grain, so that the "shelf-life" can range from a week or two to only a few days, according to the conditions.

There is some difference of opinion as to the optimum moisture content of grain to be stored in sealed silos. Some workers (Harvey, 1965) recommended 18 to 22%, others consider that it can be as high as 25%, especially in metal silos with a sweep-arm unloader, or in the "open-top" silos discussed later.

In all airtight structures the oxygen-free atmosphere is a health hazard to those emptying the silo, and suitable precautions must be taken to prevent asphyxiation to anyone entering a silo to remove the last of the grain.

Storage in Flexible Bag Silos. Flexible bags are used either as liners to conventional concrete silos or, more commonly, as silos in their own right, supported in a cylinder of spot-welded metal mesh to give adequate strength, as the sheeting itself (butyl rubber, PVC, or, occasionally, polyethylene) is not strong enough to withstand, unsupported, the lateral thrust of the grain. The silos are usually of 20 to 40-ton capacity, and are used mainly on farms (see Figure 11).

Tests in butyl-rubber silos are described by Hyde (1968, 1970), Sojak (1968), and Nicholson (1970). Grant and Macintyre (1964), Clarke and Thorn (1967), and Hyde (1970) have investigated silos with bags of PVC, which are also in commercial production. Some of these have a lining of Kraft paper between the metal mesh and the PVC. This reduces the chance of damage, and also enables a thinner gauge of plastic sheeting to be used. Small polyethylene sacks have been shown by several workers to be satisfactory (Hope, 1964; Ekström et al., 1965; Forbes, 1965), especially during the cooler winter months.

Flexible structures have the advantage over rigid silos of collapsing onto the grain as the silo is emptied, thus reducing the amount of air space above the grain (Figure 23). Care must be taken that the bag is supported from above, so that it does not sag, particularly after heavy rain, and become entangled with the emptying auger. When emptying begins, the auger is inserted through a tube which was placed in position when the silo was erected, an airtight "snoot" being provided to close the opening. The bag silos are light and easy to handle, so that they can be transported and erected on any smooth ground, and packed up and stored in a small space when not in use.

Polyethylene sacks are even more portable. They are used mainly by farmers and feed compounders wishing to store relatively small quantities of grain in segregated lots. Storage is satisfactory, especially during the winter, if the polyethylene is of adequate thickness [at least 200 μm. (0.008 in.)] and if great care is paid to sealing the sacks, which should preferably be done by a double tie, or by heat sealing.

With all flexible silos, care must be taken to prevent damage by rodents. At ground-level this can be done by removing any nearby vegetation and by fixing a 30-cm.-high metal band round the base of the silo, on the outside of the mesh. Sometimes a 10-cm. "coving" or fillet of sand around the base is adequate. Flexible silos often have a tarpaulin rain cover, to prevent pools of water collecting in the folds of the bag itself. This cover should be lifted at frequent intervals (e.g., once a week) to check that rats and mice are not attacking the bag.

Flexible bag silos and polyethylene sacks are easily damaged, and although sometimes they can be patched, they are relatively inexpensive and should be regarded as having a shorter life (2 to 5 years) than the metal silos, the costs of which are usually amortized over 10 years.

Figure 23. Partially empty butyl-rubber silo, showing the bag collapsed onto the grain. [British Crown copyright. Reproduced by permission of the Controller of Her Britannic Majesty's Stationery Office.]

Open-Top Silos and Bunkers. So far, we have considered airtight storage of high-moisture grain in structures in which the seal is mechanical, i.e., provided by the impervious wall of the container itself.

There is, however, a certain amount of storage in conventional, but proofed, concrete tower silos or horizontal bunkers. Trials and commercial tests in tower silos have been described by Heuberger (1960), Isaacs (1961), Pratt et al. (1961), Messer et al. (1965), and Nicholson (1970). Horizontal bunkers have been studied by Morris and Isaacs (1965) and Krall (1969).

In these "open-top" or "open-end" structures the seal is "biological", provided by the exposed face of the grain itself. The surface is covered with a plastic sheet during the early period of storage, to enable oxygen-free conditions to become established in the grain mass. In this unstable form of airtight storage the towers are unloaded from the top and the bunkers from the side. Oxygen-free conditions are maintained in the grain bulk by the rapid utilization of oxygen by the microorganisms in the grain exposed to the air. This layer must be removed daily, to a depth which many workers have found to be 2 to 3 in. (5 to 8 cm.), before the grain has become heated and before thermophilic organisms, many of which are harmful, have developed. Messer et al. (1965) describe extensive trials on open-top concrete stave silos, where a high concentration of thermophils was found in the air spora above the exposed grain.

These open silos and bunkers are most successful when storing very damp grain, preferably over 30% moisture content. This very damp grain, especially if it is barley, is often harvested prematurely, and wild oats are cut with it before they have time to shed their seed: a useful way of destroying this troublesome weed. Many workers have obtained the high moisture content required by adding water to the grain (Jedele et al., 1958; Isaacs, 1961) which they claim reduces the dry-matter loss normally expected at very high moistures (see p. 406). Morris and Isaacs (1965) and Krall (1969) have reported these open silos and bunkers to be most satisfactory when storing ground or rolled maize or barley, which have a greater degree of compaction—and therefore less intergranular air—than whole grain. The ground grain can be handled without difficulty by the unloading systems used.

It must be pointed out, however, that this unstable form of airtight storage is potentially more hazardous than that in the mechanically sealed silos, as there is a greater risk of harmful microorganisms developing.

It may be that these open-top silos and bunkers will find their best use in storing "whole ear silage", as suggested by Hopkins (1968) for whole-crop barley. This is cut at a moisture content of about 40 to 50%, that is, about the time when the kernels have attained full dry matter content. The main advantage is that harvest is very early (in late July in Britain) at a time when there are less demands on farm labor than when the grain is mature. The ensiled product must, however, be regarded more as silage than grain, and therefore detailed comments are inappropriate in the present context.

IV. MISCELLANEOUS PROBLEMS

There are certain problems arising in connection with the airtight storage of grain, both dry and damp, that need further consideration. One of these is how the oxygen-free condition can best be created.

With heavy insect infestations in dry grain, or when the moisture content is high, low concentrations of oxygen are produced in airtight containers within a few days by the respiration of the insects or molds present in the grain, unless the temperature is rather low (10° to 15°C.).

However, if the infestation is light or the moisture content relatively low (16 to 18%), depletion of oxygen may be too slow to control the pest organisms within a short period of time, and it may be advisable to reduce the concentration of oxygen artificially. Several workers have considered the injection of carbon dioxide gas from cylinders (Le Du, 1966; Jay and Pearman, 1969). Henderson (1969) found carbon dioxide to be more effective than nitrogen in killing insects, as with 35% carbon dioxide the oxygen only had to be reduced to 14% to obtain a good kill. Press and Harein (1967) and Harein and Press (1968) also found that artificial atmospheres could be successfully created to control insects in dry products. Tuite et al. (1967) thought that several of the failures in commercial sealed storage of damp grain, at moisture contents of 20 to 24%, might have been due to relatively slow utilization of oxygen, and found that few fungi grew in artificial atmospheres in which the oxygen concentration was below 0.5%, although there were some exceptions.

Some users have created a carbon dioxide-rich atmosphere by adding blocks of solid carbon dioxide to a silo before sealing; and in France, purging with carbon dioxide gas is a common procedure. Many early workers hoped that by such treatment the anaerobic fermentation and its effects on the grain would be reduced. Experiments have shown (Hyde, 1970) that premature creation of oxygen-free conditions did not eliminate the fermentation, although the lowered temperature produced by flushing with carbon dioxide from cylinders reduced the deterioration of the product to a certain extent.

Other means of creating an oxygen-free atmosphere include combustion of propane or other gas, but this is an expensive method which may only be justified in special circumstances (Kruger, 1960).

V. TROPICAL ASPECTS OF AIRTIGHT STORAGE

In discussing airtight storage in tropical countries one must distinguish between those regions which, although geographically in the tropics, have, because of their altitude or other factors, a climate which can be regarded as temperate, and those areas which are truly "tropical", i.e., very warm throughout most of the year. The former type, which includes high, cool regions of Mexico, Venezuela, and Colombia, does not present any particular problems in relation to airtight or other forms of storage. Practices that prevail in temperate countries can be used with success in these, as well.

In the hot tropics, however, such as parts of Asia and Africa, certain problems arise which restrict the use of airtight storage to dry grain, i.e., not above 13% moisture content. In the developing countries, particularly, care must be exercised in ensuring that the moisture content of grain stored in airtight structures does not exceed this value, as in damp grain a number of problems arise, as has been indicated by Hyde (1969). In these countries most of the grain is used for human food, not for livestock, and the taint that develops at high moistures would make the grain unacceptable to the consumer. In the warm conditions the germination capacity would fall very rapidly, so that the grain could not be used for seed, even after only a short period of storage. The climatic conditions, even in relatively cool regions, with mean air temperatures of 18° to 20°C., permit relatively rapid growth of fungi. Any molds that developed would therefore engender a self-perpetuating process of spoilage, raising the temperature of the grain still higher, whereupon the harmful thermophilic organisms mentioned on p. 407 would have a chance to develop.

The degree of airtightness needed to prevent mold growth is much more critical than that required to control insects in dry grain. In some developing countries, where the principles of airtight storage may not be fully understood by those storing the grain, there is a danger of improper sealing, and of accidental or willful damage, the effects of which may not be fully appreciated.

Although the silos would be relatively small, the grain would probably be withdrawn only a little at a time, over a considerable period. Even in a flexible bag silo the free air space above the grain might contain enough oxygen to allow growth of fungi, particularly the harmful organisms already mentioned.

The "shelf-life" of damp grain is very short in warm conditions. At harvest the grain can only be kept for a few hours before putting into the silo, without its beginning to heat and go moldy. Some of the molds, including certain strains of *Aspergillus flavus*, could be toxin-producing, so that even if they were killed by the subsequent airtight conditions, the poisons they might have produced would remain. Invasion by molds after the grain was taken from the airtight silo would be very rapid, as the grain would now be dead and therefore very susceptible to mold attack.

It is therefore recommended that in warm countries airtight storage should not be used for grain of above 13 to 14% moisture content. For grain drier than this, it can be used with success, both for short-term storage to control existing infestations, or for long-term storage of famine reserves. If the moisture content is 11 to 12% or less, it is probable that the grain could still be used for seed, when stored from season to season.

VI. FUTURE PROSPECTS FOR AIRTIGHT STORAGE

Although airtight storage is now used fairly widely, it does not yet seem to have reached its full potential. It is well established in a number of temperate countries as a means of storage for high-moisture grain for feeding to livestock, the only possible use when the grain is damp. In Great Britain its limitations are now accepted, and care is taken to avoid the dangers of improper storage, especially those resulting from the growth of microorganisms, many of them harmful, if oxygen-free conditions are not maintained.

There is a certain amount of airtight storage of relatively dry grain (up to 16 to 17% moisture content) in large installations in France; but this development has not become widespread. However, the use of simple forms of airtight storage could be much extended where dry grain is concerned, both in well-developed areas and in developing countries. It offers a simple means of holding grain in an insect-free state for long periods, for famine or strategic reserves, without the use of chemical insecticides. This is a considerable advantage in these pollution-conscious days. Its use for short-term storage, and especially its possibilities for preventing insect infestations, or controlling existing ones (as described on p. 395) without the need for toxic chemicals, does not yet seem to have been fully appreciated.

Use of "controlled atmosphere" storage by addition of inert gas (carbon dioxide, nitrogen, or "natural gas" produced by burning of propane, either by combustion or by catalytic reaction), for both dry and damp grain, needs further investigation, as it may be justified in certain circumstances. But, basically, airtight storage is a simple method, and it may be best to let it remain so.

LITERATURE CITED

ANISKIN, V. I. 1968. *Preservation of moist grain*, 288 p. Isdatel'stvo Kolos, Moscow.

ARGENTINE MINISTRY OF NATIONAL ECONOMY. 1951. Storage of wheat in underground silos. Proc. United Nations Scientific Conference on Conservation and Utilization of Resources (Lake Success, Aug.-Sept. 1949) 6: 356-358.

ATTIA, R. 1948. Typical methods of handling and storing grain in Egypt. p. 105-109 in *Preservation of grains in storage*. United Nations, Food and Agriculture Organization, Agricultural Studies No. 2.

BAILEY, C. H., and A. M. GURJAR. 1918. Respiration in stored wheat. J. Agr. Res. 12: 685-713.

BAILEY, S. W. 1955. Air-tight storage of grain; its effect on insect pests. I. *Calandra granaria* L. (Coleoptera, Curculionidae.). Aust. J. Agr. Res. 6: 33-51.

BAILEY, S. W. 1956. Air-tight storage of grain; its effect on insect pests. II. *Calandra oryzae* (small strain). Aust. J. Agr. Res. 7: 7-19.

BAILEY, S. W. 1957. Air-tight storage of grain; its effect on insect pests. III. *Calandra oryzae* (large strain). Aust. J. Agr. Res. 8: 595-603.

BAILEY, S. W. 1965. Air-tight storage of grain; its effect on insect pests. IV. *Rhyzopertha dominica* (F.) and some other Coleoptera that infest stored grain. J. Stored Prod. Res. 1: 25-33.

BLANC, A. 1938. Essais de conservation de blé en atmosphère confinée. C. R. Acad. Agr. France 24: 625-630, + 71 p. suppl.

BLANC, A. 1939. Les premiers résultats d'une nouvelle série d'essais de conservation de blé en atmosphère confinée. C. R. Acad. Agr. France 25: 1005-1015.

BROWN, W. 1922. On the germination and growth of fungi at various temperatures and in various concentrations of oxygen and carbon dioxide. Ann. Bot. (London) 36: 257-283.

BURMEISTER, H. R., and P. A. HARTMAN. 1966. Yeasts in ensiled high-moisture corn. Appl. Microbiol. 14: 35-38.

BURMEISTER, H. R., P. A. HARTMAN, and R. A. SAUL. 1966. Microbiology of ensiled high-moisture corn. Appl. Microbiol. 14: 31-34.

CALDERON, M., and E. DONAHAYE. 1963. Observations on the storage conditions of barley held in an underground pit. Hassadeh.

CHRISTENSEN, C. M., and H. H. KAUFMANN. 1965. Deterioration of stored grains by fungi. Ann. Rev. Phytopathol. 3: 69-84.

CLARKE, A. D., and P. THORN. 1967. Moist grain storage eliminates drying. Rubber and Plastics Age 48: 450-452, 454.

CLARKE, J. H., E. V. NILES, and S. T. HILL. 1967. Ecology of the microflora of moist barley. Barley in "sealed" silos on farms. Pest Infestation Research for 1966: 14-16.

CLARKE, J. H., S. T. HILL, E. V. NILES, and M. A. R. HOWARD. 1969. Ecology of the microflora of moist barley in "sealed" silos on farms. Pest Infestation Research for 1968: 17.

COLE, E. W., and M. MILNER. 1953. Colorimetric and fluorometric properties of wheat in relation to germ damage. Cereal Chem. 30: 378-391.

COTES, E. C. 1888. Notes on economic entomology, No. 1 [Quoted by H. S. Pruthi and M. Singh, 1950. Pests in stored grain and their control. Indian J. Agr. Sci. 18: 88 p.]

COTTON, R. T. 1961. What about airtight storage of grain? Northwest. Miller 265(15): 46-51.

CULPIN, C. 1969. Agricultural mechanization. Airtight storage of grain. United Nations, Economic Commission for Europe, Report AGRI/MECH/38. 15 p.

de BOISGELIN, L. 1804. p. 42 in *Ancient and modern Malta*, vol. 1. G & J Robinson, London.

DENDY, A. 1918. Report on the effect of airtight storage upon grain insects. I. Report of the Grain Pests (War) Committee, Roy. Soc., London, No. 1, part 1: 6-24.

DENDY, A., and H. D. ELKINGTON. 1918. Report on the effect of airtight storage upon grain insects. II. Report of the Grain Pests (War) Committee, Roy. Soc., London, No. 3: 3-14.

DENDY, A., and H. D. ELKINGTON. 1920. Report on the effect of airtight storage upon grain insects. III. Report of the Grain Pests (War) Committee, Roy. Soc., London, No. 6: 1-51.

DESIKACHAR, H. S. R., S. K. MAJUMDER, S. V. PINGALE, and V. SUBRAHMANYAN. 1959. Discoloration in rice: Some studies on its nature and effect on nutritive value. Cereal Chem. 36: 78-83.

DEXTER, S. T., A. M. CHAVES, and O. T. EDJE. 1969. Drying or anaerobically preserving small lots of grain for seed or food. Agron. J. 61: 913-919.

DONAHAYE, E., S. NAVARRO, and M. CALDERON. 1967. Storage of barley in an underground pit sealed with a PVC liner. J. Stored Prod. Res. 3: 359-364.

DOYÈRE, L. 1862. *Conservation des grains par l'ensilage.* Guillaumin Ed., Paris. [From A. M. Jossoud, 1959. Conservation des grains par l'ensilage il y a cent ans. Agriculture (Paris) 210: 77-85.]

EKSTRÖM, N., G. ANIANSSON, L.

THYSELIUS, and S. THOMKE. 1965. Spannmalsensilerung. Jordbrukstekniska Institutet (Uppsala), Meddelande No. 311. 75 p.

FLETCHER, T. B., and C. C. GHOSH. 1920. Stored grain pests. Rep. of the Proc. 3rd Entomological Meeting (Pusa, Feb. 1919) 2: 712-761.

FORBES, T. J. 1965. Some observations on the hermetic storage of undried barley and its use in pig-feeding. Agr. Prog. 40: 55-67.

FOSTER, G. H., H. A. KALER, and R. L. WHISTLER. 1955. Effects on corn of storage in airtight bins. J. Agr. Food Chem. 3: 682-686.

FREDERICKS, E. E. 1960. High moisture grain. Rep. Purdue Univ. Agr. Exp. Sta. 3(3): 2-5.

GILES, P. H. 1965. Control of insects infesting stored sorghum in northern Nigeria. J. Stored Prod. Res. 1: 145-158.

GOLDING, N. S. 1940a. The gas requirements of molds. II. The oxygen requirements of *Penicillium roquefortii* (three strains originally isolated from blue-veined cheese) in the presence of nitrogen as diluent and the absence of carbon dioxide. J. Dairy Sci. 23: 879-889.

GOLDING, N. S. 1940b. The gas requirements of molds. III. The effect of various concentrations of carbon dioxide on the growth of *Penicillium roquefortii* (three strains originally isolated from blue-veined cheese) in air. J. Dairy Sci. 23: 891-898.

GONEN, M., and M. CALDERON. 1968. Changes in the microfloral composition of moist sorghum stored under hermetic conditions. Trop. Sci. 10: 107-114.

GRANT, J. R., and I. M. M. MACINTYRE. 1964. Airtight storage of high-moisture grain. Scot. Agr. 44: 89-91.

GUILBOT, A., and J. POISSON. 1963. Conditions de stockage et durée de conservation des grains. Journée d'Études sur la conservation des grains de l'Institut Technique des Céréales et des Fourrages 14 June 1963: 15-27.

HALL, D. W., G. A. HASWELL, and T. A. OXLEY. 1956. Underground storage of grain. Colon. Res. Stud. No. 21. 27 p.

HAREIN, P. K., and A. F. PRESS. 1968. Mortality of stored-peanut insects exposed to mixtures of atmospheric gases at various temperatures. J. Stored Prod. Res. 4: 77-82.

HARVEY, P. N. 1965. Moist grain storage. Quart. Rev., Nat. Agr. Advisory Service 69: 10-15.

HENDERSON, L. S. 1969. Refrigerated and controlled air for insect control in stored grain. Milling 151(4): 28,30.

HEUBERGER, G. L. 1960. A study of high-moisture field-shelled corn for beef cattle production. Diss. Abstr. 21: 1312.

HOPE, H. 1964. Undried grain in plastic bags. Farmers Weekly, Aug. 7: 79-80.

HOPKINS, J. R. 1968. Whole crop barley for silage. NAAS Quart. Rev. 79: 117-120.

HURST, D. 1965. Intensive feeding of cattle with particular reference to the feeding of high moisture grain. Agr. Progress 40: 68-74.

HYDE, MARY B. 1958. Underground storage of grain and its effects on grain quality. Berichte 2. Getreidetagung, Detmold, 21-23 May 1958: 153-165.

HYDE, MARY B. 1965. Principles of wet grain conservation. J. and Proc., Inst. Agr. Eng. 21: 75-82.

HYDE, MARY B. 1968. Successful storage of high moisture grain. Research is overcoming the problems and complications involved. Esso Farmer 20(3): 11-14.

HYDE, MARY B. 1969. Hazards of storing high moisture grain in airtight silos in tropical countries. Trop. Stored Prod. Inform. 18: 9-12.

HYDE, MARY B. 1970. Storage trials with moist barley and field beans in polyvinyl chloride and butyl rubber silos. p. 178-185 in Proc. 4th Int. Colloquium on Plastics in Agriculture, Paris, June 1970.

HYDE, MARY B., and N. J. BURRELL. 1969. Control of infestation in stored grain by airtight storage or by cooling. p. 412-419 in Proc. 5th British Insecticides and Fungicides Conference, Brighton, 17-20 Nov. 1969 (British Crop Protection Council organized the conference).

HYDE, MARY B., N. J. BURRELL, GLORIA WICKENDEN, and JANET BROWN. 1961. Airtightness and insect control. Tests in a glass-fibre bin. p. 20 in Pest Infestation Research for 1960.

HYDE, MARY B., and C. G. DAUBNEY. 1960. A study of grain storage in fossae in Malta. Trop. Sci. 2: 115-129.

HYDE, MARY B., and T. A. OXLEY. 1960. Experiments on the airtight storage of damp grain. I. Introduction, effect on the grain and the intergranular atmosphere. Ann. Appl. Biol. 48: 687-710.

ISAACS, G. W. 1959. Airtight storage: Another way to handle high moisture grain. World Farming 1(5): 18-20, 36.

ISAACS, G. W. 1961. Wet storage and chemical treatment of grain. Paper to Crop Conditioning Equipment Conference, University of Nebraska, 4 Aug. 1961. 20 p. (Duplicated.)

ISAACS, G. W., I. J. ROSS, and E. R. BAUGH. 1958. Hermetic storage of high moisture corn in plastic-lined bins. Purdue Univ., Agr. Exp. Sta., Report AE-45. 8 p. (Duplicated.)

JANJUA, N. A., and M. M. NASIR. 1948. Stored grain pests and their control in Baluchistan. Bull. Dep. Agr., Baluchistan, No. 2. 32 p.

JAY, E. G., and G. C. PEARMAN. 1969. Protecting wheat in metal cans with carbon dioxide. J. Georgia Entomol. Soc. 4: 181-186.

JEDELE, D. G., F. W. ANDREW, and G. P. CARLISLE. 1958. Now—store "wet" corn in *any* upright silo. Successful Farming 56(8): 82.

JONES, H. D. 1842. Memoranda and details of the mode of building houses, etc., in the island of Malta. Professional Papers, Corps of Royal Engineers 5: 196-205.

KELLY, C. F., B. M. STAHL, S. C. SALMON, and R. H. BLACK. 1942. Wheat storage in experimental farm-type bins, 245 p. U.S. Dep. Agr. Circ. No. 637.

KLEEV, I. A. 1948. Storage of grain in anaerobic conditions. Trudy Vses. Nauch. Issledov. Inst. Zerna 15: 59-69.

KRALL, J. L. 1969. High moisture barley; harvesting, storing and feeding. Mont. Agr. Exp. Sta. Bull. 625. 45 p.

KRUGER, A. H. 1960. Inert atmosphere for the preservation and protection of feeds in storage. Bull. Pacific Coast Gas Ass. No. 181. 4 p.

Le DU, J. 1966. Valeurs boulangères, qualités technologiques du blé, sont-elles conservées après deux ans de stockage? Bull. Anciens Elèves École Fr. Meun. 213: 127-132.

Le DU, J. 1968. Conservation de blé sous vide, sous atmosphère confinée, sous atmosphère de gas carbonique. Conservation d'orge de brasserie sous atmosphère confinée. Ind. Aliment. Agr. 35: 811-821.

LINDGREN, D. L. 1935. The respiration of insects in relation to the heating and the fumigation of grain. Tech. Bull. Minn. Agr. Exp. Sta. No. 109. 32 p.

LINKO, P. 1960. Current research on the biochemistry of grain storage. Cereal Sci. Today 5: 302-306.

LÓPEZ, C. O. 1942. Almacenamiento a granel de emergencia y silos subterráneos. Min. Agr. de la Nacion, Comision de Conservación de Cereales, Buenos Aires, 32 p.

LÓPEZ, C. O. 1946. La conservación de los cereales y los silos subterráneos. Reseñas 7: 27-72.

MANESSIER, J. 1950. Silos métalliques étanches pour le stockage des grains. Information et Documentation Agricoles, No. 14: 439-445.

McFARLANE, J. A. 1970. Insect control by airtight storage in small containers. Trop. Stored Prod. Inform. 19: 10-14.

MEIERING, A. G., F. W. BAKKER-ARKEMA, and W. G. BICKERT. 1966. Short time sealed storage of high-moisture small grains. Quart. Bull. Mich. Agr. Exp. Sta. 48: 465-470.

MESSER, H. J. M., J. M. HILL, R. WHITTENBURY, and J. LACEY. 1965. The use of concrete staved silos for storing high-moisture barley. Agr. Res. Council, Exp. Farm Buildings Rep. No. 4. 24 p.

MILNER, M., C. M. CHRISTENSEN, and W. F. GEDDES. 1947a. Grain storage studies. VI. Wheat respiration in relation to moisture content, mold growth, chemical deterioration, and heating. Cereal Chem. 24: 182-199.

MILNER, M., C. M. CHRISTENSEN, and W. F. GEDDES. 1947b. Grain storage studies. VII. Influence of certain mold inhibitors on respiration of moist wheat. Cereal Chem. 24: 507-517.

MORRIS, W. H. M., and G. W. ISAACS. 1965. Preservation of high moisture grain in oxygen-free storages. Paper to C.I.G.R. Seminar, Cambridge, Sept. 20-24, 1965. 13 p. (Duplicated.)

MÜNTZ, A. 1881. Etudes sur la conservation des grains par l'ensilage. Ann. Inst. Nat. Agron. 3: 19-73.

NAVARRO, S., M. CALDERON, and E. DONAHAYE. 1968. Hermetic storage of wheat in a butyl rubber container. p. 102-110 in Progress Report, Israel Ministry of Agr., Dep. of Plant Protection, Stored Prod. Res. Lab. 1967/68.

NEWMAN, G., and R. H. BROOK. 1971. Investigation of a pressure equalising system in a sealed grain silo. J. Inst. Agr. Eng. 25(4):158-161.

NICHOLS, AGNES A., and CHRISTINE W. LEAVER. 1966. Methods of examining damp grain at harvest and after sealed and open storage: Changes in the microflora of damp grain during sealed storage. J. Appl. Bacteriol. 29: 566-581.

NICHOLSON, J. W. G. 1970. High moisture barley. p. 5-7 in News from Canada Department of Agriculture, No. 1399.

NIKITINSKII, YA YA. 1955. Storage of damp wheat grains in an atmosphere of carbon dioxide gas in an experimental silo. Trudy Vses. Nauch. Issled. Inst. Zerna 30: 5-12.

OXLEY, T. A., and MARY B. HYDE. 1955. Recent experiments on hermetic storage of wheat. Proc. 3rd Int. Bread Congr., Hamburg: 179-182.

OXLEY, T. A., and MARY B. HYDE. 1957. The airtight storage of damp grain. Farm Mechanization 9: 473-474.

OXLEY, T. A., MARY B. HYDE, K. FOULGER, GLORIA WICKENDEN, and MARY KEEPING. 1956. Underground storage of grain. Pest Infestation Research for 1955: 17-20.

OXLEY, T. A., MARY B. HYDE, and GLORIA WICKENDEN. 1957. The testing of structures for airtightness. Pest Infestation Research for 1956: 22-23.

OXLEY, T. A., and GLORIA WICKENDEN. 1963. The effect of restricted air supply on some insects which infest grain. Ann. of Appl. Biol. 51: 313-324.

PASFIELD, D. H. 1953. Confined atmosphere storage of grain. Farm Mechanization 5(1): 16-17.

PETERSON, ANNE, VERA SCHLEGEL, B. HUMMEL, L. S. CUENDET, W. F. GEDDES, and C. M. CHRISTENSEN. 1956. Grain storage studies. XXII. Influence of oxygen and carbon dioxide concentrations on mold growth and grain deterioration. Cereal Chem. 33: 53-66.

PRADHAN, S., P. B. MOOKHERJEE, and G. C. SHARMA. 1965. Pusa bin for grain storage. Indian Farming 15(1): 14-16.

PRATT, G. L., W. L. PROMERSBERGER, C. A. WATSON, and M. L. BUCHANAN. 1961. Storing high moisture barley in North Dakota. Paper to the Annual Meeting of the Amer. Soc. Agr. Eng., 61-425. 8 p.

PRESS, A. F., and P. K. HAREIN. 1967. Mortality of *Tribolium castaneum* (Herbst) (Coleoptera, *Tenebrionidae*) in simulated peanut storages purged with carbon dioxide and nitrogen. J. Stored Prod. Res. 3: 91-96.

PRUTHI, H. S., and M. SINGH. 1950. Pests of stored grain and their control. Indian J. Agr. Sci. 18: 88 p.

RIGGS, J. K. 1969. Processing moist grain sorghum for beef cattle. Trans. Amer. Soc. Agr. Eng. 12: 782-785.

SHELLENBERGER, J. A., and F. C. FENTON. 1952. Underground grain storage. Milling Production 17(7): 5, 12-16.

SHVETSOVA, V. A., and N. I. SOSEDOV. 1958. Biochemical changes during prolonged hermetic storage of wheat. Biokhimiya Zerna No. 4: 229-240.

SOJAK, M. 1968. Experience with a butyl silo at Ridgetown College of Agricultural Technology. Duplicated Report, Ridgetown Coll. Agr. Technol., Agdex 110/732-120. 4 p.

SPAFFORD, W. J. 1939. Storing loose grain in South Australia. J. Dep. Agr., South Aust. 43: 274-286.

SWAINE, G. 1954. Underground storage of maize in Tanganyika. East Afr. Agr. J. 20: 122-128.

TEUNISSON, DOROTHEA J. 1954a. Influence of storage without aeration on the microbial populations of rough rice. Cereal Chem. 31: 462-474.

TEUNISSON, DOROTHEA. 1954b. Yeasts from freshly combined rough rice stored in a sealed bin. Appl. Microbiol. 2: 215-220.

TUITE, J. F., C. G. HAUGH, G. W. ISAACS, and C. C. HUXSOLL. 1967. Growth and effect of molds in stored high-moisture grain. Trans. Amer. Soc. Agr. Eng. 10: 730-732, 737.

VAYSSIÈRE, P. 1940. La rationnement en denrées alimentaires et la protection des stocks. C. R. Acad. Sci. Paris, 1940: 798-808.

VAYSSIÈRE, P. 1948. Hermetic storage, the process of the future for the conservation of foodstuffs. United Nations, Food and Agriculture Organization, Agr. Stud. No. 2: 115-122.

CHAPTER 11

CHILLING

N. J. B U R R E L L

Pest Infestation Control Laboratory
Ministry of Agriculture, Fisheries and Food, Slough, Buckinghamshire, England

I. INTRODUCTION

To avoid a common misconception, it is essential at the outset to define the term *Chilling* as applied to grain storage. The term *Chilling* is considered here to be synonymous with *Refrigeration*, and involves the passage of air over a refrigerated coil to condition the air to a temperature usually well below ambient before blowing it into a grain bulk. Usually the relative humidity is also adjusted to a low level by reheating the cool air slightly with a second warm coil. *Chilling* should not be confused with *Aeration*, which is described in Chapter 12, because grain *Aeration* is defined as grain cooling using selected but unconditioned air at a temperature and relative humidity near ambient.

In most parts of the world the moisture content of grain at harvest is too high for safe storage, and damp grain is readily attacked by molds unless it is protected in some way. The most widely used method of preventing mold growth is to dry the grain to a safe level; but protection by airtight storage, preservative chemicals, or cooling is also used under some circumstances. Thorough drying alone, however, is not successful against all organisms, as dry grain may still be attacked and damaged by insects, particularly if the temperature is high. Grain, therefore, requires cooling after it is dried, to make it safe from insect attack.

It is widely accepted that there is a balance between safe moisture content[1] and safe temperature, so that the lower the temperature of a bulk of grain, the damper it can safely be stored (Figure 1). This leads to the conclusion that drying need not be so stringently applied as, in general, the power required to evaporate moisture from a bulk of grain is far greater than that required to cool the same bulk. For example, the energy required to evaporate 6% of moisture from a grain mass is at least six times greater than that required to cool the same bulk from 25° to 5° C. Therefore, storage by cooling may have an economic advantage over drying, as long as this advantage is not lost through grain spoilage caused by attempting to store excessively damp grain, by the need for frequent chilling, or by the excessively high capital cost of the equipment used.

---

[1]All moisture contents in this chapter are given as a percentage of the wet weight.

In some regions such as the cooler and damper countries of Europe, fuel costs are relatively high (Nijweide, 1964) and the average moisture content of freshly harvested wheat, oats, and barley is 18 to 25%, with maize corn up to 50% moisture. In such regions a balance between low temperatures and high moisture contents may reduce drying costs, although, in Europe, grain too damp for refrigerated storage is usually reduced to a suitable level by passing it rapidly through a dryer. Stringent drying is, therefore, sometimes avoided, particularly when the storage period is to be short or when the grain is to be used for stockfeed. However, grain which is to be kept for an unknown duration, for famine or strategic reserves, or for export, requires thorough drying to ensure safe storage, particularly during the extreme changes in temperature and humidity sometimes experienced during shipment. Refrigeration for dried grain during shipment could, however, be a useful insurance against insects or against damp grain heating in the holds.

There are, however, additional reasons why grain is sometimes held in a damp condition. For example, damp grain is usually considered preferable to dry grain for stockfeed, as it is more easily rolled, more easily digested, and creates fewer

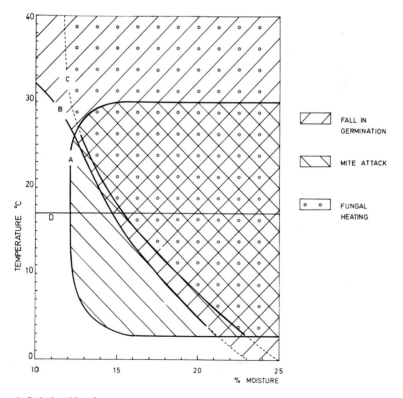

Figure 1. Relationship of storage temperature and grain moisture content to insect heating (above line D), fall in germination (to 95% in 35 weeks' storage, line B), damp grain heating, and mite attack. (After Burges and Burrell, 1964.)

dust problems. For milling, wheat is required at about 15 to 16% moisture content, and at this level mold growth and heating can occur in large bulks unless some form of cooling is applied. Refrigeration is, therefore, sometimes used to treat milling wheat or malting barley in store, particularly in the warmer areas of France (Jouin, 1965), but also in Britain (Burrell, 1965), Belgium, and Germany (Heidt and Bolling, 1965). Reports of grain stored at moistures as high as 18% have been cited by Jamet (1959) in France, but more recent observations indicate that the moisture content there does not now often exceed 16%, except for short periods. In Britain, refrigeration is sometimes taken up by farmers who, on increasing their cereal acreage or combining capacity, find their existing dryers to be inadequate, and use refrigeration to hold grain at up to 22% moisture content for a short period until existing dryers catch up with the harvest; however, once chilling machinery has been introduced into a grain-storage installation, it is usually made to pay for its keep by holding grain at lower temperatures and at higher moistures than before. Chilling is also sometimes used on small farms in remote areas in Britain to avoid the cost of installing a three-phase electrical supply, as a single-phase supply is often adequate for small-farm chillers. An alternative choice is, of course, to purchase a diesel-driven dryer.

Some farmers use their grain-chilling unit for additional purposes, such as for the temporary storage of fruit, peas, or other vegetables; and some units are used both as a heat pump for grain drying in one bin and simultaneously, or alternatively, as a chiller for another bin. However, such examples are rare, and single-purpose units are the general rule. In the U.S. more attention has been given to "dehydrofrigidation"—that is, drying while holding the grain at a low temperature—but low-temperature drying, in Europe, has not so far proven to be economical (Burrell, 1969a). In some warm climates the use of grain chillers has been considered as a means of cooling dry grain to a temperature low enough to prevent grain insects from producing an infestation, and tests in Queensland by Sutherland et al. (1970) have shown promising, but so far incomplete, success.

To determine whether a crop should be dried or chilled, one must consider the biology of the seeds and of the organisms causing deterioration and the physics of the seeds, as well as the final use of the grain. All pest organisms have optimal zones of moisture and temperature in which they thrive. For insects the temperatures are relatively high, usually above 15°C., and their moisture tolerance is often as low as 10% or even less. For mites the temperature optima are lower and the limiting moisture content higher. By contrast, various fungi have temperature tolerances covering a wide band of temperature of perhaps 0° to 50°C., but all need a relative humidity in excess of 70%. The pest hazards are, therefore, determined by the temperature-moisture combinations achieved during storage, and the ideal situation is for low temperatures to inhibit insects and for dryness to limit fungi, mites, and the metabolism of the seed.

II. BIOLOGICAL HAZARDS AT LOW TEMPERATURES

When grain is chilled, storage conditions of low temperature and high moisture content are deliberately chosen. In these circumstances, fungi are the most important pest organisms and mites may be a problem, but insects are unlikely to cause much damage. The influence of chilling on germination must also be considered.

A. Growth of Fungi

Some fungi are normally present as a mycelium under the epidermis or on the surface of the grains at harvest. Under normal dry storage conditions, and particularly at temperatures above ambient, these field organisms usually die out and are replaced by lower numbers of storage fungi (see Chapter IV, Microflora). Under damp conditions, and particularly at low temperatures, however, these field organisms survive (Pelhate, 1968) and may be found growing actively during storage, in conjunction with storage fungi, for as long as 7 months (Lagrandeur and Poisson, 1968). The presence of a heavy inoculum at the end of a period of cool storage can, however, be a considerable disadvantage. Andreson et al. (1967) demonstrated how cool damp storage allowed a high initial mold count to persist and showed that an increase in both field and storage fungi occurred on malting barley during the processes of steeping and germination. They pointed out that to reduce the final mold population the initial population should be as small as possible and that storage conditions should be unfavorable for proliferation. Kneen (1963) showed that off-flavors and instability in beer could be produced by several field and storage fungi. In other words, malting barley should normally be dried thoroughly before storage.

Musty odors often occur in bulks of damp grain even when low temperatures are maintained, although this mustiness can be prevented or even removed by the frequent passage of air through the bulk. The odors may be caused by microorganisms or mites, but above 15% moisture they are usually because of fungi. Aeration can remove only volatile substances, and any other taints produced by mold activity will remain. If the grain is to be used for human consumption, it is more satisfactory to prevent storage odors by adequate drying.

The main problem facing those considering the storage of damp grain is the question of how low a temperature is required at any given moisture content to preserve grain for the necessary storage period. The work on this subject is limited, but it is clear that, at high moisture contents, temperatures well below freezing would be necessary to prevent fungal activity, since Chistiakov and Bocharova (1938) and Berry and Magoon (1934) reported that *Aspergillus glaucus,* several species of *Penicillium, Cladosporium, Fusarium,* and *Mucor,* and some yeasts, grow at $-5°$ to $-8°C.$, and in some instances sporulate at freezing temperatures. Joffe (1962) also reported the production of fungal toxins on moldy grain at sub-zero temperatures. Table I gives an estimate of the length of time that barley can be stored free from visible mold under various conditions of temperature and moisture content. Kreyger (1967) found that oats, wheat, and rye are more subject to fungal attack than barley, but that the period of mold-free storage could be delayed by air movement. Figure 2 illustrates how mold growth occurs more rapidly at higher moisture contents, and most studies show that the damper the grain, the lower is the temperature required to prevent mold growth (Figure 1). Lagrandeur and Poisson (1968), however, found little difference in the total number of fungi growing on damp maize at temperatures from $5°$ to $22°C.$

Mold growth is usually an accelerating process even when the temperature is

TABLE I
*Estimated maximum number of weeks of mold-free storage of
barley at various temperatures and moisture contents*

Moisture Content %	Temperature, °C.						
	$-6°$ [a]	$0°$ [a]	$5°$	$10°$	$15°$	$20°$	$25°$
16	> 100	> 100	> 100	> 100	>100	40	10
17	> 100	> 100	> 100	100	30	10	4
18	> 100	> 100	80	30	12	5	2
19	> 56	> 32	40	17	6.5	3	1.5
20	56	32	9.5	5.5	3	1.5	1
20[b]	...	...	15	8	4	2	1.5
22	40	12	4	2.5	1.5	1	0.5
22[b]	...	...	9	5.5	3	1.5	1
24	32	6	2.5	1.5	1	0.5	0.5
24[b]	...	...	4.5	2.5	1.5	1	0.5
26	24	4	1.5	1	0.5	0.5	...
26[b]	...	...	3.5	2	1	0.5	...

[a]After Burrell (1966) and Kreyger (1967).
[b]With the use of adequate ventilation.

kept steady (Oxley, 1948a; Hummel et al., 1954), and the tendency for heating may not, therefore, reach its maximum for days or even for weeks. The increase in the rate of respiration with time is because of the increasing fungal mycelium present (Mattei, 1968) aided by any increase in moisture content owing to the production of metabolic water; therefore, even after the grain has been cooled, further periods of chilling may be necessary to prevent reheating. Heating may be exacerbated by mechanical damage during combining, which leads to a more rapid attack by molds and a rapid fall in germination (Arnold, 1959, 1963; Saul and Steele, 1966). This rapid fall in germination may be arrested by immediate drying, but continues under cool damp storage conditions.

B. Estimation of Losses from Fungi

The heat of metabolism that accompanies the respiration of fungi is a hindrance to artificial cooling. The rate of respiration depends on moisture content, temperature, the amount of fungal mycelium on the grain, the extent of damage to the grain, and the amount of dust present. Fungal activity metabolizes the carbohydrate, protein, and any fat in the grain, and any circumstances which increase the rate of respiration increase the amount of substrate used, and produce greater losses in the weight of seed. Although the respiration of living organisms consists of a very large number of interrelated chemical processes, the net results of these can be summarized, somewhat inadequately, by the formula for the oxidation of a hexose carbohydrate

$$C_6H_{12}O_6 + 6O_2 = 6CO_2 + 6H_2O + 677 \text{ kcal.}^2$$

[2]It can be calculated from the equation that a 1% loss in dry matter is accompanied by the production of about 14.7 g. of carbon dioxide from each kilogram of dry matter.

Thus, the rate at which the grain is destroyed by fungi can be estimated directly in terms of the weight of the grain or by measuring: a) the rate of oxygen uptake or carbon dioxide output per unit weight of grain; b) the increase in moisture content in a given time; or c) the rate of heat production.

Of these possibilities the easiest and most common laboratory or large-scale method which can be used is to measure the carbon dioxide output, and Steele and Saul (1962), Scholz (1962), Mattei (1968), and Kreyger (1967) have used this method at a wide range of conditions for various grains. Some dry-weight losses from these sources for temperatures from 2.5° to 35°C. are summarized in Table II. Nuret (1935) seems to have been the first author to use the rate of respiration of fungi on grain to derive the combinations of moisture content and temperature which give storage conditions of equal danger for grain, and the same approach has been used by many later workers. Steele and Saul (1962) defined the allowable storage time for shelled corn as the time taken by the fungi to metabolize 0.5% dry matter, and showed that the time available for drying could be extended greatly at low temperatures. Steele et al. (1969) showed the quantitative effects of time, temperature, moisture content, and mechanical damage on the rate of carbon dioxide production of fungi on maize.

Much of the work on the respiration of moldy grain has been carried out at temperatures over 10°C., as the amount of gas exchange is small at lower temperatures. At low temperatures it is sometimes more convenient to estimate loss in dry weight from slow increases in moisture content. Figure 3 relates in-

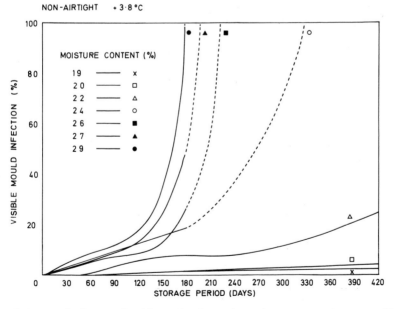

Figure 2. Increase in the rate of mold growth at increasing moisture contents (as measured by the appearance of visible fungal colonies on barley) at a mean storage temperature of 3.8 (±2°C.). (Burrell, 1966.)

TABLE II

Mean percentage loss in dry weight per day of barley (B), wheat (W), and maize (M) in relation to temperatures and moisture content

Temp. °C	Grain	Moisture Content (% of wet weight)								Reference Cited
		18	20	22	24	24–26	26	28	30	
2.5	M	...	...	0.006	0.0086	...	0.0116	0.0135	0.0166	Steele and Saul (1962)
5.0	M	...	...	0.0094	0.0135	...	0.0179	0.0217	0.0278	Steele and Saul (1962)
10	W	0.0035	...	0.0086	...	...	0.0304	...	0.050	Scholz (1962)
10	M	...	0.001	0.019	0.026	...	0.036	0.042	0.050	Steele and Saul (1962)
15	B	...	0.009	0.022	...	0.035	...	...	...	Kreyger (1967)
20	W	0.0163	...	0.056	...	...	0.137	...	0.170	Scholz (1962)
20	B	...	0.016	0.04	...	0.065	...	...	...	Kreyger (1967)
25	B	...	0.025	0.055	...	0.09	...	...	...	Kreyger (1967)
30	B	...	0.03	0.075	...	0.12	...	...	...	Kreyger (1967)
30	W	0.0583	...	0.13	...	...	0.321	...	0.335	Scholz (1962)
35	B	...	0.37	0.094	...	0.15	...	...	...	Kreyger (1967)

crease in moisture to the average loss in dry weight in bins of chilled wheat and barley over a period of 6.5 months when the temperatures were reduced rapidly from 17° to 5°C. Daily mean heat production is also given and is related to the mean temperature rise likely to occur in cooled grain of more than 18% moisture. As demonstrated in Figure 3, the costs of power for chilling are likely to increase in grain stored at more than 18% moisture and to increase rapidly at over 22% moisture because of the need for repeated chilling to prevent damp grain heating.

C. Mites

Grain storage mites are active in grain at high moisture contents and at moderately high temperatures but soon die at temperatures much above 30°C. or at low moisture contents. Cunnington (1965) showed that the limits of favorable temperature for complete development of the grain mite *Acarus siro* ranged from about 3° to 31°C. and that it could develop at a relative humidity as low as 62.5% (13-14% moisture content) provided the temperature was not much below 10°C. or much above 20°C. Further studies (Cunnington, personal communication) showed that the mite developed slowly at 5°C. at moistures above 15% and most rapidly at 25°C. and at about 20% moisture content when the population increase was more than sevenfold per week. Grain mites are, however, often resistant to low temperatures and their resistance can be increased by previous exposure to moderately low temperatures. Sinha (1964) found that after rearing *Acarus siro* at 6(±2)°C., it survived exposure to a temperature of –18°C. for 7 days, during which others, reared at 21°C., all died. Mites and fungi are often found abundantly together, partly because both thrive

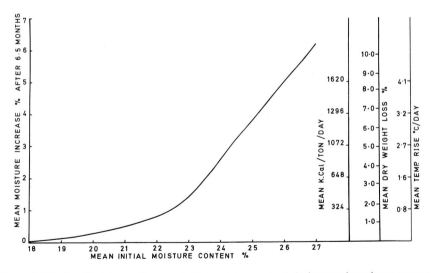

Figure 3. Relationship between the mean initial moisture content, the increase in moisture content, and calculated loss in dry weight of wheat and barley during a storage period of 6.5 months at a temperature of 7.5°C. Mean heat production and estimated temperature rise per day are given. (Burrell, 1969b.)

TABLE III

Number of mites present in samples taken at 1- and 2-ft. intervals down the center of a 100-ton bin of damp refrigerated barley 2 months after chilling[a]

Depth		Moisture Content	Approximate Mean Temperature	Mites
ft.	m.	%	°C.	per kg.
1	0.31	19.2	11.4	4,310
2	0.61	20.3	11.4	3,440
3	0.92	19.7	11.4	7,300
4	1.22	20.1	11.4	1,360
5	1.52	20.0	11.7	2,100
6	1.83	19.4	11.7	4,810
8	2.44	19.0	11.7	2,190
9	2.75	19.1	11.7	2,380
11	3.35	20.4	7.3	1,780
12	3.66	19.8	7.3	1,860
14	4.27	19.3	7.3	860
16	4.88	16.7	4.5	110
17	5.19	16.7	4.5	0
19	5.80	16.6	4.5	80

[a]Burrell and Laundon, 1967.

in the same conditions and partly because certain storage fungi are attractive to and are eaten by mites (Griffiths et al., 1959; Sinha, 1964).

Sinha (1964) recorded that *Acarus siro* and *Glycyphagus destructor* were common in grain stored in the prairie provinces of Canada, especially in a shallow upper layer of the grain bulks, but that midwinter temperature fluctuations of 1° to −18°C. in this layer caused a high mortality among them. The same mites predominate in British farm-stored grain (Table IV). The numbers of mites in barley chilled once after harvesting and sampled 2 months later from various depths down the center of a 100-ton bin of refrigerated grain are given in Table III. This population of mites is higher than that usually found in bulks of grain refrigerated regularly, as the numbers in damp refrigerated grain do not often exceed 1,000 per kilogram of grain, even after storage for 8 months (Table IV).

Since *Acarus siro* feeds almost entirely on the germ, infested grain stored at a high moisture content may suffer a loss of germination (Solomon, 1946) unless the grain temperature is reduced rapidly and permanently to below 5°C., especially at the upper surface where most mites occur. Although it is often possible, in time, to achieve 5°C. throughout the main bulk, it is too expensive to achieve this at the periphery in the fall when air temperatures are still favorable for mite development, and some mites must normally be expected to occur there at this time.

Some mites have long been known as hazards to both human and animal health. Recent research has shown that certain species play an important role in respiratory allergy as causal agents of bronchial asthma and rhinitis. Although not the most important species associated with respiratory disorders, some of the common grain mites, including *Acarus siro* and *Glycyphagus destructor*, have

TABLE IV
Changes in moisture content, germination, and density of mite infestation; main mite genera present; running periods; and costs of treatment in six bins of damp barley stored for 6 months. Bin 6 was then dried by heat pump[a]

	Bins						
	1	2	3	4	5	6	6
Refrigerated (R) or Ventilated (V)	R	V	R	V	R	V	Dried
Moisture Content, %							
Initial mean	19.2	15.7	17.3	16.7	16.9	18.7	18.1
Final mean	18.1	16.3	17.3	17.0	16.7	18.1	13.8
Change	−1.1	+0.6	0.0	+0.3	−0.2	−0.6	−4.4
Mites per kg.							
Initial mean	106	117	13	30	3	47	246
Final mean	181	2,460	538	806	837	257	217
Final genera							
Glycyphagus	107	1,202	413	382	331	65	110
Acarus	44	1,240	61	360	439	182	65
Tarsonemids	26	16	62	61	66	4	13
Cheyletus	3	0	1	1	0	5	29
Gamasids	1	2	1	2	1	1	0
Hours run	1,007	1,267	1,007	566	1,007	566	357
Power cost per ton, £	0.42	0.08	0.42	0.09	0.42	0.09	0.20

[a]Burrell, 1969c.

been shown to possess potent allergens and to provoke strong allergic reactions in sensitized subjects (Maunsell et al., 1968, Brown and Filer, 1968). Grain or forage mites, as they are sometimes called, may also cause dermatitis to persons coming into contact with them frequently (Rogers, 1943; Nixon, 1944) and have also been reported as the cause of gastrointestinal and other internal disorders in both man (Mackenzie, 1922, 1923; Mekie, 1926; Hinman and Kampmeier, 1934; Smith and Jones, 1961) and in animals, although reports about the latter are somewhat contradictory. Parish (1954) observed certain deleterious effects in rabbits after prolonged feeding with heavily mite-infested foodstuffs, but Polish workers (Szwabowicz and Miedzobrodski, 1957; Szwabowicz et al., 1957, 1958a; 1958b) reported no ill effects in similar trials with horses, sheep, and small laboratory animals.

Although the small numbers of mites likely to occur in chilled grain may not immediately present problems of any real economic, medical, or veterinary importance, they are a potential hazard, and their presence, even at relatively low levels of infestation, is one disadvantage of this form of storage.

D. Insects

Burges and Burrell (1964) showed that cooling grain to 20° C. greatly reduced the hazard from insects. If the highest temperature in a grain bulk was 17° C., the grain was secure against all the major granivorous insects unless the infestation was so numerous that it could raise the grain temperature. If the cooling period was protracted the period of risk was lengthened. A summary of their investigations on safe storage is given in Figure 1. With refrigeration, or with aeration, the grain temperature in temperate or cold climates can be brought to a level at which security is given even against heavy infestations. Cooling to 5° to 10° C. will not kill some insect pests and will kill some stages of others only very slowly. The different stages of every species show different resistances to low temperatures, the resistance of the adult differing from that of the eggs, larval stages, or pupae; and some species have diapause stages capable of surviving long periods under adverse conditions (Solomon and Adamson, 1955). As with mites, differences or changes in the environmental conditions of insects may produce changes in their cold-hardiness.

The grain weevil *Sitophilus granarius* is one of the most resistant pests and will survive for over 2 months at 0° C. (Solomon and Adamson, 1955). In tests with this species Burrell (1967) found that 97% of the adults moved from a cold bulk during storage, and only 0.5% remained and survived the storage period. However, larvae and pupae of *S. granarius* live within the kernels during development, and so cannot migrate.

One of the most common grain insects, the saw-toothed grain beetle, *Oryzaephilus surinamensis,* survived for over 10 weeks at 5° to 10° C. in a heavily infested, 100-ton bin of dry barley (Burrell, 1967). Although the insects were not killed by the treatment, grain below 10° C. showed little tendency to reheat because this species does not breed at this temperature and their activity and heat production were greatly reduced.

Mathlein (1968) suggests that refrigeration of infested goods is cheaper than fumigation for killing insect pests in rice and in other commodities, and also eliminates the problem of residues in the commodity. He gives a temperature of −20° C. as being sufficient to kill most pests after exposure for 1 to 24 hr., but suggests that a temperature of −30° C. is preferable for complete eradication. In some areas use can be made of low winter temperature to achieve destruction of insect pests (Pulkki, 1966), but in temperate or warm climates such low temperatures could only be attained by using a refrigerated chamber, possibly after passing the grain through a stream of air chilled to −35° to −40° C.

Refrigerated air has been used by Sutherland et al. (1970) for cooling wheat bins in Queensland where ambient temperatures are too high for successful insect control by aeration with untreated air. The refrigerated concrete bins used were of 1,000 tonnes capacity, being 6.5 m. diameter and 26 m. high. These were chilled when the temperature of a sensor buried near the top of the bin rose above 18° C., which was considered a safe storage temperature. Over 85% of the bulk was reduced to a temperature below 18° C. within 2 months, but heat conduction through the concrete walls prevented cooling in the outer layer up to nearly 1 m. thick for a period of about 6 months, and permitted higher insect numbers to develop there than were considered acceptable. Sutherland et al. (1970) conclude that power costs could be reduced by thermal insulation. However, it is unlikely that this would be economically practicable for the bins described, but might be possible in underground stores.

E. Germination

Data on the effects of storage at temperatures close to freezing on the viability of cereal grains are limited and fragmentary, but some indication of the effect of low temperatures on germination can be made by extrapolating the results of some authors. For example, Roberts (1960) showed that there was a simple mathematical relationship between the temperature, moisture content, and period of viability, which he expressed as $\log p = Kv - C_1m - C_2m - C_2t$, where $p =$ half viability period, $Kv = 4.222$, $C_1 = 0.108$, $C_2 = 0.050$, $m =$ percent moisture content (wet-weight basis) and $t =$ temperature. Roberts also showed that it is possible to predict the time taken for viability to drop to any given level of germination and found the equation to be applicable to wheat, oats, and barley.

Linko (1960) produced a nomogram for estimating the storage period of wheat under a wide range of conditions, and Figure 4 illustrates how storage at high

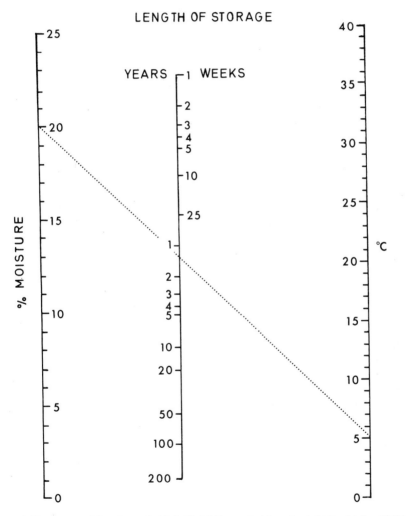

Figure 4. Nomogram giving the probable half-viability period for wheat. (After Linko, 1960.)

moisture contents can be extended by low temperatures; 50% germination is taken as the standard for judgment. This is not a very stringent standard and is clearly inadequate for malting barley. For this, Kreyger (1958,1959) points out that barley is useless for malting if the germinative energy is below 95% (Figure 5). Jansen (1965) suggested a figure of 97.5, and Bewer (1957) stated that any measurable fall in germination was detrimental for malting purposes. For milling wheat, a fall in germination to 70% was considered acceptable by Guilbot and Poisson (1963) as long as the mold count did not exceed 32,000 per g. and no organoleptic or serious physical or chemical changes had occurred. The conditions stated by these various authors to be necessary for safe storage, therefore, vary considerably, as do the experimental methods used. The initial conditions of different batches of grain also vary considerably, and the weather before harvest has been shown by Pollock (1956), Wellington (1956), Strand (1965), and Shands et al. (1967) to seriously affect germination, and thus the storage potential of cereal grains. Different batches of grain, therefore, may behave differently when exposed to the same set of storage conditions, and, for preservation of high germinability, drying is preferable to chilled storage.

Agena (1961) measured the effects of temperatures from +6° to −24° C. and at moisture contents of 20 to 26% on the percentage germination of grain. He found that for wheat, barley, and rye, temperatures below −6° C. caused a fall in germination, and this damage increased with increasing moisture content and

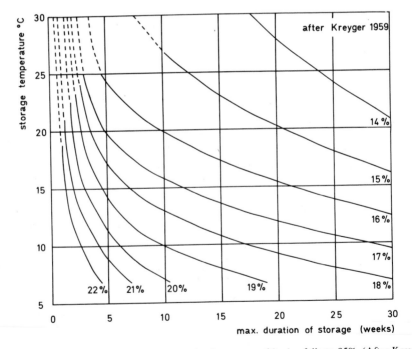

Figure 5. Storage periods in which the germinative energy of barley falls to 95%. (After Kreyger, 1958, 1959.)

decreasing temperature. Similar results were obtained for sorghum by Robbins and Porter (1946) and by Carlson and Atkins (1960) who found no damage to seed with low moisture contents. Barton (1960), Sundstol (1966), Goodsell et al. (1955), Houston et al. (1959), and Brunson (1949) found drier grain to be less damaged by low temperatures than was damp grain.

It is now well established that the dormancy of some grains, particularly some varieties of barley, is maintained for long periods unless the grain is thoroughly dried and then stored for 2 to 3 weeks at 20° to 30° C. in order to break dormancy (Essery and Pollock, 1957; Essery et al., 1955; Pollock, 1957). Cool, damp storage, such as that experienced in chilling, prolongs natural dormancy (Schuster and Jung, 1961) and also imposes a secondary dormancy or "water sensitivity" which prevents barley from germinating after steeping it in water during the malting process. Blum and Gilbert (1957) ascribed this phenomenon to microbiological attack and to the secretion of inhibitors by the fungus. They found that water sensitivity could be removed by surface sterilization with fungicides such as solutions of hypochlorites or mercuric chloride. Pionnat (1966) found salicylic acid, produced by *Penicillium viridicyclopium* on grain, to be phytotoxic and to inhibit germination enzymes. Inhibition could be removed by various chemical treatments but these are uneconomic for large-scale malting. To avoid dormancy problems in grains subject to them and which are to be used for malting or for planting, the grains should not be stored cool and moist.

III. PHYSICAL CONSIDERATIONS

In addition to the biological factors already described, some of the physical characteristics of grain play an important part in the process of chilling.

A. Moisture Content — Relative Humidity Equilibria

The importance of the equilibrium relationship between the moisture content of the grain and the relative humidity of the air surrounding the grain is given in detail in Chapter 1. For the present purposes it is enough to say that when grain is exposed to air, the air may give up moisture to the grain or the grain may release water into the air until a state of equilibrium is reached governed by the vapor pressure of water in the air and that of water leaving the grain.

The equilibrium relationship (e.r.h.) can, however, be displaced by any change of temperature, and for grain at any given moisture content the relative humidity is slightly reduced by a fall in temperature (see Chapter 1). Since the activity and growth of mites and molds are reduced both at a lower relative humidity and at a lower temperature, the fall in e.r.h. that accompanies a fall in temperature will reinforce its inhibitory effect on their activity.

If cool air at a high relative humidity is passed into grain at a lower equilibrium relative humidity, the grain moisture content will rise once the temperature of the two media becomes similar. It is important, therefore, to ensure that air leaving the refrigeration unit has a drying effect on the chilled grain; and it is necessary to reheat the chilled air after it passes through the cold coil of the refrigeration unit and before it enters the grain bulk, otherwise an appreciable increase in moisture content may occur in the grain around the duct (Burrell and Laundon, 1967). The chilled air may be reheated by using waste heat from the condenser, or by using the refrigerator as a heat pump or as a partial heat pump; but the heat produced by the ventilation fan is sometimes substantial and may be sufficient for reheating purposes.

B. Mechanics of Refrigeration

The main principles of the process of refrigeration as used in most grain chillers may be of interest to some readers. A typical grain-chilling unit (Figures 6 and 7) contains a compressor, composed usually of a reciprocating piston working inside a cylinder. The piston compresses the refrigerant gas, causing it to heat up. The hot compressed refrigerant gas is then forced under pressure through a valve into a copper coil called the condenser—which may be air or water cooled and which usually has metal fins to permit rapid heat exchange between the hot gas inside the coil and the cooling medium, which is usually air or water flowing over the outer surface of the coil. (In cool climates fresh air is normally preferred to water for cooling the condenser on chillers because of the possibility of freezing and breakages during cold weather, but elsewhere water is more effective as a coolant.) Inside the condenser, the latent heat of condensation of the compressed gas is removed by the cooling medium and the vapor is condensed to a liquid which collects in a reservoir. The liquid refrigerant, still under pressure from the compressed gases, is then forced along narrow tubing through an expansion valve and is sprayed into a long and wide evaporating coil, which is at a lower pressure, on the suction side of the compressor. In the evaporator, the droplets of liquid refrigerant absorb heat from the coil, boil, and

Figure 6. Fifteen horsepower compressor unit used to chill a minimum of ten bins, each containing 100 tons of grain, to 0° to 4°C. at an airflow of 1,500 to 2,500 ft.³ air per min. (42 to 71 m.³ per min.).

Figure 7. A 3-ton, farm chilling unit used to chill ten bins, each containing 50 to 60 tons of grain, to 5° to 10°C. at an airflow of 800 ft.³ air per min. (23 m.³ per min.).

are reconverted into a gas. The latent and sensible heats necessary for the boiling process are absorbed from air passing over the evaporating coil, and this chilled air is passed into the grain after slight reheating to adjust its relative humidity to the required level.

As it passes over the evaporator, moisture is condensed from the chilled air as water or, possibly, as ice if the air temperature required is close to freezing. If ice forms on the evaporator the ability of the coil to chill is reduced, as the coating of ice is a poorer heat conductor than metal. In addition, excessive uncontrolled icing may eventually block the path of the chilled air. If low temperatures are required, therefore, an automatic defrost system such as reverse-cycle defrosting becomes necessary to melt and remove the ice. This may reduce the time available for chilling, and increase running and capital costs; but if the refrigeration unit is a dual-purpose chiller/heat pump, the reverse cycle system may be an intrinsic, necessary part of the equipment. To avoid the extra costs incurred by defrost systems, however, the units supplied to many European farms are controlled thermostatically, the compressors being set to cut out at air temperatures below about 40° F., thus preventing ice formation.

The condensed water must, of course, be drained from the chilling unit to avoid flooding the building. A refrigerator can be constructed to attain and maintain any desired temperature, particularly in well-lagged chambers with recirculated air. In such chambers temperature control is simple, as the chiller is continuously available and is governed thermostatically to provide further cooling as required. With grain bins, however, recirculation and lagging are often impracticable unless the building is purpose-made. Much power is therefore

TABLE V

Useful conversion factors

1 Frigorie = 1 kcal. = 3.968 B.t.u.
1 U.K. ton = 1,016 kg. = 1.016 metric tonne = 2,240 lb.
1 U.S. ton = 2,000 lb.
1 metric tonne = 1,000 kg. = 2,204.6 lb. = 10 Quintals
1 lb. = 7,000 grains = 453.6 g.
1 Bushel (U.S.) = 1.24 ft.[3]
1 Bushel (English) = 1.283 ft.[3]
1 ton of refrigeration = 288,000 B.t.u./day = 12,000 B.t.u./hr.
1 h.p. = 0.7457 kwh. = 641.3 kcal. = 746 watts = 2,545 B.t.u.
Latent heat of ice = 144 B.t.u./lb. = 79.7 cal./g.
Latent heat of condensation of water = 1,000 B.t.u./lb. = 590 cal./g.
Specific heat of air = 0.24 B.t.u./lb. (at 14.0 ft.[3]/lb. dry air)
1 B.t.u. = 252 cal.
1 cubic meter = 35.314 cubic feet
A dry weight loss of 0.01% per day produces approximately 1,490 B.t.u. (376 kcal.)/ton/day and a temperature rise of about 1.4°F. (0.8°C.)/day, assuming that no heat losses occur and that the specific heat of the damp grain is 0.5 B.t.u./lb.

wasted in removing heat entering through ducts and walls, and also in removing latent heat from water vapor released by the grain (Table V). Further power may then be wasted during defrosting periods, which may occur hourly under some conditions.

C. Grain Cooling

The quantity of heat required to be removed from a grain bulk depends upon the temperature drop required and the moisture content of the grain. Disney (1954) showed that the heat content, or specific heat, of grain at 23% moisture content was about 16% higher than the heat content at 15% moisture (Figure 8). In addition, the production of metabolic heat at low temperatures is appreciable at 23% moisture and negligible at 15% moisture. The effect of these two factors is offset to a large extent, during chilling, by the loss of moisture from damp grain, which results in evaporative cooling. The reverse process may occur, and the temperature of the grain may rise as a result of the liberation of latent heat from grain dampened by the air passing through it.

The quantity of heat (H) required to be removed from a given weight of grain may be calculated as follows:

$$H = m (t_o - t_l) C$$

where m = mass, t_o = original temperature, t_l = temperature after cooling, and C = specific heat.

For example, if 1 tonne (1,000 kg.) of wheat at 23% moisture (C = 0.5 cal. per g. per °C.) is to be cooled from 20° to 5°C. in one day then

$$H = 1,000 (20-5) 0.5 = 7,500 \text{ kcal.}$$

To this must be added the mean heat production of the respiration of a tonne of grain at 23% moisture at temperatures falling from 20° to 5°C. This may be es-

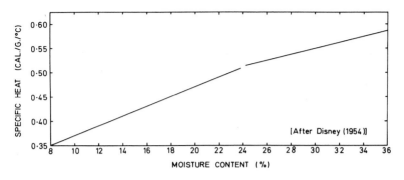

Figure 8. Relationship between moisture content and specific heat of wheat. (After Disney, 1954.)

timated approximately from the mean dry-weight loss per day of grain at 23% moisture content—about 0.03% (Table II)—which is equivalent to around 1,100 kcal. per day (Table V), so making a total of 8,600 kcal. In a recirculation system, additional heat gains through the walls or ducting can be estimated from Table VI.

The effect of evaporative cooling can be demonstrated by taking, as an example, two bins of wheat containing the same tonnage of grain at 20° C., one at 23 and the other at 15% moisture contents. If an equal quantity of air at 5° C. and 70% r.h. (enthalpy 3.4 kcal. per kg. of air) is blown simultaneously into both bins, air leaving the dry grain at about 18° C. and 73% r.h. will carry about 10 kcal. per kg. air, whereas that leaving the damp grain will be at 18° C. and 95% r.h. and have an enthalpy[3] of 11.7 kcal. per kg. of air. The exhaust air from the damp grain will remove over 25% more heat than that from the dry grain, largely cancelling out the extra load imposed by damp grain due to respiration and to higher specific heat.

From this example, and using a psychrometric chart (also see Table VII), it can be calculated that each kilogram of refrigerated air will extract 8.4 g. of water from the damp grain while the bulk is still warm. During chilling, however, the temperature of the air leaving the grain falls, and by the time the grain has been cooled to 7° C. only 2.1 g. of water is removed by the same quantity of air. Therefore, once the cold front has passed completely through a bin of grain, drying occurs at a very low rate.

The calculation of the heat load imposed by the grain is, however, of more theoretical interest than practical value, since the grain is not chilled directly by the chilling unit, but indirectly by the air passing from the unit into the grain. Therefore the load imposed on the chiller is governed by ambient conditions rather than by grain temperature and moisture. In most European installations grain refrigeration is a two-stage process. First the refrigeration unit is used to cool fresh air, and then the cold air is blown through the grain. As described later, it may take up to 1,400 cubic meters of air to cool a tonne of grain close to the temperature of the inlet air. Taking as our example the extreme load imposed

---

[3]Enthalpy, or heat content, which includes the heat of vaporization (latent heat) of moisture in the air as well as the measurable or "sensible" heat calculated from the temperature and specific heat of the air.

TABLE VI

A. *Thermal conductivities of grains, common building materials, and insulants*

Substance	Moisture Content % wet basis	Thermal Conductivity		Reference
		B.t.u./hr./ft.^{2}/°F./in.	g. cal./sec./cm./°C.	
Wheat	11.7	1.046	0.00036	Oxley (1948b)
Wheat	17.8	1.132	0.00039	Oxley (1948b)
Wheat	...	1.046	0.00036	Babbitt (1945)
Yellow maize	13.2	1.22	0.00042	Oxley (1948b)
Oats	12.5	0.90	0.00031	Oxley (1948b)
Oats	9.0	0.444	0.000153	Kazarian and Hall (1965)
Oats	27.7	0.639	0.00022	Kazarian and Hall (1965)
Oats	...	0.444	0.000153	Bakke and Stiles (1935)

B. *From Bureau of Standards letter circular No. 227*

Substance	Density lb./ft.^{3}	Thermal Conductivity	
		B.t.u./hr./ft.^{2}/°F./in.	g. cal./sec./cm./°C.
Kapok between paper	1–2	0.24	0.000082
Hair felt	11	0.26	0.000089
Glass wool	4	0.29	0.0001
Granulated cork	8.1	0.31	0.000107
Sawdust	12.0	0.41	0.000141
Cinder concrete	...	2–3	0.00069–0.00103
Concrete	...	6–9	0.00206–0.0031
Plaster	...	2–5	0.00069–0.00172
Brick	...	3–6	0.00103–0.00206
Glass	...	5–6	0.00172–0.00206
Dry soil	...	0.096	0.00033

during warm wet weather, the study of a psychrometric chart illustrates that 20,000 kcal. may be extracted from 1,400 m³ air in order to remove only 8,600 kcal. of heat from the tonne of grain. During cool weather, however, the air may be so cold that no refrigeration is required, and cooling can then be carried out using the fan alone. There is, therefore, a tremendous variation in the power required to cool a tonne of grain under different weather conditions. Clearly this variation in load could result in a widely variable temperature of the chilled air and of the grain. Such wide variations are usually overcome by a thermostatically controlled valve which regulates the amount of air passing through the cold coil in order to provide a stream of air at a steady temperature.

D. Lagging

If a grain bulk is at a different temperature from the air surrounding it, exchange of heat will occur from the warmer to the cooler medium. In general, refrigerated grain is normally below the mean ambient temperature and a rise in temperature of the grain can be expected. Grain is itself a comparatively poor conductor of heat; and although only about one-third as effective as granulated cork, its thermal conductivity is six to nine times lower than that of concrete (Table VI).

Estimates of the rate at which heat enters a grain bulk can be obtained from formulae used by Oxley (1948b) and by Kazarian and Hall (1965). However, the data required for the calculations, mean ambient temperature, mean bulk temperature, thermal conductivity, specific heat, and bulk density are very variable, and the computation is therefore complicated. In any case, refrigeration is normally used frequently enough to prevent waves of heat from entering far into the bulk; and for wet grain over 18 to 20% moisture, temperature increases deep in the bulk are more likely to be caused by fungal activity than by heat entry. It is simpler, therefore, to quote figures for heat entry under conditions found commonly rather than to calculate these.

In uninsulated metal bins (Figure 6) 10 m. deep containing 100 tonnes of grain exposed to the sun and to a mean ambient temperature of 18°C. (range 10° to 23°C.), the grain was initially cooled to below 5°C. in a period of 60 hr. (Burrell and Laundon, 1967). The grain temperature 0.25 m. from the wall rose to above 15°C. after 2 weeks; the temperature of peripheral grain rose to over 10°C. at 0.6 m. and to over 15°C. at 0.3 m. from the wall. Temperatures of 17° to 18°C. were common at distances of up to 0.08 m., but only rose above 20°C. during hours of direct sunlight (Figure 9). Many modern lagging materials are two to three times as effective as grain for reducing heat entry (Burrell, (1966). Consequently, a layer 5 cm. (0.05 m.) thick of insulation on the outer surface of a metal bin would be expected to reduce the depth of penetration of the various temperature rises reported above by about 0.1 to 0.15 m.

In a 1,000-tonne concrete bin 26 m. high, Sutherland et al. (1970) found that the main bulk of grain was cooled from 33° to 15°C. in 17 days, but, owing to entry of heat, a peripheral layer increasing to up to 1 m. thick near the top was not cooled adequately for insect control for a further 6 months. In both stores described above lagging does not appear to be an economic proposition, but grain chilling under specially made, thermally insulated domes has been described by

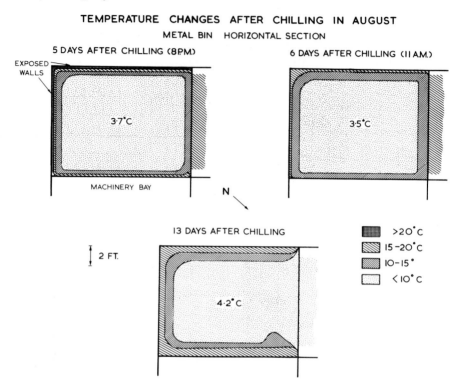

Figure 9. Heat entry horizontally through the metal walls into a refrigerated bin of grain. (Burrell and Laundon, 1967.)

Shove (1966). Lagging is an advantage for refrigerated stores of grain, since for any given power consumption the presence of thermal insulation will enable lower temperatures to be reached. Alternatively, the same temperature may be achieved by a smaller plant at a lower capital cost or with the same chilling plant by a lower power cost; of course, once the grain has been cooled to the required level, heat gains will be reduced and refrigeration will be required less frequently. In Europe, however, the usual practice is to move the refrigeration unit along a row of bins or along a series of ducts in a floor store so that the unit is only likely to be returned to a bin at infrequent intervals and, as has been described, reheating at the periphery cannot be prevented in warm weather if the bins are left unchilled for a week or more, even if lagging is applied. The use of underground pits for chilling could be advantageous in limiting heat entry, as earth provides a considerable degree of insulation; but as far as is known, no attempt has yet been made to do so.

IV. METHODS

There are four main methods of using refrigeration machinery for grain storage or drying, but some additional minor variations occur. The common methods are: a) grain drying at a high temperature, using the refrigerator merely as a heat pump; b) dehydrofrigidation, or drying at a low temperature; c) chilling alone, to cool the grain without any attempt to dry it; and d) use of conditioned air to maintain the moisture content and temperature at any required level.

A. Drying by Heat Pump

A heat pump operates on the same principle as a refrigerator and is sometimes described as a refrigerator in reverse, but this is inaccurate. The refrigeration unit of a heat pump operates in exactly the same way as for chilling, but the cool air is allowed to go to waste while the warm air is collected. Under some circumstances it is possible to use a refrigeration unit simultaneously for chilling one bin and, by use of the heat extracted from the air during this process, to dry an adjacent bin (Cooper, 1965); the only extra equipment required for this is a more powerful condenser fan and a length of ducting to direct the warm air into the damp grain.

The main advantage of using a heat pump as a source of energy is its high coefficient of performance. For example the consumption of 1 kwh. of electricity in an electric heater produces 860 kcal., whereas the same quantity of electricity absorbed by an electric motor in a refrigeration unit can be made to collect over 3,000 kcal. from a convenient heat source (Flikke et al., 1957) such as the air, or a river or lake, and move it to an area where the heat is needed. For details of the history and development of the principles of the heat pump or reversible heat engine, postulated by Carnot in 1824 and developed by Lord Kelvin in 1852, the reader is referred to textbooks such as that of Jordan and Priester (1957).

A refrigeration unit is more efficient at producing an air temperature rise than it is for cooling a similar quantity of air, since the latent heat produced by condensation of water or ice from the air is made available for heating in addition to the heat produced by the motors and fans. If a high temperature is required, any such heat gain is beneficial; but for chilling, the temperature rise from motors and fans may be detrimental (compare Figures 10 and 11). Care must, therefore, be taken when a refrigeration unit planned for use as a grain chiller is used as a heat pump, as the air temperature rise may be excessive (Figure 11) and lead to overdrying around the ducts and mold growth higher up (Massie et al., 1964). For this reason a highly variable airflow is required for dual-purpose chillers, and correct fan selection is most important to avoid an excessive rise in air temperature owing to fan heat when chilling at a low rate of airflow. It may sometimes be necessary to use a low-powered fan on the refrigeration unit when chilling, and to replace this with a high-powered fan when using the unit for drying by heat pump.

Although heat pumps are often used as sources of heat, electricity is expensive in some European countries and, in addition, the refrigeration unit has a comparatively high capital cost, so that the apparent advantages of cheap heat are lost. Comparative running costs for drying by heat pump, storage by chilling, and ventilation with selected ambient air are given in Table IV.

Flikke et al. (1957) found that for every 6 lb. of water removed per hour, a refrigeration capacity of 10,000 B.t.u. per hour was required, and that drying was more efficient at high temperatures and high airflows; but they recommended an airflow of 320 cfm. for every 10,000 B.t.u. per hour of refrigeration capacity. They also showed that the higher the air velocity through a bed of grain, the closer were the conditions of the air leaving the grain to those at the inlet.

Drying by heat pump differs from dehydrofrigidation, since a heat pump is a refrigeration unit where all the available heat is used for heating, whereas dehydrofrigidation makes only limited use of the heat available.

B. Dehydrofrigidation

As the term suggests, dehydrofrigidation is the reduction of the moisture content of grain while keeping the temperature low, in order to prevent—or to limit—mold growth in excessively damp commodities such as freshly harvested corn (Shove, 1966). The main object of the process is to reduce power consumption and capital costs below those of rapid-drying methods by extending the drying period. Steele and Saul (1962) showed how the allowable storage time for shelled corn at 26% moisture and 20° C. could be extended from 5 to 30 days if cooled to 5° C. As described earlier, however, the volume of air required to remove a given quantity of water is increased considerably once the temperature of the grain is reduced, and it does not seem possible to avoid a large fall in the drying rate once the grain has been cooled to the desired temperature. The

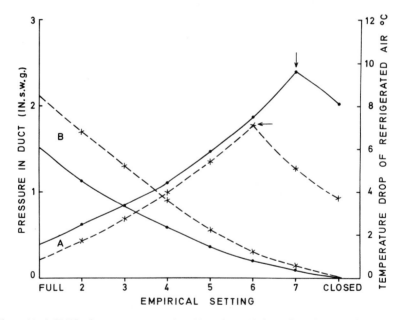

Figure 10. A, Fall in air temperature produced by a farm chilling unit during the refrigeration of 20-ton bins of grain at various rates of airflow controlled by a damper valve. B, Air pressures in ducts during chilling. Dotted line indicates results of chilling bins two at a time. Solid line for a single bin. The arrow indicates that the compressor motor was set to cut out thermostatically when the temperature of the evaporator coil reached –20° C. Note: The temperature of the refrigerated air was between 5° and 15° C.

relative humidity of the chilled air can easily be reduced, but this could lead to overdrying of the lower layers of grain without any appreciable reduction in the moisture content of grain further away from the air inlet. Drying at a low temperature appears, therefore, to be inefficient compared with high-temperature drying, but the rate of power consumption is reduced, machinery costs may be less, and the final condition of the dried grain may possibly be improved.

The limitations of low-temperature drying can be clearly seen by a comparison of the moisture-carrying capacities of cold and of warm air (Table VII). As illustrated, drying at 30° C. removes moisture five times as rapidly as drying at 5° C., but high-temperature drying is normally only practicable in shallow depths of grain or in continuous dryers.

C. Chilling

In France, Leroy (1950) suggested using a refrigeration system to store grain at 18 to 20% moisture and to dry it slowly to 16 to 18%. The first French patent, taken out in 1953 (Centre National de la Recherche Scientifique, 1953), made use of a cold evaporator coil inside the top of the bin above the grain. When warm air rising from the grain bulk by convection came into contact with the cold coil, its water-holding capacity (Table VII) was reduced, and the excess water condensed on the coil and was drained off. The cool, drier air then passed down through the grain bulk, by convection. Grain drying from 17.5 to 14.5% moisture in a 40-ton

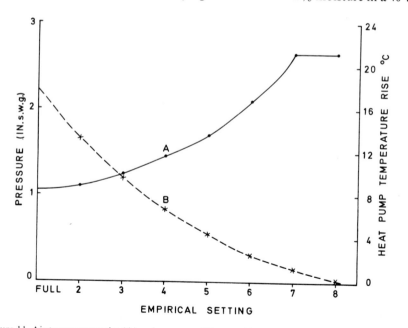

Figure 11. Air temperature rise (A) and pressures (B) caused by a heat pump used for drying a 20-ton bin at various rates of airflow. Compare this temperature rise with the fall in temperature caused by the same unit when used as a chiller (Figure 10).

TABLE VII

Moisture-carrying capacity of air (g. water per kg. air)

Dry Bulb °C.	% Relative Humidity					
	50	60	70	80	90	100
0	1.9	2.3	2.7	3.1	3.4	3.8
5	2.7	3.2	3.8	4.3	4.8	5.4
10	3.8	4.6	5.4	6.2	6.9	7.6
15	5.4	6.4	7.5	8.6	9.6	10.7
20	7.3	8.8	10.2	11.7	13.2	14.7
25	9.9	11.9	13.9	16.0	18.0	20.1
30	13.3	16.1	18.9	21.6	24.4	27.4

bin was reported to take 2 months, with a final temperature of 7° C. at the top, rising to 14.5°C. at the center. An improved patent, describing a forced-air circulation, appeared later (Centre National de la Recherche Scientifique, 1958), and was amended to provide either chilling at a low temperature or heat-pump drying at a high temperature.

The main aim of grain chilling in Europe now seems to be to cool the grain and to store it at a higher moisture content than was previously considered safe. Recent observations in France and Belgium, where hundreds of refrigeration units have been in use since the 1950's, indicate that grain arriving at up to 17% moisture is often chilled and undried, and that damper grain is usually dried to below this level before chilling. Typical grain temperatures achieved by chilling after harvest in the warmer areas of France and Belgium indicate that temperatures of 12° to 16°C. are considered acceptable for storing grain at up to 16 to 17% moisture content.

During chilling, cold air from the refrigeration unit is heated slightly, sometimes by a secondary condenser or an extra heat source, or merely by fan heat, to reduce the relative humidity of the air, usually to 70 to 80%. This air is then injected into the base of the grain bin or floor store through widely spaced perforated ducts. The grain at the base is cooled first; above this is a zone of cooling grain; and yet higher up the grain remains uncooled (Figure 12). During chilling the grain does not lose heat throughout, and heat from a warm layer is transferred to the layer above, causing a rise in temperature there (Burrell and Laundon, 1967). Reports of apparent grain heating when chilling is started are believed to be due to this phenomenon. The cooling curves shown in Figure 13 illustrate that five out of eight thermocouples used to record temperatures in a bin of chilled grain showed an immediate increase in temperature while the other three cooled immediately. It seems probable that the immediate temperature increases were due to upwards transfer of heat from warmer regions below, whereas areas which cooled immediately were above cooler regions.

Assuming the grain to be freshly harvested and damp, the exhaust air from the top of the bin will normally have a higher heat content than that of the outside air, particularly at night. Figure 13 demonstrates how in a bin 33 ft. deep, grain near the top (thermocouples 7, 21, and 14) remained at a higher temperature than ambient for about half the cooling period. Calculations based on the temperature and humidity of the exhaust air showed that its enthalpy was above

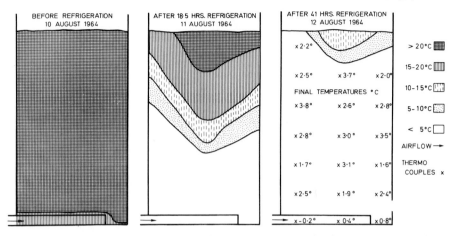

Figure 12. Progress of cooling in a 33 ft. high bin containing 100 tons of grain. (Burrell and Laundon, 1967.)

that of the ambient air for about 90% of the cooling period. Under these circumstances, and in tall bins, the need for recirculation, which would be costly, is limited. For shallow bins, however, recirculation is more efficient, particularly for farm chillers which are normally low-powered and are unable to obtain low temperatures at the first chilling period. Under these circumstances the exhaust air should be allowed to escape until its enthalpy is below that of the fresh air. On coupling of the recirculation ducting, chilling can then be carried out progressively to lower temperatures.

On British farms, however, the need for recirculation is often avoided by chilling in stages. Under farm conditions, a chilling unit is normally expected to be capable of refrigerating each day's intake of grain and of dealing with a row of several bins (Figure 7). If the chiller is not moved to each bin as it is filled, those filled last may stand unchilled for several days or weeks, and damp grain may heat. It is often the practice, therefore, to start chilling at a high rate of airflow, and at a temperature only a few degrees below ambient, in order to pass a cold front completely through each bin on the day following harvest. At a later date a further, longer, chilling period is completed at a lower rate of airflow and, consequently, with a larger temperature drop (Figure 10). Recirculation is, therefore, rarely used on British farms, but is more common in French and Belgian Co-operatives. Jouin (1965) also suggests that, for economy, chilling should be carried out in stages.

The rate of airflow is usually selected according to the total quantity of grain to be chilled and the length of the harvest period. Jouin (1965) suggested that to cool a cubic foot or a cubic meter of grain, 600 times the volume of air were required. Matthies (1956) and McCune et al. (1963) found 720-725 times the volume to be necessary, but in deep bins Burrell and Laundon (1967) found a variation from 750 to 1,120 times the volume according to the moisture content and the evenness of airflow which was adversely affected by packing and dust deposits. Their work suggests, therefore, that it may take up to 1,400 m.^{3} of air to cool a tonne of grain.

McCune et al. (1963) showed that at an airflow of 0.1 cfm. per ft.[3], grain could be cooled from 35° to 10° C. in 125 hr. when air at 7° C. was recirculated through the grain and Shove (1970) gives a figure of 0.5 cfm. per bu. (0.4 cfm. per ft.[3]) for cooling in 24 hr. Munday (1965) suggested that the power of chilling plants should be related to the tonnage of grain cooled per day, and should be about 8 tonnes of grain per h.p. per day. He also stated that the temperature of the air entering the grain should be at least 3° C. below the final required grain temperature.

D. Conditioning

McCune et al. (1963) used conditioned air to maintain the moisture content of grain at any desired level, and suggested that over-drying, reported to occur in bulks of grain ventilated with fresh air, could be avoided by chilling. The tests were successful, but the cost of running the chiller for 1,000 to 7,000 hr. seems uneconomical.

E. Ducts

Due to the large number of variable factors involved, no rigid recommendations can be made for duct spacings in bulks of chilled grain. The main variables are: the quantity and depth of grain, its moisture content, final required temperature, future use, length of storage period, whether it is intended to

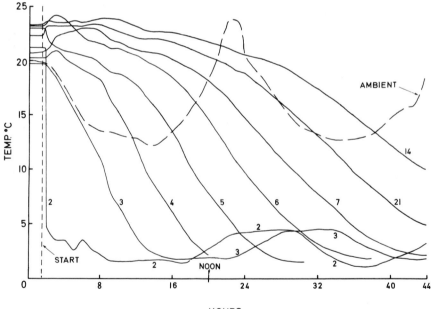

Figure 13. Rate of cooling of thermocouples 2 to 7 placed at intervals of 5 ft. up a 33-ft. bin of wheat at 16 to 18% moisture. Thermocouples 7, 21, and 14 are in the top grain layer, as shown in Figure 12. (Burrell and Laundon, 1967.)

dry the grain (by dehydrofrigidation or by warm air from a heat pump) or whether it is to be kept cool without any serious attempt to alter its moisture content.

However, certain guide lines exist: as in all systems where air is blown into grain, the duct sizes and spacing depend mainly upon the rate of airflow selected as being suitable for the purpose. For a very high rate of airflow, a completely perforated floor, or closely spaced ducts, may be necessary. Shove (1966) describes a dome specially erected for dehydrofrigidation, with built-in lagging, with the air supply ducts embedded in a porous mass of rocks, so achieving what amounted to a perforated floor and an even air distribution. In tests in Britain, however, airflows of 3 to 10 ft.^{3} air per min. (0.1 to 0.3 m.^{3} air per min.) per tonne have been used to maintain low temperatures in grain up to 19% moisture content (Burrell, 1969c) and at these rates of airflow widely spaced ducting is adequate. In general, grain chilling is rarely practiced in Europe at moisture contents much above 18%, and drying is usually very limited. Floor storage at such moistures is usually restricted to relatively small bulks 3 to 4 m. deep, although greater depths are common in grain bins where a more even air distribution is normally expected. In floor stores the distance between the ducts rarely exceeds the grain depth and is often less than this, but where drying is required, ducts must be spaced more closely to prevent areas of slow drying occurring and to prevent heating of the grain in those areas during intervals between chilling periods.

Duct sizes are calculated, as for aeration systems, from the rate of airflow selected, the aim being to provide a sufficient cross-sectional area to limit the air velocity in long ducts to below 2,000 ft. per min. (610 m. per min.) although higher velocities are practicable in short ducts. The surface area of the perforated duct is selected to restrict the velocity of air passing through the grain surrounding the duct to below about 30 ft. per min. (9 m. per min.) so avoiding a large resistance to airflow in this area. The ducts themselves may be constructed of any convenient materials available but, in general, the larger the free surface area the better.

F. Costs

As described earlier, the power costs involved in chilling a bulk of grain from 20° to 5°C. are not great, and during the winter very little further chilling may be necessary to maintain low temperatures and to prevent visible mold growth in bulks of grain below 20% moisture. However, musty odors occur in damp, ·unventilated grain and, to avoid this, frequent passage of air through the grain is necessary. The amount of chilling necessary to prevent musty odors appears to vary from about 500 to 2,000 hr. for a storage period of up to 8 months; the damper the grain the more frequently is chilling necessary. If the grain is for stockfeed, musty odors may not be important, and experience in the United Kingdom indicates that running costs may be low, but for taint-free grain the running costs rise considerably.

Where comparisons were made on a farm scale (Table IV) the power cost for drying grain from 18.1 to 13.8% by heat pump was only half that required to refrigerate the grain and keep it free of taint for 6 months. In ventilated bins, however, where fresh air was used to cool the grain, the power costs were even

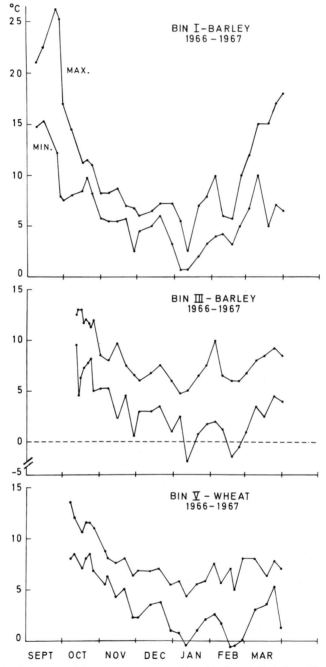

Figure 14. Maximum and minimum temperatures achieved in three chilled, 20-ton bins of grain at 17 to 23% moisture content at a variable airflow of 2 to 30 ft.[3] air per min. per ton of grain.

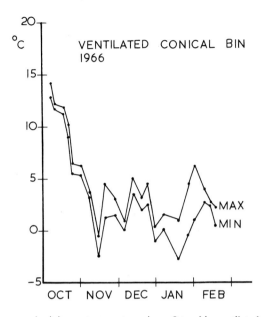

Figure 15. Maximum and minimum temperatures in an 8-ton bin ventilated with ambient air at an airflow of 30 ft.³ of air per min. per ton of grain. Fan operation was controlled by a differential, wet-bulb thermostat.

lower, and the final condition of the grain was very similar to that in the bins of chilled grain. Published figures on the capital and total annual costs of grain chilling are too limited to furnish any accurate estimates at present.

V. CONCLUSION

Grain chilling is rarely used by Dutch farmers as the low ambient temperatures in Holland prevent rapid spoilage and enable much grain to be dried with air heated by fan energy alone. Similar results are obtained in other temperate regions, and comparative temperatures in refrigerated and ventilated bins in Britain, given in Figures 14 and 15, demonstrate that the advantages of refrigeration over ventilation with untreated air are not great in such cool climates. Kreyger (1963) concluded that keeping seeds at a low temperature to prolong the period of drying might seem to be advantageous, but he was doubtful of the real value of this practice, as refrigeration was expensive and drying was still necessary. Many of the biological and physical factors described in this chapter lead to the conclusion that the risks involved with grain chilling are appreciable and the benefit gained is doubtful.

Jouin (1965) also, while discussing the advantages of cool storage, concludes that grain must normally be dried to the normal commercial level of 16% moisture content and he suggests that since it is not possible for most farmers to dry their grain immediately it is harvested, storage of the damp grain can be prolonged in a continental climate by ventilation at night, but that in a maritime climate refrigeration may be necessary. There is no doubt, however, that in many instances substantial economies have been claimed by the users of grain chilling systems (Farquharson, 1965).

LITERATURE CITED

AGENA, M. U. 1961. Untersuchungen über Kälteeinwirkungen auf lagernde Getreidefrüchte mit verschiedenem Wassergehalte. Dissertation for D. Agr. Univ. Bonn. 112 p.

ANDRESON, K., P. GJERTSON, and B. TROLLE. 1967. The microflora of barley and its effect on wort and beer. Brew. Dig. 1967: 76–81.

ARNOLD, R. E. 1959. The effect of harvest damage on the germination of barley. J. Agr. Eng. Res. 4: 24–29.

ARNOLD, R. E. 1963. Effects of harvest damage on the rate of fall in viability of wheat stored at a range of moisture levels. J. Agr. Eng. Res. 8: 7–16.

BABBITT, J. D. 1945. The thermal properties of wheat in bulk. Can. J. Res. 23: 388–401.

BAKKE, A. L., and H. STILES. 1935. Thermal conductivity of stored oats with different moisture content. Plant Physiol. 10: 521–527.

BARTON, L. V. 1960. Life span of frost damaged corn seeds. Contrib. Boyce Thompson Inst. 20: 403–408 [Int. Abstr. Biol. Sci. 22: 4021 (1961)].

BERRY, J. A., and C. A. MAGOON. 1934. Growth of micro-organisms at and below 0°C. Phytopathology 24: 780–796.

BEWER, H. E. 1957. Getreidekonservierung mit kalter Nachtluft. München Wolfrathausen: Berichte Landtechnik Inst. f. Landtechnik, Bonn. No. 47. 53 p.

BLUM, P. H., and S. G. GILBERT. 1957. Mechanism of water sensitivity. Amer. Soc. Brew. Chem. Proc. 1957, p. 22 [J. Inst. Brew. London 3: 250 (1958)].

BROWN, H. M., and J. L. FILER.1968. Role of mites in allergy to house dust. Brit. Med. J. 3: 646–647.

BRUNSON, A. M. 1949. The effect of storage conditions on the longevity of seed corn. Purdue Univ. Exp. Sta. Ann. Rep. 1948-49: 42.

BURGES, H. D., and N. J. BURRELL. 1964. Cooling bulk grain in the British climate to control storage insects and to improve keeping quality. J. Sci. Food Agr. 15: 32–50.

BURRELL, N. J. 1969a. The chilled storage of grain. Ceres 5: 15–20.

BURRELL, N. J. 1969b. Mould growth, moisture production and dry weight losses. Pest Infest. Res. 1968: 24–25.

BURRELL, N. J. 1969c. Damp grain storage by refrigeration and aeration. Pest Infest. Res. 1968: 20–22.

BURRELL, N. J. 1967. Grain cooling studies. II. Effect of aeration on infested grain bulks. J. Stored Prod. Res. 3: 145–154.

BURRELL, N. J. 1965. Refrigeration of damp grain. Farm & Country 88-90.

BURRELL, N. J. 1966. Refrigerated damp grain storage. Pest Infest. Res. 1965: 17–19.

BURRELL, N. J., and J. H. J. LAUNDON. 1967. Grain cooling studies. I. Observations during a large-scale refrigeration test on damp grain. J. Stored Prod. Res. 3: 125–144.

CARLSON, G. E., and R. E. ATKINS. 1960. Effect of freezing temperature on seed viability of sorghum. Agron. J. 52: 329-333.

CHISTIAKOV, F. M., and Z. Z. BOCHAROVA. 1938. The influence of low temperature on micro-organisms. II. and IV. Influence of low temperature on the development of moulds. Microbiology (USSR) 7: 498-514, 838-842.

COOPER, T. 1965. Combined cooler-drier for grain. Farmer Stock Breed. 79: 84.

CUNNINGTON, A. M. 1965. Physical limits for complete development of grain mite *Acarus siro* in relation to its world distribution. J. Appl. Ecol. 2: 295–306.

DISNEY, R. W. 1954. The specific heat of some cereal grains. Cereal Chem. 31: 229-239.

ESSERY, R. E., and J. R. A. POLLOCK. 1957. Studies in barley and malt. X. Note on the effect of desiccation and of heating on the germinative behaviour of dormant barley. J. Inst. Brew. 63: 221–222.

ESSERY, R. E., B. H. KIRSOPP, and J. R. A. POLLOCK. 1955. Studies in barley and malt. II. Tests for germination and water sensitivity. J. Inst. Brew. 61: 25–28.

FARQUHARSON, R. 1965. Chilled grain storage. Agriculture 72: 579–582.

FLIKKE, A. M., H. A. CLOUD, and A. HUSTRULID. 1957. Grain drying by heat pump. Agr. Eng. (St. Joseph, Mich.) 38: 592–597.

FRANCE. Centre National de la Recherche Scientifique. 1953. Brit. Pat. 699,462; 1958, Brit. Pat. 801,585.

GOODSELL, S., F. HUEY, and R. ROYCE. 1955. Effect of moisture content and temperature on the cold test reaction of *Zea mays* stored in air, carbon dioxide and nitrogen. Agron. J. 47: 61–64.

GRIFFITHS, D. A., A. C. HODSON, and C. M. CHRISTENSEN. 1959. Grain storage fungi associated with mites. J. Econ. Entomol. 52: 514–518.

GUILBOT, A., and J. POISSON. 1963. Conditions de stockage et durée de conservation des grains. J. Etud. Conserv. Grains: 15–27.

HEIDT, H., and H. BOLLING. 1965. Körnerkühlung. Muhle 102: 3–11.

HINMAN, E. H., and R. H. KAMPMEIER. 1934. Intestinal acariasis due to *Tyroglyphus longior* Gervais. Amer. J. Trop. Med. 14: 355–363.

HOUSTON, D. F., R. E. FERREL, I. R. HUNTER, and E. B. KESTER. 1959. Preservation of rough rice by cold storage. Cereal Chem. 36: 103–107.

HUMMEL, B. C. W., L. S. CUENDET, C. M. CHRISTENSEN, and W. F. GEDDES. 1954. Grain storage studies. XII. Comparative changes in respiration, viability, and chemical composition of mold-free and mold-contaminated wheat upon storage. Cereal Chem. 31: 143–150.

JAMET, P. 1959. La conservation des orges de brasserie en atmosphère refrigerée. Brasserie 14: 163–167.

JANSEN, J. 1965. Resultaten van enkele bewaarproeven met zaaigranen. Resultaten van zaaizaadonderzboek. I.B.V.L. Wageningen 3: 77–82.

JOFFE, A. Z. 1962. Biological properties of some toxic fungi isolated from overwintered cereals. Mycopath. Mycol. Appl. 16: 201–221.

JORDAN, R. C., and G. B. PRIESTER. 1957. Refrigeration and air conditioning. Constable & Co., Ltd., London. 555 p.

JOUIN, C. 1965. Le froid et la conservation des céréales. Bull. Anciens Élèves École Fr. Meun. 205: 9–13.

KAZARIAN, E. A., and C. W. HALL. 1965. The thermal properties of grain. Trans. Amer. Soc. Agr. Eng. 8: 33–37.

KNEEN, E. 1963. Proc. Irish Malsters Conf. 1963: 51.

KREYGER, J. 1967. Drogestoffverliezen en verandering van de gebruikswaarde van tarwe bij geventileerde bewaring. Jaarb. Inst. Bewar. Verwerk. Landb. Prod. I.B.V.L. 1966, 1967: 33–34.

KREYGER, J. 1963. General considerations concerning the storage of seeds. Proc. Int. Seed Test. Ass. 28: 827–836.

KREYGER, J. 1958, 1959. Recherches sur la conservation des orges de brasserie. Petit. J. Brass. 66: 811–816; 67: 7–10.

LAGRANDEUR, G., and J. POISSON. 1968. La microflore du mais: son évolution en fonction des conditions hydriques et thermiques de stockage en atmosphère renouvelée. Ind. Aliment. Agr. 85: 775–788.

LEROY, H. 1950. La conservation des grains et le méthode du point froid. Bull. Anciens Élèves Ecole Fr. Meun. 120: 193–196.

LINKO, P. 1960. The biochemistry of grain storage. Cereal Sci. Today 5: 302–306.

MACKENZIE, J. 1922. Endo-parasitic Acari as a cause of urinary diseases with notes on several cases. J.R.A.M.C. 39: 339–347.

MACKENZIE, J. 1923. Acari in specimens of urine. J.R.A.M.C. 41: 157–158.

MASSIE, D. R., E. F. OLVER, and G. C. SHOVE. 1964. Extended time of drying corn with a controlled atmosphere. Trans. Amer. Soc. Agr. Eng. 7: 332–333.

MATHLEIN, R. 1968. Artificial cooling of infested goods in Sweden. Rep. Int. Conf. Prot. Stored Prod., Lisbon-Oeiras.

MATTEI, J. N. 1968. Mesures de l'intensité du dégagement de gaz carbonique de divers graines et grains. Ind. Aliment. Agr. 1968: 789–794.

MATTHIES, H. J. 1956. Resistance of grains to airflow. Agr. Eng. (St. Joseph, Mich.) 37: 778.

MAUNSELL, K., D. G. WRAITH, and A. M. CUNNINGTON. 1968. Mites and house-dust allergy in bronchial asthma. Lancet 1: 1267–1270.

McCUNE, W. E., N. K. PERSON, and J. W. SORENSON. 1963. Conditioned air storage of grain. Trans. Amer. Soc. Agr. Eng. 6: 186–189.

MEKIE, E. C. 1926. Parasitic infection of the urinary tract. Report of a case of infection of the urinary tract by Acari together with an analysis of previously reported cases. Edinburgh Med. J. 33: 708–719.

MUNDAY, G. D. 1965. Refrigerated grain storage. J. Proc. Inst. Agr. Eng. 21: 65–74.

NIJWEIDE, R. J. 1964. Observations on aeration and drying practices in Europe. Paper. Winter Meeting, Amer. Soc. Agr. Eng., New Orleans, Dec. 8–11.

NIXON, J. A. 1944. Cheese itch and itchy cargoes in reference to workers compensation. Proc. Roy. Soc. Med. 37: 887–889.

NURET, H. 1935. Bull. Anciens Élèves École Fr. Meun. 42: 193; 43: 223.

OXLEY, T. A. 1948a. The spontaneous heating of stored grain. p. 43-48 in *The Scientific Principles of Grain Storage.* Northern Publishing Co. Ltd.: Liverpool. 103 p.

OXLEY, T. A. 1948b. The movement of heat and water in stored grain. Trans. Amer. Ass. Cereal Chem. 6: 84-99.

PARISH, W. 1954. Report on the animal health services in Great Britain. H.M.S.O. London: 48-57.

PELHATE, J. 1968. Evolution de la mycoflore des blés en cours de conservation. Ind. Aliment. Agr. 85: 769-773.

PIONNAT, J. C. 1966. Étude des alterations fongiques des grains d'orge en cours de conservation. Ann. Epiphyt. 17: 203–214.

POLLOCK, J. R. A. 1957. Dormancy in seeds. J. Brew. Guild 43: 342–356.

POLLOCK, J. R. A. 1956. Incidence of dormancy in different barleys. Brit. Ind. Res. Found. 62: 331–333.

PULKKI, L. H. 1966. Pests in flour mills. Milling 20: 417.

ROBBINS, W. A., and R. H. PORTER. 1946. Germinability of sorghum and soybean seed exposed to low temperatures. J. Amer. Soc. Agron. 38: 905-913.

ROBERTS, E. H. 1960. The viability of cereal seed in relation to temperature and moisture. Ann. Bot. (London) 24: 12–31.

ROGERS, G. K. 1943. Grain itch. J. Amer. Med. Ass. 123: 887–889.

SAUL, R. A., and J. L. STEELE. 1966. Why damaged corn costs more to dry. Amer. Soc. Agr. Eng. (St. Joseph, Mich.) 47: 326-329, 337.

SCHOLZ, B. 1962. Atmungsverluste bei Weizen in Abhangigkeit von Temperatur, Lagerzeit und Wassergehalt. Landtech. Forschung 212: 48–52.

SCHUSTER, K., and O. M. JUNG. 1961. Variable malting properties of brewing barley with special reference to the influence of low temperature on dormancy. Brauwissenschaft 14: 359-362 [J. Sci. Food Agr. 13: Abstr., col. 35 (1962)].

SHANDS, H. L., D. C. JANISCH, and A. D.

DICKSON. 1967. Germination response of barley following different harvesting conditions and storage treatments. Crop. Sci. 7: 444–446.

SHOVE, G. C. 1966. Application of dehydrofrigidation to shelled corn conditioning. Ann. Meeting, Amer. Soc. Agr. Eng., Amherst, Mass., June: 26–29.

SHOVE, G. C. 1970. Potential energy in use in low temperature grain conditioning. Trans. Amer. Soc. Agr. Eng. 13: 58–60.

SINHA, R. N. 1964. Effect of low temperatures on the survival of some stored product mites. Acarologia 6: 336-341.

SMITH, H. A., and T. C. JONES. 1961. *Veterinary Pathology.* Lea & Febiger, Philadelphia. 569 p.

SOLOMON, M. E. 1946. Tyroglyphid mites in stored products. Nature and amount of damage to wheat. Ann. Appl. Biol. 33: 280.

SOLOMON, M. E., and B. E. ADAMSON. 1955. The powers of survival of storage and domestic pests under winter conditions in Britain. Bull. Entomol. Res. 46: 311–355.

STEELE, J. L., and R. A. SAUL. 1962. Laboratory measurements of the rate of deterioration of grain during drying. Paper pres. Ann. Meeting Mid-Central Section of Amer. Soc. Agr. Eng.

STEELE, J. L., R. A. SAUL, and W. V. HUKILL. 1969. Deterioration of shelled corn as measured by carbon dioxide production. Trans. Amer. Soc. Agr. Eng. 12: 685–689.

STRAND, E. 1965. Studies on seed dormancy. Meld. Norg. Landbrukshogsk. 44 p.

SUNDSTOL, F. 1966. Virkingen af frost pa spireevnen hos havre. Meld. Nord. Landbrukstigsk 45: 1–28 [Biol. Abstr.: 48. No. 108703 (1967)].

SUTHERLAND, J. W., D. PESCOD, and H. J. GRIFFITHS. 1970. Refrigeration of bulk stored wheat. Paper pres. Jubilee Federal Conf. of Aust. Inst. Refrig. Air Cond. and Heat., Melbourne. April 6–10.

SZWABOWICZ, A., and K. MIEDZOBRODZKI. 1957. Toxicity of *Tyroglyphus farinae* for animals. I. Experiments on white mice, guinea pigs, pigeons and hens. Med. Wet. 13: 478.

SZWABOWICZ, A., K. MIEDZOBRODZKI, and W. SCHMID. 1958a. Toxicity of *Tyroglyphus farinae* for animals. III. Experiments on pigs. Med. Wet. 14: 344-346.

SZWABOWICZ, A., K. MIEDZOBRODZKI, J. PANKOWA,

and B. HOLNICKA. 1958b. Toxicity of *Tyroglyphus farinae* for animals. IV. Experiments on chickens and ducks. Med. Wet. 14: 556-558.

SZWABOWICZ, A., K. MIEDZOBRODZKI, and K. DONIGIEWICZ. 1957. Toxicity of *Tyroglyphus farinae* for animals. II. Experiments on horses and sheep. Med. Wet. 13: 724.

WELLINGTON, P. S. 1956. Effect of desiccation on barley dormancy. Nature (London) 176: 601.

CHAPTER 12

AERATION

N. J. BURRELL

Pest Infestation Control Laboratory
Ministry of Agriculture, Fisheries and Food, Slough, Buckinghamshire, England

I. INTRODUCTION

Aeration of grain consists of blowing or drawing ambient air through the grain mass, usually by means of fans attached to perforated ducts. Its major function is to establish and maintain a moderately low and uniform temperature throughout the bulk. The rate of airflow is variable and usually low, ranging from 0.05 to 0.3 volumes of air per unit volume of grain per min., only 1/10th to 1/20th of the rate used for grain drying. Occasionally, aeration with a higher than normal airflow or closer than normal duct spacing is used to cool or to dry damp grain slowly, so that aeration systems are not always sharply distinguishable from drying systems.

Aeration greatly reduces the risk of damage from insects, mites, and fungi by establishing and maintaining a low temperature throughout the bulk. Granivorous insects become inactive (and some slowly succumb) at temperatures below 63° F. (17° C.). Mites and a few kinds of storage fungi are able to develop slowly at temperatures down to freezing (*Penicillium* can grow at temperatures as low as 23° F. (–5° C.) if the moisture content is high enough) but below 50° F. (10° C.) their development is exceedingly slow. Maintenance of a uniform temperature throughout the grain mass reduces moisture transfer, which otherwise almost inevitably occurs, and this prevents the development of local and often hidden or unexpected hot spots with their accompanying deterioration.

The use of aeration to maintain high quality in stored grains is not new. du Monceau (1753, 1765) described a ventilated bin with a capacity of 90 tons which was aerated with an airflow rate of up to about 5 m.³ per min. by a pair of bellows operated by a windmill. He also described manually operated bellows for smaller bins. However, it was not until the early 1950's that aeration came into general use with mass production of the necessary equipment such as ducts and fans. In the 1954 edition of *Storage of Cereal Grains and Their Products*, for example, about the only mention of aeration is that by Barre (1954) in the chapter on Country Storage of Grain. On page 312 he states, "Mechanical ventilation has been employed to keep high-moisture grain cool, thereby prolonging the storage period, and also to cool dry grain in cold weather in order to control insects and to minimize moisture migration. Although this development is recent, it appears very promising, so that it will probably be one of the accepted practices in the future, even in the larger storages." Principles and practices involved are discussed by workers in many countries: Hukill (1953), Shedd (1953), Johnson (1957), and Holman (1960) in the United States; Bewer (1957) in Germany, Navarro et al. (1969) in Israel, Jouin (1961) in France, Kreyger et al. (1960) in Holland, Griffiths (1967) and Elder (1968) in Australia, Golik (1951) in the U.S.S.R., and Williamson (1961) in the United Kingdom.

II. BIOLOGICAL CONSIDERATIONS

A. Insects

In general, the drier and cooler cereal seeds are stored, the longer they remain sound (see the preceding chapter on Chilling). However, as most freshly harvested grain is dried artificially or naturally before storage to prevent spoilage by molds and mites, it is usually placed into store in a warm condition. Although dry, it may still be attacked by insect pests harbored within the building or

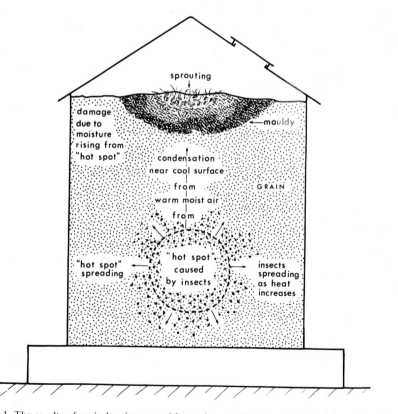

Figure 1. The results of grain heating caused by an insect infestation (British Crown Copyright).

brought in with the grain, for example, from other infested stores. Insects are active and proliferate rapidly in sufficiently warm grain. During the various stages of their life cycle, insects respire, consuming food and oxygen and producing carbon dioxide, water, and heat. Their heat production causes a local temperature increase or a hot spot, which can lead to migration of moisture to the cooler upper surface, resulting in sprouting and mold growth there (Figure 1).

The optimum temperature for the most important granivorous insects is between 82° and 100° F. (28° and 38° C.) (Table I). At temperatures below their optima, insects increase less rapidly. If grain is cooled to 63° F. (17° C.) or less, any insects present are unable to complete their life cycles or are unable to breed quickly enough to cause significant damage (Burges and Burrell, 1964). One of the main uses of an aeration system, therefore, is to cool the grain as far as possible below 63° F. (17° C.) and so prevent insect infestations arising.

Although aeration is normally used to prevent damage, it may also be used to minimize the effects of an existing heavy infestation. Burrell (1967) reported a heavy infestation of *Oryzaephilus surinamensis* in large stores provided with an aeration system which had not been used. The infestation was subdued by subsequently cooling the grain from about 104° F. (40° C.) to less than 50° F. (10° C.). In grain cooled to 41° to 50° F. (5° to 10° C.), heating ceased, and a layer of damp grain at the upper surface was dried during periods of aeration in an upward direction.

Complete control of insects is only likely to be obtained in cool climates, but aeration is nevertheless fairly widely used in warm climates, and Navarro et al. (1969) found that a large degree of insect protection was obtained by selective aeration during suitable weather. In the southern parts of the U.S., aeration is also used to preserve damp rice or maize for short periods before drying and between passes through the dryer (Calderwood and Hutchison, 1961). Myklestad (1968) prevented mold growth by aeration alone when the moisture content was not excessive.

B. Mites

The importance of mites in damp grain is described fully in Chapter 11 (Chilling), and only a summary is given here. Mites are rarely found in grain dried to less than about 13% moisture content but are likely to be common or abundant in damper grain. Figure 2 illustrates the wide variation of mite numbers found in grain samples at a wide range of moisture contents taken from farm stores of aerated grain. A temperature below 41° F. (5° C.) is required to prevent an increase of mites in damp grain.

C. Mold Growth

Although fungi grow in bulks of warm grain even at moisture contents of from 13.5 to 15% if given sufficient time (Christensen, 1955), studies in Britain by Burrell et al. (1965–1970) show that visible fungal growth rarely occurs in bulks of cooled grain at 41° to 50° F. (5° to 10° C.) if the moisture content is below about 18%, during a storage period of up to 8 months. The musty odors that occasionally arise are usually prevented, or even removed, by prolonged aeration. Burrell (unpublished results) found no significant change in fungal

TABLE I

Optimum temperature for rapid insect growth and the temperature at which the developmental cycle from egg laying to the emergence of the adult from the pupa takes place in a mean of 100 days. (After Burges and Burrell, 1964)

Species	Species	Optimum Temperature °C.	Safe Temperature (Life cycle >100 days)			Authority	
			°F.	°C.	°F.		
Saw-toothed grain beetle	*Oryzaephilus surinamensis* L.	34	93	19	66	Howe	1956b
Grain weevil	*Sitophilus granarius* L.	28 to 30	82 to 86	17	63	Eastham and Segrove	1947
Rust-red grain beetle	*Cryptolestes ferrugineus* (Steph)	36	97	20	68	Rilett	1949
Rust-red flour beetle	*Tribolium castaneum* Herbst	36	97	22	72	Howe	1956a
Confused flour beetle	*Tribolium confusum* J. du V.	33	91	21	70	Howe	1960
Khapra beetle	*Trogoderma granarium* Everts	38	100	22	72	Hadaway	1956
Rice weevil	*Sitophilus oryzae* (L.)	29 to 31	84 to 87	18	64	Kuschel / Birch	1961 / 1945
Lesser grain borer	*Rhizopertha dominica* F.	34	93	21	70	Birch	1945
Flat grain beetle	*Cryptolestes pusillus* Schonherr	32	90	19	66	Davies	1949

counts during the aerated storage of wheat and barley at up to 18% moisture although there was slight deterioration at 19%. Kreyger (1968) also reports mold-free storage for long periods under similar conditions and showed that the onset of mold growth could be delayed by passing air through the grain. In Sweden, Anianson and Noren (1964) reported that it was not necessary to dry grain below 17 to 19% moisture content in their cold climate and Bewer (1957) found that aeration with cold night air greatly reduced the need for drying. It is clear, however, that the preservation of damp grain by aeration is only possible in cool climates as Calderwood and Schroeder (1968) noted the growth of the dangerous fungus *Aspergillus flavus* and the production of aflatoxin in bins of aerated rice in a warm area. However, Calderwood and Hutchison (1961) found that periods of cool air aeration, alternating between periods of warm air drying, were a useful aid in preserving rice, and that from 31 to 55% of the drying occurred during periods of aeration. Schroeder (1963), however, found that aeration at low airflow rates had little effect in reducing mold growth, and to do this, high airflow rates were required.

In general, therefore, it appears that in cold climates it may be possible to store grain at up to about 18% moisture content until the spring, but in warm climates stringent drying to 12 to 13% moisture content soon after harvest is necessary to prevent appreciable fungal growth.

D. Germination

Effects of cool storage on grain germination have been described in detail in the preceding chapter on Chilling. It should be noted that the dormancy of some barley varieties may be greatly extended if stored at a low temperature, particularly after a cool, damp harvest, unless the grain is first dried and stored in warm conditions for a few weeks to break its natural dormancy (Pollock, 1956). Cool storage of damp grain may reduce germination, particularly if the grain has been damaged during combining (Arnold, 1963). Inhibition of germination can result from fungal activity at high moisture contents (Blum and Gilbert, 1957).

E. Summary of Biological Considerations

The combined effects of temperature and moisture content on the major criteria affecting safe storage are summarized in Figure 3. Activities of seed and any microorganisms present are reduced to negligible proportions and will not cause heating in conditions shown below line C; germination is well maintained for 8 months at line B, and for increasing periods the lower one goes below it; insect attack is normally prevented below line D, and mite activity is negligible outside the shaded area bounded by line A. The "safe" area shown in the diagram is restricted to the lower left corner. In practice, however, it is common to find conditions suitable for the development of mites in farm-stored grain.

III. PHYSICAL CONSIDERATIONS

Basic engineering data for planning ventilation systems have existed for many years and are detailed in numerous publications. One of the most comprehensive

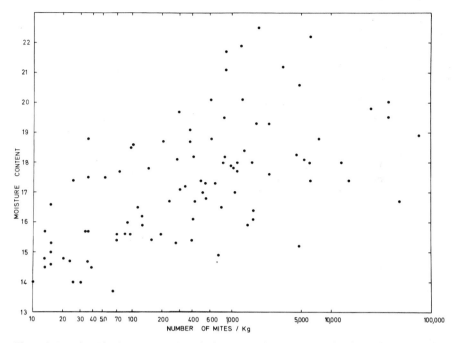

Figure 2. Relationships between number of mites and moisture content of grain samples taken down the centers of 19 farm stores (Burrell and Havers, 1970).

is that of the U.S. Department of Agriculture (Holman, 1960). The following chapter provides the basic information necessary to understand and plan an aeration system.

A. Resistance of Grains to Airflow

Size and shape of the various grains govern their resistance to air flowing between them. Resistance to airflow is increased by smaller grains, faster airflow, and greater depth, but considerable variations can occur because of dust deposits and packing effects (Shedd, 1953). Figure 4 demonstrates how the resistance to airflow of a bulk of wheat is proportional to the air velocity through the grain and to the depth of the grain. For example, to cool a bulk of grain to near mean ambient temperature in 48 hr. requires an airflow of about 0.2 c.f.m. per cu. ft. of grain. In grain 10 ft. deep, this airflow rate corresponds to an air velocity through the upper surface of the bulk of 2 ft. per min. Figure 4 illustrates that a resistance of 0.04 in. standard water gauge (in. swg) is produced by each ft. of grain depth so that the total resistance of 10 ft. of grain to this airflow is 0.4 in. swg.

To cool a grain mass 20 ft. deep in a similar period of 48 hr., the same airflow rate (0.2 c.f.m. per cu. ft. grain) is necessary, but to achieve this, twice the air quantity must be passed through the grain and the air velocity must, therefore, be increased from 2 to 4 ft. per min. As Figure 4 shows, the pressure drop per ft. of grain depth is doubled. Since the grain depth is also doubled, an overall fourfold increase in resistance occurs, to 1.6 in. swg. Similarly, the same airflow rate in grain 30 and 40 ft. deep requires a pressure of about 3.6 and 7.2 in. swg, respectively.

The power consumed in aerating deep grain bulks increases even more rapidly than the resistance to airflow. For example, if a fan delivers 1,000 c.f.m. into grain 10 ft. deep, at a pressure of 0.4 in. swg, then to cool bins of grain 20, 30, and 40 ft. deep in the same time, the fans must deliver 2,000, 3,000, and 4,000 c.f.m. at 1.6, 3.6, and 7.2 in. swg, respectively. The large increase in both air quantity required and resistance increases power consumption enormously (Osborne, 1961) and requires far larger and more expensive fans and ducting. There are two main methods of avoiding high power consumption in deep bulks of aerated grain: either the airflow rate must be diminished, for example, from 0.2 to 0.05 c.f.m. per cu. ft. of grain or, alternatively, the depth of grain through which the air passes can be reduced. This can be done in tall, narrow bins by placing aeration ducting vertically down opposite corners or opposite sides of a bin with air drawn or blown laterally across the bin (Hohner and Brooker, 1965). In deep, floor-storage, however, lateral aeration is not usually practical, and a lower

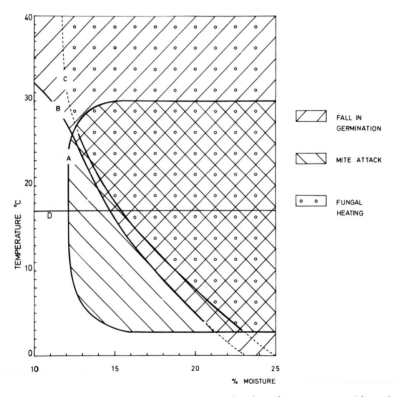

Figure 3. Relationship between storage temperature and grain moisture content and insect heating (above line D), fall in germination (to 95% in 35 weeks' storage), damp grain heating and mite attack (after Burges and Burrell, 1964).

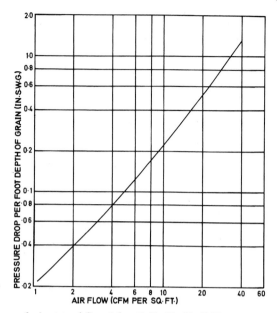

Figure 4. Resistance of wheat to airflow (after C. K. Shedd, 1953).

airflow rate may be preferred to a large increase in power consumption. A compromise between increased power consumption and a reduced rate of airflow is, however, often feasible. If the airflow rate is reduced to one-quarter of the desired rate, cooling will take four times as long. An estimate of the time necessary to cool a bulk of grain can be obtained. It takes roughly 600 (Jouin, 1965) to 720 (McCune et al., 1963) volumes of air to cool a single volume of grain, assuming that an even air distribution occurs (Burrell and Laundon, 1967).

Shedd (1953) found that resistance to airflow sometimes increased by more than 50% when grain was tightly packed. He showed that the resistance to airflow in damp grain was up to 20% less than in dry grain. He also found that increased resistance because of dust depended not only on the quantity present but also on the particle size. It is clear, therefore, that thorough cleaning is necessary before storage, if slowly cooling areas are to be reduced to a minimum. Despite this care, however, variations in resistance due to packing effects are still likely to occur in different positions within a bulk of grain.

B. Air Distribution

A thorough study of air distribution through grain may result in appreciable economies in ducting, which incurs the major cost of aerating a floor store or a lateral aeration system. In small bins of grain the fan is likely to be the most expensive part of the equipment, but the cost can often be reduced by using the fan to ventilate more than one bin.

Ideal bin systems. A ventilated bin with a perforated false floor is sometimes referred to as an "ideal" system, as all air paths between the perforated floor and

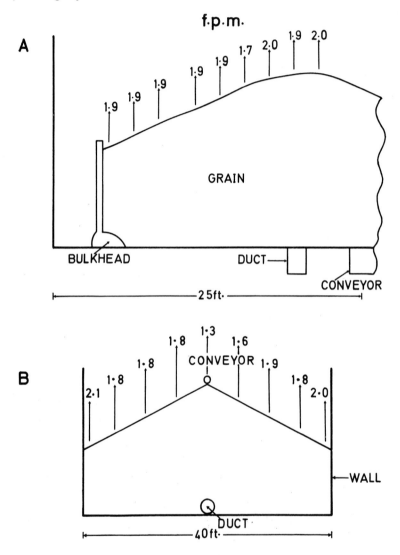

Figure 5. Cross sections through large grain stores, with upward aeration showing even distribution of air achieved in peak-loaded stores. Numbers indicate air velocity through the upper grain surface in ft. per min. (fpm). Note the lower rate of airflow at the peak of diagram B in the dusty area beneath the peak (Burrell, 1970).

the upper surface are equal and the air, therefore, moves through a homogeneous grain mass in parallel paths and with a uniform velocity. Shedd (1953) described this air movement as linear air flow. In such ventilated bins, usually used for grain drying rather than for aeration, air pressure falls evenly as air passes through the grain. If the aeration fan produces an air pressure of 2 in. swg in the grain at the base of a bin filled to a height of 10 ft., the pressures at intervals of 1 ft. up the bin will be 1.8, 1.6, 1.4, 1.2, etc., until at the upper surface the fan produces no measurable pressure (Brooker, 1961). Similar results are obtained in a suction system, with the air moving down, except that the pressures are negative in this case, i.e., they will be −2 in. swg in the grain above the duct and −1.8, −1.6, −1.4, etc., at intervals of 1 ft. up the bin. In such a bin, the cool front may remain more or less horizontal and move steadily up or down the bin according to the direction of air movement. As described earlier, however, packing effects and dust deposits often produce variations of airflow which modify the cooling pattern.

Floor ducts. Brooker (1965) showed that a duct system compared favorably in air distribution with a perforated false floor at any given rate of airflow, if the air escape area of the ducts equaled one-fourth of the floor area. However, since ducts are expensive in large floor stores, they are usually kept to a minimum and spaced at wide intervals over the floor of the store or bin.

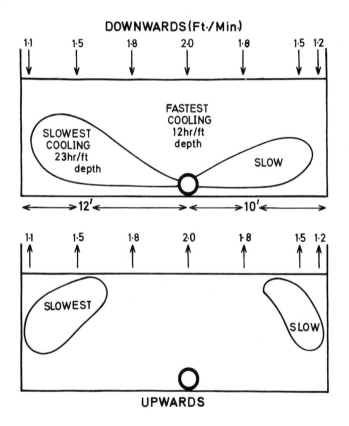

Figure 6. Cross section through a level-loaded floor store showing the air velocity through the upper surface when sucking or blowing using the same centrifugal fan turned through 90°. The times taken to cool grain along the shortest and longest air paths are given and positions of residual warmer areas are shown (Burrell, 1970).

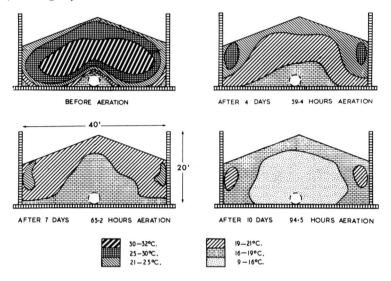

BEFORE AERATION   AFTER 4 DAYS   39.4 HOURS AERATION

←——— 40' ———→   20'

AFTER 7 DAYS   65.2 HOURS AERATION   AFTER 10 DAYS   94.5 HOURS AERATION

30–32°C.		19–21°C.
25–30°C.		16–19°C.
21–25°C.		9–16°C.

Figure 7. Cross section through a 1,000-ton store, showing the cooling pattern produced by upward ventilation from a single longitudinal duct (Burges and Burrell, 1964).

Leaving a floor duct, the air spreads radially from it along divergent air paths with a consequent rapid drop in velocity and pressure. The air spreads through a semicylindrical region around the duct until it reaches a distance equal to half the distance to the next duct where air from the two adjacent ducts combines and is then forced to move vertically upward (Henderson, 1958). In a single-duct system, an even air distribution can only occur if the grain depth above the duct is similar to the distance from the duct to the sides of the heap. Therefore, a more even air distribution is normally obtained when the duct lies longitudinally beneath a peak (Figure 5) than when the store is level-loaded, i.e., loaded to the same depth all over the floor (Figure 6).

If temperatures are measured in many positions through several cross sections along a store (Burges and Burrell, 1964), cooling occurs equally along the length of the store, and the cooling pattern produced by the divergent air from the duct cools a more or less semicircular region around the duct with this region spreading upward gradually (Figure 7).

Radial air movement away from floor ducts can be demonstrated in other ways. Measurement of air pressures within a bulk shows a similar pattern (Figure 8), and air paths are assumed to be at right angles to isobars. Hukill and Shedd (1955) computed the time it takes air to travel from a duct to any given point in the bulk and defined this as the traverse time usually measured in seconds. Lines of equal traverse time represent the shape of the cooling or drying front as it passes through the grain bulk.

With downward ventilation the reverse situation occurs, with the warmest areas persisting longest around the duct.

Lateral air movement in level-loaded bins. When a floor duct is covered by a shallow layer of grain loaded evenly over the floor of the store, air will travel most

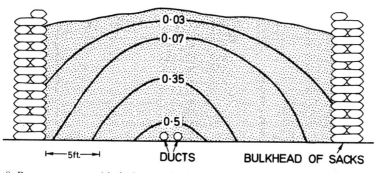

Figure 8. Pressures measured in inches standard water gauge in a cross section through a 600-ton ventilated store, retained within a bulkhead of sacks (Burrell, 1970).

easily and rapidly through the shortest path to the surface. Figure 9 shows that the velocity of air passing upward or downward through the upper grain surface in a bin loaded evenly to a depth of 3 ft. and later to 8 ft. is greatest directly above the duct, and that it falls evenly until a position is reached about 1 to 2 ft. from the wall, where the velocity increases slightly.

The results for depths at intervals of 1 ft. from 3 ft. to 8 ft. are summarized in Figure 10. These detailed measurements show clearly that air distribution from ducting extends laterally to a great extent even when the difference between the shortest and longest air paths from the duct to the surface is large.

Path ratio, velocity ratio, and cooling ratio. As already described, the lengths of all air paths are virtually identical in ideal bin systems with a perforated floor and also in cylindrical, radially ventilated bins with a central vertical perforated duct. In all other aeration systems, however, the air paths are unequal. Brooker (1965) pointed out that slow cooling or slow drying areas always remain at the ends of the longest air paths. This is also shown in Figure 7. Burrell and Havers (1970) reported, however, that even in ideal bin systems, dust deposits and differences in packing prevented even cooling and showed air channeling to occur in bins with perforated floors. Although an even air velocity might be expected to occur through the top surface of ideal bins, differences of up to 1.9:1 occurred.

The importance of the velocity ratio was stressed by Burrell and Laundon (1967), whose measurements showed that a velocity ratio of 1.7:1 in a bin of grain 33 ft. deep was associated with a cooling time of 34 hr. in the most rapid cooling area and 60 hr. in the slowest, i.e., a cooling ratio of 1.8:1. In shallower bins, however, a lower difference in the cooling ratio may be expected.

Care must be taken, however, to avoid applying the results of tests in level-loaded bins (Figure 10) to peak-loaded bins (Figure 5). A comparison between air velocities through the top surface shows how the relationship between path ratio and velocity ratio in the level-loaded bin (Figure 10) does not apply to the velocities through the upper surface in the peak-loaded stores (Figure 5). This difference in air distribution from ducts to upper surface amply illustrates the great advantage of peak loading over level loading. For any given floor store and aeration system, however, path and velocity ratios are reduced as grain depth increases, and this results in a more even air distribution (Figure 10).

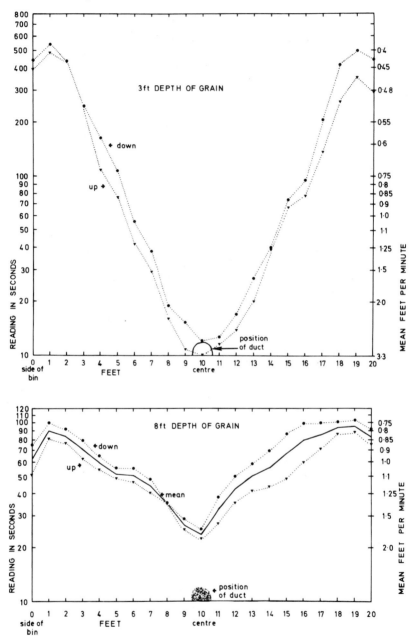

Figure 9. Air velocities, during upward and downward aeration, through the upper surface of a ventilated grain bin 20 ft. wide loaded with 3 ft. of grain (upper diagram) and 8 ft. of grain (lower diagram). Note how velocity ratios approach unity as grain depth increases and the path ratio is reduced.

C. Duct Positions and Spacing

The size of the grain bulk as well as its geometry should be considered in all aeration systems when selecting duct spacing and position. Bulks of grain dry and free from insect pests eventually cool naturally without aeration, but the larger the bulk the greater is the effect of thermal insulation and the more slowly it cools at the center. Even without aeration, the periphery of each grain bulk soon cools naturally (Figure 7). Burges and Burrell (1964) showed that it may take several months for the temperature at the center of a large unaerated bulk to cool to a safe level. During this time any insects invading the store could increase in number. Therefore, in large stores, little advantage can be taken of natural cooling processes, and the ratio between the longest and shortest air paths is usually kept to between 1.5 and 1.8:1 (Holman, 1960; Burges and Burrell, 1964). In small grain stores, natural cooling occurs more extensively, and temperatures suitable for insects do not persist for more than a few weeks. Thus in small, level-loaded floor stores of 8 to 10 ft. depth in Britain, more reliance is placed on natural cooling, and economies are often gained in duct spacings (Burrell and Havers, 1970). Air path ratios as high as 2.7:1 have been reported by these authors to achieve adequate cooling in shallow level-loaded bulks in the United Kingdom if the grain is below about 15% moisture. A ratio of 2:1 was considered adequate for grain at 15 to 18% in small stores. They concluded that the path ratio for damper grain should not greatly exceed 1.5:1 even in small stores due to the risk of damp grain heating in areas far from the duct.

Examples of satisfactory duct systems for large stores are given in Figure 11A and 11C where a duct ratio of 1.8:1 has been adequate for aerating dry grain. In the store whose performance is illustrated in Figure 11C, however, warm areas remained toward the sides of the store, as also shown in Figure 7. In Figure 11B, natural cooling in the shallower grain toward the sides of the store would permit

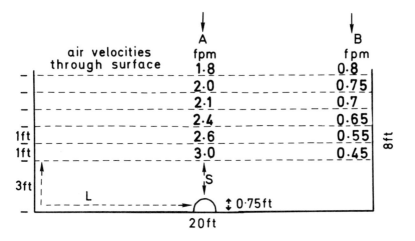

Figure 10. Cross section through a grain bin 20 ft. wide, showing maximum air velocities through the upper surface immediately above the duct and minimum velocities about 1 ft. from the sides. The bin was loaded with cleaned barley initially to a depth of 3 ft. and later to depths of 4, 5, 6, 7, and 8 ft. (Burrell, 1970).

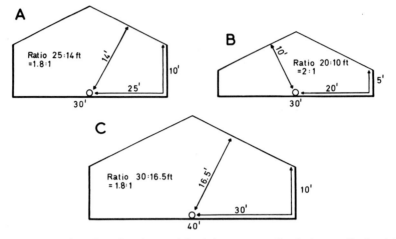

Figure 11. Cross sections through various peak-loaded stores aerated by single centrally placed ducts. Path ratios of 1.8:1 in A and C were satisfactory (see Figure 7). B illustrates how the path ratio increases as grain depth decreases (Burrell, unpublished).

a path ratio of up to 2:1 to be used if ventilation were in an upward direction. It is less certain if a similar system would be satisfactory for downward aeration, as the warmest areas would remain near the center of the store where natural cooling would probably be less effective.

In the wider store illustrated in Figure 12, three or more ducts would normally be selected for even airflow, but future developments, discussed later, may probably allow economies in the amount of ducting used.

IV. PRACTICAL CONSIDERATIONS

A. Sucking or Blowing

Whether air should be blown through the grain from the fan and ducting or whether it should be drawn, or sucked, through the grain to the duct and then be exhausted out of the building by the fan seems to arouse most controversy during discussions on aeration. The aim of this section is to try to present the arguments for and against these two procedures.

Advantages of blowing. 1) Temperature measurement in the grain is easier when air is blown upward since the warmest areas are near the surface and can be easily measured with simple temperature probes. This factor is particularly important in deep and extensive bulks of grain where it is difficult, or even practically impossible, to measure the temperatures deep in the bulk in all positions which may be in danger of heating. 2) Natural cooling can occur more rapidly as the warmest areas lie near the surface. 3) If warm grain is loaded on top of grain that has already been cooled, the warm air is driven from the store and is not drawn downward, rewarming the grain below as in downward ventilation. This is particularly important if a grain dryer is in use in the building, discharging warm, damp air into the space above the grain. 4) In humid weather, slight heating of the air by 1° to 2°C., which can sometimes be achieved by fan heat alone, can reduce the relative humidity of the air, thus greatly reducing the chance or extent of moisture increases in the grain.

Disadvantages of blowing. 1) There is a greater possibility that warm air from aerated grain may cause condensation under the roof, particularly if the grain has been allowed to heat up and the weather is cold. Chances of condensation are increased in outdoor metal bins with only a small distance between grain and metal roof. In large stores of dry grain, condensation rarely occurs unless the grain is already heating. The existence of a large space above the grain also helps to prevent condensation. 2) If the fan heat is negligible, it is possible for the grain to absorb moisture around the duct, but in practice the moisture content of grain around the duct is unlikely to rise above about 17%. 3) If the fan is operated near a grain cleaner or other dusty area, ducts could become blocked. 4) Unless the ducts are provided with internal valves to block the airflow, aeration cannot normally be started until the ducts are completely covered with grain. 5) If fans are positioned against outside walls of the store, it is usually necessary to erect a substantial shelter over them to prevent rain water from being blown into the ducts.

Advantages of downward aeration. 1) There is usually no condensation, provided the exhaust air is led out of the building. But if grain heating has occurred, warm air is sometimes drawn downward and produces condensation in the cold grain around the ducts. This may result in sprouting of grain causing partial blockage of the ducts with root growth. 2) Any moisture increase is spread over a wide area at the upper surface. However, it should be remembered that in damp weather with no solar heat falling on the roof, the relative humidity of the air entering the grain will be similar to ambient. Tests in Britain (Burrell et al., 1969) have shown that in such circumstances larger moisture content increases can occur with sucking than with blowing. 3) Dust floating in the air can be drawn down rapidly into the grain thus removing a nuisance to workers in the building. 4) Aeration ducts are unlikely to be blocked with dust even when operating close to cleaning machinery. 5) In sunny weather, solar heat may warm the air as it passes down into the grain, thus producing a drying effect. 6)

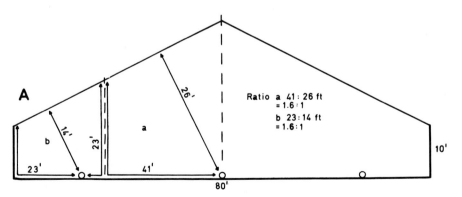

Figure 12. Cross section through a large grain store illustrating a method of duct positioning to obtain even path ratios around each duct (Burrell, unpublished).

Aeration can be started before the ducts are completely covered by grain, as the uncovered duct can be temporarily blocked by covering it with a loose plastic sheet. 7) Air can be encouraged to pass more rapidly through slow cooling areas, or hot spots, in the bulk by covering parts of the upper surface with thin plastic sheets.

Disadvantages of downward aeration. 1) In bulks of damp grain, the dampest areas are likely to be deep in the bulk where their presence may remain unsuspected. 2) The warmest areas also may be deep in the bulk where they are difficult to find. 3) Fan heat is wasted. 4) It is impracticable to add heat to control the relative humidity of the air, apart from the uncontrollable solar heat gain through the roof in good weather. 5) When warm grain is loaded on top of cool grain, the cold layer is rewarmed by the warm air drawn from above.

Conclusions. The advantages and disadvantages of blowing and sucking appear to be approximately equal, but for damp grain, blowing is preferable. In some buildings there is no choice, as conditions may impose the selection of one particular method. For example, downward aeration would probably be rejected where hot or damp air from an industrial process would be drawn into the grain. Similarly, blowing would be rejected if there were a possibility that dust-laden air might contaminate some other food product.

B. Effect of Loading Schedule on Duct Arrangement

In some large industrial stores containing thousands of tons of grain it may take months to fill the store. If cooling is delayed until the ducts are completely covered, any insect infestation may increase before aeration can be carried out. It is therefore necessary to start cooling within 3 to 4 weeks after initial loading. The aeration system should be planned to begin cooling before the store is filled, and the following methods are suggested.

Method 1. An ideal system is to provide butterfly valves or sliding valves inside the ducts which can be opened or moved along the duct as they are covered with grain. In practice this system is difficult to arrange in large stores.

Method 2. Where longitudinal ducting has been selected, the grain may be loaded in shallow layers along the building, covering the ducting from one end to the other and making it possible to start aeration soon after loading begins.

This method has various disadvantages:

1. Not all loading methods permit loading to be carried out in layers. Even when this is possible, it is often inconvenient to arrange.

2. With a downward ventilation system, cooling will take longer. For example, one store loaded initially with 550 tons of warm wheat was cooled to below 63°F. (17°C.) after 124 hr. of ventilation in a downward direction. A further layer of 150 tons was then added and ventilation continued. The grain layer that had been cooled was rewarmed by the air from the warm grain above being drawn down into the cool grain and a further 150 hr. of ventilation was required to recool the grain to 17°C.

3. In large stores of malting barley, different layers of grain may be at different stages of dormancy. None of the grain can be used for malting until dormancy is broken throughout the store.

Method 3. It is usually more convenient to begin loading a grain store at one end, to fill that part, and move on to the next section. Most large stores are peak loaded along the center with a large difference in the depth of grain at the center and at the sides of the store. The most widely used duct layout in such stores is a multiduct system where each duct provides cooling over a limited area within the store. The ducts may be placed laterally, but this layout usually leads to slower cooling beneath the central peak and may require long periods of aeration to cool this resistant area.

A complicated but efficient multiduct system can be built by placing main ducts longitudinally beneath the peak from each end of the store, with peripheral grain being aerated by other ducts entering through sides or ends of the store.

It is often necessary to adjust the duct spacing to permit access for vehicles during loading and unloading. In these cases under-floor ducting is beneficial but the cost of excavating and supporting the ducts may be considerable. For examples of various possible duct systems in many types of storage the reader is referred to the work of Holman (1960).

C. Temperatures Achieved by Aeration

Temperature ranges found in aerated bins depend on a number of factors, some of which are controllable and others, such as climate and weather, are not.

The rate of airflow. If the airflow rate is high and air is distributed evenly from the ducts, a cooling front will pass rapidly through the grain. During cool weather or if a series of cold nights follows the harvest, grain temperatures can be reduced rapidly. If the airflow rate is low, there is far greater likelihood that the grain bulk will not be thoroughly cooled by the time the cold period ends.

Control equipment. The days after harvest tend to be warm with a low relative humidity, and nights are usually cooler and more humid. There is, therefore, a choice between cooling at night to achieve the lowest possible temperatures but with the risk of dampening the grain if it has been thoroughly dried. Alternatively, ventilating during the day results in higher temperatures, but reduces the risk of dampening, and may even achieve a limited amount of drying if the grain is damp.

Grain is cooled most rapidly if thermostatically controlled switches operate the fans. To reduce the chance of raising the moisture content, more complicated differential thermostats are often used to switch on the fan when the air temperature is several degrees below the highest grain temperature. Another recent development in Australia is a thermostat whose setting is automatically adjusted (Elder, 1969). Wet-bulb differential thermostats, described by Griffiths (1967), have also been used with satisfactory results (Burrell, 1967).

If the grain is to be aerated during periods of low relative humidity, the fan may be switched on by humidistat, or manually after consulting a hygrometer or psychrometer. Time switches are often used to operate fans during the day to make use of lower relative humidities or at night to make use of lower temperatures. An overriding humidistat or thermostat may also be used to avoid periods of high humidity or temperature.

The practice of operating fans continuously 24 hr. a day is inefficient unless the grain is in imminent danger of heating, as the low temperatures achieved at night are increased the following day, with the possibility that condensation may result as warm morning air is passed into cold grain.

Cooling stages. Temperature ranges which can be achieved in temperate climates such as in the United Kingdom are shown in Figure 13. Because of the normal difficulty of obtaining low temperatures during warm postharvest weather, aeration is normally carried out in stages to obtain progressively lower temperatures as winter approaches.

Evaporative cooling. If wet grain is exposed to a stream of dry air, moisture is evaporated, and the grain cools to near wet-bulb air temperature. The damper the grain or the drier the air, the more likely is evaporative cooling to play some part in cooling the grain. Under conditions where no moisture loss occurs from the grain, no evaporative cooling can occur. If moisture is absorbed by the grain from air passing through it, slight warming occurs as latent heat is released.

Climatic effects. In warm areas, insects cannot be completely controlled by aeration. By selective aeration, however, it is possible to reduce grain temperatures below those which are optimal for insect development and so reduce their rate of increase and the amount of damage caused by their activity. Despite a warm climate, Navarro et al. (1969) obtained a useful reduction of temperature and insect infestation in Israel. Myklestad (1968) also found beneficial results when aerating rice in a warm climate.

D. Moisture Changes

One of the most useful methods of preventing excessive dampening in bulks of aerated grain, whatever fan control is used, is to select a fan and duct system which produces a small temperature rise of 1° or 2°C. In a cool or temperate

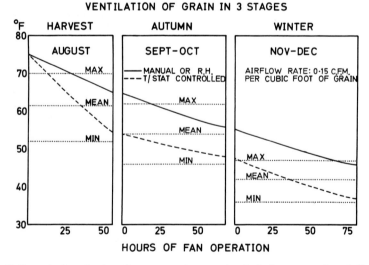

Figure 13. Stages in the reduction of temperature in aerated grain during storage. In each diagram the upper sloping line shows the probable mean temperature achieved by aerating during periods of low humidity. The lower sloping dotted line shows the temperature achieved by thermostatic control. The horizontal dotted lines show the mean daily maximum, minimum, and mean temperatures (1901-1930) for the months of August to December for Southern England (Burrell, 1970).

climate, such a rise reduces the relative humidity of air by about 7 to 14%. Although this arrangement seems inefficient and the temperature rise indicates that some fan power is wasted in the production of heat rather than in moving air along the duct, enormous benefits can result. The need for supervision can be reduced, and it is possible to aerate a grain bulk, whatever the air humidity, thus reducing grain temperatures rapidly without running the risk of dampening the

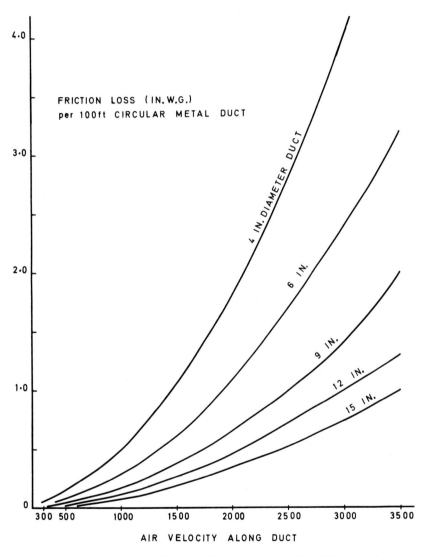

Figure 14. Friction loss along a 100-ft. length of circular metal ducting. Friction loss increases with increase in duct length or air velocity and with decreasing duct diameter (after Osborne and Turner, 1952).

grain to any important extent (Burrell and Laundon, 1965). Such systems are, of course, only workable when air is blown through the grain.

Not only does the rise in air temperature reduce the possibility of dampening the grain, but as the resultant aeration is more or less independent of atmospheric humidity, aeration can be carried out more frequently, lower rates of airflow may be used or, alternatively, economies can be made in duct sizes and spacings.

Use of slightly heated air is particularly suited to the aeration of damp grain, as slow drying may be achieved, even in cool, damp climates, and there is no risk of dampening grain further. As discussed above and earlier in the Chapter on Chilling, aerated storage is possible in a cool climate at up to about 18% moisture content. Above this level, however, increasingly large rates of airflow are necessary to prevent mold growth and losses in dry weight during storage.

E. Friction Loss in Air Ducts

Air moving in a duct experiences a resistance to its movement caused by friction between duct walls and air stream. As air velocity or duct length increases or duct diameter decreases, the friction between air and duct walls increases (Figure 14). To avoid a large reduction in airflow due to duct resistance, or large power waste, the cross-sectional area of air ducts is usually made sufficiently large to permit the required air volume to pass along the duct at a velocity limited to 1,500 to 2,000 ft. per min.

However, this limitation of air velocity is not always desirable and, as explained in the previous section, a small rise in air temperature may make it possible to extend the periods of ventilation from a few hours a day to continuous aeration if desired. Therefore, not only is smaller ducting cheaper, but it may also be used, purposely, to decrease the efficiency of the aeration system so that an air velocity of 3,000 ft. per min. or more is required in the duct to supply an adequate flow of air to the grain. The increased velocity in the duct results in a greater resistance to air movement. To overcome this, a more powerful fan and larger power consumption are necessary. An increased rise in air temperature results from the use of more power necessary to achieve the required rate of airflow.

The same temperature rise may, of course be obtained with a small heater to provide 1 kw. of heat per 1,000 c.f.m. which, when added to fan heat, produces a rise in air temperature of about 4°F. However, there will be no economy in the cost of ducting to offset the increased power consumption, as the same wide ducting is required.

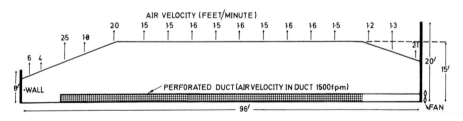

Figure 15. Air velocities in a peak-loaded store, showing even air distribution except (left) where the shallow grain permitted some air waste despite the shortened duct (Burrell, 1970).

Excessive friction losses in ducts can lead to irregularities in air velocity through grain from one end of a store to the other, particularly in ducts more than 100 ft. long. Air velocities through the upper surface of a floor store are illustrated in Figure 15. Velocity readings were taken a few feet below the peak of the store, to avoid thick dust deposits at the peak beneath the conveyor outlets. Cross sections through this store are illustrated in Figures 5B and 11C. The airflow through the main bulk is reasonably even but some waste of air occurs through the shallow grain at the end of the store away from the fan. It appears also that the duct need not have extended quite so far. Near the fan, however, the reverse situation occurs, and the duct appears to be blanked off too far from the inlet, as the airflow through the upper surface is reduced in this area.

F. Planning an Aeration System

A sound plan and a cross section are the basis for construction. By way of example consider the case of a store of dry wheat as illustrated in Figures 7 and 11C. This store is nearly 100 ft. long and contains slightly more than 1,000 tons of grain.

1. Indicate the position of the upper grain surface, assuming the angle of repose of dry grain to be about 26°. This angle varies according to the grain size and shape and any factor which increases friction between seeds such as high moisture content, angular shape, or presence of dust increases the angle of repose. In practice, however, the angle is unlikely to exceed 30°.

2. Calculate grain volume and tonnage, e.g. 1,000 tons.

3. Decide what rate of ventilation to use. This may vary from as little as 2 c.f.m. per ton in deep, dry grain to 10 c.f.m. per ton in shallow grain or in damp grain with 18% moisture content. In this example consider 6 c.f.m. per ton.

4. Multiply tonnage by airflow rate: $1,000 \times 6 = 6,000$ c.f.m.

5. Decide on the number of ducts to use and where to place them according to the path ratios desired. In Figure 11C, only one duct is used, but to reduce warm areas remaining at the sides shown in Figure 7, two ducts 10 ft. (3 m.) apart would be preferable.

6. Divide total required airflow of 6,000 c.f.m. by the number of ducts: $6,000 \div 2 = 3,000$ c.f.m. per duct.

7. Each duct should normally have a sufficient cross-sectional area to keep air velocity along the duct to below 2,000 ft. per min. In this instance the ducts should have a cross-sectional area of $3,000 \div 2,000 = 1.5$ sq. ft.

8. Arrange that in level-loaded stores perforated ducts pass from one side of the building to the other. Where the grain depth at the sides is less than that at the center, however, the duct should end several feet from the wall so that the distance from the end of the duct to the wall, plus grain height against the wall, equals the longest air path elsewhere in the store.

9. Calculate the perforated surface area of the duct to ensure that the velocity of the air leaving the duct surface does not exceed 30 ft. per min. (Holman, 1960). The velocity in floor stores is usually well below this figure, but in some stores with under-floor ducting or in narrow bins the surface area may be inadequate, and modifications are then necessary to increase the duct surface area.

10. Estimate the resistance of the grain to airflow from published graphs relating to the particular commodity involved (Shedd, 1953; Holman, 1960).

Figure 4 may be used for wheat. It gives 1.5 in. swg as the resistance of grain 20 ft. deep to this rate of airflow.

11. Derive the resistance owing to the duct system from Figure 14. In the example the duct resistance is about 0.2 in. swg.

12. The total resistance is 1.7 in. swg. Two fans are then selected which will each give 3,000 c.f.m. at 1.7 in. swg.

G. Fault Finding

Occasionally faults occur in ventilation systems. They usually result from accidental duct blockages but are sometimes caused by excessive economy in duct spacing or sizes, by faulty placing, or faulty fans. To check the airflow produced by a fan blowing air into or sucking out of a duct, an additional straight duct may be attached to the fan inlet or outlet outside the store, so that a pitot tube, a manometer, or a mechanical airflow meter can be used to estimate airflow through the external duct while aerating the grain. For small fans on small bins it is sometimes possible to attach the fan to thin-gauge polyethylene tubing and to measure the time (in sec.) necessary to inflate a measured length and calculated volume of the tubing (Burrell et al., 1970).

However, when the duct is faulty, other detection methods are necessary. One of the simplest methods which can be used in bins is to press a piece of metal tubing of perhaps 1/8 in. (3.0 mm.) diameter a few feet down into the grain to measure the air pressure there, by attaching the free end of the tubing to an accurate inclined manometer. Example: the pressure in a mass of wheat at 5 ft. depth is 0.2 in. swg. This pressure is divided by the depth in ft. to obtain the pressure drop per ft. depth; in this instance 0.04 in. swg. Read this pressure drop on the vertical axis of Figure 4, and the velocity of air through the grain is 2 c.f.m. per sq. ft. of surface area. If the bin is 10 ft. square, the volume delivered by the fan is approximately 200 c.f.m., and if the grain depth is 20 ft., the rate of airflow is about 0.1 c.f.m. per cu. ft. of grain.

In large floor stores, however, it is not usually possible to find a fixed surface where an inclined manometer can be used, and other more complicated methods are necessary. Unfortunately specially made equipment must be used, since many of the better known types of float, rotating vane, or hot wire anemometers are too insensitive for air velocities of 0.5 to 3 ft. per min., which commonly occur in bulks of aerated grain. Some instruments increase the velocity to a measurable level by collecting air in a wide funnel before leading it through a narrower tube to the anemometer. Other interesting methods have been used such as that of Cromarty (1968) who injected a halogenated hydrocarbon refrigerant into the duct and measured the time taken for the refrigerant gas to affect a refrigerant gas detector placed on the upper surface of the bulk.

A simple but well-tested apparatus that indicates areas of low air velocity at the upper surface is illustrated in Figures 16 and 17. Its basic principle is air passing upward or downward through the grain surface is led by means of a metal tube and rubber adaptor through a glass or plastic tube whose interior has been lubricated with a detergent solution and which contains a film of detergent across the glass tube. Rapid movement of the soap film indicates rapid air movement; sluggish movement indicates low air movement in that area. The apparatus is supported in the grain by means of a rod clamped to the metal tube.

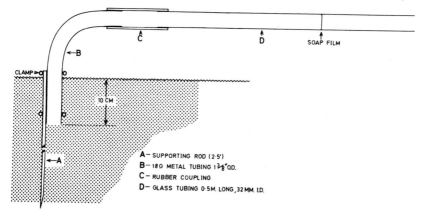

Figure 16. A simple apparatus used to measure or compare velocities of air passing upward or downward through the upper surface of ventilated grain bulks (Burrell, 1970).

The time taken for the soap film to travel a given distance (e.g. 1 ft.) is measured in seconds. If the dimensions of the tubes are the same as those given in Figure 16, the velocity of the air passing through the grain surface can be read off the calibration curve (Figure 17) which covers a range of 0.5 to 30 ft. per min. The calibration curves for wheat and barley in an upward and downward direction are all very similar but differ slightly for larger seeds, such as maize and beans (Burrell et al., 1963).

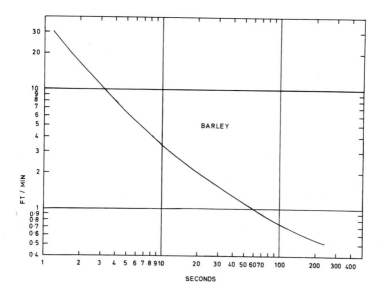

Figure 17. Mean calibration curve for upward and downward air movement through barley from 0.5 to 30 ft. per min. (Burrell, 1970).

V. CONCLUSION

In cool or temperate climates a well-planned and well-managed aeration system can greatly reduce the danger of damage by insects, mites, and fungi, the chief hazards to quality in stored grains and seeds. Even in warm climates, selective ventilation can effectively limit damage caused by these agents, and so can be of tremendous value in preserving quality. The prevention of moisture transfer, through maintenance of a uniform temperature throughout the bulk, greatly reduces the chance of development of hidden or unexpected local areas of deterioration within the bulk. Unquestionably, the development of effective aeration systems has been a major contribution of modern engineering technology to grain storage. Combined with the use of temperature detection systems and a program of regular sampling and testing, it has revolutionized grain-storage practices and has brought these far along the road from a somewhat chancy art to at least a moderately exact science.

LITERATURE CITED

ANIANSON, G., and O. NOREN. 1964. Drying with unheated air. Span 7: 42-44.

ARNOLD, R. E. 1963. Effects of harvest damage on the rate of fall in viability of wheat stored at a range of moisture levels. J. Agr. Eng. Res. 8: 7-16.

BARRE, H. J. 1954. Country storage of grain. Ch. 7, p. 312, in *Storage of Cereal Grains and Their Products*, J. A. Anderson and A. W. Alcock, eds. Amer. Ass. Cereal Chem.: St. Paul, Minn.

BEWER, H. E. 1957. Getreidekonservierung mit kalter Nachtluft. München Wolfrathausen: Ber. Inst. Landtechnik No. 47, Bonn.

BIRCH, L. C. 1945. The influence of temperature on the different stages of development of *Calandra oryzae* L. and *Rhizopertha dominica* Fab. Aust. J. Exp. Biol. Med. Sci. 23: 29-35.

BLUM, P. H., and S. G. GILBERT. 1957. Mechanism of water sensitivity. Amer. Soc. Brew. Chem., Proc. 1957, pp. 22-25.

BROOKER, D. B. 1961. Pressure patterns in grain drying systems established by numerical methods. Trans. Amer. Soc. Agr. Eng. 4: 72-74.

BROOKER, D. B. 1965. Non-linear air flow patterns in grain drying systems. Missouri Univ. Agr. Exp. Sta. Bull. 892.

BURGES, H. D., and N. J. BURRELL. 1964. Cooling bulk grain in the British climate to control storage insects and to improve keeping quality. J. Sci. Food Agr. 15: 32-50.

BURRELL, N. J. 1967. Grain cooling studies. II. Effect of aeration on infested grain bulks. J. Stored Prod. Res. 3: 143-154.

BURRELL, N. J. 1970. Low-volume ventilation and cooling patterns in grain. Paper to Inst. Agr. Eng., West Midlands Branch.

BURRELL, N. J., C. G. DACKE, and J. H. J. LAUNDON. 1963. Measurement of low rates of airflow. Res. Develop. Ind. 27: 32.

BURRELL, N. J., J. H. GRIFFITHS, J. H. J. LAUNDON, and L. A. HOLLINGWORTH. 1967. Cooling dry bulk barley with untreated air: Refrigerated damp grain storage. Pest Infest. Res. 1966: 20-23.

BURRELL, N. J., and S. J. HAVERS. 1970. Survey of some farm stores of ventilated grain. J. Sci. Food Agr. 21: 458-464.

BURRELL, N. J., S. J. HAVERS, and S. L. GORDON. 1969. Damp grain storage by refrigeration and aeration: Mould growth, moisture production and dry weight losses. Pest Infest. Res. 1968: 20-25.

BURRELL, N. J., S. J. HAVERS, and S. L. GORDON. 1970. Aeration of damp and dry bulk grain: Measurement of fan airflow. Pest Infest. Res. 1969: 17-24.

BURRELL, N. J., and J. H. J. LAUNDON. 1965. Cooling barley with untreated air. Pest Infest. Res. 1964: 20; 1965: 16.

BURRELL, N. J., and J. H. J. LAUNDON. 1967. Grain cooling studies. I. Observations during a large-scale refrigeration test on damp grain. J. Stored Prod. Res. 3: 125-144.

CALDERWOOD, D. L., and R. S. HUTCHISON. 1961. Drying rice in heated air dryers with aeration as a supplemental treatment. Rice J. 65(2): 21-28; (3) 23-28; (4) 25-39.

CALDERWOOD, D. L., and H. W. SCHROEDER. 1968. Aflatoxin development of undried rough rice following prolonged storage in aerated bins. Rep. U.S. Dep. Agr., ARS 52-26.

CHRISTENSEN, C. M. 1955. Grain storage studies. XVIII. Mold invasion of wheat stored for sixteen months at moisture contents below 15 percent. Cereal Chem. 32: 107-116.

CROMARTY, A. S. 1968. A gas tracer technique for predicting chilling patterns in stored barley. Agr. Eng. Res. 13: 1-11.

DAVIES, R. G. 1949. The biology of *Laemophloeus minutus* Oliv. (Col. Cucujidae). Bull. Entomol. Res. 40: 63-82.

EASTHAM, L. E. S., and F. SEGROVE. 1947. The influence of temperature and humidity on instar length in *Calandra* (*Sitophilus*) *granaria* Linn. J. Exp. Biol. 24: 79-94.

ELDER, W. B. 1968. Aeration and cooling of stored grain. Power Farming (Aust. and N.Z.) 28(3): 8-11.

ELDER, W. B. 1969. CSIRO develops aeration system for farm-stored grain. Power Farming, and Better Farming Dig. (Aust.) 78: 10-13.

GOLIK, M. G. 1951. Forced ventilation of grain in floor stores and silos. Moscow State Publisher on Technical and Economic Literature on Food.

GRIFFITHS, H. J. 1967. Wet-bulb control of grain aeration systems. Aust. Commonw. Sci. Ind. Res. Organ. Div. Mech. Eng. No. 3.

HADAWAY, A. B. 1956. The biology of the Dermestid beetles, *Trogoderma granarium* Everts and *Trogoderma versicolor*. Bull. Entomol. Res. 46: 781-796.

HENDERSON, S. M. 1958. Air pressure requirements for tunnel systems in deep-bed grain dryers. Trans. Amer. Soc. Agr. Eng. 1: 9-11.

HOHNER, G. A., and D. B. BROOKER. 1965. An analog of grain cooling by cross flow aeration in tall structures. Trans. Amer. Soc. Agr. Eng. 8: 56-59, 62.

HOLMAN, L. E. (Compiler). 1960. Aeration of grain in commercial storages. Marketing Res. Rep. 178. U.S. Dep. Agr. Agr. Marketing Serv. Res. Div.

HOWE, R. W. 1956a. The biology of the two common species of *Oryzaephilus* (Coleoptera, Cucujidae). Ann. Appl. Biol. 44: 341-355.

HOWE, R. W. 1956b. The effect of temperature and humidity on the rate of development and mortality of *Tribolium castaneum* (Herbst) (Coleoptera, Tenebrionidae). Ann. Appl. Biol. 44: 356-368.

HOWE, R. W. 1960. The effects of temperature and humidity on the rate of development and mortality of *Tribolium confusum* Duval (Coleoptera, Tenebrionidae). Ann. Appl. Biol. 48: 363-376.

HUKILL, W. V. 1953. Grain cooling by air. Agr. Eng. (St. Joseph, Mich.) 34: 456-458.

HUKILL, W. V., and C. K. SHEDD. 1955. Non-linear airflow in grain drying. Agr. Eng. (St. Joseph, Mich.) 36: 462-466.

JOHNSON, H. K. 1957. Cooling stored grain by aeration. Agr. Eng. (St. Joseph, Mich.) 38: 238-241, 244-246.

JOUIN, C. 1965. Le froid et la conservation des céréales. Bull. Anciens Eleves Ecole Fr. Meun. 205: 9-13.

KREYGER, J. 1968. Praktische grondslagen voor de bewaring van gemaidoorst graan. Jaarb Inst. Bewar. Verwerk. Landb. Prod. 1967, 1968: 73-94.

KREYGER, J., G. R. Van BASTELAERE, and J. JANSEN. 1960. Investigations into ventilated storage and slow drying of malting barley. Petit J. Brass. 68: 238-241.

KUSCHEL, G. 1961. On problems of synonomy in the *Sitophilus oryzae* complex (30th Contribution, Co., Curculionidae). Ann. Mag. Nat. Hist. 4: 241-244.

McCUNE, W. E., N. K. PERSON, and J. W. SORENSON. 1963. Conditioned air storage of grain. Trans. Amer. Soc. Agr. Eng. 6: 186-189.

du MONCEAU, D. 1753. Traité de la conservation des grains, Paris, Hippolyte-Louis Guerin and Louis-Francois Delatour. 294 p.

du MONCEAU, D. 1765. Supplement au traité de la conservation des grains. Hippolyte-Louis Guerin and Louis-Francois Delatour. 144 p.

MYKLESTAD, O. 1968. Controlled aeration

of rice in bulk. J. Sci. Food Agr. 19: 41-46.

NAVARRO, S., E. DONAHAYE, and M. CALDERON. 1969. Observations on prolonged grain storage with forced aeration in Israel. J. Stored Prod. Res. 5: 73-81.

OSBORNE, L. E. 1961. Resistance to airflow of grain and other seeds. J. Agr. Eng. Res. 6: 119-122.

OSBORNE, W. C., and C. G. TURNER. 1952. Woods' practical guide to fan engineering. Colchester: Woods of Colchester Ltd. 227 p.

POLLOCK, J. R. A. 1956. Incidence of dormancy in different barleys. Brew. Ind. Res. Found. 62: 331-335.

RILETT, R. O. 1949. The biology of *Laemophiloeus ferrugineus* (Steph). Can. J. Res. 27: 112-148.

SCHROEDER, H. W. 1963. The relation between storage molds and damage in high-moisture rice in aerated storage. Phytopathology 53: 804-808.

SHEDD, C. K. 1953. Resistance of grains and seeds to airflow. Agr. Eng. (St. Joseph, Mich.) 34: 616-619.

WILLIAMSON, W. F. 1961. Cooling grain in silos. J. Agr. Eng. Res. 6: 51-58.

CHAPTER 13

GRAIN DRYING

W. V. HUKILL

U.S. Department of Agriculture
Iowa State University, Ames, Iowa

I. INTRODUCTION

The amount of moisture contained in grain has a definite effect on its suitability for ordinary processes such as harvesting, storing, feeding, germinating, and milling of various kinds. For many processes there is an optimum or critical moisture content above or below which results are not satisfactory. While grain is growing, the moisture content is high. As it ripens the percentage of moisture decreases, and moisture normally continues to leave kernels after ripening until they are what we call "dry." In this condition, however, grain still contains water in amounts that may be surprising. A bushel of "dry" wheat, for example, is likely to contain from 1/2 to 1 gal. (2 to 4 l.) of water (7 to 15 lb. per 100 lb.).

For most purposes it would not be desirable to free grain completely of water even if it were convenient to do so. Perhaps the most important practical reason for concern about the moisture content of grain is that molds, yeasts, and other microorganisms require moisture for their growth (see Chapters 3 and 4). They do not get the necessary moisture unless grain contains a relatively high percentage of water. The minimum moisture content of grain above which microorganisms may cause damage is within roughly 10 to 15%. The exact level depends upon kind of grain, temperature, nature of the organism, and the duration of exposure.

The following discussion of grain drying is divided into three sections: general considerations, theoretical considerations, and practical considerations. The treatment of theoretical considerations is necessarily somewhat technical, and some readers may not wish to follow the development in detail. For this reason, an attempt has been made to keep each section as independent as possible of the others.

II. GENERAL CONSIDERATIONS

The drying of grains is similar to air drying of other solid materials. However, many other materials that are dried, such as fresh fruits and vegetables, contain much more water. General discussions of drying wet materials indicate that, in the normal range of moisture in grains, the rate of drying is limited by resistance to moisture flow within the kernel to a greater extent than by the resistance to vapor flow from the surface. When drying grains we are usually concerned with removal of a limited amount of moisture. In practice, grain does not need to be dried from initial moistures higher than perhaps 35% nor below about 10% (wet basis), and this discussion will be confined to this practical range of moisture.

A. Methods of Reporting Moisture Content

The amount of moisture in grain is usually expressed in percent by weight. A given percentage of moisture by weight, however, may have either of two meanings. For example, if we are told that grain has a moisture content of 25%, we might expect this to mean that 100 lb. of grain contains 25 lb. of water. This is right if the moisture content is expressed in percent *wet basis*. On the other hand, it is just as reasonable to assume that the 25% moisture content is expressed on a *dry basis;* in this case 100 lb. of grain contains 20 lb. of water and 80 lb. of dry matter since 20 is 25% of 80. Accordingly, when the moisture content is reported as percentage, it is necessary to know which basis is used. One is neither more correct nor more logical than the other. For some purposes it is more convenient to use the wet basis; for others, dry basis. In the United States, particularly for commercial purposes, it is customary to express grain moisture content in percent wet basis, and in the Official Grain Standards of the United States the wet basis is used.

B. Grain-Air Equilibrium

Grain is hygroscopic and holds an appreciable amount of water even after long exposure to relatively dry air. If the relative humidity of the air is increased, grain will absorb moisture. Accordingly, grain that is exposed in thin layers to air with fluctuating humidity absorbs and gives off moisture, tending at all times to reach

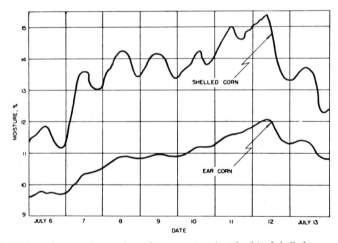

Figure 1. Typical continuous changes in moisture content (wet basis) of shelled corn and ear corn completely exposed to the atmosphere.

TABLE I

Moisture contents in equilibrium with air of various humidities at room temperature
(approximately 77° F.; 25° C.)

	Moisture Content (Wet Basis)							
	15% r.h.	30% r.h.	45% r.h.	60% r.h.	75% r.h.	90% r.h.	100% r.h.	Authority
Barley	6.1	8.5	10.0	12.1	14.4	19.5	26.8	C & F[a]
Buckwheat	6.7	9.1	10.9	12.7	15.0	19.1	24.5	C & F
Shelled corn, YD	6.4	8.4	10.5	12.9	14.8	19.1	23.8	C & F
Shelled corn, WD	6.6	8.5	10.4	12.9	14.7	18.9	24.6	C & F
Shelled corn, pop	6.8	8.5	9.8	12.2	13.6	18.4	23.0	C & F
Flax seed	4.5	5.6	6.3	7.9	10.0	15.2	21.4	C & F
Oats	5.7	8.1	9.6	11.8	13.8	18.5	24.1	C & F
Rice, milled	6.8	9.0	10.7	12.6	14.4	18.1	23.6	C & F
Rye	7.0	8.7	10.5	12.2	14.8	20.6	26.7	C & F
Sorghum	6.5	8.6	10.5	12.0	15.3	18.8	21.9	C, R, & F[b]
Soybeans	...	6.2	7.4	9.7	13.2	...	...	R & G[c]
Wheat, white	6.8	8.6	9.9	11.8	15.0	19.7	26.3	C & F
Wheat, durum	6.6	8.5	10.1	11.5	14.1	19.3	26.7	C & F
Wheat, soft red winter	6.3	8.6	10.6	11.9	14.6	19.7	25.6	C & F
Wheat, hard red winter	6.4	8.5	10.5	12.5	14.6	20.1	25.4	C & F
Wheat, hard red spring	6.8	8.5	10.1	11.8	14.8	19.7	25.0	C & F

[a] Coleman and Fellows (1925). Moisture content determined by water-oven method.
[b] Coleman, Rothgeb, and Fellows (1928). Moisture determined by official air-oven method.
[c] Ramstad and Geddes (1942). Moisture determined by vacuum-oven method. Values in above table interpolated from published graph.

equilibrium with the air. Figure 1 illustrates typical changes in moisture content in shelled corn and ear corn exposed to changes in atmospheric humidity, but protected from rain.

While relative humidity of air is not shown in this figure, on typical days the humidity is low in the afternoon and high in the early morning. Grain dries during periods of low humidity, and when humidity is high it picks up moisture. For this reason, moisture is usually highest around noon and lowest shortly before midnight. The moisture content curve follows the relative humidity roughly, but the peaks lag several hours behind. Shelled corn follows the humidity changes more closely than does ear corn.

Experiments have shown that for each kind of grain there is a definite relation between grain moisture content and relative humidity of the air with which the grain is in moisture equilibrium. That is, for any given percentage of moisture in grain, there is a definite relative humidity of air to which grain might be exposed without losing or gaining moisture. The grain moisture content in equilibrium with a given relative humidity is frequently called the "equilibrium moisture content" for that humidity. The equilibrium moisture content for a given relative humidity changes slightly as air temperature changes. Equilibrium moisture contents for several of the grains at various humidities at 77° F. (25° C.) are shown in Table I. At higher temperatures, the moisture content for each humidity will be lower than that shown.

C. Drying of Fully Exposed Grain

Grain and air are in equilibrium when the vapor pressure of grain moisture is equal to that in the air. In equilibrium, the flow of moisture to or from grain is zero, and its moisture content does not change. When the moisture content is higher than the equilibrium value, moisture flows from the grain, drying it. The rate at which moisture leaves grain depends upon how much grain is out of equilibrium with the surrounding air, temperature, and on the nature, size, and shape of the kernels.

Various experimenters have measured the drying rates of various grains exposed to constant conditions of air temperature and humidity. A typical drying curve is shown in Figure 2. In this case, a sample of oats in a layer only one kernel deep was exposed to air having a temperature of 129.5° F. (54.2° C.) and a relative humidity of 30.3%. The grain was weighed periodically and the moisture content, dry basis, was computed. As is characteristic of experiments on drying rates, the moisture content dropped off rapidly at first, then more and more slowly. At the end of the experiment, when the moisture content was almost at equilibrium with the air, the drying was so slow that it could hardly be detected by the change in weight.

This description applies to the drying of any grain that is fully exposed to an atmosphere of constant temperature and humidity. In general, the rate of drying is faster if the initial moisture content is high, if the temperature is high, or if the humidity is low. With very slow air movement, increasing the air velocity also causes faster drying. Under other conditions, the effect of air velocity change is negligible. The individual effects of each of these variables combine to cause the grain to dry in a particular manner such as, for example, that for the oat experiment illustrated in Figure 2. However, the way in which each of the above variables affects the drying rate of fully exposed samples has not been worked out completely enough for accurate prediction of the exact rate of drying under any given set of conditions.

Figure 2 showed that the rate of drying drops off as the moisture content goes down. The data of the experiment may be examined to see if the rate of drying at each moment is proportional to the amount of moisture yet to be removed at that time. The simplest test is a semilogarithmic plot of the data. If the points fall on a straight line in such a plot, the rate of drying at all times is proportional to the amount of moisture yet to be removed, and a simple formula expresses the relation of moisture content to exposure time. Data from Figure 2 have been plotted in this way in Figure 3. Time in hours is represented as before, but in this case the equilibrium moisture content is first subtracted from the observed moisture, and the logarithm of the percentage of moisture remaining to be removed is then plotted on the ordinate. The moisture content for these plots is expressed as percentage dry basis. For this purpose, percentage wet basis will not do.

The semilogarithmic plot of these data is not a straight line. Had it been, the relation between moisture content and time could have been expressed by the formula,

$$M - M_E = \Delta M e^{-Kt} \tag{1}$$

where: M is the moisture at any time; M_E the equilibrium moisture content; ΔM is the original moisture (M_o) minus M_E (all moisture contents expressed in

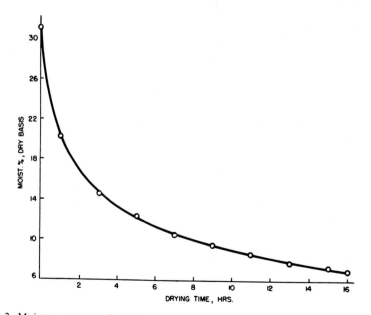

Figure 2. Moisture content of a fully exposed oat sample in an air stream having a constant temperature and humidity.

percent dry basis); e is the base of natural logarithms; K is a constant which expresses the slope of the plotted line; and t is time in hours.

Under some conditions, observed drying rates are such that data do plot approximately as a straight line. The slope of line K can then be used to express the characteristic drying rate of the particular kind of grain observed under the particular conditions of exposure. Sherwood (1936) discusses the relation between moisture content and time for drying of solids in general, and suggests a modification of the above equation that might be used to describe certain cases of drying. Newman (1931) shows other modifications that might be applied to materials with particles of various shapes.

If changing the temperature and running a new experiment yields a different value of K, and if the observed values of K have a definite relation to the temperature, a drying formula can be written with the effect of temperature included. Similarly, if the effect of various initial moisture contents, relative humidities, and air velocities could be included, a complete formula for predicting the drying rate of exposed samples could be written. While the above equation (Eq. 1) describes the drying rate only approximately, and under some conditions the approximation is poor, no other algebraic expression has been demonstrated to have general application.

Holman (1948) and Page (1948) have analyzed their results by using the equation,

$$M - M_E = \Delta M e^{-K_2 t^n} \tag{2}$$

With the limited data reported, values of K_2 and n could be found such that the drying curve for all observed cases could be described. In each case n is less than 1 and varies from about 0.55 to 0.85 in the tests reported.

The drying rate is increased by higher temperatures. The change in the drying rate K with humidity might also be expressed as a function of the wet- and dry-bulb temperatures. As an approximation to the effect of changing humidity upon K, Hukill (1947) suggested that, at a given wet-bulb temperature, K is proportional to the difference between the dry-bulb temperature and the temperature at which grain moisture would be in equilibrium with air at the given wet-bulb temperature. For very wet grain, having a relative humidity equilibrium of 100%, this would be the difference between the dry- and wet-bulb temperatures of the air; for drier grain the difference would be less.

D. Drying of Grain in Bulk

The foregoing discussion has been confined to rates of drying of fully exposed samples. That is, grain is exposed in such a way that each kernel is continually in contact with air of specified temperature and humidity. In practical drying procedure this is not generally true. Because most experiments reported on grain drying rates have been concerned with practical application, little of the drying rate data in the literature is useful in establishing the laws governing exposed drying rates. In practice, air at some constant initial temperature and humidity is passed through or over grain and picks up some moisture. It then moves past more grain, but is no longer in its initial condition, so that only the first kernels with which it comes in contact dry at the maximum rate. The rate at which the rest of the grain dries depends not only on the character of the grain and the initial condition of the air but also upon the amount of grain present and the volume of circulating air.

The rates at which air temperature and humidity change, as air progresses through a batch of grain, depend upon how fast moisture is being evaporated from the grain. Thus, all changes taking place in the bin — decrease in grain moisture content, increase in air humidity, decrease in air temperature — are controlled by the rate at which moisture is leaving each kernel as an individually exposed element. For this reason, knowledge of the effect of grain moisture content, character of grain, temperature and humidity of air, and air velocity upon *fully exposed* drying rate is essential to an understanding of how drying may be expected to proceed in any process.

Unfortunately, no general formula has been developed which accurately describes the exposed drying rate, into which each of the above variables would fit. The previous discussion of the various tentative formulas proposed by experimenters indicates that approximations are available. Until a more exact analysis of fully exposed drying rates is formulated, these approximations may be used to develop an understanding of the way in which drying may be expected to proceed in any bulk drying process. Inasmuch as the exposed drying rate is described only approximately, the bulk drying rate developed from it will also be an approximation.

Hukill (1947) described a method of predicting bulk drying rates, based upon approximations to true exposed drying rates. The computed bulk drying rates predict the actual rates only approximately but closely enough for practical

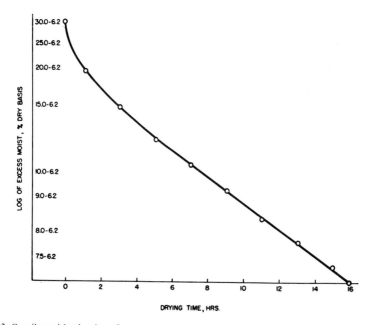

Figure 3. Semilogarithmic plot of same data as shown in Figure 2.

application. Figure 4 shows the approximate moisture content of successive layers of grain in a bin being dried as a batch. It applies to grain having a uniform initial moisture content, through which a constant volume of air, of constant initial temperature and humidity, is continually blown in one direction.

In applying the chart of Figure 4 to determine the moisture content at any point in a drying bin, after any period of dryer operation, it is necessary to express moisture content, depth of grain to that point, and time of operating the dryer in appropriate units. The required moisture content can then be read off the chart. The method of arriving at the proper units will be presented later, after a discussion of what takes place in a batch-drying process.

E. Specific Heat and Heat of Vaporization

Data in the literature on heat of vaporization of water in grains and on the specific heats of grains are incomplete. Specific heats of wheat at a few percentages of moisture and temperatures are reported by Kelly (1940). For purposes of approximation, Siebel's (1911) formula may be applied to grain. No claims for its exactness have been made. It assumes that the specific heat of the water content of the grain is 1.0 and that of the dry material is 0.2, and that there is no interaction. The formula is

$$S = 0.2 + 0.008 \ M_w \tag{3}$$

where S is the specific heat of the material in Btu/lb.° F., and M_w is the moisture content, percent wet basis.

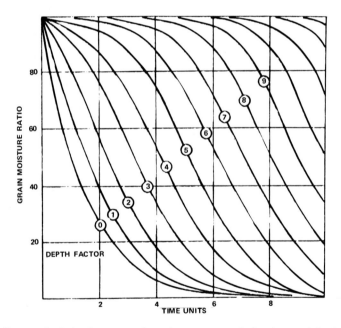

Figure 4. Computed relation between grain moisture content, drying time, and depth.

The heat of vaporization for water in grain is higher than that for free water at the same temperature. The difference may be assumed to equal the heat of wetting, but experimental data on heat of wetting are also scarce. The latent heat is greatest at low moisture content, and is very nearly the same as for free water at high moisture content. Winkler and Geddes (1931) measured the heat of hydration of flour and starches. Their results are expressed in heat units per unit weight of dry material and cannot be translated directly to Btu per pound of water absorbed at each level of moisture content, because this would require analysis of the rate of change of hydration heat. However, the data include the total heat of hydration when material of various initial moisture contents is wetted with excess water. The results indicate that the quantity of heat released when increments of water are added to flours and starches of very low moisture content (as low as 1.7%) is approximately 200 cal. per g. They also show that, above 16%, added increments of water release much less heat. Two hundred calories per gram is 360 Btu per lb. Assuming, as appears logical, that the heat of hydration is the difference between the heat of vaporization of water in flour and that of free water, we can conclude that the heat required to dry flour (or grain) must be the heat of vaporization of free water (approximately 1,000 Btu per lb.) plus 360 Btu. This is for removal of water at extremely low moisture contents. For drying at between 10 and 20% moisture content, the heat of vaporization is considerably less. In the absence of accurate data Hukill (1947) used a value of 1,120 Btu per lb.

Schrenk et al. (1947) measured hydration heat of starch and found higher values than those of Winkler and Geddes, although the data are not strictly comparable. Results for various starches were from about 23 to 30 cal. per g. of starch, as compared with about 20 cal. measured by earlier workers. These experiments were all made with completely dry starch so that the heats of hydration for various moisture contents cannot be estimated from them.

The heat of vaporization may be computed from data on vapor pressure of the moisture in grain by the following close approximation of the Clausius-Clapeyron equation:

$$H_{fg} = V_{fg}T\frac{\delta P}{\delta T} \tag{4}$$

in which H_{fg} is heat of vaporization, ft.-lb. per lb.; V_{fg} is volume of the vapor, cu. ft. per lb.; T is absolute temperature, °R.; and P is vapor pressure, lb. per sq. ft. Unfortunately, accurate measurements of vapor pressure of moisture in grain are also lacking.

F. General Comment

The preceding discussion provides a general picture of the current status of basic research on grain drying. All principal factors that affect drying rates appear to be known. But nothing like sufficient observational data are available to make possible the formulation of precise mathematical laws for grain drying. There is a wide field here for further experimental work. The key problem obviously relates to the simplest case in which each kernel is fully exposed to air of constant temperature and humidity. Until this problem is solved — that is, until an equation has been developed for these conditions that takes account of all variables involved — bulk grain drying must remain an essentially empirical operation. The deficiencies in our knowledge will be apparent from the next section, which deals with some of the fundamental aspects of bulk drying and with the mathematics of the process as far as it seems possible to develop it from presently available information.

III. THEORETICAL CONSIDERATIONS

In this section, the relations among various factors in bulk drying are discussed. The mathematical treatment of this section illustrates a way in which various drying processes may be interpreted to arrive at a general pattern of moisture changes in any grain bulk, although only the expressions for the simple batch process are derived. The heat balance which is expressed as a differential equation is valid in any adiabatic bulk drying process — whether batch, continuous counterflow, reversed air movement, or other — and is an essential part of any engineering analysis of bulk drying. Because an attempt has been made to keep this section independent of the others, a certain amount of repetition is unavoidable.

A. Significance of Wet-Bulb Temperature

Consider a batch of moist grain of uniform initial moisture content in a bin with vertical sides. Drying air is forced into the grain through a perforated floor. The air moves upward at a constant rate, leaving through the upper grain surface. Temperature and humidity of the air entering the grain are assumed to be constant. As the air moves upward, its humidity increases as a result of moisture evaporation from the grain. The increase in air humidity is accompanied by a decrease in air temperature. The increase in air humidity and the decrease in its temperature take place simultaneously and, since both are almost proportional to the quantity of heat used in vaporizing water, the total heat of the air remains practically unchanged. The wet-bulb temperature is very nearly an expression of the total heat of the air, so the wet-bulb temperature is almost constant as it passes through the grain. For practical purposes, it may be considered to be constant. The condition of the air as it passes through the grain therefore follows a wet-bulb line on a psychrometric chart. The rate at which the air temperature drops depends upon how fast moisture is evaporated from the grain.

B. Heat Balance

The heat used in evaporating moisture from a kernel must equal the heat supplied to that kernel by the drop in air temperature, plus any heat supplied by a change in grain temperature, plus any heat supplied by conduction or radiation from the surrounding grain or bin walls. For practical purposes, heat lost or gained through bin walls is small and may usually be neglected; for simplicity, it will be neglected in this discussion. This leaves the heat balance between heat of vaporization, sensible heat of the air, and sensible heat of the grain. For further simplicity, the case when sensible heat of grain is negligible will be considered, although under some conditions this factor may have an appreciable effect on drying rates. When it does, a correction can be applied to find how the initial grain temperature affects the computed moisture contents.

This reduces the heat balance to one in which the heat for vaporizing moisture from grain is equal to the sensible heat loss in air passing through the grain. This balance must prevail at every point in the bin at all times.

Consider a thin layer (δx) of grain at any height (x) in the bin. During a short time interval (δt), the moisture content (M) decreases slightly (δM). The quantity of heat required to decrease the moisture content by this amount is given by the product of the amount of water evaporated and the unit heat of vaporization. In symbols, this may be expressed as

$$L = W \, A \, \delta x \frac{\delta M}{100} \cdot V \qquad (5)$$

where W is the density of dry matter in grain, A is the cross-sectional area of air stream through grain, and V is the unit heat of vaporization of moisture in grain.[1]

During the same time interval, the air moving through the thin layer undergoes a slight temperature drop (δT). The heat loss associated with this temperature drop is given by the product of the mass of air passing through the thin layer during the time interval, the specific heat of air, and the drop in temperature. In symbols, this may be expressed as

$$L' = 60 \, Q \, A \, \delta t \, S_A \, \delta T \qquad (6)$$

where Q is the mass rate of airflow, and S_A is the specific heat of air. Since the heat balance prevails throughout the bin, $L = L'$, and

$$W \, A \, \delta x \frac{\delta M}{100} V = 60 \, Q \, A \, \delta t \, S_A \, \delta T \qquad (7)$$

or

$$\frac{\delta M}{\delta t} = \frac{6{,}000 \, Q \, S_A}{W \, V} \cdot \frac{\delta T}{\delta x} \qquad (8)$$

This expression may be written as

$$\frac{\delta M}{\delta t} = P \cdot \frac{\delta T}{\delta x} \qquad (9)$$

Where $P = \dfrac{6{,}000 \, Q \, S_A}{W \, V}$, a constant for any given set of drying conditions.

This differential equation (Eq. 9) may be phrased in the following way: The time rate of drying at a given point and a given time is proportional to the space rate of decrease in temperature of the air at that point and at that time. If an

---

[1] A list of the symbols in this discussion, together with their definitions and dimensions, is given at the end of this section (p. 501).

expression were available for the way in which the moisture content of fully exposed grain changes for various conditions of air temperature, air humidity, air velocity, and character and moisture of grain, this relation could be combined with the above heat balance equation to give the general expression for moisture content in bulk drying.

C. Fully Exposed Drying Rate

As stated earlier, the exact relation between the exposed rate of drying and drying conditions has not been determined. An approximation is given by the equation for exposed drying,

$$M - M_E = \Delta M e^{-Kt} \qquad (1)$$

In the absence of a more exact expression, this equation is used in combination with the heat balance equation to give the general moisture chart of Figure 4. To make use of the above equation for this purpose, it is necessary to know how K is related to temperature, humidity, and air velocity. Experiments have shown that, in most conditions, the exposed drying rate is affected very little by air velocity. This does not refer to the effect of varying the volume of air in bulk drying but to the effect of varying the velocity past a fully exposed kernel. For the present purpose, the effect of varying air velocity on exposed drying rate is considered negligible. When sufficient experimental data have been compiled to show just what effect changing air velocity has on exposed drying rate, this effect can be included in a more complete analysis.

D. Air Temperature Changes in Bulk Drying

The effect of changing temperature and humidity of the air upon exposed drying rate has already been discussed briefly. It was pointed out that in bulk drying these two variables change simultaneously in such a way that the wet-bulb temperature is almost constant. Since humidity depends on the dry-bulb temperature in a given drying operation, it is only necessary to consider changes in the air temperature. At the very start of drying, as air moves upward through the grain in a drying bin, the time-rate of grain drying, and therefore the space-rate of drop in air temperature, decreases as the air ascends. The temperature drops at a slower and slower rate, approaching, toward the top of the bin, a temperature of equilibrium below which it will not fall. This limiting temperature (T_G) is that at which (having cooled at constant wet-bulb) the relative air humidity is in equilibrium with the grain moisture content. On the psychrometric chart, T_G is located by first finding the point representing the initial condition of the air, i.e., the initial dry-bulb temperature (T_o) and the wet-bulb temperature (T_w). From this point, the line of constant wet-bulb is followed to the relative humidity of equilibrium with the initial grain moisture content. Read the dry-bulb at this point to get T_G. For very wet grain, $T_G = T_w$ and for drier grain T_G is greater than T_w.

The rate at which T approaches T_G when all grain is at a uniform moisture content depends upon the rates at which moisture leaves the grain. As pointed out, the exact relation has not been determined, but for this discussion we will use the approximation

$$T - T_G = \Delta\, Te^{-Cx} \tag{10}$$

in which $\Delta T = T_o - T_G$, C is the rate of cooling, and x is the distance from the bottom of the bin. This is equivalent to saying that when grain is at a uniform moisture content, air decreases in temperature, as it rises in the bin, at a rate proportional to the difference between the temperature at that point and the temperature T_G.

E. Separate Relationship among Factors

In summarizing, we have arrived at the following approximations:
For grain fully exposed to constant drying conditions (such as grain at the very bin bottom),

$$M - M_E = \Delta\, Me^{-Kt} \tag{1}$$

For air moving through grain of uniform moisture content (such as a batch of grain at the beginning of the drying process),

$$T - T_G = \Delta\, Te^{-Cx} \tag{10}$$

Also, if conduction and radiation losses and the sensible heat of grain are neglected,

$$\frac{\delta M}{\delta t} = P\, \frac{\delta T}{\delta x} \tag{9}$$

With these conditions assumed, we can derive an expression for the moisture content at any time at any level in a bin in which air of a constant initial condition is blown at a constant rate through grain having a uniform initial moisture content. Such an expression would give M as a function of t and x. A similar expression for the air temperature at each point in the bin could be derived giving T as a function of t and x.

We know that: when $t = O$, $M = M_o$, and $T = \Delta Te^{-Cx} + T_G$;

when $t = \infty$, $M = M_E$;

when $x = O$, $T = T_o$, and $M = \Delta Me^{-Kt} + M_E$;

when $x = \infty$, $T = T_G$;

and that, for any values of t and x, $\delta M/\delta t = P\, \delta T/\delta x$

F. General Relationship among Factors

The functions

$$M - M_E = \frac{\Delta M e^{Cx}}{e^{Cx} + e^{Kt} - 1} \tag{11}$$

and

$$T - T_G = \frac{\Delta T e^{Kt}}{e^{Cx} + e^{Kt} - 1} \tag{12}$$

in which

$$C = \frac{K \Delta M}{P \Delta T'} \tag{13}$$

satisfy all the above conditions, so that

$$M = \Delta M \frac{e^{Cx}}{e^{Cx} + e^{Kt} - 1} + M_E \tag{14}$$

and

$$T = \Delta T \frac{e^{Kt}}{e^{Cx} + e^{Kt} - 1} + T_G \tag{15}$$

These expressions for M and T make it possible to predict approximately grain moisture and drying air temperature at any level in the bin at any time for a given set of drying conditions.

Since Equations 1, 9, and 10, and the assumption regarding effect of air velocity, are only approximately true, the bulk drying equations derived from them are also only approximate. Hukill (1947) shows that the approximation is accurate enough to be useful, but results in underestimation of the time required for drying to low moisture levels. When more exact relationships are developed for exposed drying rate, a process similar to the above will yield a more exact expression for bulk drying rate.

G. Simplified Form of General Equation

The equation for M is useful in predicting the effect of variation in each of the factors affecting drying rate. However, because of the large number of constants and in order to plot the equation as in Figure 4, it is simpler to use a form in which the units of moisture content, temperature, time, and depth are defined in such a way as to simplify the constants. First, the moisture content can be expressed in terms of a ratio, i.e., the moisture ratio,

$$m = \frac{M - M_E}{\Delta M} \tag{16}$$

Before drying, m = 1.0, and at equilibrium, m = 0. The time can be expressed in terms of periods of half response; i.e., one period (H hours) is the time required for fully exposed grain to reach a moisture ratio of 0.5 under any given set of conditions. Accordingly, $e^{-KH} = 0.5$ or $e^{KH} = 2$; and the time, in periods of half response, is

$$Y = t/H \qquad (17)$$

The unit of equivalent depth (D) can be defined as the depth which contains enough grain to make the heat requirement for evaporating its moisture, from an initial moisture ratio m = 1.0 to a final moisture ratio m = 0, equal to the sensible heat supplied by all air in one unit of time if its temperature is dropped from T_o to T_G. At any level in the bin, the equivalent depth is D if

$$D = \frac{s \, WV \, \Delta M}{6{,}000 \, Q \, S_A \, H \, \Delta T} \qquad (18)$$

If these units are used, Figure 4 is a graphical representation of the equation

$$m = \frac{2^D}{2^D + 2^Y - 1} \qquad (19)$$

This is the simplified form of the general drying equation. By translating a given set of drying conditions to these units and using the equation or Figure 4, it is possible to estimate when the top layer (or any other layer) will reach a desired moisture content. By thus estimating the drying time and final moisture content for various sets of drying conditions, the effect of changing rates of airflow or other factors on economy or uniformity of final moisture content can be estimated.

H. Application of General Equation

The use of Figure 4 is illustrated in the following example:

Grain sorghum 10.8 in. deep is to be dried in a bin by blowing 20 c.f.m. per sq. ft. of air upward through it from a space under a perforated floor. The conditions are as follows:

Density of dry matter in grain, W = 35.2 lb./cu. ft.
Initial moisture content, M_o = 21.9%, dry basis.
Depth of grain in bin (10.8 in.), x = 0.9 ft.
Initial condition of drying air: dry-bulb T_o = 86.5° F. (30.3° C.)
                                        wet-bulb T_w = 69.6° F. (20.9° C.)
                                    and relative humidity = 42%.

Quantity of drying air (20 c.f.m.) Q = 20/14.0 = 1.43 lb./sq. ft. min. From moisture-humidity equilibrium curves, M_E = 12.1%, dry basis. From tests of exposed drying rate for sorghum at 86.5° F. (30.3° C.), H = 1.8 hr. Assume V = 1170 Btu/lb. and S_A = 0.24 Btu/lb. ° F. From psychrometric chart,

T_G = 73.0° F. (22.8° C.)
ΔM = 21.9 − 12.1 = 9.8°,
ΔT = 86.5 − 73.0 = 13.5° F. (7.5° C.)

From these values, and considering a column of grain 1 sq. ft. in cross section, the equivalent depth D of 10.8 in. of grain is

$$D = \frac{0.9 \times 35.2 \times 1170 \times 9.8}{6{,}000 \times 1.43 \times 0.24 \times 1.8 \times 13.5} = 7.25 \text{ (from Eq. 18)}.$$

The top layer of grain in the bin will dry along the line D = 7.25.

If we wish to know when the top layer will reach 17% dry basis, for example, we compute the moisture ratio for 17%:

$$m = \frac{17.0 - 12.1}{9.8} = 0.50 \text{ (from Eq. 16)}.$$

We then read from the chart, Figure 4, the time at which line D = 7.25 crosses m = 0.50. This occurs at Y = 7.4. Since Y = t/H, the time in hours is YH = 13.3; i.e., the top layer will reach 17% in 13.3 hr. The moisture in any other layer or at any other time can be estimated similarly.

I. Nonadiabatic Drying

The effect of initial grain temperature is neglected in the equation represented in Figure 4. When the grain is much warmer or colder before drying than its final temperature, the heat given up or absorbed in changing its temperature may be a substantial part of the heat balance. This is particularly true when the change in moisture content is small. In this case the computation can be made more accurate by treating the sensible heat as part of V in the formula for D. To make this correction use V_1 in the equation instead of V. The sum of the sensible heat and heat of vaporization is thus:

$$V_1 = V + (T_0 - T_i) \left(1 + \frac{20}{\Delta M}\right) \tag{20}$$

in which T_i is the initial temperature of the grain, °F.

J. Thermal Efficiency

When artificial heat is used in drying grain, thermal efficiency is important. In most grain-drying processes, the heat for vaporizing moisture is supplied by air which is heated and passed through the grain. Generally, only part of the heat supplied to air is available for drying. The heat supplied to air is the quantity of air times the specific heat times the temperature rise. The heat used for drying is that given up by air while passing through grain; it is the quantity of air times its specific heat times the temperature drop. The thermal efficiency, neglecting radiation losses, may be defined as the ratio, expressed as a percentage, of the temperature drop of air on its way through grain to the temperature rise of air as it is heated before passing through grain.

$$E = 100 \frac{T_0 - T_F}{T_0 - T_a}$$

in which E = thermal efficiency, percent,

T_o = temperature of heated air, °F.,

T_F = temperature of air leaving grain, °F., and

T_a = atmospheric temperature, °F.

(Note that the thermal efficiency may be greater than 100%. When this occurs, part of the energy for evaporation is supplied from superheat of the atmosphere.)

As pointed out earlier, air may leave the grain at temperature T_G or higher. Evaporation cannot reduce the air temperature below T_G, so that the maximum theoretical thermal efficiency is

$$100 \; \frac{T_o - T_G}{T_o - T_a}$$

If air does not stay in contact with grain long enough to pick up its maximum moisture load, the efficiency is less than the theoretical maximum. In a batch-drying process, such as that discussed earlier, if drying is continued until the upper layer is partly dry, T_F will be higher than T_G, and the maximum drying efficiency will not be attained.

Examination of Figure 4 will illustrate this. Line 0 shows how the moisture in the bottom layer of grain changes. Line 1 shows the changing moisture content of the grain at a depth of one unit. If there are "D" pounds of grain (depth factor of one) in the dryer, line 1 shows the moisture at the top of the grain, that is, where the air exhausts from the grain. If there is more grain, the upper layers will change as shown by the successive lines. When the drying air reaches the grain corresponding to line 1, it still has capacity for removing moisture at that point but less rapidly than when it entered the bin. As air passes successive layers, its capacity for removing moisture becomes less and less. For example, by the time it has reached line 5 it has become almost saturated and does very little drying until the dryer has been in operation for some time. After a period of 2 or 3 time units the moisture content at line 5 drops more rapidly because, by that time, the grain below has dried considerably and the air at that point has not become so nearly saturated by moisture from the grain below.

If there are only "D" pounds of grain (depth factor of one), it will be seen that the air is exhausted from the grain without having become nearly saturated. It still has considerable drying capacity, and the efficiency is low because the air is exhausted from the bin without picking up its maximum load of moisture. If there is more grain, more of the drying capacity of the air is used, and the efficiency is higher. In general, the more grain in the bin the higher the efficiency, but beyond a depth factor of 4 or 5 the efficiency may not increase very fast.

K. Drying Front

At the end of any drying period there is not much difference in moisture content between top and bottom layers of the bin when grain is only 1 unit deep. At 5 units, on the other hand, the top has dried little when the bottom is almost completely dry. At greater depths, "zone drying" is very noticeable; that is, drying occurs first in the lower layers only. When they have dried, the grain next above starts to lose moisture, and the zone in which drying takes place moves gradually upward until the whole bin is dry.

Grain is still at its initial moisture content above the drying zone. The moisture content varies within this zone. If we were to select a moisture content between the initial and final moistures, e.g. 14%, we could visualize all kernels with this moisture content as lying in a very thin layer within the zone. Later, the thin layer of 14% grain would be at a higher level in the bin. The advancing location of the

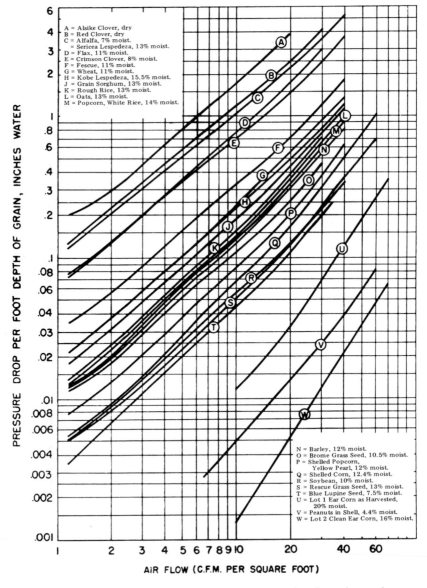

Figure 5. Relation between rate of airflow and pressure drop per foot for various grains.

layer of kernels having the given moisture is known as a "drying front." In a bin with a uniform depth of grain and uniform upward airflow, the drying front is a horizontal plane moving upward through the grain. How the shape of the drying front is influenced by nonlinear airflow will be discussed and illustrated later.

L. Airflow through Grains

When air is forced through grain, pressure is required to overcome the resistance to flow. The amount of pressure depends on the kind of grain, the airflow rate, and the length of airpath through the grain. Figure 5 shows curves by Shedd (1953) of the relation between airflow rate (c.f.m. per sq. ft.) and pressure drop (in., water gauge, per ft. of depth) for various grains. The chart is for linear airflow.

M. Drying Front in Nonlinear Airflow

In bin drying the airflow is often not uniform in all sections of a bin. This may result from uneven depth of grain or from air entering the grain unevenly, as for example when drying air is introduced through spaced ducts. Whatever the cause, nonuniform airflow results in distortion of the drying front. Hukill and Shedd (1955) show a method of applying data of Figure 5 for determining the shape of the drying front when flow lines are not straight and pressure gradients in grain are known. This method is not given in detail here, but it includes estimating "traverse time" or the length of time an air particle is in the grain when it travels along a given path. All points on the drying front, at any time during drying, have equal traverse times. Drying is completed only when the most delayed part of the drying front reaches the top of the grain. The most delayed part is where the air has taken longest to traverse the grain.

Figure 6 shows typical nonlinear airflow lines in grain. The two bins shown have transparent end walls so that dense smoke injected at various points can be seen traveling along the flow lines. Air is exhausted from the upper bin at the lower right-hand corner and from the lower bin at openings spaced along the bottom. These pictures were taken when air was moving downward through the grain, but the flow lines would have had identical positions if air movement had been upward from the same openings. It is clear that air would take longer to traverse the curved flow lines than the straight ones, not only because the path is longer but also because the air is moving more slowly. If one could mark the place on each of the flow lines where the air had been in the grain a given length of time, e.g. 1 sec., the marks could be connected by a line from one side of the bin to the other. This line would be the location of the drying front at one time in its passage through the grain. Each successive position of the drying front would be the locus of points having equal traverse times.

The shape of the drying front when airflow is not linear is illustrated in Figure 7 which is a cross section of a model drying bin with a transparent wall. The grain in the photograph was treated to change color as it dried. Drying air entered the grain from two ducts just visible at the bottoms of the photograph. The drying front in the grain shows up as light gray. When the picture was taken, the front was well up in the bin over the air entry, but had progressed little, if at all, halfway between the ducts. Had another picture been taken later, the front would be seen at a higher level but would still have approximately the same shape. The entire bin would be dry when the lowest portion of the drying front reached the top surface of the grain.

Figure 6. Airflow streamlines in model Plexiglas bins (Ives et al., 1959).

N. General Comment

This section has shown how a mathematical formula can be derived for predicting approximate moisture content of grain at any level in a batch dryer under a given set of conditions. Before an exact formula can be developed and used for accurate performance predictions of practical grain dryers, much additional information for various grains will be required regarding these factors: (1) moisture vaporization heat at different grain moisture levels; (2) moisture-humidity equilibriums; and (3) exposed drying rates at different grain moisture levels using air at different temperatures, humidities, and velocities.

O. Definitions and Dimensions of Symbols Used in This Section

M = moisture content of the grain, percentage dry basis, lb./lb.x100.
t = time from start of drying, hr.
x = distance from bottom of bin, ft.
T = dry-bulb temperature of air, °F.
L = heat involved in heat balance, Btu.
V = unit heat of vaporization of moisture in grain, Btu/lb.
A = cross-sectional area of air stream through grain, sq. ft.
W = density of dry matter in grain, lb./cu. ft.
Q = mass rate of airflow, lb.min.sq.ft. (60 Q = lb./hr./sq.ft.).
S_A = specific heat of air, Btu/lb. °F.
M_E = equilibrium moisture content, percent, dry basis (see p. 484).
M_o = initial moisture in grain before drying, percent, dry basis (see p. 484).
ΔM = $M_o - M_E$, percent dry basis (see p. 484).
K = drying constant in Equation (1) (see p. 485).
C = cooling rate of air passing through grain of uniform moisture content (see p. 492).
T_o = initial temperature of drying air, °F (see p. 492).
T_G = air temperature of moisture equilibrium at constant wet bulb, °F. (see p. 492).
ΔT = $T_o - T_G$, °F. (see p. 493).
m = moisture ratio $M - M_E/\Delta M$ (see p. 494).
H = period of half response, hr. (see p. 495).
Y = time in dimensionless units = t/H (see p. 495).
D = equivalent depth = $x\, W\, V\, \Delta\, M/6{,}000\, Q\, S_A\, H\, \Delta\, T$ (see p. 495).

IV. PRACTICAL CONSIDERATIONS

A number of different methods for practical grain drying are being used. Principal considerations in choosing a dryer are drying capacity, cost of installation, safety of operation, control of drying temperature, uniformity of output, and suitability of handling equipment. Ease of cleaning is also important, particularly if the dryer is to be used for seed grain. Types of damage that may occur to grain from drying include: loss of germination; scorching; hardening of kernels, which makes milling difficult; reduction in baking quality; checking, especially in rice, which results in broken kernels; and possible reduction in palatability or nutritive value in feed grains. Molding during drying may occur if the drying process takes too long.

A. Batch and Stage Drying

In batch drying, that is, drying an entire lot of grain to completion before adding more grain, the thermal efficiency may be high, but only if the grain is several units deep. On the other hand, the final moisture content is relatively uniform only if the depth of grain is shallow or if drying is continued until all grain is near the equilibrium moisture content. Usually it is neither economical nor desirable to dry grain to extremely low moisture content. In batch drying, then, the choice is between fuel economy and uniformity of final grain moisture.

Stage drying is a modified batch process in which more uniform final moisture can be achieved without sacrifice in economy. The air is passed in series through two or more bins. While the grain in the first bin is being dried to the desired moisture content, the grain in the second bin is partially dried by exhaust air from the first. At the conclusion of this stage, air funneled directly from the heater completes the drying in the second bin and the exhaust air is passed to a third. Meanwhile, the first bin is emptied and refilled. Extreme overdrying is thus avoided though the drying air is used almost to capacity. If each batch in this process contains about 2 or 3 depth units, uniformity and economy may be relatively good. Many processors of hybrid seed corn use two or three stages in drying ear corn for seed.

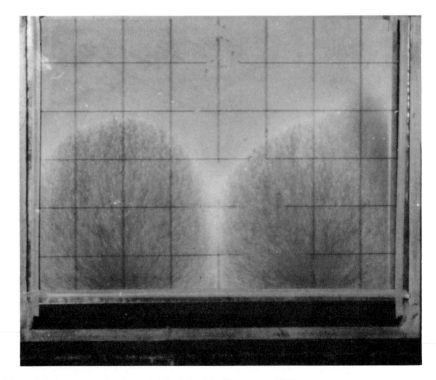

Figure 7. Distorted drying front in Plexiglas bin (Ives et al., 1959).

B. Sweating during Batch Drying

When heated air is used for batch drying, the top layers of grain frequently become wetter during the early part of the drying period. This is sometimes called "sweating." It occurs if grain is initially colder than the exhaust air temperature or if heat is lost by radiation from the upper surface. If the grain depth is more than 4 or 5 units, sweating is likely to occur. The effect of this temporary wetting on fuel economy is not serious because moisture condensed on grain releases its heat of vaporization to the grain. Sweating may be serious, however, because molds may develop on grain if grain moisture and temperature are maintained at high levels for long periods. When heated air is used, it is important to have sufficient airflow capacity in the equipment to dry all layers completely before any damage from high humidity and temperature can occur.

C. Continuous Drying

Continuous-flow dryers are used for shelled corn and small grains. The grain may be made to flow by gravity while the discharge rate is controlled by mechanical means. Air is passed through grain as it moves downward in several different ways. With respect to the drying rates in successive layers of grain, continuous-flow dryers are not necessarily different from batch dryers. For example, if air moves horizontally through an unagitated downward-moving column of grain, the drying proceeds as in a batch dryer, and the limitations with respect to economy and uniformity are about the same as for batch drying. If air is passed successively through a lower section of the column, then through an upper section, the process is about the same as in a two-stage batch dryer. If grain is thoroughly agitated in a single-pass continuous dryer, the uniformity of final moisture content may be good but the thermal efficiency cannot be high. In order to have high thermal efficiency, the leaving air must have been in contact with wet grain long enough for its temperature to have dropped almost to the level (T_G) at which the relative air humidity is in equilibrium with the grain moisture content.

Commercial dryers are usually installed at processing plants or grain elevators and, as a rule, utilize either gas or fuel oil. In most dryers the products of combustion are mixed with the drying air to avoid the necessity for expensive heat exchangers and the accompanying stack heat losses. With complete combustion, stack gases do not affect grain adversely. A certain amount of water is formed during combustion; with fuel oil, for example, about a gallon of water from each gallon of oil, and even more from propane or butane. But this addition of moisture to the drying air has a relatively small effect.

Commercial dryers used for wheat, shelled corn, and oats are usually designed to operate with air heated to about 200° F. (93° C.). High temperatures result in high capacity in pounds of water removed per hour. The maximum theoretical thermal efficiency is also usually higher at high temperatures.

Grain dryers have been used at terminal elevators for years in the United States and Canada. A large number of local elevators, particularly in the corn belt, have installed drying equipment. Artificial drying of wheat, oats, corn, and similar grains used to be looked upon as an emergency measure to prevent deterioration in occasional damp lots of grain. Changes in farming methods, however, including more complete mechanization, are resulting in more dependence on artificial drying as part of the farm routine in handling grain.

D. Effects of Drying

Mechanical drying may have various effects on the grain dried. Whether a given drying treatment damages the grain, or how severe the damage is, depends partly on the kind of grain and what it is to be used for. For example, corn (maize) of zero germination because of exposure to high temperature may have lost none of its value as livestock feed.

Effect on Milling Quality. Wheat dried at high temperature becomes case hardened and is more difficult to mill than normal wheat. The baking quality of wheat flour can be impaired by drying the grain at temperatures over 175° to 180° F. (about 80° C.). Corn dried at high temperature is not suitable for wet milling. The starch does not separate readily, and millers will not knowingly accept corn dried with heated air.

Successful rice milling depends on turning out a high percentage of unbroken kernels. Drying temperatures of more than about 130° F. (about 55° C.) tend to result in stress cracks in the kernels. Cracked kernels are likely to break during milling, so both temperature and duration of exposure during drying are limited. Unlike most other grains, rice is usually milled and dryed by the same management, so that damage to the dried product is more apparent to the operator than is the case with other grains. Sometimes the same lot of rice is put through a dryer several times, removing a relatively small percentage of water in each "pass." With a tempering period between passes, kernel checking can be minimized.

Effect on Germination. Grain to be used for seed, or barley for malting, cannot be dried at excessive temperature without destroying the germinating power. In drying seed corn and malting barley it is customary to limit drying air temperatures to about 110° F. (about 43° C.). For other grains, temperature limits may be somewhat higher. The temperature above which germination is impaired depends on initial grain moisture. The higher the moisture, the lower the temperature limit must be. Seed corn is sometimes dried on the ear, partly because it is difficult to shell high-moisture corn without damaging kernels. In some seed corn operations high-moisture corn is dried to between 16 and 20% on the ear. The corn is then shelled from the ear, and final drying is done in a shelled-corn dryer.

Effect on Nutritive Value. Feeding value is so complex that it is difficult to determine by test what effect various drying treatments may have on animal nutrition. Each of the nutritional components such as carbohydrates, proteins, and vitamins reacts differently to temperature treatment, and various animals such as pigs, poultry, and ruminants are not equally sensitive to the quality of these elements. For these and other reasons information on the effect of drying on nutritive value of grains is limited. Cabell et al. (1958) point out that protein nutritive value is more sensitive to heat than other nutritional factors. They used rats to measure the protein nutritive value of corn dried in various ways. They found that corn dried from approximately 30% moisture with air temperature of 240° F. (about 115° C.) was not damaged, but an air temperature of 280° F. (about 138° C.) did damage the corn. Limited observations on the same corn showed no significant losses in carotene and no marked increase in fat acidity. Cabell et al. did observe loss of protein nutritive value and increase in fat acidity in corn dried from 28% with unheated air at low airflow rates. Increased airflow prevented these losses by shortening the period of exposure to high moisture content, thus limiting development of molds. The consequences of not drying quickly enough will be discussed further under "Drying with Unheated Air" (page 506).

Effect on Market Acceptability. Much grain is sold in the open market, and the buyer of dried grain may not know its ultimate destination. Official grade standards have been established and define the quality of grain bought and sold but may reflect very poorly the value of mechanically dried grain. For example, corn discolored from high temperature is likely to be graded as "heat damaged." In naturally dried corn, "heat damage" usually reflects an appearance brought about by mold activity. The same appearance caused by high temperature does not necessarily mean impaired value. On the other hand if the germ is killed by high temperature, the official grade may not be affected at all. Corn kernels dried at high temperature may have stress cracks. If these cracks result in actual breakage of the kernel into small pieces the official grade will reflect their presence, but otherwise not. Stress-cracked corn is vulnerable to breakage during subsequent handling and tends to result in troublesome fine dust during handling.

Temperature limits for preventing these effects are not well defined. Thompson and Foster (1963) discuss the relation between drying conditions and stress cracking. The severity of stress cracking from a given drying operation can be reduced by cooling the grain slowly after drying or tempering it for a few hours. Foster (1964) describes a sequence of operations which he calls "Dryeration," in which corn is dried at high temperature, transferred to a tempering bin, held for 6 to 10 hr., then cooled. This procedure minimizes the cracking and is further discussed by McKenzie et al. (1966).

E. Ear Corn Drying

Corn, ripening as it does in the early fall, usually contains too much moisture at harvest time to be shelled and stored immediately. If it has dried to about 20% moisture in the kernels while on the stalk, the husked ears can be put into a ventilated crib where the wind further dries it. By late spring the ears may be dry enough to shell and produce shelled corn that can be stored safely. If the growing season is unfavorable, or if the weather at harvest is unusually poor for natural drying, special handling is necessary to prevent spoilage. Changes in farming methods are making natural drying less desirable. Since a large part of the corn crop is consumed on the farm, and because of transportation costs, particularly for corn on the cob, central drying plants cannot meet the entire need for mechanical drying. Practically no ear corn drying is done off the farm, except for hybrid seed corn.

Ear corn is often dried artificially on the farm in an ordinary storage crib with heated or unheated air. Air must be introduced in such a way that it moves more or less uniformly through all the corn. Drying with unheated air may require several weeks. For drying ear corn with heated air, temperatures of less than 60° to 70° F. (about 16° to 21° C.) result in slow drying. Most units are designed to operate at 60° to 80° F. (about 33° to 44° C.) above atmospheric temperature, although some use 200° F. (about 93° C.) or higher.

To reduce the moisture content to a safe level, it may be necessary to evaporate 2 gal. or more of water from each bushel of ear corn. Corn shrinks while drying, and the top may settle as much as 3 ft. in a crib 14 ft. deep at the start. Much of the water in ear corn is in the cob, especially immediately after harvest. Considerably more heat is required to dry corn on the cob than when it is shelled before drying. Schmidt (1948) discusses the relation between moisture in kernel and that in cob.

F. Drying with Unheated Air

Virtually no grain was dried mechanically on the farm prior to World War II. Some of the developments in grain drying are related directly to on-the-farm drying. Drying with unheated air is confined largely to farm operations, and it is usually done in a bin used for storage as well. When unheated air is blown upward through the grain from a perforated floor, the drying front moves upward more slowly than with heated air. If the drying front reaches the top and all grain is dried before it has spoiled, the process is a success. The only bad effect of drying with unheated air on grain is deterioration that may occur because of failure to dry quickly enough or to a low enough moisture level.

G. Respiration and Permissible Drying Time

Respiration of grain, associated molds, and other microorganisms is discussed in Chapter 4, but a few comments here will show how permissible drying time is related to weather conditions, kind of grain, and initial moisture content. Grain respires continually, using atmospheric oxygen and giving off CO_2 among other things, thus using up grain constituents. Respiration of both the grain itself and associated molds is sustained by the kernel substance. Continuous respiration is accompanied by continuous deterioration and loss of dry matter. Eventually the grain will reach a stage in which it is considered unsuitable for use. At low temperatures and low moisture this might occur only after many years. At high moisture content respiration proceeds many times as fast as at low moisture. High temperatures, within limits, also accelerate respiration so that warm, wet corn may spoil in a few days or hours. How far the deterioration process is allowed to go before grain becomes unacceptable depends somewhat on the use to be made of it. Saul and Steele (1966) conclude that when typical field-shelled corn has lost 0.5% of its dry weight from respiration it is likely to be on the verge of failing to meet No. 2 grade. At that time it has produced 7.35 g. of CO_2 per kg. of dry matter. They observed how long it takes corn with 28% moisture and up to

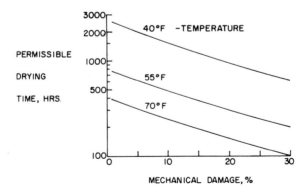

Figure 8. Permissible drying time to get No. 2 corn. Corn moisture content is 28%.

30% mechanically damaged kernels to sustain a 0.5% dry matter loss at various temperatures. The result is shown in Figure 8. Saul and Steele show how to estimate the permissible drying time for other moisture contents as well. These estimates provide the best available guide to how quickly the drying front must be passed through a drying bin to avoid spoilage in the top layer.

The temperature to which Saul and Steele refer is the temperature of the kernel itself. Until it is dried, the grain in a drying bin is at a temperature equal to the wet-bulb temperature of air used for drying. Schmidt and Waite (1962) have prepared maps of the United States showing monthly average wet-bulb temperature. They also show monthly average wet-bulb depression, which partly determines how fast the drying front moves through a bin. These maps, together with the Saul and Steele data, make it possible to estimate how quickly corn having an average amount of mechanical damage must be dried at any given location and time of year. They also provide the climatic information necessary for estimating airflow requirements to complete drying in a given time.

H. Mechanical Damage before Drying

The amount of mechanical damage sustained by shelled corn during harvest has a marked effect on the rate of deterioration or respiration. If corn could be harvested and shelled without mechanical damage, unheated air dryers with very low airflow rates would be entirely satisfactory. Undamaged kernels would tolerate delay two to three times as long as typical field-shelled corn.

I. Final Moisture Content

The final moisture content of grain after drying with unheated air depends largely on the atmospheric humidity during drying. If, after the drying front has passed through the grain, the grain moisture content is too high, further drying can be accomplished by operating the dryer during selected periods of low humidity. If corn is dried to 15% moisture, for example, this is too wet for long-time storage but is satisfactory for sale as No. 2 corn. How long it can be stored at this moisture without loss in grade depends on how much of the tolerable 0.5% dry matter loss has already been incurred. The desirable grain moisture content depends, therefore, on its intended use and how long it will be necessary to hold grain before use.

J. General Comment

All methods of drying grain after it is harvested, from spreading in thin layers in the sunshine or wind to the use of heat and forced ventilation in special drying compartments, depend on having each kernel exposed to a drying environment long enough to lose the desired amount of moisture. The time necessary to get a substantial loss in moisture presents a very real problem in farm drying. The method of drying used, or whether mechanical drying is used at all, may depend on how many man-hours can be spared for the job, what kind of mechanical conveying equipment can be made available, and how the drying process can be fitted in with other farm operations. Since World War II, mechanical grain drying on the farm has become more and more common and, for corn particularly, is depended upon as a routine for removing some of the hazards of weather and climate.

LITERATURE CITED

CABELL, C. A., R. E. DAVIS, and R. A. SAUL. 1958. Relation of drying air temperature, time, and air flow rate to the nutritive value of field-shelled corn. A technical progress report. ARS 44-41. Agr. Res. Service, U.S. Dep. Agr.

COLEMAN, D. A., and H. C. FELLOWS. 1925. Hygroscopic moisture of cereal grains and flaxseed exposed to atmospheres of different relative humidities. Cereal Chem. 2: 275-287.

COLEMAN, D. A., B. E. ROTHGEB, and H. C. FELLOWS. 1928. Respiration of sorghum grains. U.S. Dep. Agr. Tech. Bull. 100.

FOSTER, G. H. 1964. Dryeration—A corn drying process, progress report. Agr. Marketing Serv., U.S. Dep. Agr., AMS 532.

HOLMAN, L. E. 1948. Basic drying rates of different grains. Pres. at A.S.A.E. Annual Meeting.

HUKILL, W. V. 1947. Basic principles in drying corn and grain sorghum. Agr. Eng. (St. Joseph, Mich.) 28: 335-338.

HUKILL, W. V., and C. K. SHEDD. 1955. Non-linear air flow in grain drying. Agr. Eng. (St. Joseph, Mich.) 36: 462-466.

IVES, N. C., W. V. HUKILL, and R. A. SAUL. 1959. Grain ventilation and drying patterns. Trans. Amer. Soc. Agr. Eng. 2: 95-101.

KELLY, C. F. 1940. Methods of ventilating wheat in farm storages. U.S. Dep. Agr. Circ. 544.

McKENZIE, B. A., G. H. FOSTER, R. I. NOYES, and R. A. THOMPSON. 1966. Dryeration—Better corn quality with high-speed drying. Coop. Ext. Serv. Purdue Univ. AE72.

NEWMAN, A. B. 1931. The drying of porous solids. Trans. Amer. Inst. Chem. Eng. 27: 203-220 and 310-333.

PAGE, G. 1948. Basic drying rates of different grains. Pres. at A.S.A.E. Annual Meeting.

RAMSTAD, P. E., and W. F. GEDDES. 1942. The respiration and storage behavior of soybeans. Minn. Agr. Exp. Sta. Tech. Bull. 156.

SAUL, R. A., and J. L. STEELE. 1966. Why damaged corn costs more to dry. Agr. Eng. (St. Joseph, Mich.) 47: 326-329, 337.

SCHMIDT, J. L. 1948. How to reduce ear corn to bushels of shelled corn. Agr. Eng. (St. Joseph, Mich.) 29: 294-296.

SCHMIDT, J. L., and P. J. WAITE. 1962. Summaries of wet-bulb temperature and wet-bulb depression for grain drier design. Trans. Amer. Soc. Agr. Eng. 5: 186-189.

SCHRENK, W. G., A. C. ANDREWS, and H. H. KING. 1947. Calorimetric measurements of heats of hydration of starches. Ind. Eng. Chem. 39: 113-116.

SHEDD, C. K. 1953. Resistance of grains and seeds to airflow. Agr. Eng. (St. Joseph, Mich.) 34: 616-619.

SHERWOOD, T. K. 1936. Air drying of solids. Trans. Amer. Inst. Chem. Eng. 32: 150-168.

SIEBEL, J. E. 1911. Compend of mechanical refrigeration and engineering (8th ed.). Nickerson and Collins Co.: Chicago, Ill.

THOMPSON, R. A., and G. H. FOSTER. 1963. Stress cracks and breakage in artificially dried corn. Marketing Res. Rep. 631. U.S. Dep. Agr. Agr. Marketing Serv.

WINKLER, C. A., and W. F. GEDDES. 1931. Heat of hydration of wheat flour and certain starches including wheat, rice, and potato. Cereal Chem. 8: 455-475.

CHAPTER 14

PACKAGING OF
CEREAL PRODUCTS

C. A. SOUTHWICK, JR.

Technical Editor, Modern Packaging Magazine
New York, New York

I. INTRODUCTION

Cereal products, like many other foods, have a wide range of composition, processing, and marketing requirements with a need for a large number and variety of package types and materials.

New cereal products alone or combined with other foods are being and will continue to be developed and marketed. An important factor in their success will be attractive, protective, and economical packaging. Because of the nearly infinite number of combinations and permutations that can result from such a large family of products, the many choices of packages and materials, plus marketing demands, it is only possible in a single chapter to state basic principles and guidelines, and to describe a few specific examples.

A package must protect the product from physical damage, from losses or deterioration during storage and display, and must be convenient in use. It must also be an attractive billboard for product trademark identity, and it must perform these functions at minimum cost, since the package itself has no intrinsic value to the consumer. In recent years, growing pressure has developed requiring that a package be easily disposable or recycleable. Packagers of cereal products should be aware of this pressure even though their industry does not appear to be a current target.

Many package failures arise from the inability of the manufacturer to exercise control after packaged goods leave the plant and are exposed to common carriers, ambient conditions of humidity and temperature and, in most cases, for indeterminate times.

The cereal producer can precisely control all manufacturing steps and can produce uniform products; the packaging engineer can qualitatively determine the kinds of functions that the package must possess. However, because it is not generally possible to develop numbers or values for the external requirement of marketing and for the effects of ambient conditions, packaging is not, in many of its phases and at present, a scientifically integrated function.

The objective of packaging is to provide a carrier and a protective atmosphere

509

so as to conveniently deliver the product to the user in the best possible condition and to establish identity, invite purchase at the point of sale, and contribute to resale by being convenient in use.

This chapter will cover fundamentals, describe typical materials and package forms, and show how typical cereal products are packaged. Reading this chapter should help develop an appreciation of the subject and an understanding of the problems peculiar to packaging.

II. GENERAL CONSIDERATIONS

Problems of packaging cereals and cereal products and methods of developing packages for them are similar to those met when dealing with other products. Cereal products have certain characteristics and marketing requirements which demand special consideration or emphasis, but the general techniques, theory, and engineering approach are the same as for any other commodity.

An engineering approach is the only route for developing an adequate and efficient package for a standard article or for a new and specialized cereal product. This approach, together with judgment and experience, ensures product preservation at the lowest package cost commensurate with merchandising and product requirements.

Basic cereal products can generally be characterized as having good stability, moderate densities, and low costs. For example, at one end of the product stability range are flours and similar products that have not been heated and do not carry unstable additives. At the other end are some snack foods and baked goods where high temperatures and many additives put a maximum demand on the package and/or require frequent deliveries. However, it is neither wise nor necessary to characterize or generalize the packaging requirements of any new product by comparing it to other products on the market, since there are test methods and reports on how to evaluate a product for packaging. Apparently trivial differences in formulation or processing can change the stability and thus change the preservation requirement of a product.

Widely ranging demands in merchandising and distribution, which affect preservation by varying time and conditions of exposure and storage, confront the cereal industry with further packaging requirements. Packaging is further complicated by available machinery and knowledge of consumer habits, both of which limit free choice of forms. Shortages of supplies or other difficulties may necessitate changes in package specifications. Differences in raw materials or in merchandising methods are sometimes responsible for variations in the packages used by different manufacturers of similar products.

Results of these conditions can be seen in the large variety of packages and materials used today for cereals and cereal products. In the following discussion, however, only typical products can be discussed, only basic packaging needs be outlined, and only a general description be given of commercial packages.

Though packaging must be considered mainly as a means of preservation and distribution, other factors are also involved. In the United States where self-service is a dominant method of merchandising, the package must be attractive and must also carry the trademark to the customer. To encourage repeat sales, it must also be designed with the ultimate use in mind; it must be convenient in size, and easy to open and reclose. Its cost must be kept as low as possible, but it is doubtful if any meaningful relationship can be established to the cost of the product. These conditions impose restrictions on the packaging of many cereals and cereal products because of their low selling price. Cost limitations are usually less stringent on specialty products, and on nationally advertised trademarked brands, because these must have better packaging for preservation, distribution, and point-of-sale appeal.

Packaging of all products is increasing at the expense of bulk handling for many compelling reasons. Packages provide better preservation for long-term storage and shipment, and make more economical use of warehouse space. They save labor in both distribution and selling. They lend themselves to the distribution of an identified product which can be effectively advertised. And finally, they provide adequate economical preservation, meeting growing customer demand for "perfect" products.

Many of these considerations apply to retail units for home use, but some apply also to industrial or institutional units. The larger units generally move through distribution channels in less time than small units, and preservation is less of a problem. Lower-grade packaging materials can often be used for larger sizes, provided they have the required strength and durability, qualities whose importance increases with package size. Also, for large units little extra cost is incurred for decoration beyond that required to establish brand, source, and composition of the product.

III. PACKAGE ENGINEERING

Many cereal products are merchandised in packages which are superficially similar in shape, size, and materials, but the possible combinations of materials and package types are so great that packaging can well be a confusing subject.

A number of approaches to package engineering are based on combinations of laboratory testing and field reports. Also, an increasing number of standard test methods for both materials and packages have been developed and issued by associations and government agencies. (See Associations list, page 539.) However, meaningful and detailed package and/or material specifications are used only by some larger companies and by government and other agencies. Although package and material suppliers provide more and more basic data on their products, users tend not to have complete data on the packaging characteristics of their products. This lack of basic product information is probably the single greatest cause of package failure. Package engineering must be based on three groups of factors: packaging characteristics of the product; merchandising, distribution, and use factors; and the physical and preservation functions of the package and its materials of construction.

A. Packaging Characteristics of the Product

Factors affecting a product's packaging characteristics can be determined in the laboratory by various tests with a knowledge of the formulation of the product. But, although packaging characteristics of a product depend upon formulation, processing, and chemical composition, they are often not predictable from even a complete knowledge of these criteria and must be determined empirically by special means. Thus special tests, of the nature of performance trials, are usually needed to establish packaging qualities of a product.

Equilibrium humidity is the relative humidity at which a product neither gains nor loses moisture. It is usually measured at or slightly above the typical storage temperature. The lower the value of a product's equilibrium humidity the more likely it is to gain moisture from the atmosphere. Conversely, as these values rise above normal atmospheric humidities, products tend to lose moisture.

Cereal products like normal white flours of about 13% moisture content have equilibrium values around 65% relative humidity and so do not need package protection against moisture migration, since vapor pressure differentials between product and atmosphere are usually small. However, cereal products that have been heat-processed or mixed with some types of additives may have values around 30% relative humidity. An example of a product with a low equilibrium humidity is the white cake mix whose data are plotted in Figure 1. Such products require a careful choice of moisture barriers and well-sealed packages to prevent excessive moisture pickup in storage. Determination of a new product's equilibrium value is most important as a guide to materials and construction of the package.

Causes of Product Deterioration. Gain or loss of moisture generally causes some deterioration of the product. The value of the equilibrium humidity shows the humidity at which the product starts to gain or lose moisture, but it is also necessary to know how much the moisture content can change without making the product unusable or unsalable. In other words, the capacity of a product to lose or gain moisture without deterioration is an extremely important fact for the package designer, since it helps to determine the required degree of moistureproofing of the package.

An empirical expression for the relationship between equilibrium humidity

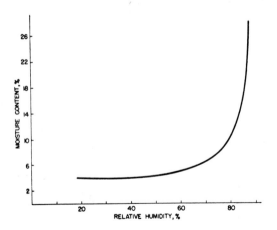

Figure 1. Relation between equilibrium moisture content of a white cake mix and relative humidity of the atmosphere.

and capacity to lose or gain moisture can be developed, provided that the rate of water vapor transfer through a package barrier is assumed to be proportional to the water vapor pressure difference existing across the barrier. Actually, this assumption is not valid for some barrier materials or for some levels of humidity or differences in vapor pressure.

In mathematical symbols, the assumption may be written:

$$\frac{dW}{dt} = B(P_a - P_p) \tag{1}$$

where W = mass of water vapor transmitted:

$\frac{dW}{dt}$ = rate of transmission of water vapor in units of mass per package per day;

P_a = water vapor pressure of the atmosphere;

P_p = water vapor pressure established by the product inside the package;

B = a constant of proportionality which must be determined experimentally for the package material and package type in question.

B is probably constant only for a limited range of temperatures and exterior humidity and depends upon the water vapor transmission rate of the package barrier and the efficiency of its use in forming and sealing of the package.

Equation 1 when integrated becomes

$$W = B (P_a - P_p)t \tag{2}$$

and the loss or gain, W, can be calculated for a given time, t. If m_1 is the initial moisture content, the moisture content m_2 after an elapsed time, t, will be:

$$M_2 = \frac{\frac{m_1 M}{100} + W}{M + W} \times 100$$

where M is the initial total weight of the package content.

If P_p is greater than P_a, their difference will be negative and W will also be negative; i.e., the package will lose weight by losing moisture. In any case, the package must be designed to hold the values for m_2 within the safe range.

These equations are sometimes useful in estimating storage effects under carefully controlled laboratory conditions, but they are not a reliable basis for predicting shelf life under actual field conditions, because of the effects of large changes in ambient temperatures and humidities. Oswin (1945) and others have attempted to estimate shelf life using only a few constants derived from laboratory studies. However, all such attempts require many assumptions, most of which are valid only for simple products or for limited ranges of atmospheric conditions. The equations are given here only to emphasize that in considering changes in moisture content of a packaged product with time, product, package, and atmospheric conditions must all be taken into account.

Many cereal products are susceptible to the development of rancidity, and it is necessary to know the degree of this susceptibility and its effects on the acceptability of the stored products. Suitable package construction and specification ensure that the package does not catalyze the oxidation of absorbed fat and helps to prevent development of rancidity by excluding light or oxygen, or both; or, if rancidity is unavoidable, mitigates the effects by allowing rancid odors to escape. Obviously, no package can protect a product from temperature changes, but if a product must be stored and handled within a specific temperature range, the package must be designed to perform under those conditions.

Many products carry volatile flavors or other additives. Loss of these components can change the product's character and acceptability. It is not possible to determine the specific permeability of package materials to aromatic mixtures, although such data are available for pure gases. However, well-sealed sample packages can be formed from a variety of materials, and storage tests indicate those which are most effective in keeping loss of volatiles at acceptable levels.

Freeness of Fats. It is necessary to know if fats, whether naturally occurring or additives, carried by a product are free to migrate to the surface and so coat or be absorbed by package materials in contact with the product. Freeness of fats has no direct relationship to the amount of fats present or their composition, although the higher the fat content and the lower its melting point increase the need for greaseproofing.

Several methods are available for measuring the freeness of fats. A typical test consists of placing the product on a piece of soft, white, unsized paper and holding it for 24 hr. at 90° to 100° F. (32.22° to 37.78° C.). It may be necessary to place a small weight on the sample to ensure contact with the paper. Examination of the paper shows the degree of fat staining. With only a few stains it may not be necessary to use packaging material of a greaseproof type. However, if the test paper shows extensive staining, package materials in contact with the product must serve as a barrier to keep fats from appearing on the package surface.

With marginal freeness of fats, package materials in contact with the product may be allowed to absorb the small amounts of fats, but care must be taken to select grades and types of material that do not catalyze the breakdown of absorbed fats. This problem is particularly acute with many kinds of baked goods in which the shortening used is degraded by the baking process, or the product picks up fats used to coat baking pans.

Some cereal products, either because they contain a sufficiently high percentage of added fats or because they have been cooked in fats, require truly greaseproof materials as well as tight seals and closures to prevent fat migration. Among such greaseproof materials are glassine, parchment paper, cellophane, some plastic films, and special coatings on paper. With most cereal products, however, a greaseproof package is not required.

Staleness is a problem with many baked cereal products and, since it is caused by internal changes in the product, it cannot be inhibited by packaging alone. A typical case is bread where shelf life is very limited, and product freshness requires frequent store delivery.

Physical Properties. Certain of the product's physical properties must be known to the packaging engineer. A partial list of such physical properties includes: bulk density, abrasiveness, fineness, flow characteristics, and brittleness. Some unusual characteristics may require special consideration in package design. The package must assure the delivery of its contents without loss and without excessive physical breakdown. Also, contents should not sift between package components, should not abrade package materials, and should not distort the package shape. Many physical properties cannot be measured or values established for them, but laboratory package tests, together with trial shipments, should establish and confirm the general suitability of the package, its materials, and coatings. It is particularly important that in such tests both the package and the filled shipping case (freshly packed as well as after storage) be exposed to compression and rough handling.

Chemical Properties. In addition to properties discussed in the preceding paragraphs, cereal products and their additives can react with certain types of package materials to cause some form of deterioration of the product, package material, or both. Thus some coatings or plastic films may be softened and their physical and protective properties degraded by fatty substances. Cellophane and glassine may become brittle by loss of moisture caused by the dehydrating action of cereal products of very low moisture content; plasticizers, resins, and inks may be affected by volatile components or the products of oxidation; and products may absorb some of the volatiles from the package with resulting undesirable flavors.

There are no test procedures to establish or measure these interactions which can best be guarded against by accelerated and long-term tests duplicating as nearly as possible the conditions encountered in commercial shipments. Food & Drug Administration criteria, relative to safety standards and acceptance for all materials and additives for both food packages and food products, are established. It is, therefore, vitally important for cereal product manufacturers to secure from their package and packaging material suppliers a statement of composition and suitability for the type of food and package, and of Food & Drug Administration compliance.

Most qualitative requirements of the package and its materials can be established by knowing the product's requirements for its preservation, coupled with a knowledge of interactions between product and package materials. But for a complete description of the required package performance, more than knowledge of packaging characteristics of the product is needed. The second group of factors — those dependent upon merchandising and handling methods — must now be considered.

B. Merchandising, Distribution, and Use Factors

Information about factors pertaining to merchandising and distribution should make it possible to fix size and type of package, physical requirements such as stiffness, and specifications for decorative and printing requirements.

Knowledge of these factors should also decide questions regarding the use of such conveniences as pouring spouts or opening means. Most importantly, it should provide data about the time the product will remain in various distribution channels, particularly as a single unit at the points of sale and use. The time factor and the climate of the distribution area have a bearing on the degree of preservation required, and so affect the choice of materials.

Another consideration concerns the type of failure which is least unacceptable to the consumer. Many products can become unsalable or unusable from different causes. The choice of package material can in some cases control or influence these causes of failure, and it then becomes important to decide the kind of product deterioration which is least objectionable. In this case, the extent of deterioration that can be permitted must guide the packaging engineer in evaluating various materials and packages. He cannot be held responsible for and cannot, from his own testing, develop values or the necessary information in this area. These answers and decisions must come from marketing and consumer research personnel.

Most information required is based upon estimates or opinion. Few companies have valid and reliable information on most of the factors involved in merchandising, distribution, and use. But, in most cases, some guidance in the packaging of a new product is provided by experience with established products of similar composition or properties. With an entirely new product, a great deal of uncertainty necessarily occurs, and the general rule is to make estimates sufficiently pessimistic so as to produce considerable overprotection by the package. It is better to overly protect a new product initially, and then to reduce cost and degree of protection with time and experience, than to have failures on introductory shipments.

The system of distributing the package to the point of sale has an important effect on the package's protection. There are two basic distribution systems: 1) frequent and rapid delivery by truck from point of manufacture to retail store with little or no warehousing and with a driver-salesman policing shelf stocks and delivering fresh supplies; 2) central warehousing, common carriers, with policing and ordering left to the store manager.

Many important makers of snacks with a short shelf life consider truck delivery a necessity even though it is expensive. Such snacks are generally packaged in moistureproof, opaque or transparent pouches or bags. They are inexpensive, and drivers remove torn, crumpled, and outdated packages, and packages are in transit for only a short time.

While the system entailing the services of a common carrier and central warehousing is least expensive, transit time from plant to shelf can be quite long, in spite of inventory controls. The package must therefore be made more protective and the product more stable. Bags and pouches can be used for some products, but gas or vacuum packing may be necessary. However, the trend in this distribution system is to use folding cartons, fiber, metal or even glass jars since they are less liable to cause product breakage or to become shopworn, and they give maximum protection.

Some snack makers use combinations of these two systems in an attempt to reduce costs of both shipping and package. As a result of the increasing cost of the driver-salesman system, many makers try to find packages, packing systems, product processing, and formulations that will give products a sufficiently long shelf life to go through normal channels of distribution.

Certain exact data can emerge from considering package life (distribution time plus time on the shelf) or if the product has sufficient inherent stability when packaged. For example, package size in terms of both weight and dimensions affects the final choice among the materials and perhaps the package type. A package carrying 1 oz. of product has a larger surface per unit of weight than a 1-lb. package. Since moisture transmission into a package is directly related to surface area, the package area per unit of weight can affect cost and shelf life.

For example, 1 oz. of a dry cereal product can be packaged either in a folding carton $1 \times 2 \times 3$ in. or in a flat envelope of 4×5 in. The carton has a surface area of 22 sq. in. and the envelope of 40 sq. in. Assuming comparable tightness of seals and seams, the envelope material must possess twice the moisture protection, i.e., one-half the value of the water vapor transmission rate to achieve the same shelf life.

C. Functions of the Package

By combining product requirements and those of satisfactory merchandising and distribution (see preceding subsections), properties and functions required of package material and package can be qualitatively determined. "Function" can also cover certain decorative features as well as physical and preservation characteristics of package materials. Next, data on various materials and package forms should be surveyed to select those combinations most likely to meet the requirements. Complete data of this kind are not usually available in most companies, and it is, therefore, necessary to select several package combinations on the basis of more or less uncertain information.

Many physical, decorative, and preservative properties of package materials can be measured in the laboratory by test methods which have some official approval. For many package requirements, however, test methods have no official basis or proven reliability. However, the need for more and product-related test methods has been recognized. This deficiency is steadily being corrected.

Samples of the selected combinations should be made into packages approaching commercial practice and tolerances. Through process of elimination, a few combinations will remain, ready for laboratory evaluation to determine their protective and other qualities. Unfortunately, there is no universal agreement on accelerated package tests. In general, test conditions should simulate typical deterioration as it occurs during the desired shelf life. For example, tests on a package expected to have a shelf life of less than 30 days could safely be accelerated so that laboratory failure would occur in approximately a week. If the shelf life is expected to be about a year, it would be desirable to have laboratory failure occur in from 1 to 2 months. Whatever the conditions and manner of making the test, it should be performed to ensure reproducibility so that the data developed can always be compared with previous and future tests. In all tests a few packages should be included which contain a standard material as an absolute basis of comparison, thus affording a means of directly comparing various material combinations and package forms tested at different times. For example, a standard material for the evaluation of moistureproofness of packages might be anhydrous calcium chloride.

The laboratory testing of packages under controlled conditions of temperature and humidity (Figure 2) is generally accepted as the most satisfactory means of evaluating package protection, interactions between packages and product, and product deterioration. However, there are some who insist upon actual field tests or the translation of laboratory data into days of shelf life in a specific region. At first sight, field tests would appear to be a practical way to discover actual package performance in a given area of storage and distribution. Such tests have been tried by many companies but have generally been abandoned because of the long time required, the expense of sending samples to many typical areas, and the inconclusive character of the results.

Uncertainties surrounding interpretation of field tests arise because of short-term abnormalities in weather conditions in test areas during the test period, and also because test packages are not exposed to a free atmosphere, but to one which depends upon many local factors, including location and type of buildings in which packages are stored. Field tests must therefore be conducted on a very large scale if they are to provide a basis for valid conclusions.

Laboratory tests, on the other hand, furnish an accurate, rapid, and reproducible means of comparing package function, of accumulating valuable

Figure 2. A controlled humidity cabinet in a packaging laboratory.

data, and of researching package development. Laboratory data, interpreted in the light of accumulated experience, thus constitute safe grounds for recommendations for packaging a new product. It is usually impossible to correlate laboratory test results with those obtained from usual field tests because the latter are influenced, as already explained, by many unknown factors. In the end, conclusions based on laboratory work must stand the test of subsequent general field experience, a situation familiar to all control chemists who use laboratory tests to measure the utility of a product.

After an initial series of laboratory tests, more of the proposed packages are discarded. A second accelerated test is then made on the remainder, perhaps with some additional packages suggested by the previous results. This usually concludes the laboratory work. If successful, a few packages are generally satisfactory in all respects. The final choice is made by the merchandising group on the basis of appearance and convenience, and by the production department on the basis of costs and performance on existing packaging machines.

As soon as semiproduction samples are available, a large number of packages and filled shipping cases should be given shipping and rough-handling tests and returned to the laboratory. The laboratory should evaluate these returned samples for physical damage to both product and containers and retest typical packages for possible changes in their preservation quality.

Tentative specifications for all materials and the package should be developed as soon as production standards are known. Since sample packages may vary considerably from those commercially produced, the results for handmade packages should not be used as the basis for specifications.

The final package or packages that meet all requirements and conditions should represent some degree of "overpacking;" i.e., they should preserve the product for longer than the normal or mean life expectancy. As experience with commercial shipments is acquired, and as goods returned because of package failures may indicate, it is possible that gradual and tested alterations can be made to lower the package cost.

Conversely, commercial shipments and returned goods may indicate the need for package improvement. This usually means the package is not performing as planned, or that some estimates of merchandising and handling factors were too optimistic, or were based on erroneous reports of the times and conditions of storage, sale, and use. However, there will always be some returned goods attributable to package failure through exposure to unusually adverse conditions or faults in individual packages. The package must deliver nearly all goods in satisfactory condition, but it is economically impossible to try to make a package to deliver all goods in a usable condition.

Packaging can neither improve an inferior product, nor can it control the effect of such elemental influences as temperature and normal product aging. Certain cereal products are subject to staleness, an example of a product aging effect that cannot be inhibited by any package. If a product is processed under carefully controlled conditions, proper packaging will serve to deliver it to its point of use in an acceptable condition. Packaging, therefore, must be considered as a means of maintaining the quality of a product during its distribution, marketing, and use periods.

D. Package Types

Cereal products can be packaged in practically all existing package types, although most are packaged in so-called flexible-type containers including bags and folding cartons of different types and construction. The most popular packages are: bags of cloth, paper, transparent films, foils, or laminations; folding or set-up cartons, with or without liners or overwraps; and fiber cans either composite or all-fiber. There is a limited use of metal cans and glass jars, mainly for export packaging or for very unstable products. Plastic and all-aluminum trays find important and increasing uses for baked and precooked cereal-based foods, especially frozen products. Also, formed plastic sheeting is used increasingly for dividers and shaped pads. These are used in bags, trays, and cartons to reduce breakage and improve appearance.

Bags. Many cereal products are packaged in bags. These vary in capacity from a few ounces of a household product to 100 pounds of feeds or flours for institutional or industrial use. In general, larger bags are multi-ply paper, cloth, or cloth-paper combinations. Large units of standard flours and feeds are hardly affected by atmospheric conditions. The most important problem is usually one of finding the most economical means of shipping and handling and to provide a container which meets use requirements, such as ease of opening, reuse, identification, and other factors.

Some years ago cotton and burlap bags were used almost exclusively for

Figure 3. Packing flour in paper bags with built-in valves.

Causes and Prevention of Typical Forms of Deterioration. The following list shows how various forms of product damage can be reduced by package changes.

Deterioration	Cause	Prevention
Breakage	Rough handling or improper package type	Bags or wrapped trays can allow excessive breakage; change to rigid or carton-type package. Use heavier gauges of paperboard or use trays and dividers.
Caking, lumping	Moisture change	Improved seals and closures. Greater moistureproofness of materials. Change of package type.
Staleness	Moisture changes and other causes	The package has very little influence.
Oxidative rancidity	Oxygen plus fat instability	Use of oxygen-tight packages or ventilation of package to reduce concentration of rancid odors. Use of opaque or light-screening materials.
Loss of aromatic or volatile portions	Diffusion through package materials or seal	Improved seals and closures. Use of package material of low permeability to volatile components.
Infestation	Storage in contaminated space	Complete protection only by use of tight metal or glass containers. Metal foils, well-sealed plastic film, heavy coating or layers of waxes, resins, or asphalt, etc., inclusion of repellents, and use of multiple plies can improve package resistance to penetration.
Dehydration (freezer burn) of frozen foods	Loss of surface moisture.	Insufficient moistureproofness, poor seals, large voids.

packing of larger sizes of such products, but cost reduction of paper bags and constant improvement in materials, construction, and means of handling have led to a steady increase in the use of paper at the expense of cotton bags. Either cloth or paper bags successfully carry many cereal products under normal conditions of storage, distribution, and use in this country. Advantages of paper bags are smooth and lint-free surfaces, suitability for multicolor printing, ease of filling by means of built-in valves combined with high-speed packing machinery

(Figure 3), and ease of opening. The paper bag with pasted bottom or sewn construction can be made to incorporate one or more plies of asphaltic laminations, plastic coatings or other protective barriers to increase the resistance to moisture penetration, or can be made with greaseproof linings to prevent fat-staining. Because all-paper, multi-ply bag construction lends itself to incorporation of many kinds of protective materials as one or more of its plies, such bags are used for the more complex and highly processed cereal products.

Cloth bags can be used for many trips and reused for other purposes[1]. For these reasons, they are in demand in certain markets and for certain products. There is a wide variety of possible cloth-to-cloth or cloth-to-paper laminations, but these greatly increase the cost and reduce the possibility of reuse for nonpackaging purposes. Neither the paper nor the cloth bag is rodent resistant, but the multi-ply bag is not easily penetrated by many kinds of insects.

Plastic bags of all sizes up to 100 pounds are now being used for cereal products, from animal feeds to ready-to-eat cereals. These bags are generally of some grade or gauge of polyolefin film, usually a polyethylene. They find growing acceptance because they are strong, moistureproof, inert, can be transparent, and can be formed, filled, and sealed on automatic equipment.

Another important development in feed bags is the trend to 50- and 100-pound bags made of heat-set, woven polypropylene strands made from tensilized, twisted, narrow-width film. These tightly woven side and bottom-sewn, open-mouth bags were originally developed for military sand bags. They exceed burlap and treated cloth bags in rot resistance and strength. This new and unique plastic-woven bag is less expensive than burlap bags, is domestically produced, and shows relative price stability as compared to jute. The new bag also has better water, insect, and rodent resistance and is easily cleaned and reused.

Smaller bags are made in a great variety of ways (gussets, bottoms, or closures), usually determined by merchandising and use since nearly any material or combinations of materials can be made into any bag.

As products become more complex or are packaged in smaller sizes, improved protection against moisture pickup, staining, etc., often becomes necessary, requiring modern materials and better closures, seams, and seals. Self-service stores have increased the need for product visibility and for multicolor printing. Therefore, smaller sizes are found in a great variety of combinations of materials and construction. Small bags are often made of heat-sealing materials with coatings or laminating agents for moistureproofing.

Bags, envelopes, or pouches of smaller sizes (carrying less than 1 lb. of product) are commonly made of cellophane; cellophane-paper combinations; glassine-paper, either plain or laminated; plastic films or extrusion-coated polyethylene on many substrates. In exceptional cases aluminum foil may be used on the exterior or as one of the combined plies. Bottom and side seals are often made with adhesives, with the top either double-folded and held in position by clips or wire ties or closed by heat-sealing. Exterior surfaces of these small bags are usually printed in multi-colored designs. Today most smaller quantities are packaged in pouches or bag-like structures on form, fill, seal machines that

---

[1] Because second-hand bags are often a source of insect infestation, their use for flour is not favored by the milling industry. Collection, cleaning, and other steps required in reuse also become increasingly uneconomical.

operate from rolls of preprinted stock using only heat-sealing. Some models can also pack with inert gas.

Bags in the middle-size range carry from 1 lb. up to 25 lb. The larger of these are identical with the 50- or 100- lb. size, that is, a straight paper or cloth bag in either single or multi-ply. Sizes approaching 1-lb. capacity are made of less decorative and less protective materials than those of still smaller size but either have more plies or are made of stronger materials. Plastic and plastic combinations are becoming predominant in this range, and, again, the form, fill, seal system is used.

The final choice of exterior surface ply depends on quality and amount of printing and strength requirements. The choice of the interior ply is dictated by many considerations. For example, it is customary to put white flour in bags with blue interior surfaces to enhance the whiteness of the product, and to use a particular type of bag construction with long acceptance in the trade. Any free fat must be kept from migrating or being absorbed by means of a greaseproof liner or inner surface. Greaseproofness in a package must be established at the point of contact with the product. Premade bags can be used as liners for folding cartons. They must be distinguished from those formed by high-speed automatic equipment, though they are more or less interchangeable in performance.

Folding Cartons. It would be difficult to establish whether bags or folding cartons are most used for packaging of cereals and cereal products, but both are used in substantial numbers. Folding cartons protect fragile products from impact and crushing, and certain dense or easily flowing products can be held in better shape by the carton structure. Simpler products such as hot breakfast foods, corn meal, or other ground cereal products with low moisture pickup and no added fat can be successfully packaged in a folding carton without a liner or a wrapper.

The gauge (thickness) of the required paperboard depends upon product density and package size. As a general rule, folding cartons are not used for more than a few pounds of product. Many kinds of paperboard can be used for folding cartons. For cereals, however, grades of better color and strength are usually selected, and some attention is paid to odor. The paperboard can be *lined* board, that is, interior and/or exterior surfaces can be made of pulp of improved color, printability, or quality. One of the most important requirements for this type of package is that the carton be carefully die-cut and glued to prevent pin holes and mechanical openings in corners.

Because some cereal products are finely ground or contain fines, and are subject to infestation from outside, carton liners or exterior wrappers are used. Liners or "tight" wrappers are particularly well suited to prevent sifting, while either tight or loose wrappers are used to increase resistance to infestation. "Tight-wrapped" printed paper wrappers are put on by automatic equipment so that they adhere at all points of contact with the carton. Paper wrappers also improve exterior appearance since label paper can be printed by more processes and in more detail than most carton surfaces.

The use of "tight wrap" is decreasing because it must be put on damp, then dry to shrink into conformation and adhesion. This added moisture and the complexity of the process make it incompatible and undesirable with moisture-sensitive products and high-speed operations.

The most popular overwrapper today for many cookies, crackers, and snacks is a printed paper overwrapper with a hard, bright, and moisture-resistant, hot-melt-type coating on the outside and a softer and easily heat-sealed coating on the inside. A similar wrapper consists of a heat-cured coating on the outside over the printing with a hot-melt coating on the inside. The outer coating is bright and durable, and the inner coating is moistureproof and heat-sealable. These wrappers can be heat-sealed on high-speed equipment and are scuff resistant, protective, and attractive. For this reason, hot-melt coatings have displaced unmodified paraffin waxes which were easily scuffed and did not make strong heat seals. Hot melts are wax blends with as much as 40 percent of synthetic polymers similar to ethylene vinyl acetate. Amount and kind of polymer used determine gloss, seal strength, and other important properties of the coatings. Viscosities and other important coating characteristics of these modern hot melts are such that special coating equipment must be used.

Also used for overwraps are coatings of polyethylene resin applied over printing by the extrusion coating process. Polyethylene extrusion coating and, in some cases, high-polymer-coated hot melts are used for folding cartons as coatings, either interior or exterior.

Hot melts and extrusion coatings can be used with laminated wrappers or with carton stock where higher levels of protection are indicated and where an overwrap is not desired. Many companies prefer these hot melts and extrusion-coated structures to transparent film wrappers because of their attractive appearance, durability, and moistureproofness.

With more complex cereal products, requiring more protection against moisture migration, some type of liner or loose overwrap or laminated carton stock, singly or combined, must be used. The problem with cereal products having a low bulk density and a large surface, such as cold breakfast cereals, is to obtain a high level of resistance to moisture penetration at the lowest possible cost. In general, most cereal product packages are moistureproofed with waxed paper formed on automatic machinery into a sealed or semisealed carton liner or overwrapper. The degree of moistureproofness of a lined package depends upon type of base paper, amount of wax, and efficiency in forming seals and closure of the liner. For products requiring a still greater degree of moistureproofness, wax-laminated and coated liners or, in some cases, foil laminations are used.

Polyvinyledene chloride (P.V.D.C.) coatings on thin, dense paper, such as glassine, are increasingly used as cereal liners because of their superior moistureproofness, strong heat seals, and more attractive appearance. To a lesser extent, moistureproofness is obtained by use of wax or plastics to laminate carton board to a paper. Cartons of this type are successfully used but have several disadvantages since the laminating agent is plastic and makes the board less rigid, particularly in warm weather. Also the laminating agent, by adhering to the cutting dies, tends to reduce production speeds in the manufacture of the carton.

Overwraps are generally as efficient and effective as liners or interior bags for moistureproofing and, in some cases, are used as the sole moistureproofing barrier. They protect the carton from handling stains and guarantee the purchaser that the carton has not previously been opened (i.e. tamperproofness).

Carton overwraps may provide an additional, if slight, barrier to the passage of insects.

Aluminum foil laminated to paper has been used for products which require an extreme degree of moisture protection. These foil-paper combinations can be used as carton liners, printed carton overwraps, or the foil may be laminated to the interior or exterior of the carton stock. If heavier gauges of foil are used (about 1/1,000 in.) and tight seals and closures are made, the finished structure will afford the maximum protection possible in a flexible-type package against both infestation and moisture change. However, very few cereal products require this degree of protection, which is also very expensive.

Cartons with transparent overwraps must be made as siftproof as possible; otherwise the product will sift out of the carton and lodge between carton and wrapper. This effect is less noticeable if the wrapper is opaque and printed. Nevertheless, it should be avoided since some products are fairly granular and tend to emboss or even perforate the wrapper. Either effect renders the package less salable.

Composite and All-Fiber Cans. The all-fiber can usually consists of a spiral or convolute, wound body, the ends of which have been die-formed into paper caps. The package is completed by a tightly adherent printed paper label which usually covers the entire body area and extends over the edges of the caps. The resulting low-cost, strong package can be made in many sizes and used for many cereal products, particularly corn meal, rolled oats, or bread crumbs. Moisture- or greaseproofness can be imparted to the package with certain laminated paperboards for the body; special adhesives in making the body; or by a lining ply of greaseproof material, like glassine or aluminum foil. End caps can be made from similarly laminated or lined materials, and an effective level of moistureproofness thus developed. This type of container is somewhat superior to the folding carton for protection against insect infestation.

Special fiber can constructions are used for cookie and biscuit doughs that must be kept refrigerated. Special openers or dispensers are available for these dense and firm-bodied products.

A composite fiber-metal can is constructed similar to the all-fiber can but has a metal for either one or both ends. Friction plugs or similar reclosure means can be used with metal ends, and package rigidity and strength are greatly increased. Also composite cans can be made much more protective against moisture migration than all-fiber cans, since the metal end and the method of clinching it to the body eliminate two points of moisture entry.

A special form of the fiber can is the large-size heavy-duty fiber drum designed for shipping special or concentrated products up to 200 lb. This container is made by winding heavy paper into a tube using pastes or glues for ply adhesion. There are many means and devices for shaping and securing the bottom and also many types of closures. The cost of the fiber drum and the similar plywood drum is too great in comparison with paper or cloth bags to allow its use for any but higher-cost products.

Metal Cans. All-metal cans are occasionally used for some cereals and cereal products, particularly for extremely long storage or for export shipping where rough handling and severe climatic conditions are encountered. The metal can is usually not a hermetic or packer can, but is the so-called "general line" can, usually made up without compound or soldering of ends or side seams. These metal cans give complete protection against rodent infestation or attack. However, spoilage and infestation can occur in metal cans if the product is not properly processed, harbors insects and insect eggs when packed, or if the moisture content is not properly controlled.

Trays. A few years ago frozen pre-baked rolls, pies, cakes, and more appeared in frozen-food cabinets. The package used is unlike any other cereal product container. These products require moisture protection to prevent freezer burn (surface moisture loss), a package that allows high-temperature reheating, and multi-color product identity. The package meeting these requirements is a formed aluminum tray with a crimped-on lid of foil-laminated paperboard carrying process printing of the product. These products and this package have opened new markets for completely prepared baked goods that can be held frozen for long periods and yet be quickly heated for use. There certainly will be new products and increased volume for these cereal products.

Some time ago overwrapped, deep aluminum trays carrying bread or roll dough or partially baked doughs in a paper, cellophane, or special film bag were on the market. The user completed the baking cycle, in some cases with the product in the bag. Doughs in special high-temperature films, such as certain nylons, have also been on the market. These products, however, have apparently not found consumer acceptance, and were probably displaced by the frozen baked goods that can be prepared much more quickly.

Shipping Cases. After packaging most cereal products are placed in an outer container for shipment. Years ago they were shipped, like most other products, in lightweight wooden cases because no other containers were available. With the development of fiberboard it became possible to make containers which were lighter in weight, lower in cost, and easier to use than wooden boxes. At first, solid fiberboard was used, but at the present time the overwhelming preference is for the corrugated container. Use of wooden boxes is now limited to export shipments and military supplies. For the shipment of flour packed in small paper bags (10 lb. and less) multi-wall paper shipping sacks are sometimes used instead of corrugated containers.

Corrugated shipping containers are acceptable for all types of cereal products for domestic use. They are dealt with in Rule 41 of the "Corrugated Freight Classification," a document issued by the Association of American Railroads Uniform Classification Committee. The title of Rule 41 is, "Solid or Corrugated Fiber Board Containers," and certain portions of this rule must be complied with or a higher shipping rate is applied as a penalty. The classification tables do not specify materials or details of construction but use the Mullen test or Cady test as an index of container strength. Cases for most cereal products need not hold more than 65 lb. and can therefore be made of 200-lb. test board. The most important change in this area in recent years is that, under specified conditions, hot-melt adhesives may be used for sealing case flaps in place of liquid, water-based adhesives.

Corrugated board is made of either Kraft or jute paper for the face, with Kraft or straw board as the corrugating medium. The corrugating itself can be either "A," "B," or "C" flute. These are simple designations for the number of corrugations per foot and their height. Much of the board used in the cereal industries is made with the "A" flute because this particular construction gives the greatest compression resistance in top-to-bottom loading of the case.

Several machines are now in use to test compression on shipping cases in the laboratory. Tests on empty, sealed cases give a good indication of the general quality of materials and construction, whereas results on filled cases supply information about the maximum safe height of stacking — an important consideration, especially if pallets are used. Many case goods are now handled on pallets for warehousing and transfer to and from trucks and freight cars. As a rule the greatest possible resistance to compression from top to bottom is required because most stacking puts the load in that direction. These tests, of course, can also be used to measure resistance of cases to compressive forces in any direction.

Domestic shipping cases covered by Rule 41 are not suitable for most export applications. The cases can be strengthened by adding steel strapping and by using heavier board, but it is recommended to enclose the container in a second case or to slip it into a sleeve and use strapping. For military use, or whenever very severe handling must be withstood, a weatherproof, solid fiber case or wooden box with strapping is necessary.

Comparative Properties of Packaging Materials. Materials used for packaging cereal products in bags, folding cartons, and fiber cans can affect the type of deterioration which the product undergoes in storage. For example, there is a substantial difference in the degree of permeability to organic vapors of cloth and untreated papers on one hand, and metal foils, plastic films, glassine, and cellophane on the other. Thus, if a product contains aromatic portions essential to its character and to its acceptance for final use, a packaging material and construction must be selected which will hold the major portion of these aromatics until final use. This not only means a careful selection of the material for its impermeability toward these volatiles, but care in the construction of the package for a minimum of free openings.

Permeability to organic vapors is sometimes a desirable feature. Cereal products subjected to heat or mixed with other materials may become rancid. Experience shows that oxidation products responsible for rancid odors do not escape through some packaging materials, and the result is an unpleasant accumulation of odors by the time the package is opened. By selecting proper packaging materials, these undesirable odors can be dissipated through the package walls, without reducing the moistureproofing efficiency of the package in any way. While product stability is desirable, complete inhibition of the development of all forms of rancidity is rarely possible.

Cellophane, glassine, parchment paper, certain plastic films, and aluminum foil can be generally considered impervious or nearly so toward organic vapors. On the other hand, papers and paperboard other than those mentioned, whether waxed or not, can be considered as easily permeated by such vapors. This is important in packaging cereals since an improper packaging material can shorten the shelf life and change the type of failure.

Plastic films and coatings are based on many different types of polymers and resins and each is permeable in some degree to certain classes of gases, flavors, and volatile ingredients. It is not possible to tabulate the values for the innumerable films and coatings with the very large number of gases or volatile ingredients, so empirical testing must be done for special cases where unique permeation problems arise.

Some properties and uses of principal packaging materials for cereals are given in Table I. Only a brief summary is given since it would be beyond the scope of this chapter to list and characterize the many packaging materials resulting from laminating, coating, and combining that are commercially available today. More detailed information on any specific material and its suitability for a given requirement can be obtained from various trade associations and manufacturers and from the literature. Such information, as well as the results of special laboratory tests, must be related to the requirements of any particular product. Costs also greatly influence the final selection of the material and package.

IV. PACKAGING PRACTICES IN THE CEREAL INDUSTRIES

This section considers which packages are commonly used for each of the different groups of cereal products. Some repetition of what has already been said will be unavoidable; and, indeed, it seems important to repeat at the outset that similar products can be packaged in a number of different ways, depending upon methods of distribution and the merchandising approaches of the manufacturers. This complication makes it necessary to limit the discussion to the most generally accepted types and styles of package used for each class of product. Even with that limitation it is not feasible to write detailed specifications for the packaging materials used because different sizes of packages require different weights of board and paper and because the materials themselves are subject to variation.

A. Cold Breakfast Cereals

Cold breakfast cereals vary greatly in their need for both moistureproofness and physical protection since they range from crisp and thin products to others that are dense and hard. Puffed cereals, including those that have been given a sugar coating, are often packaged in large, printed cellophane-plastic film bags. In many cases duplex bags made of two plies of moistureproof film are used, because the resistance to the transmission of water vapor of a single film is reduced by the printing.

Cold cereals are also packaged in folding cartons of from 1 oz., for individual servings, to about 12-oz. capacity. Because of the highly competitive nature of these products, the package is generally made to appear as large as possible by increasing the size of the front panel with a corresponding reduction in depth. This fact, together with the bulky nature of the product, produces a carton with a very large surface area which must yet have a high degree of moistureproofness. Because of the large surface area of the package and the relatively low cost of its contents, the most economical carton construction compatible with the physical, protective, and printing requirements is essential.

These folding cartons have the shortest possible flaps to reduce the amount of board. The carton board is usually news stock or other reused stocks made on a cylinder machine with a thin surface of a white pulp for printing. These cartons are set up and lined on automatic equipment which forms the liner by heat-sealing and inserts it into the carton. The liner is usually a 22-lb. basic weight,

TABLE I

General Properties and Uses of Principal Cereal Packaging Materials[a]

Material	Composition	Use	Function	Remarks
Cellophane	A regenerated cellulose plus coatings	Bags or overwraps, printed or plain	Moistureproofness, heat-sealing, greaseproof	A transparent, decorative, and protective film
Plastic films	Made from many types of resins	Bags, all sizes	Dependent on film and composition	Ideal for bags
Aluminum foil	Aluminum metal rolled to 0.001 to 0.00035 in.	Usually combined to paper for carton wrappers, liners, bags	Decorative, highly moistureproof	Can be printed and coated to make heat-sealing
Waxed papers	Well-finished papers, waxed to give surface coatings	Plain or printed as wrappers, liners, or bags	Heat sealable, moistureproof liners	Semitransparent or opaque, good gloss
Hot-melt coatings	Paraffin waxes with special polymers	Coatings and laminations	Moistureproof, heat-sealing,	Strong heat seals, high gloss, durability
Polyethylene extrusions	Low-density polyethylenes	Coatings and laminations	Moistureproof, very strong heat seals	Form, fill, and seal and bags because of strong heat seals
Glassine, pouch paper	A supercalendared paper of special process and pulps	Bags, liners, laminations, and wrappers	Greaseproof, heat-sealing moistureproof by coating and laminating	Excellent surface for printing; opaque to semitransparent
Carton board	Made from many kinds of pulp and processes	Folding cartons, trays, fiber cans etc.	Stiffness and strength	Base for coating and printing

[a]See Modern Packaging Encyclopedia and similar sources for more details of physical and functional properties of all packaging materials.

glassine-type paper carrying about 2 lb. of wax on each surface. After filling, the top of the liner is heat-sealed or double-folded and crimped.

At certain seasons of the year or for shipment to southern markets, the carton may be overwrapped with a loose transparent wrapper of waxed sulfite paper, waxed glassine, or cellophane. Some cold cereal products are also packaged in a lined but unprinted carton similar to the foregoing but with a loose outer wrap of opaque, printed wax paper. Heat sealing of both liner and wrapper produces the greatest possible protection against moisture penetration and insect infestation obtainable with an all-paper package.

Denser and less moisture-sensitive cold cereals are sold in similar packages except that either a liner or overwrap is used, but usually not both. Sugar-coated cold cereals require a very high degree of moisture protection, and a combined foil-waxed paper inner liner is used to ensure adequate protection.

B. Hot Cereals

Hot cereals are always free-flowing, relatively dense products which have not been greatly altered in processing and are not particularly sensitive to moisture changes. Most products of this type are packaged in a heavy-gauge folding carton (up to 0.030 in. thick) without a liner and with a printed paper wrapper on the outside. The paperboard is usually of better grade than that used for cold cereals and may have an interior surface of a semibleached or bleached pulp to improve its appearance and to reduce interaction between the product and the reused pulps of the body stock. The printed paper wrapper is firmly applied to the carton surface with an all-over adhesive and is designed to prevent sifting of the product and to reduce the possibility of infestation. A similar package construction is used for corn starch, corn meal, and other products having similar physical properties and preservation requirements.

Hot cereals, corn meal, cracker crumbs, and others are sometimes packaged in all-fiber cans, apparently because the consumer has long been accustomed to certain brands in this type of container. These packages are usually made from spirally wound paper tubes of more than one ply, the adhesive being a vegetable paste. The ends are cup-shaped and are formed by stamping a heavy-gauge paperboard which has been steamed or moistened before forming. The formed ends are slipped over the fiber body and are allowed to dry in position, which shrinks them firmly to the body. The filled package is labeled with a paper label which comes up over the end caps and is all-over glued. This gives a strong, non-sifting, low-cost package with some resistance to infestation. It can be made with varying degrees of moistureproofness depending on the material used for the inner ply, the label, or the laminating agent.

C. Macaroni Products

Macaroni, spaghetti, and similar products are nearly always packaged in a particular style of folding carton which has been used so long that it is always associated with these products. The package, relatively long as compared with its cross section, is a lock-end type carton with a tucked top. Locking is done by inserting special flaps into slots on the narrow end; the tuck top extends the full length of the package. The carton, made of low-cost stock with a good printing surface on the exterior, is usually set up with a piece of lining paper which folds in with end tucks to form what is known in the trade as a Peters-style carton and liner. After the product is loaded, the ends of the liner are folded over and the carton top tucked into position. If the carton is unprinted, a loose, printed paper wrapper is used. The liner is made of any good grade of white paper, glassine, or cellophane. The resulting package is not moistureproof but gives some physical protection to the product, is inexpensive, and adaptable to automatic or semiautomatic packing operations.

D. Bread Flours

Consumer packages of bread flour vary from a few pounds to a hundred pounds in weight. This product does not require moistureproofness, the principal requirement being a strong, attractive bag resistant to sifting and to infestation. Paper bags used for flour vary little in character from one size to another, but more plies or greater thickness of ply must be used as size is increased. Thus 5-lb. bags are made of paper of about 70-lb. weight and 10-lb. bags of 80-lb. paper; for bags holding 25 lb. of flour, paper of about 125-lb. basic weight is required. In still larger sizes more than one ply of paper may be used, depending upon the paper stock and its weight.

The paper is usually manufactured from rope or jute stock or from long-fiber, high-strength Kraft. It must be soft and relatively porous to air so that little flour will puff out when the bags are filled on high-speed, automatic machines. For smaller bags the paper is sometimes embossed to increase its softness and improve its appearance, while the exterior surface is always treated with a white pigment or pulp to give a better surface for printing. As mentioned previously, the interior surface may be colored blue to enhance the whiteness of the flour.

The construction of paper bags varies according to the type of machine on which they are made and the way they are to be filled and closed. There are several different types of closures; a simple wire or string tie, a sewn top, a folded and pasted-down top which, when carefully opened, provides a pouring means, and a top turned down several times and pasted against the body of the bag.

E. Cake Flours

Cake flours are usually packaged in folding cartons holding 2 or 3 lb. The carton is about a 30-point (0.030-in.) board made from a good grade of reused pulps. To minimize the danger of contamination, the interior surface of the board is often made of a still better grade of pulp. Filled and sealed cartons are overwrapped with a tight-wrapped, printed paper label. There may be scored and preperforated lines on the carton and wrapper to facilitate opening and reclosure. The package is not moistureproof, but is strong and stiff enough not to be bulged by the weight of the contents, and has reasonable resistance to infestation.

F. Cake Mixes

The packaging of cake mixtures is complicated by the inclusion of leavening agents, sugar, flavor, and coloring materials which may be hygroscopic and moisture-sensitive in varying degrees. The package often consists of a folding carton of about a 24-point board with a machine-formed liner of laminated glassine or an inserted, laminated glassine bag. After the lined carton is filled, the liner or bag closure is heat-sealed or well folded and crimped, the flaps are sealed, and the carton is overwrapped with a printed, tight wrapper. There is no particular need for a high-quality board since the product is placed in laminated glassine to prevent any contact of product with the carton wall. The laminated glassine also gives protection against loss of volatile flavorings, prevents fat penetration, and provides excellent moistureproofness. Aluminum foil, less than 0.001 in. thick, laminated to paper makes an attractive wrapper and, when properly applied, greatly improves the moisture resistance of the package and also its resistance to infestation. Another satisfactory package consists of a lined and printed carton with a moistureproof cellophane overwrap. An unlined carton of high-grade paperboard may be used with a printed hot-melt, coated overwrap.

G. Cookies and Crackers

Cookies and crackers include an extremely wide range of products, ranging from hard, dense types having little moisture sensitivity, to complex products carrying oils and fats and having various surface coatings or fillings, usually of a sugary nature. Simpler and more stable products such as graham crackers, or soda crackers can be packaged in a Peters-type carton (see Macaroni Products), using a liner of plain or waxed glassine and a loose, printed paper overwrap. Liners in these packages are left unsealed to allow the escape of any odors resulting from fat oxidation.

Many cookies with a high sugar content and requiring moistureproofness are packaged in a folding carton with full flaps and a tuck top. The liner, machine-formed or inserted bag, is made of waxed or laminated glassine, wax sulfite papers, or, more rarely, moistureproof cellophane. The carton may be printed, but if not, a printed overwrap is used which is an opaque, hot-melt, coated wrapper sealed by heat. Other packages for sweet cookies consist of a paperboard tray or stiffener slipped into a film bag. The problem here is to prevent undue breakage. Because of their irregular shape and brittleness, cookies of this sort must often be packed by hand or by semiautomatic means. Other problems in the packaging of fancy cookies are to prevent excessive staining or penetration of the packages by fats and to provide a high level of protection against moisture absorption. Both must be done without undue cost increases or unduly complicated package construction. Many companies use folding cartons for larger packages and transparent film bags for the smaller ones. If the film is unprinted, paper labels may be applied by heat-sealing, or printed paper may be stapled or sealed over the bag closure. Transparent films are very popular for packaging sweet cookies, because product visibility is considered helpful in merchandising.

In the same general class are many complex products sold as snack or cocktail items. These may be fried, puffed, or surface-treated with flavoring ingredients. Many are packaged in small sizes in printed, laminated glassine bags, duplex cellophane, or a combination of films and glassine. Sometimes a colored or tinted ply is used to enhance the color of the product or in the belief that the color screen will reduce the rate of rancidity development. Such color screens are of doubtful value since light is not the only cause of rancidity, and the packages are rarely exposed to direct sunlight in normal distribution. The bag should be well made and sealed to give protection for short periods only against rancidity and infestation. No package can do more than this for such unstable products. Even in a completely moistureproof package rancidity and staling cannot be long delayed. A decorative bag that gives a reasonable degree of protection at low cost is therefore used. To prevent products from becoming unattractive or unsalable there must be close control of stocks and sales outlets. Some companies prefer printed, transparent bags or pouches while others use a white, opaque surface or large areas of white ink. Since either opaque or transparent structures can give the same level of protection, the option is a merchandising decision.

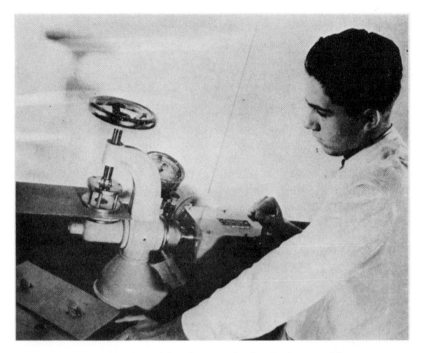

Figure 4. A Mullen tester for determining the strength of packaging materials.

H. Bread

Bread has been packaged in heat-sealed wrappers of printed waxed paper (23 lb. per ream), although a special grade of moistureproof cellophane is popular for special loaves. The necessity for having the most economical wrapper limits the use of cellophane for white bread. The wrapper should not be too moistureproof, as this may induce mold growth on the bread surface. However, in recent years, bread packaging has been almost completely converted to a thin, transparent, printed bag of polyethylene film with the end closure a clipped or tied bunched end with a considerable free section. This package required a complete change in packaging machinery but apparently had immediate consumer acceptance, because the package was easy to open and reclose. Bread is another product that must have a rapid turnover to reduce the volume of returned goods. The package must prevent excessive moisture losses, carry the maker's trademark, and keep the product clean in handling. Rolls and similar baked goods can be packaged like bread, but often trays or open-sided cartons are used with the wrapper on the outside.

I. Cakes

The many kinds of cakes vary widely in stability and durability. Firm cakes can be packaged like bread or rolls, while those having icing or soft structures require a rigid carton to prevent disfiguration. Fancy and holiday cakes are often

Figure 5. Multipacker for assembling and overwrapping single-serving cartons into a ten-pack. *(Courtesy of Battle Creek Packaging Machines, Inc.)*

packaged in lithographed metal cans, plastic boxes, or in set-up boxes with cellophane, foil, or other decorated films as overwraps. Similar packaging is used for other baked goods having fillings, top dressings, and delicate structures where physical damage and too much moisture loss must be prevented. Long storage is never necessary, and the usual cost limitations often do not apply. Too much moistureproofness produces sogginess and accelerates mold growth. If icings are used, very little or no moistureproofness is desirable.

The most recent and important new product and marketing innovations in cereal products are cakes, rolls, pies, and other ready-to-eat baked goods that are quick-frozen to be reheated by the consumer. The package is a formed foil tray with a printed foil-paperboard crimped-on cover, and the package is used to re-heat the contents or allow rapid thawing, depending on the product (Figure 4). This is the first appearance of baked goods in the frozen food cabinets of retail outlets. Its acceptance has been rapid and extensive. This development assures important and great growth for many ready-to-eat-and-serve cereal products.

Precooked, frozen waffles and French toast are generally packaged in a polyethylene film bag in a printed folding carton. The inner bag is easy to open and can be tightly reclosed to preserve the remaining contents. The products are reheated, often in a bread toaster, at the time of use. The success and acceptance of these frozen, precooked products will certainly result in many new cereal products going to market via the quick-frozen route.

Small, flat pastries which are prebaked, then reheated in a toaster at the point of use are new and unique cereal products. Strong pastry shells are filled with fruit pastes and sugar or other toppings. The moisture content is low, and the

Figure 6. Fresh-baked Danish pastry packaged in formed aluminum tray and then frozen. (*Courtesy of Ekco Products, Inc.*)

product is stable at ambient conditions, so that it can be handled and stored without refrigeration or special storage. Each pastry or tart is in a well-sealed, printed pouch of a paper-aluminum foil lamination or a similar protective material, packaged by a form, fill, seal machine. Several of these filled pouches are placed in a printed folding carton as the unit of sale. Product and package are excellent examples of new products developed as convenience food and requiring a coordinated effort by marketing, package development, and product development people.

V. TRENDS AND DEVELOPMENTS

Packaging of cereals and cereal products has been affected and will continue to be influenced by certain general trends in packaging methods and package construction. The most important of these trends are: use of more decoration and transparency, simplification of package construction, adoption of unit packages (single servings), production of packages by automatic means, and increased use of heat-sealing. Cereal packaging will use increasing quantities of formed plastic containers, trays, and films and also aluminum foil trays for frozen items and foil laminations for improved protection and increased shelf life.

Packages for cereal products should not be the target of any specific criticism for waste disposal reasons. By far the bulk of cereal packages are flexible materials and almost none are metal cans or glass, so that returning for reuse is not a consideration. Flexible packages as a class can be incinerated, used as land fill, and sorted for recycling of the various components. There is no reason for packagers of cereal products to have any special concern about possible ecological or waste disposal problems with their packages or package materials. They should have no difficulty in meeting any general regulations that may be applied to packages made from flexible materials.

All packagers of food products must be aware of the growing insistance by various regulatory agencies on readably dating each package. The concept is sometimes called "freshness dating," but there seems to be some present confusion as to whether the date stamped on the package shall be the day the product is packaged or whether it is based on expected shelf life.

The multiplication of self-service retail outlets has greatly increased the importance of the package as a merchandising tool. Modern distribution methods have made it essential to have a package of the most attractive appearance if the customer's favor is to be won. Thus we find present-day packages distinguished by good art work, striking colors, and glossy surfaces. Product identification is often accomplished by process printing, so that the package may carry an attractive and authentic reproduction of the product. This

Figure 7. A high-speed "Expresso" machine for heat-sealing membranes in folding cartons. *(Courtesy of Rexham Corp., Packaging Machine Div.)*

requires the use of more complex printing processes and the selection of package materials with improved surfaces. Inspection as well as identification of some products is made possible by using transparent material for all or part of the package, though this is not always feasible because of the need for protection or some other requirement.

Consumer research indicates that the user desires a package which is convenient to handle and open, and is adapted to the way in which the product is used. This requirement can best be met by keeping the construction as simple as possible, by the use of easy means for opening and reclosing and, in some cases, by the addition of opening or pouring devices. It is difficult to satisfy these requirements and at the same time meet the increasing need for improved preservation and low cost.

The growing demand for packages carrying sufficient product for a single use, or so-called "unit packages," has resulted in a greatly increased number of single-serving packages for cold breakfast cereals. A unit package must be carefully designed and automatically produced because, with these smaller packages, preservation becomes more difficult and more packaging material is required.

The use of automatic machinery for making packages and for filling and closing them has been brought about by the great increase in the production of packaged goods and by steadily rising labor costs. Developments have led to the production of certain basic types of package-making machinery which are modified for particular uses. There are few special problems in adapting machinery to handle most cereal products. However, some cereal products, such as cookies and crackers, because of their irregular shape and brittleness, require special machines for the filling operation and, although many problems have been solved, there is still much work to be done. The use of automatic machinery is made easier by the simplification of packages and the use of heat sealing, since these measures reduce the number of machines required or allow higher production rates to be attained.

Besides increasing speed and simplicity of automatic machines, the use of heat-sealing materials has been an important factor in improving the preservative functions of packages, and in making them more attractive and convenient. New package materials are continually being produced, and many of them come from the plastics industry. These materials, whether films or resins used in coatings or adhesives, hold great promise in the manufacture of flexible or paperboard packages which, by heat sealing, can improve protection or be made hermetic and thus permit the use of inert gases or vacuum, or even the packaging of sterile products. An example of a machine that uses heat-sealable materials to make a unique folding carton is the "Expresso" machine. It seals a liquid and moisture-tight membrane across the open end of a folding carton, first on the bottom and then the top after filling, but before the flaps are glued down (Figure 5). The result is a linerless package with improved performance.

An important development finding rapid acceptance is the use of preprinted, hot-melt adhesives on carton flaps. This eliminates liquid glue applicators in the forming and closing steps and substitutes hot pads resulting in neater and faster operations. Hot-melt adhesives must be tailored for each application and material, and no changes should be made without carefully checking performance.

Many of the latest cartoning machines use flat blanks and make the side seam in the set-up operation which reduces costs and lowers scrap losses.

Computers are being increasingly tied into machine operations to control various steps, to shut down if malfunctions occur, to indicate points of failure, to record performance, and to scan and totalize product weight—to mention some of the many present and possible uses. Some of the more advanced computerized machines signal breakdown or malfunction by diagrams, recording tapes, and signals to indicate and assist in finding the cause and location of trouble.

With the growing complexity of products and the trend toward smaller selling units, improved and novel functional properties are demanded of the package. This trend has been accelerated by the centralization of facilities for the manufacture of cereal products, which results in a longer storage time and increased handling. As each new package material comes on the market, it is immediately evaluated and, if it has unusual properties or can affect economics, it may be expected to solve some existing problem or make possible an improved package for some product. The annual dollar volume of packaging materials and machinery is so large that a great deal of research and development work is being done by the many companies who are already in this business or who are attracted by its volume and potentials. This results in a continuous flow of new resins, films, coatings, processes, and combinations of materials and equipment which must be evaluated before they can find their proper place in packaging. The package user who does not continually evaluate new materials, constructions, and machinery with scientific methods, and who is not aware of trends and the needs of his customers, may rapidly fall behind under today's competitive conditions.

Packaging is now accepted as a vital and necessary part of storage, handling, display, and preservation of goods in our present economy. The package must accomplish all its functions at the lowest possible cost. The continuing need for improving packages and reducing their costs, coupled with the rapid progress in packaging, makes it imperative for every large company to insure its future by organizing and staffing an integrated packaging section. The company that does not keep pace with package developments will find itself in economic difficulties regardless of its skill as a producer or the quality of its product.

BIBLIOGRAPHY

AIKEN, W. H., P. M. DOTY, and H. MARK. 1945. Water vapor permeability—What it is and how it works. Mod. Packag. 18(12): 137-140, 166, 169.

ANONYMOUS. 1970. UCC relaxes rules on use of hot-melt adhesives. Mod. Packag. 43(6).

ANONYMOUS. March, 1971. Snack packaging, a market game. Today's Packager, pp. 10-14.

BRODY, A. L. 1971. *Flexible packaging of foods.* C.R.C. Press, Cleveland, Ohio 44128.

CAGE, J. K. 1971. Package specification. Mod. Packag. 44(9).

FELT, C. E., A. C. BUECHELE, L. F. BORCHARDT, R. C. KOEHN, F. A. COLLATZ, and F. C. HILDEBRAND. 1945. Determination of shelf life of packaged cereals. Cereal Chem. 22: 261-271.

GRAEBNER, W. A. 1944. The application of humidity equilibria to package engineering. Amer. Management Ass., Packag. Series 11, pp. 11-23.

HALLADAY, J. F. 1942. An engineering approach to solution of packaging problems involving water vapor resistance. Pap. Trade J. 115: 153-162.

HANLON, J. F. 1971. *Handbook of package engineering*. McGraw-Hill Book Co., New York, N.Y. 10036.

LANDROCK, A. F. 1950. Stored-food product insects and their relationship to packaging problems. Ph.D. Thesis, Boston Univ.

LANDROCK, A. H., and B. E. PROCTOR. 1951. Free oil in packaged foods. Mod. Packag. 24(12): 107-112.

LEONARD, E. A. 1971. The economics of packaging. Modern Packaging, New York, N.Y. 10019.

LEONARD, E. A. 1971. Packaging specifications, purchasing and quality control. Modern Packaging, New York, N.Y. 10019.

MORRIS, J. S. 1971. Making standard package tests fit the exact product. Package Eng. 16(10).

OSWIN, C. R. 1945. The kinetics of package life. II. The temperature factor. J. Soc. Chem. Ind. (London) 64: 224-225.

SOUTHWICK, C. A., Jr. 1947. Package characteristics of products. Mod. Packag. 20(11): 147-149.

SOUTHWICK, C. A., Jr. 1947. Return goods. Mod. Packag. 21(1): 149-151, 182-183.

ASSOCIATIONS AND SOURCES OF TEST METHODS, DATA, STATISTICS

AMERICAN SOCIETY FOR TESTING AND MATERIALS
1916 Race Street
Philadelphia, Pa. 19103

MODERN PACKAGING ENCYCLOPEDIA (published yearly)
McGraw Hill, 1301 Avenue of the Americas, New York, N.Y. 10019

(Statistics, costs, machinery, and charts of data on packages and materials)

NATIONAL FLEXIBLE PACKAGING ASSOCIATION
12025 Shaker Blvd., Cleveland, Ohio 44120

(Guidelines for testing snack food, flexible packaging, and similar reports)

PACKAGING INSTITUTE
342 Madison Avenue, New York, N.Y. 10017

(Glossary of packaging terms, test methods, and reports of conferences)

THE TECHNICAL ASSOCIATION OF THE PULP AND PAPER INDUSTRY
1 Dunwoody Park, Atlanta, Georgia 30341

(Test methods)

INDEX

Notes

The extensive system of headings and subheadings used in the text will be of help to the reader, in addition to the index.

To avoid ambiguity, some key words are repeated several times—for example, Moisture, Moisture in Grain, Moisture Content.

Most entries indicate the beginning page but not the full range of a discussion that continues on following pages.

541

PAGE

PAGE